McClain

D1595568

FLUID POWER SYSTEMS & CIRCUITS

By Russell W. Henke, P.E.

Edited by Tobi Goldoftas

Published by HYDRAULICS & PNEUMATICS Magazine

Library of Congress Catalog Card Number: 83-61875

ISBN 0-932905-04-8

Current printing (last digit):

10   9   8   7   6   5   4   3

Printed in the United States of America

Preface to the Second Edition

Things should not be made any more complex than necessary to convey an idea. Russ Henke (with deference to Albert Einstein)

In the Preface to the First Edition of this book I stated that it was written for my students. Its acceptance reflects the verity of this approach. The necessity for a second printing supports our perception of a need for a pragmatic treatment of the subject and for this we are grateful. I will continue to adhere to this premise in future works.

R.W.H.
Elm Grove, Wisconsin
March 1986

Preface

Everything should be made as simple as possible. But not simpler. Albert Einstein

This book was conceived and written to bridge the gap between elementary treatments of fluid power circuits and the highly sophisticated, analytical treatises on system theory. However, this application-oriented work also remains pragmatic — an engineering must.

During the past 15 years, as the fluid power technology matured, it experienced a normal technological evolution. The contents of this work reflect many of the developments which have taken place. Some topics which were the rage only two decades ago, *i.e.,* fluidics, are omitted. Others such as energy conservative systems, hydrostatic transmissions, noise control, and contamination control are discussed in detail. This book also considers electrical controls and discusses microcomputers, microprocessors, component selection, and troubleshooting.

The overriding thrust of this book is to provide a practical methodology for designing fluid power circuits and systems — methods based on careful analysis and definition of the job to be done. This definition approach, called the *Load Cycle Profile,* is based on the essence of sound design: a detailed load analysis is presented in graphic form.

Seldom is any book the culmination of the sole efforts of the author. This one is no exception. I want to acknowledge and thank those whose help, thoughtfulness, and contributions were of material assistance in making this book possible. I extend my sincere appreciation to:

My wife Connie for her continuous support and encouragement,

The Milwaukee School of Engineering, where the seeds for this book were planted years ago,

Professor Warren Wilson, a pioneer in the fluid power education, and founder of the National Conference on Fluid Power during his tenure at the Illinois Institute of Technology in Chicago,

Mr. Walter Ernst, another great pioneer, whose early writing had a profound influence on me,

My former students, who provided me with the motivation for writing this book,

My many friends and colleagues, who helped shape and influence my perception of the fluid power technology.

Finally, we all owe a debt of gratitude to the person most responsible for making this book a reality — Tobi Goldoftas, Chief Editor of HYDRAULICS & PNEUMATICS Magazine. If ever patience and perseverance were requisites to success, this project proved to be an acid test. He brought an abundance of both to the making of this book.

R.W.H.
Elm Grove, Wisconsin
September 1983

CONTENTS

CONTENTS

CONTENTS

CHAPTER I

ENERGY TRANSFER SYSTEMS

INTRODUCTION

This book deals with the technologies of basic *energy transmission systems* as used by the product/process oriented industries, the military, etc. The diagram, Figure 1.1 illustrates the essence of these types of systems.

These classes of Energy Transmission Systems can be characterized by:

1. **Mechanical rotary input** in the form of
   - an input speed, N_i — which can be *constant,* or *variable*
   - an input torque, T_i which is *variable,* responding to the instantaneous demand of the Energy Transmission System, *i.e.,* the output impedance of the prime mover

2. **Mechanical output** in two basic forms:
   - *Linear*
     a. An output linear velocity v_o (or $\dot{x}$) which can be *constant* or *variable*
     b. An output force reaction, F_o which can be *constant* or *variable,* responding to the instantaneous changes in load reaction,

i.e., the output impedance of the actuator
- *Rotary*
  a. Limited rotation actuators
     - An output *rotational* velocity, ω (or $\dot{\theta}$), which can be constant, N_o, or variable, $\dot{\theta}$
     - An output *torque* reaction, T_o which can be constant or variable responding to load changes
  b. Continuous rotation motors
     - An output angular velocity which can be constant, N_o (usually shown as speed, N, instead of ω_o) or variable, $\dot{\theta}$.
     - An output reaction torque, T_o which can be *constant* or *variable,* responding to load changes.

In the diagram illustrated in Figure 1.1, the Energy Transmission System is an *interface* between an *input* (prime mover) and an *output* (load). The Energy Transmission System must next be broken down into its *functional* sections, as shown in the block diagram Figure 1.2.

Functional segments

An Energy Transmission System has three

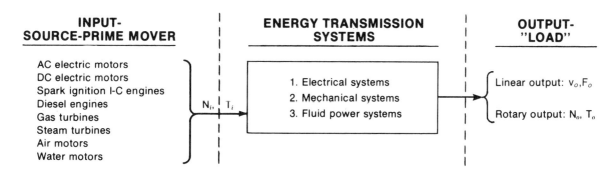

Fig. 1.1. Diagram shows the Energy Transmission System is an interface between an input element such as a prime mover and an output element such as a load.

1

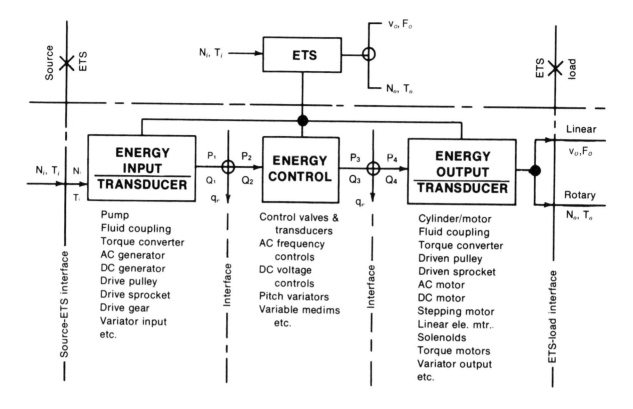

Fig. 1.2. Block diagram of typical Energy Transmission System subdivided into its three major functional categories.

functional sections:

1. Energy Input Devices receive the energy from the prime mover across the *Source-Energy Transmission System* interface.

    a. The input variables are: input speed, N_i and input torque, T_i.

    b. Output variables are represented by symbols p_1 and Q_1, pressure and flow respectively.

    c. Typical examples of energy input devices are shown in Figure 1.2.

2. Energy Output Devices receive the energy transmitted by the Energy Transmission System, transduce it into a mechanical output and deliver it across the "Energy Transmission System-Load" interface to the LOAD.

    a. Input variable to the Energy Output Devices are called p_4, Q_4.

    b. Output variables from the Energy Output Devices are
      •Linear output, v_o, F_o
      •Rotary output, N_o, T_o

    c. Typical examples of Energy Output Devices are shown in Figure 1.2. Commercially, there is a wider variety of available Energy Output Devices than Energy Input Devices.

3. Energy Control Devices receive energy from the Energy Input Devices in the form of input variables p_2, Q_2. Energy Control Devices modulate the energy as they transmit it and deliver it in the form of output variables p_3, Q_3.

Note that the intersectional interfaces are shown within the Energy Transmission Systems thus,

    a. There is an interface between the Energy Input Devices and Energy Control Devices section

    b. There is an interface between the Energy Control Devices and the Energy Output Devices section of the overall Energy Transmission System, and

    c. Intersectional energy losses (i.e. transmission losses), symbolized by q_e are shown lumped at a summing point located at the internal interfaces.

There is a fourth section to a fluid power Energy Transmission System, the "Auxiliaries." This section consists of all the components needed to implement a practical system. However these components participate in neither energy transfer nor control. Typically these are: piping, fittings, hoses, reservoirs, fluid, and filters.

The next step is to consider the relationship of the control function to the other sections of the

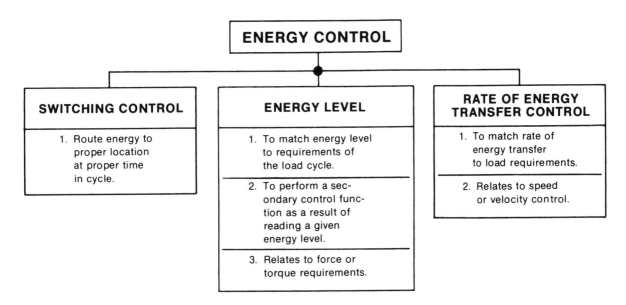

Fig. 1.3. Block diagram illustrates relationship of control functions to other sections in overall system.

overall system, Figure 1.3.

Most control situations are a combination of two or more of these three basic functions. The term *control* tells how these three control functions relate to the other sections of the total Energy Transmission System.

LOAD DOMINATED ENERGY TRANSMISSION SYSTEM

One more factor must be considered before the designer can approach the subject of fluid power circuit design effectively, namely, the *Load-*

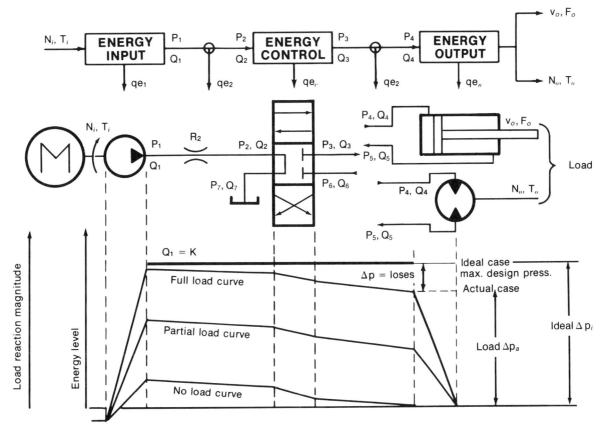

Fig. 1.4 Diagram illustrates "Load-oriented" nature of Energy Transmission Systems.

3

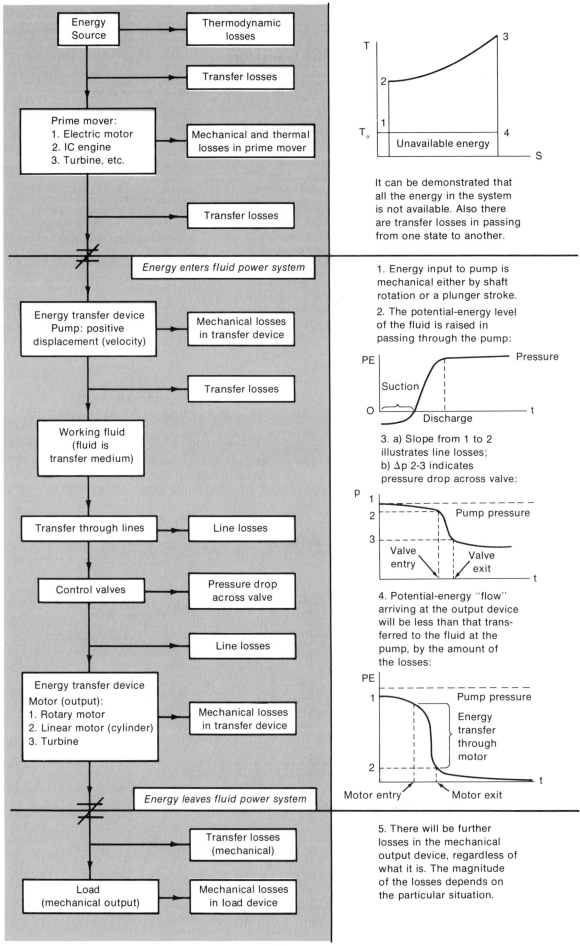

Fig. 1.5. Energy transfer steps and relationships in an Energy Transmission System from prime mover to load.

4

Oriented nature of the kinds of Energy Transmission Systems previously defined. The fact that these systems *are Load-dominated* is illustrated in Figure 1.4, which uses a single hydraulic Energy Transmission System as the example.

The block diagram shown is that of Figure 1.2. Below the functional representation is a schematic of the hydraulic system consisting of one pump, one control valve and either a linear actuator or continuous rotation hydraulic motor. The curves below the schematic illustrate the key point: the *load-domination* of the system.

Hydraulic systems, which ordinarily use positive displacement input-output devices such as pumps, actuators and motors, transfer energy by means of potential energy changes in the fluid transfer medium, that is, by virtue of hydrostatic fluid pressure level differentials, Δp. The rate at which the energy is transferred is a function of flow, Q. These two variables — pressure and flow — are essentially independent of each other.

There is a common misconception concerning fluid power systems — that a pump generates pressure in the fluid transfer medium. It does not. A positive displacement pump transfers fluid at a controllable rate into a system *against* an impedance, namely some resistance to fluid flow. A small part of the resistance emanates from the piping, hoses, fittings, orifices, and other restrictions in the fluid conducting components. Energy losses due to this part of flow resistance show up as pressure drops — and account for the downward slope of the energy level curves, Figure 1.4. The shapes of these curves remain the same for any constant flow in any given system, **regardless** of overall pressure level. By far, the largest part of resistance to fluid flow comes from the load itself. Pressure[1] is an indication of the potential energy level of the fluid caused by load reaction distributed across the actuator interface area. As load reaction varies, pressure varies accordingly.

As illustrated in Figure 1.4, the effect of a varying load reaction is that of shifting the load-curve up and down between the no-load-level, representing the summation of pressure differentials ($\Sigma\Delta p$) only around the circuit; and the maximum load curve representing the upper load-reaction limit for which the system was designed for safe operation.

Other types of potential energy level transfer systems would exhibit analogous characteristics. Although kinetic energy transfer systems would show different characteristics, the concept would be similar.

---

1. *Russell W. Henke, Introduction to Fluid Mechanics (Addison Wesley, 1966) p. 5-9; p. 27.*

The preceding is a functional *definition* of energy transmission. It is within this context that this book on fluid power circuits and systems is written.

Figure 1.5 illustrates the energy transfer steps and relationships in an Energy Transmission System, from *prime mover* to *load*. The flow diagram at left (shaded section) represents the steps in the transfer process; the curves at right the energy level relationships corresponding to each step.

Design vs Analysis

Fluid power circuits and systems can be considered from a twofold standpoint:

1. **Design:** Design of a circuit implies a synthesis of an energy transfer system to perform a specific task.
2. **Analysis:** Analysis of a circuit implies the existence of a circuit to be analyzed with respect to its performance characteristics.

Design is a deductive process; *analysis* is inductive. This book provides a step-by-step approach to the deductive process of fluid power circuit design.

Important Terms

Fluid Power — A technology that deals with the transfer of power by means of potential energy changes in a fluid flowing at a controlled rate.

Kinetic Energy — Energy of motion. KE = 1/2 mv^2. In CU units: KE = $wv^2/2g$ = ft lb or in. lb. In SI metric units: KE = $kgm^2/2s^2$

Load — The complete performance characteristic of a machine expressed in load reaction (force) magnitude, sense and velocity for one complete machine cycle.

Potential Energy — Energy of state or stored energy. It is the capability of doing work. It can be expressed as *PE = Wh*. In CU units: lb × ft (or in.) = ft lb or in. lb. In SI metric units: $N \bullet m$

Power — The rate of doing work, or the rate of energy transfer. In CU units: HP = 550 ft lb/sec. = 33,000 ft lbs/min. In SI metric units: PW = joules/sec = watts.

Work — The use of energy. It is generally considered to be the product of a force and the distance through which it acts. In CU units: lb × ft (or in.) = ft lb or in. lb. In SI metric units: *Nm*

REVIEW EXERCISES

1. Name the three basic types of energy transmission technologies.
2. What common input-output characteristics are shared by the technologies named in question 1?
3. What are the three functional sections of an Energy Transmission System?
4. Describe the function of each section named in Question 3.
5. What three basic control functions exist in Energy Transmission Systems? Describe each.
6. Discuss the concept of "Load Domination" of an Energy Transmission System.
7. In a hydraulic system, what are the common terms used to denote the kinds of components used to implement each of the three function sections?
8. Discuss the effect of load-reaction magnitude on energy level in a hydraulic Energy Transmission System.
9. What physical variable is used to express energy level in a fluid power system?
10. Discuss the difference between the energy level variable in an "ideal" case and in an "actual" case.
11. Losses in a fluid power Energy Transmission System depend on what physical variable?
12. Explain why the two fluid system physical variables representing energy level and rate of energy transfer are said to be independent of each other.
13. Positive displacement pumps are erroneously called "pressure generators." What are they?
14. Distinguish between *design* and *analysis*.
15. Define *fluid power*.

CHAPTER 2

DEFINITIONS AND A SYSTEM OF CLASSIFICATION OF CIRCUITS

Having established the concept of fluid power systems as energy transfer systems, we must develop a language to use in talking about them. This chapter outlines a basic vocabulary to help design fluid systems in a logical and orderly manner.

OPEN-LOOP AND CLOSED-LOOP CIRCUITS

Fluid power systems can be divided into two major groups: open-loop and closed-loop.*

In a **closed-loop** system, a *feedback* mechanism continually monitors system output, generating a signal proportional to this output, and comparing it to an input or command signal. If the two match, there is no adjustment and the system continues to operate as programmed. If there is a difference between the input command signal and the feedback signal, the output is adjusted automatically to match command requirements.

There is no feedback mechanism in an **open-loop** system. The performance characteristics of the circuit are determined entirely by the characteristics of the individual components and their interaction in the circuit. A typical open-loop circuit is illustrated in Figure 2.1. Most industrial circuits fall in this category.

An *electrohydraulic servo system* is a feedback system in which the output is a mechanical position or function thereof, Figure 2.2

Open-loop circuits can be grouped by:

1. FUNCTIONS PERFORMED

Classification of open-loop circuits by function is related to the basic areas of control used in a fluid power system:

1. *Directional* controls regulate the direction of distribution of energy

2. *Flow* controls regulate the rate at which energy is transfered by adjusting flow rate in a circuit or branch of circuit

3. *Pressure* controls regulate energy transfer by adjusting pressure level or by using a specific pressure level as a signal to initiate a secondary action.

2. CONTROL METHODS

Directional control

Valve controls make use one of many types of directional control valves to regulate the distribution of energy throughout the circuit. These

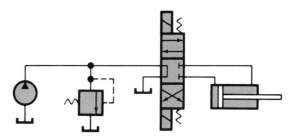

Fig. 2.1. Typical open loop circuit.

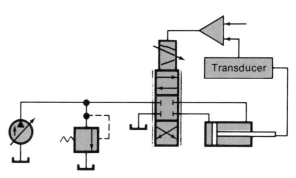

Fig. 2.2. Typical closed loop circuit.

The terms system *and* circuits *are used interchangeably.*

7

valves switch flow streams entering and leaving the valve.

Pump control is limited to reversal of direction of flow from a variable-displacement, reversible pump.

Fluid motor control is similar to pump control: it uses reversible, variable-displacement motors.

Flow Control

Valve controls use one of several types of pressure compensated or non-compensated flow control valves. The position of the flow control valve in the circuit determines the appropriate type to use:

Meter-in: flow control valve is between the source of energy (the pump) and the actuator, Figure 2.3(a).

Meter-out: flow control valve is in the return line from the actuator and controls energy transfer by limiting the rate of flow out of that actuator, Figure 2.3(b).

Bleed-off: flow control valve is in parallel with the actuator. It limits the rate of energy transfer to the actuator by controlling the amount bypassed through the parallel circuit, Figure 2.3(c).

Pump control involves the use of one of two methods, depending on the type of pump used. *Multiple* pumps provide a step variation in flow, Figure 2.4(a); *variable*-displacement pumps deliver infinitely (from zero to maximum) variable flows, Figure 2.4(b).

Fluid motor controls use techniques similar to pump controls and this involves the use of multiple motors, Figure 2.5(a) for step variation or variable-displacement motors, Figure 2.5(b), for infinite variation in output speeds.

Pressure control

Valve controls use one or more of six types of pressure control valves:

Relief valves limit the maximum energy level of the system by limiting maximum operating pressure, Figure 2.6.

Unloading valves regulate pressure level by bypassing return fluid to tank at a low energy level. Unloading valves shift when system pressure reaches a preset level, Figure 2.7.

Sequence valves react to a pressure signal to divert energy from a primary circuit to a secondary circuit, Figure 2.8.

Reducing valves react to a pressure signal to throttle flow to a secondary circuit, thus delivering energy at a lower level to the secondary than to the primary circuit, Figure 2.9.

Counterbalance valves control the potential energy differential across an actuator by maintaining a preset backpressure in the return line, Figure 2.10. Their purpose is to prevent a load from drifting.

Decompression valves provide controlled release

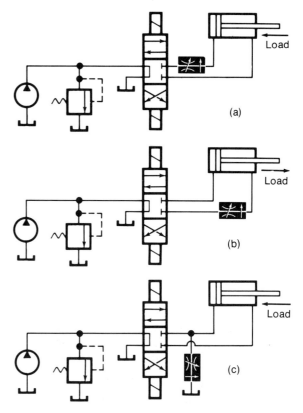

Fig. 2.3. Valve controls for open loop circuits: (a) meter in; (b) meter-out: (c) bleed-off.

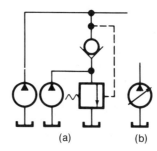

Fig. 2.4. Pump controls for open loop circuits: (a) multiple pumps, (b) variable displacement.

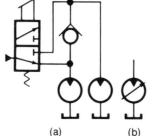

Fig. 2.5. Actuator controls for open loop circuits: (a) multiple fluid motors, (b) variable displacement.

of energy stored in high-pressure systems because of elasticity in the system, Figure 2.11.

Pump control of pressure fluid in open-loop circuits is generally achieved with pressure-compensated variable-displacement pumps. Energy transfer is controlled by varying flow from the pump in response to a pressure-level signal across the compensator, Figure 2.12.

Rotary actuator control of fluid pressure is not generally used.

3. TYPES OF OPEN-LOOP CIRCUITS

There are two basic types of open-loop circuits, constant flow and demand flow.

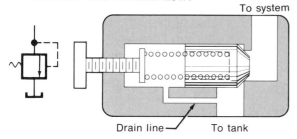

Fig. 2.6. Pressure relief valve regulates system output fluid pressure.

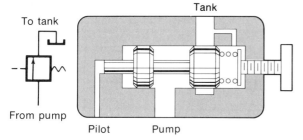

Fig. 2.7. Pressure unloading valve unloads pump output to tank at low pressure when high pressure flow is not required.

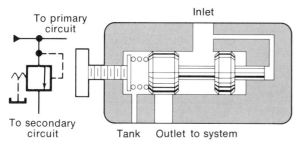

Fig. 2.8. Sequence valve prevents fluid from entering one branch of a circuit until a preset pressure is reached in the main circuit.

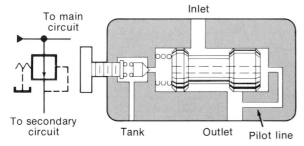

Fig. 2.9. Pressure reducing valve allows one branch of a circuit to operate at a lower pressure than the main system.

Constant flow circuits

In a typical *constant* flow circuit, Figure 2.13, the directional control valve bypasses fluid to tank when the valve is in center or neutral position, (shown) thus unloading the pump to reservoir. This circuit has a fixed displacement pump protected by a relief valve, a design frequently used in fluid power systems.

Energy transfer starts from a low (essentially zero) level when the valve is in neutral, and builds as the operator shifts the valve. As the valve continues to shift, the fluid stream flows into the actuator — linear or rotary — and thus begins to act against a load resistance.

Internal leakage is normally minimal when the valve is in center position, unless the actuator is supporting a load in an elevated position. Gener-

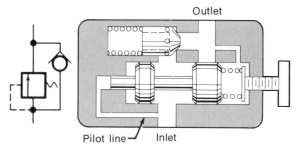

Fig. 2.10. Counterbalance valve holds fluid pressure in part of a circuit to counterbalance weight on external force.

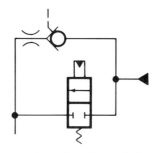

Fig. 2.11. Decompression valve releases fluid at controlled rate energy stored in high pressure system.

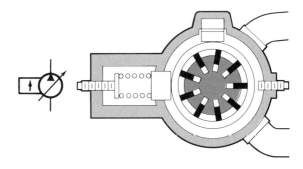

Fig. 2.12. Pressure compensated, variable displacement pump. Governor spring loads pump toward full displacement position. As output pressure rises, it supplies required force to stroke cam ring toward deadhead position.

ally, constant flow circuits are the most economical, provided they meet performance requirements.

Demand flow circuits

Figure 2.14 illustrates a typical *demand* flow circuit. This circuit uses a fixed-displacement pump, an unloading valve, and an accumulator.

Demand flow circuits have these characteristics:

All ports are blocked when the directional control valve is in center or neutral position, (shown).

If a fixed-displacement pump is used, an accumulator is ordinarily included and an unloading valve is required.

Energy transfer starts from the maximum pressure setting of the system. The energy is available

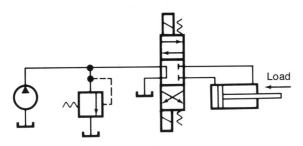

Fig. 2.13. Typical constant flow circuit. When 4-way, 3-position, solenoid actuated valve is in center (neutral) position, pump flow unloads to tank at atmospheric pressure.

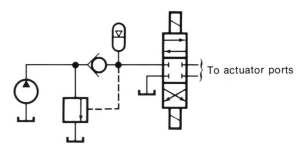

Fig. 2.14. Typical demand flow circuit. All ports are blocked when valve is in center position, as shown.

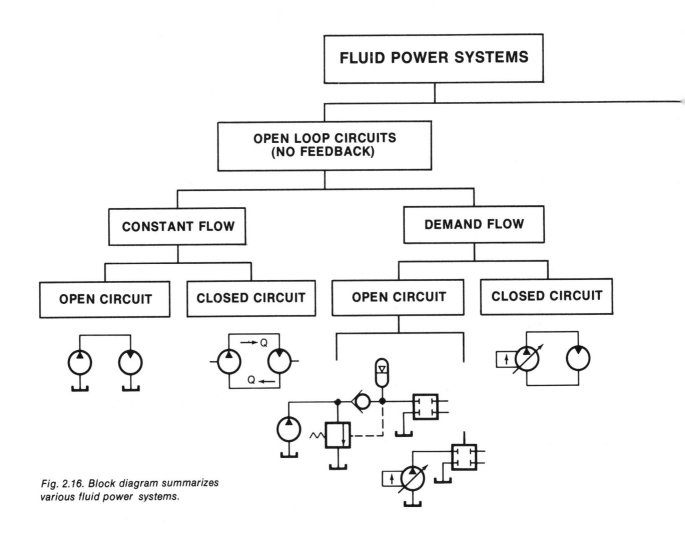

Fig. 2.16. Block diagram summarizes various fluid power systems.

to the actuator as soon as the valve is shifted. Internal leakage is of greater concern here than in constant flow circuits because the valve is holding against full system pressure at all times.

Figure 2.15 shows another version of a *demand* flow circuit. This one uses a pressure-compensated, variable displacement pump instead of the combination of fixed-displacement pump, accumulator, and unloading valve illustrated in the circuit in Figure 2.14. The charac-

teristics of the circuit in Figure 2.15 are the same as those in Figure 2.14. Figure 2.16 summarizes these circuits.

4. APPLICATIONS

1. Metal cutting machines tools
Feed circuits regulate the speed of an actuator by providing flow control.

Transfer circuits provide direction control primarily. They are used where it is desirable to regulate acceleration, velocity, or deceleration. A transfer circuit also provides secondary flow control.

Clamping circuits provide direction control, and possibly pressure control as a secondary function.

Spindle-drive circuits provide flow control primarily, but may be used for secondary pressure control.

2. Metal forming machines
Heavy stamping presses
  • Prefill circuits (primarily direction control)
  • Work-stroke circuits (pressure control)

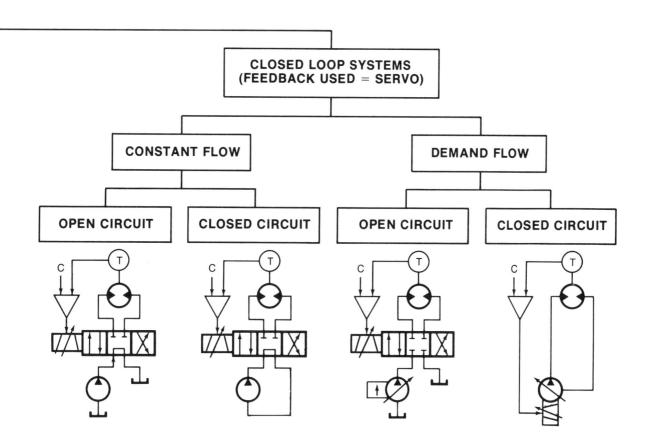

Fig. 2.15. Alternate demand flow circuit equipped with variable displacement, pressure compensated pump.

To actuator ports

•Retraction circuits (primarily direction control) — their function includes decompression

•Knockout circuits (auxiliary circuit applications, and also direction control)

•Transfer circuits (directional control)

3. Materials handling

These applications use *positioning circuits*, which operate as one of two kinds of mechanisms:

•*Transfer mechanisms* which provide direction control, and are equipped with a mechanical stop or limit switch.

•*Indexing mechanisms* which provide direction control.

4. Mobile equipment, aircraft, aerospace, marine

These applications use a variety of circuit functions, depending on machine type.

Mobile Equipment

These circuits use positioning and velocity control, both linear and rotary.

•Attachment mechanisms use linear actuators with direction, flow — and sometimes pressure — control

•Lift mechanisms use linear actuators with directional, flow and pressure control

•Steering mechanisms use linear actuators with directional and flow control

•Hydrostatic transmissions use rotary pumps and motors with directional and flow — and sometimes pressure — control.

Aircraft/Aerospace

•Landing gear retract mechanisms use linear actuators with directional control,

•Flaps and wing slots use linear or rotary actuators with directional, flow and pressure control

•Control surfaces are operated primarily by linear actuators with directional and flow control

•Cargo handling mechanisms use linear and rotary actuators with directional and flow control

Marine

These circuits utilize positioning, flow and pressure control in a variety of functions

•Winches and windlasses use rotary drives with directional and flow — and sometimes pressure — control

•Steering mechanisms use linear actuators with directional and flow control

•Cargo handling mechanisms use linear and rotary actuator with directional and flow control

•Hydroplane control mechanism use linear actuator with directional and flow control.

This chapter has classified and brought into perspective some industrial types and uses of fluid power circuits. It also developed a basic technical vocabulary. It is essential that the student of fluid power master the proper terminology and language at the outset.

Important Terms

Open-loop circuit - one without feedback.

Closed-loop circuit - one with feedback.

Valve control - where control is exercised by valving components.

Pump control - where control is exercised by pump components.

Actuator control - where control is exercised by fluid motor components.

Constant flow circuit - a circuit in which the directional control valve directs fluid flow from a fixed displacement pump to tank (instead of to the actuator) when the valve is in neutral (center) position.

Demand flow circuit - a circuit in which all ports of the directional control valve are blocked when the valve is in neutral position. A demand flow circuit consists of a pressure compensated pump or a fixed displacement pump and an unloading valve.

REVIEW EXERCISES

1. Discuss the differences between *open loop* and *closed loop* systems.

2. Why is it important to keep these terms (Question 1) specific and unambiguous?

3. What is a *feedback* signal? How is it used?

4. On what factor(s) do the performance characteristics of an *open loop* system depend?

5. What is a *servo-system*?

6. What is meant by an *open circuit*?

7. What is meant by a *closed circuit*?

8. How do the terms of Questions 6 and 7 differ from *open loop* and *closed loop*?

9. What are the three functions of *open loop* circuits?

10. By what methods can *open loop* circuit control functions be achieved?

11. Discuss *open-loop* circuit flow control.

12. Discuss *open-loop* circuit pressure control.

13. What are the basic types of *open loop* circuits? Discuss characteristics of each.

14. Describe and characterize each of the kinds of circuits and systems summarized in Figure 2.16.

15. Make up your own list of circuits as classified by types of applications.

CHAPTER 3

CRITERIA FOR DESIGNING OPEN-LOOP CIRCUITS

As defined in chapter 2, an open-loop circuit is one in which there is no feedback. In such a circuit, the characteristics of the components and their interactions determine the degree of control with which the circuit transfers energy from an energy source to an output device. Since different applications call for different circuit designs, how does one design a circuit that is most appropriate for a particular application?

Before we can start designing a fluid power circuit competently, it is necessary to develop an analytical technique that will enable us to approach the design problems in an orderly and systematic manner. The basic task in developing this technique is creating a **design check list** which specifies and describes the:

1. job to be done,
2. time per work cycle,
3. flow pattern for the work cycle,
4. pressure pattern for the work cycle, and
5. horsepower demand pattern.

This list says nothing about hardware components and their selection; it includes only items related to the basic character of the design problem. Evaluating the items on the check list provides the designer with a **"cycle profile"** which will enable him to do a better job of selecting and matching components to the particular circuit performance requirements. An analysis of each of these five elements will help develop a *cycle-profile technique*. An ideal case is discussed in this chapter.

1. JOB TO BE DONE

The purpose of every fluid power circuit is to transfer energy to an output device, or actuator, for the purpose of doing useful work, such as moving a load. Before attempting to design a circuit, it is essential to fully understand the concept of a *load*.

Types of loads

There are three types of loads:

A **resistive load**, Figure 3.1, is one which opposes the motion of the actuator. The direction of the load reaction is **opposite** to the direction of motion of the actuator. A resistive load, sometimes called a *positive load*, may be either *constant* — where the magnitude of the load remains the same — or *variable* — where the magnitude of the load varies.

An **overrunning load,** Figure 3.2, is one which joins forces, so to speak, with the motion of the actuator. Load reaction is in the **same** direction as the actuator motion. An overrunning load is sometimes called a *negative* load. Like a resistive load, an overrunning load may be either constant

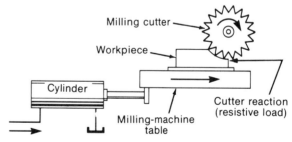

Fig. 3.1. A resistive load is one in which load reaction on the output device opposes the motion of the actuator.

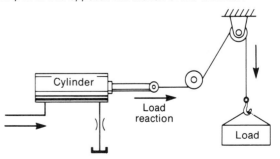

Fig. 3.2. An overrunning load is one in which load reaction on the output device has the same direction as the motion of the actuator, or augments it.

13

or variable.

An **inertial load**, Figure 3.3, best illustrated by flywheel, is one in which load reaction on the actuator is essentially characterized by Newton's Second Law of Motion:

$$F = ma \text{ or } T = J\alpha$$

These three types of loads, singly and in combination, represent the range of situations that the designer may encounter while designing fluid power circuits.

It is important to mention that a purely *resistive load* can exist **only** in a system in which load velocity is *constant*. This also applies to a purely overrunning load. All fluid power systems, however, undergo *changes* in velocity. During these periods of changing velocities, the load is of the inertial type. This point is discussed in detail in chapters 4 and 5.

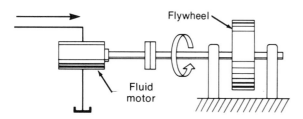

Fig. 3.3. An inertial load is one in which the load is predominantly in a steady state of motion so the reaction on the output device, when a change of state occurs, follows Newton's Second Law of Motion.

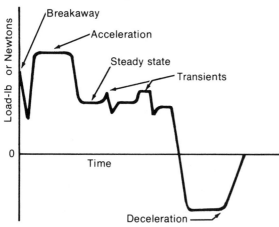

Fig. 3.4. Typical load-magnitude cycle plot for a cylinder.

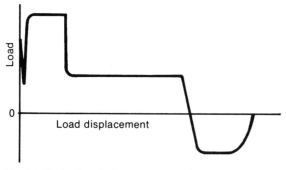

Fig. 3.5. Typical load-displacement cycle plot for a cylinder.

Cycle plot

After he has determined the type of load he is dealing with, the designer's next step is to make a *load-magnitude cycle plot*: a graphic representation of the magnitude of the load reaction during the various portions of the work cycle. If a linear actuator is used, the work cycle takes place while the piston rod is stroking. In this case load magnitude (in pounds or Newtons) is plotted on the ordinate as a function of stroke, which is plotted on the abscissa. Figure 3.4 shows a typical load-magnitude plot for a cylinder.

Five factors affect the shape of the curve:

• *Breakaway force or torque*. The magnitude of the load reaction is high at the beginning of the work cycle because energy must be supplied to overcome static friction in addition to any direct load reaction applied to the actuator in its resting state.

• *Acceleration*. The magnitude of the load reaction rises again because energy must be supplied to overcome inertia and a dynamic friction component.

• *Steady state*. During this phase of the work cycle the actuator moves the load at *constant* velocity. A dynamic friction force component is also involved here.

• *Transient load variations*. These are due to any changes in load magnitude during the load cycle.

• *Deceleration*. The magnitude of the load reaction drops because of the stopping reaction that occurs (implied in Newton's Second Law of Motion). Once again, there is a dynamic friction force component.

Once the designer has drawn a load-magnitude cycle plot, he can characterize the load even more specifically by making a *load-displacement cycle plot*. This involves plotting load magnitude against the percentage of the cycle over which each magnitude is applied, Figure 3.5. Later, after a total cycle time has been determined, the time for each part of the cycle can readily be found from the plot. If a linear actuator, such as a cylinder, is used, cycle displacement is measured in terms of *stroke*. If a rotary actuator is used, cycle displacement is measured in *radians*.

2. TIME PER WORK CYCLE

Cycle time must be determined before the other circuit parameters can be evaluated. Time affects circuit design in two important ways: it sets the

• flow requirements relative to the cycle displacement pattern.

• horsepower requirements of the circuit or branch of the circuit.

Cycle Timing

Cycle times can be determined from four criteria:

1. **Minimum overall cycle time**. The designer uses

this criterion when his basic purpose is to get the job done as fast as is reasonably and safely possible. This approach is likely to result in the highest horsepower demands.

2. **Critical sector.** One segment of the cycle is of paramount importance, and it dictates the time span. This segment might well be the time during which the useful work of the cycle is performed, the rest being allocated to such related functions as transfer, clamping, and retraction.

3. **Constant power.** The designer's uppermost concern is to use a constant flow of energy during periods of varying load. For example, he might want shorter times when load levels are low (*i.e.*, when flow is high and pressure is low), such as occur during "rapid traverse" in a feed circuit. Or he might want longer time intervals during periods of heavy load (*i.e.*, when flow is low and pressure is high), such as occur while feeding through a milling cutter.

4. **Constant speed, variable power.** The designer applies this criterion when he plans to use a constant-displacement pump with a variable load — provided there is no loss of pressure fluid over a relief valve, which would, otherwise introduce a discontinuity into the cycle.

When the designer reaches the point where he must determine the cycle time for a real circuit, he must almost always compromise between his desire to achieve the fastest, most efficient cycle possible and the need to minimize the costs of equipment and controls. Thus, in practical circuit design it is likely that the question of cycle time will be considered from more than one of the above points of view.

Effect of Actuator Selection

Before evaluating circuit parameters any further, the designer must *tentatively* select an actuator because combination of actuator displacement and cycle time, will establish fluid flow rates. In addition, the design pressure level, P_l, required for the load cycle will determine the geometry of the actuator.

If the actuator is a cylinder, the required stroke can be determined from the load-displacement cycle plot. The stroke will reflect one of the basic parameters of the design: namely, how the actuator is to transfer the load. The cylinder bore will be a function of the design pressure level, $A_p = F_l/p_d$. As a practical matter, pressure level is selected in accordance with accepted practice, and the cylinder bore is then jointly determined from the pressure level and load reaction. Sometimes another consideration, *i.e.* the structural (columnar) strength of the cylinder's piston rod, will dictate the cylinder bore.

When a fluid motor is used, the design pressure level is usually established before a specific motor is selected. The designer substitutes the pressure

level into the torque equation
$$T = \Delta p V m/2\pi,$$
and the resulting value for torque helps determine the geometric characteristics that the motor must have to fulfill its function. He can calculate flow, Q, from the displacement of the fluid motor and rotational velocity, $Q = V_m \times N$ and horsepower from
$$HP = (\Delta p \times Q)/1714$$
where pressure differential Δp is in psi and flow rate Q is in gpm. He now has enough data to select an appropriate actuator. Once selected, the system designer can draw the three remaining plots necessary to complete the cycle profile.

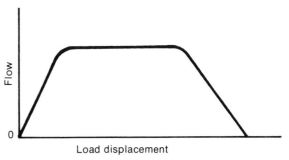

Fig. 3.6. *Typical flow-displacement profile plot for a cylinder.*

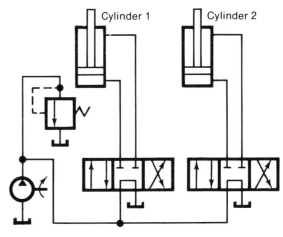

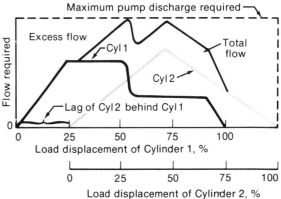

Fig. 3.7. *For circuits with multiple branches, the sum of the flows for all branches gives the total flow rate the pump must deliver at any point in the cycle.*

3. FLOW PATTERN PLOT

The designer must prepare several flow plots. The first is the **flow pattern**, based on the nature of the actuator and the (previously determined) cycle time. Flow rate is not necessarily constant throughout the cycle: in fact, the designer should calculate flows for the various segments of the cycle, then plot flow against the displacement (or time) pattern, as was done for the load-displacement profile, Figure 3.6.

The flow pattern is very important because it shows how flow rate varies in different segments of the cycle. Note that for circuits with multiple branches, the **sum** of the flows for all the branches yields the total flow rate the pump must deliver at any point in the cycle, Figure 3.7. This plot can therefore suggest ways in which you might solve subtle and complex questions of design, such as how to use the flow from one branch of a circuit to regeneratively supply another; or when to switch from a constant flow to a demand flow system.

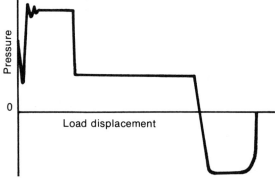

Fig. 3.8. *Pressure vs load displacement plot shows how fluid pressure varies during cycle.*

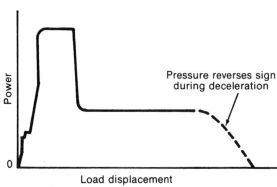

Fig. 3.9. *Power cycle profile is obtained by synthesizing flow and pressure pattern plots.*

4. PRESSURE PATTERN PLOT

The second plot that hinges on the selection of the actuator is the pressure pattern. This can be

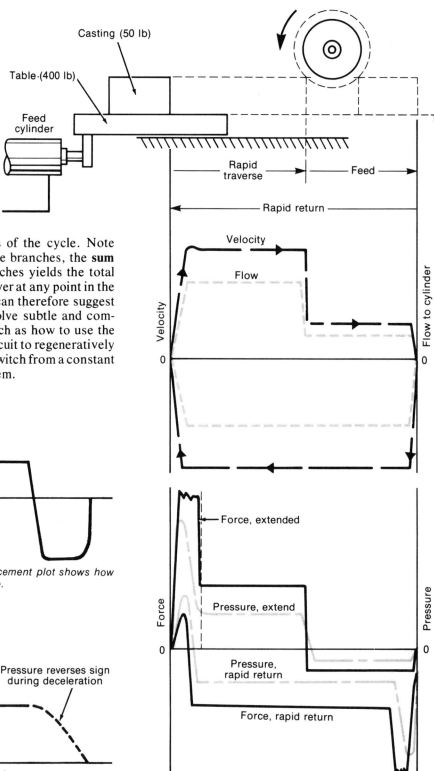

Fig. 3.10. *Typical complete profile diagram of a work cycle.*

determined from the load-displacement cycle plot and the geometry of the actuator. A plot of pressure against load displacement will show how fluid pressure varies during the cycle, Figure 3.8.

5. POWER DEMAND PATTERN PLOT

The final plot in the cycle profile can be made by synthesizing the flow and the pressure pattern plots. This is the power pattern: the variation in the power requirement during the load cycle as determined from the flow and pressure plots, Figure 3.9. The pattern provides a graphic image of power demands on the pump as the load moves through its cycle.

A typical complete cycle profile appears in Figure 3.10. This profile diagram is also discussed in more detail in Chapter 5.

So far the designer has been concerned with analyzing and characterizing the load of a fluid power circuit as completely as possible. The experienced designer will follow intuitively many of the steps outlined, perhaps even without realizing that he is doing so.

In complicated circuits, however, even the most experienced designer may overlook an important feature unless he takes the trouble to prepare a visual guide that lists the sequence of events that must take place in the circuit. The techniques outlined in this chapter are designed to help develop that visual guide.

Once he has made a cycle profile of a real application, the designer can explore the many possibilities for circuit design and be confident that he has not overlooked a vital step or operation.

Nomenclature	
a - Linear acceleration	p - Pressure
F - Force	Q - Flow
J - Mass moment of inertia	T - Torque
m - Mass	A - Angle in radians

Important Terms

Cycle profile — the name of a method for graphically displaying the condition of circuit variables at *any point* during the work cycle.

Resistive load — one for which the load reaction opposes (is opposite in sense to) the motion of the actuator input element.

Overrunning load — one for which the load reaction has the same sense as the motion of the actuator input element.

Inertial load — one for which the condition of the output from the system tends to remain in a given state unless some external force acts to change that state. The most common example is the flywheel.

Review Exercises

1. What factors determine the energy transfer and control characteristics of an open loop circuit?
2. What is a *cycle-profile* for an application of a hydraulic system?
3. Why should a system designer use a *cycle-profile*?
4. What is the *load* as it relates to a fluid power system?
5. Name the types of *loads* encountered by fluid power systems.
6. What factor characterizes each type of *load*?
7. Write the algebraic equation for Newton's Second Law of Motion in linear and rotary form.
8. Discuss each of the variables included in the equations of Newton's Second Law.
9. Discuss the implications of inertia effects on fluid power system performance.
10. Discuss why actual *loads* on fluid power systems occur only in combinations of two or three of the load types discussed in question 5.
11. What kinds of plots constitute a *cycle-profile*?
12. Discuss the implications of each of the plots for fluid power system design.
13. What is the difference between *load* and *load magnitude*?

14. What factors affect the load-magnitude plot? Discuss each as it relates to circuit design.
15. Describe the difference, if any, between a load-displacement plot and a load-magnitude plot.
16. Is there any relationship between the terms load-displacement and actuator/motor displacement? Discuss.
17. What are the effects of cycle time on a fluid power circuit design?
18. What time criteria can be used in designing a fluid power circuit? How many criteria are there?
19. Discuss the implications of each of the time-criteria for circuit performance.
20. Who makes a decision on which time-criteria to use as the basis for a circuit design? How is this decision made?
21. Discuss the difference, if any, between design pressure level and system pressure level. Are they ever the same?
22. What determines system pressure level? What or who determines design pressure level?
23. Where does the pressure-plot come from?
24. Discuss the role of design pressure in sizing actuators and motors.
25. Given a design-pressure of 3000 psi, a cylinder

has:

a. a resistive load of 900,000 lb acting on its piston rod. Calculate the theoretical area required on the cap end of the piston to balance this load reactor;

b. an overrunning load of 450,000 lb acts on the piston rod. What head end piston area would be required to counterbalance this load with a back pressure of 3000 psi?

c. assume that the resistive load decreases to 600,000 lb, what would be system pressure on the cap end of the piston, calculated in part 25a, above?

d. if the designer sized the cylinder according to the above calculations, discuss whether or not it would work in an actual application involving these parameters.

26. Optional Exercise: Recalculate problem 25 using SI metric units.

27. Given a design pressure of 2000 psi, an hydraulic motor has:

a. a resistive load torque of 1593 lb-in acting on its shaft. Calculate the theoretical motor displacement required to balance this load reaction;

b. if the same motor had an overrunning load torque of 1593 lb-in acting on its shaft, what backpressure would be required to balance it?

c. assume the above motor had a backpressure of 400 psi at its return port under conditions of part 27a, above, what effect would this have on input pressure?

d. if the above motor were used in an actual application, would it function as intended? Discuss.

28. Optional Exercise: Recalculate problem 27 using SI metric units.

29. Outline the design sequence required to size an actuator and the effect it has on establishing circuit parameters.

30. What factors influence constricting the *flow-profile* plot?

31. Is it necessary to use the pressure-plot to size the actuator or motor before calculating the required flow rates? Discuss.

32. Referring to problem 25: Use the actuator sized in solving problem 25. Assume the stroke is 36 inches and it takes 10 seconds for the actuator to move the load 36''.

a. calculate the average load velocity,

b. calculate the average input flow rate,

c. if the designer specifies a pump that can deliver exactly this calculated flow rate, would performance requirements of the application be met? Discuss.

33. Optional Exercise: Recalculate problem 32 using SI metric units.

34. Referring to problem 27: Using the motor sized in problem 27 and assume a maximum steady state speed of 2000 rpm.

a. calculate the average flow rate required,

b. if the pump was sized to meet this average flow rate, would the system meet performance requirements of the application? Discuss.

35. Optional Exercise: Recalculate problem 34 using SI metric units.

36. Discuss the implication of a flow rate plot such as shown in Fig. 3.7 for circuit design. Discuss the relationships between branch cylinder performance requirements and specifications and the circuit flow profile plot.

37. Referring to problem 32: Calculate the hydraulic horsepower for the cylinder.

a. is this the horsepower delivered to the load? Discuss.

b. optional exercise: recalculate power using SI metric units.

38. Referring to problem 33: Calculate the hydraulic horsepower for the motor.

a. is this the horsepower delivered to the load? Discuss.

b. optional exercise: recalculate power using SI metric units.

39. Referring to Fig. 3.10: Discuss the cycle-profile illustrated.

a. relate the velocity plot to the flow rate plot. Explain variations and discuss implications for controlling the circuit.

b. discuss the force plot and relate it to the pressure plot.

c. explain why the force is plotted below the axis (negative) during the "*feed*" part of the cycle.

d. what causes the high force peaks at start up during the rapid traverse and rapid return parts of the cycle?

e. why does the plot show a load reversal at the end of each of these parts of the cycle?

f. what is the implication of "points-of-inflection" (points where the load force plots cross the axis) of the force plot for control of the circuit?

g. discuss the implications of "positive" and "negative" pressures as plotted in the pressure-profile. Does "negative" pressure mean a vacuum, in this situation? Discuss.

40. Explain the statement: "The *cycle-profile* for a hydraulic circuit application provides a graphic representation of what the circuit is required to do." Explain how a *cycle-profile* increases the confidence level of a fluid power circuit designer.

CHAPTER 4

ANALYZING
RESISTIVE LOADS

The design of any circuit must begin with a thorough understanding and analysis of the functions the circuit is to perform. The first design step is an analysis of the load and of the load cycle, then the sequence in which events will take place as the circuit performs its functions. In Chapter 3, we classified loads into three basic types. Before discussing resistive loads in detail, let us first review three basic types of loads.

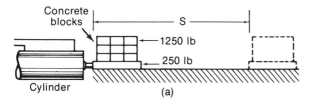

Concrete blocks
S
1250 lb
250 lb
Cylinder
(a)

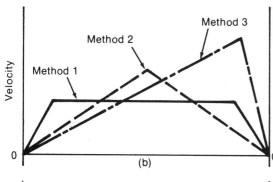

Method 3
Method 2
Method 1
Velocity
0 (b) 0

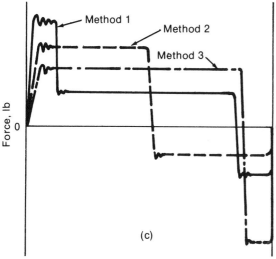

Method 1
Method 2
Method 3
Force, lb
0 0
(c)

Fig. 4.1(a). Simple resistive load: cylinder must move a pallet weighing 250 lb and supporting a load of concrete blocks weighing 1250; (b) three typical methods for moving the load; (c) typical force plots for the methods illustrated in Fig. 4.1(b).

1. A **resistive load** is one in which the load reaction on the output device opposes the motion of the actuator.
2. An **overrunning load** is one in which the load reaction on the output device has the same direction as the motion of the actuator, or increases it.
3. An **inertial load** is one in which the load is predominantly in a steady state of motion, linear or rotary, so that when a change of state occurs, the reaction on the output device follows Newton's Second Law of Motion: $F = ma$ or $T = J\alpha$.

These loads can be either **constant** or **variable**, namely steady-state or time-variant. As a practical matter, there is no such thing as a constant resistive load. Every system must start from a zero-velocity condition and accelerate to some operating velocity; during this start-up phase, the load is partly inertial. However, a load can be predominantly resistive, and this is what the term "resistive load" means.

Some resistive loads are predominantly resistive even during startup, such as extrusion press rams, broaches, and burnishing machine rams. Others, however, such as machine-tool carriage feed cylinders, have a variable-resistance load with a strong component of inertial load during acceleration.

RESISTIVE LOAD

To illustrate load analysis for a simple resistive load, consider, for example, the application of Figure 4.1(a). In this transfer application, we want to move a 1250-lb load of concrete blocks on a pallet, weighing 250 lb, through a distance S.

Several methods

One of the first problems the designer must resolve is: What motion cycle will be used? Three typical cycles or methods are illustrated in Figure 4.1(b). The *first* consists of an acceleration to a predetermined velocity, a constant-velocity transfer to some point, and a deceleration to the end of the stroke. The *second* method consists of an acceleration for a distance of $1/2S$, then a deceleration over the remaining $1/2S$. In the *third* method illustrated, the load is accelerated over the greater part of the stroke and decelerated quickly at the very end. Other methods might include simple harmonic motion.

Which of these methods offers the optimum design is really a matter of engineering judgment.

19

In Method 1, the slope of the acceleration portion of the velocity curve is quite steep; hence, initial pressure would have to be high to generate the force necessary, according to the equation $F = ma$. In addition, some consideration would have to be given to the type of load being moved. You can accelerate rapidly a stack of blocks in a relatively safe manner. However, if you attempted this with a pallet load of shafts headed for a heat-treat furnace, the results might be less than satisfactory. On the other hand, the low, constant velocity required by Method 1 would make it possible for the designer to specify a smaller, more economical pump.

In Method 2, operating pressure would likely be less than for Method 1, as indicated by the more gradual slope of the acceleration curve. However, maximum velocity reached is greater. If we assume, for the moment, that the same size cylinder is specified, then a larger pump would be needed. Actually, the need for a larger pump might be partly offset by the possibility of using a smaller cylinder.

With Method 3, the acceleration force would be smaller than with either of the other two. However, final velocity would be greater, and thus Method 3 would require the largest pump.

Force analysis

The problem still remains: which is the best design approach? If minimum, absolute cycle time is the dominant criterion, then the three methods would have to be analyzed to determine which would require the least transfer time. If cycle time is relatively unimportant, then Method 1 would likely be the simplest. However, other considerations might make it necessary to adopt different selection criteria.

Typical force plots are shown in Fig. 4.1(c). Method 1 requires more force than either of the other two methods during acceleration, but less during constant-velocity transfer because all the cylinder must do during that phase of the cycle is to overcome the frictional resistance to motion of the pallet. During deceleration the force becomes negative, but because of the effect of friction it is not quite as high as the start-up force.

With Method 2 the acceleration force is not as high as with Method 1, but it is applied during the full half-cycle; the force, then, becomes negative during deceleration. It would appear that the *total* force required is greater for Method 2 than for Method 1.

Method 3 requires the lowest force, but it is applied for the longest time. Because the system reaches a high velocity, the deceleration force is considerably larger than the acceleration force. This fact, coupled with the differential area in the cylinder, could cause pressure problems on the head end of the cylinder.

Let us assume that we have decided to use Method 1 for the application in Fig. 4.1(a), and that the pallet load of concrete blocks must be moved a distance of 6 ft. Therefore, cylinder stroke must also be 6 ft, or 72 in. We further assume an average coefficient of friction between the pallet and the surface of the ramp of 0.15 for dynamic friction and 0.25 for static friction.

Step 1. We calculate friction force from
$$F_f = \mu W$$
where μ is the coefficient of friction and W is the force normal to the direction of motion. Thus we have two friction forces: a *breakaway* force due to static friction:
$$F_{fb} = 0.25 \times 1500 \text{ lb} = 375 \text{ lb}$$

and a *running* force, due to dynamic friction:

$$F_{fr} = 0.15 \times 1500 \text{ lb} = 225 \text{ lb}$$

Step 2. The acceleration force or reaction on the piston rod can be calculated from Newton's Second Law:
$$F_a = ma$$
where mass $m = W/g$, and acceleration $a = (v_2 - v_1)/t$.
Since $v_1 = 0$, then $a = v_2/t$,
$$F_a = (1500/32)(v_2/t)$$
The designer must now determine the velocity, time available for acceleration, and time available for deceleration. In general, the requirements for the application will determine the time available for the cycle. In this example, such requirements might include the desired number of pallet loads to be transferred per unit time and the time it takes to load and unload a pallet at each end of the stroke. Let us assume that we have considered these requirements and have decided on a cycle time of 1 min. We allow 10 sec for the return of the empty pallet and 15 sec for the actual transfer. We further assume that it takes $0.1t$ of the transfer time to accelerate the load to a constant transfer velocity, and $0.1t$ for decelerating. This leaves $0.8t$ for constant-velocity transfer. For this open-loop application we can make sufficiently precise calculations using average values of velocity, acceleration, and deceleration.

Step 3. Let us determine the average velocity of transfer. As indicated, the total stroke of the cylinder is 72 in. or 6 ft. During the first $0.1t$ sec, the load will move a distance of
$$S_1 = 1/2at^2_1$$
But, since $a = v_2/t_1$
$$S_1 = 1/2(v_2/t_1)t^2_1 = 1/2v_2t_1$$
During the next $0.8t$ sec, the load will move a distance

$$S_2 = v_2 \times 0.8t$$

at constant velocity, and during deceleration the load will travel the remaining distance. In this example, $S_3 = S_1$, since deceleration time equals acceleration time. (Note, however, that this need not always be the case.)

We can now equate the total distance of 72 in. that the load will move with the sum of the three partial distances S_1, S_2, and S_3:

$$S = 72 \text{ in.} = S_1 + S_2 + S_3$$
$$= 1/2v_2t_1 + 0.8v_2t + 1/2v_2t_3$$

However, since $t_1 = t_3 = 0.1t$,

$$S = 72 \text{ in.} = 0.05v_2t + 0.8v_2t + 0.05v_2t$$
$$= 0.9vt$$

Since we set $t = 15$ sec,

$$S = 72 \text{ in.} = 13.5v_2$$

Then,

$$v_2 = 5.44 \text{ ips or } 0.445 \text{ fps}$$

Step 4. We can now calculate the force required to accelerate the load. From Step 3, we see that

$$a = v_2/t_2 = 0.445 \text{ fps}/1.5 \text{ sec}$$
$$= 0.296 \text{ ft/sec}^2$$

and

$$m = W/g = 1500 \text{ lb}/(32.2 \text{ ft/sec}^2)$$
$$= 46.6 \text{ slugs}$$

Thus,

$$F_a = ma = 46.6 \times 0.296$$
$$= 13.8 \text{ lb}$$

Step 5. The total force required to start the load moving is the sum of the breakaway friction force and the acceleration force:

$$F_t = F_{fb} + F_a$$

$$= 375 \text{ lb} + 13.8 \text{ lb} = 388.8 \text{ lb}$$

However, we must also include a factor for cylinder friction. If we assume that the cylinder has an efficiency of 90 percent,

$$F_{t1} = 388.8/0.9 = 430 \text{ lb}$$

This breakaway force, Figure 4.2, is required to get the load started and to accelerate it to the constant-velocity portion of the transfer cycle.

Step 6. We can now calculate the force needed during constant-velocity transfer—namely the sum of the resistive loads on the piston rod. Since, in this example, the friction force constitutes the only load during constant-velocity transfer, the total force on the rod will be

$$F_{t2} = \mu W = 0.15 \times 1500 \text{ lb} = 225 \text{ lb}$$

Step 7. Next, we calculate the deceleration force on the piston rod:

$$F_{t3} = \text{inertial force} + \text{resistive friction force}$$
$$= mW - \mu W$$

(the minus sign indicates that the forces oppose motion); thus

$$F_{t3} = (46.6 \times 0.296) - (0.15 \times 1500)$$
$$= 13.8 \text{ lb} - 225 \text{ lb} = -211.2 \text{ lb}$$

Note that this calculation is similar to the one for the total force required to start the load moving, Step 5. However, the calculation in Step 5 involved *static* friction, whereas this one involves *dynamic* friction.

We should now discuss a subtle point which we purposely skipped earlier. As soon as the load starts moving, friction resistance changes from static to dynamic. Thus, while the breakaway force calculated must be supplied, the actual force over *most* of the acceleration period will be the same as that just calculated for deceleration. There is still another consideration: the acceleration we calculated is the average acceleration over the relatively long initial time period. However, consider the instant between zero velocity and the point when the system just starts to accelerate. In this infinitesimally short period of time, the system must undergo a finite change in velocity; thus it would appear that the acceleration at this instant would have to approach infinity. This, of course, is impossible.

But this analysis does help account for the initial pressure peak, Figure 4.2, which exceeds that calculated using breakaway friction and acceleration forces alone. Conceivably, we could never start such a system from a dead stop were it not for the ever-so-slight compressibility of the fluid and slip flow in circuit components, which provide the necessary finite time interval over which acceleration can start.

Step 8. The force and time cycles for this application have been plotted. The designer must now make one of his intuitive decisions: at what pressure level will the system operate? This is necessary because the cylinder bore will depend on the design pressure level.

For example, if we assume an operating pressure of 1000 psi, the required piston area is

$$A_p = F/p = 430 \text{ lb}/1000 \text{ psi}$$
$$= 0.430 \text{ in}^2$$

This would correspond to a cylinder bore of about 3/4 in. Thus, it should be apparent that the *structural requirements* of the piston rod will be the limiting parameter. A 1-in diameter rod would be needed to safely sustain the 430-lb-force through the 72-in. stroke. Thus, we must increase the cylinder bore to, say, 2 in. Now we recalculate system operating pressure:

$$p = F/A_p = 430 \text{ lb}/3.1416 \text{ in}^2$$
$$= 137 \text{ psi}$$

Although this is a low pressure level, it is, nevertheless, controlled by the structural requirements of the rod.

Step 9. We saw in Step 7 that a force of only 13.8 lb

applied during the $0.1t$ sec interval is enough to decelerate the load. However, if the load had been moving over a frictionless surface, this would have required a "back pressure" of

$$13.8 \text{ lb}/(3.1416 - 0.7854) \text{ in}^2 = 5.9 \text{ psi}$$

on the head end of the piston. However, since there is a resistive friction force of 225 lb, we must continue to drive the cylinder positively during part of the "deceleration" period to enable it to complete its full stroke. This is not the general rule; usually the velocity is fast enough and friction low enough that a deceleration pressure must be applied to the head end of the piston. However, this analysis points up the fact that one cannot arbitrarily assume this to be the case.

Step 10. The next step is to determine the flow-rate pattern over the cycle. In our simple example, maximum flow rate occurs during the constant-velocity transfer period:

$$Q = A_p v_2 = 3.1416 \text{ in}^2 \times 5.44 \text{ in/sec}$$
$$= 17.1 \text{ in}^3/\text{sec} = 4.43 \text{ gpm}$$

In a more complex application there may be several flow-rate changes during the course of the cycle. If a multibranched circuit is involved, the flow rates must be superimposed. The peak flow rate determined in this way dictates the required pump output capacity.

Step 11. In this example enough delay must be provided to enable a workman to unload the pallet

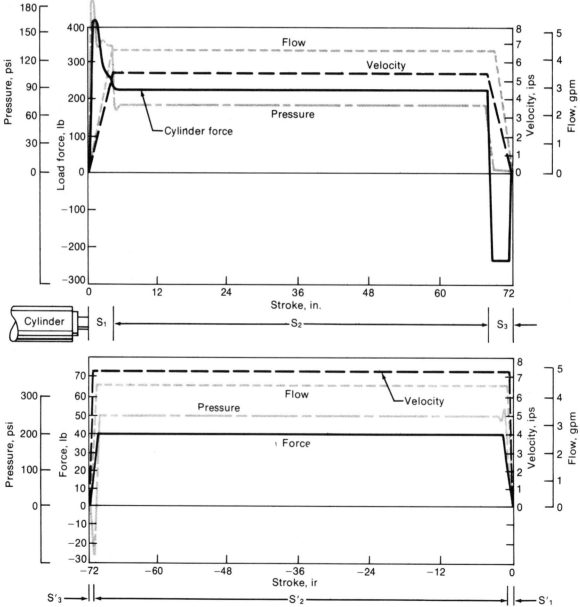

Fig. 4.2 Cycle profile for system shown in Fig. 4.1 shows relationship between load reaction (force) and pressure; and load velocity and flow rate during complete cycle.

22

before the cylinder is reversed. The usual procedure is either to have the workman initiate the return stroke manually or to interlock the return stroke with the unloading motion. In either case, the cylinder must return the empty pallet in the 10 sec allowed. The designer should try to utilize the full 4.43-gpm output from the pump, bypassing a minimum quantity over the relief valve during acceleration.

We now calculate the time t'_1 required for acceleration on the return stroke. The piston area on the rod side is

$$A_n = A_p - A_r = 3.146 \text{ in}^2 - 0.7854 \text{ in}^2$$
$$= 2.3562 \text{ in}^2$$

With an output of 4.43 gpm, the flow rate is 17.1 in³/sec. and piston velocity will be

$$v'_2 = Q/A_n = (17.1 \text{ in}^3/\text{sec})/2.3562 \text{ in}^2$$
$$= 7.27 \text{ ips}$$

Acceleration on the return stroke will be
$$a' = (v'_2 - v'_1)/t'_2$$
Since $v'_1 = 0$, then
$$a' = v'_2/t'_1 = 7.27/t'_1$$

If we set the relief valve to open at 250 psi, (remember that 137 psi were required during the extension stroke), the maximum force available for acceleration on the return stroke is:

$$F' = p'A_n = 250 \text{ psi} \times 2.3562 \text{ in}^2$$
$$= 590 \text{ lb}$$

Frictional resistance to motion on the return stroke is:

$$F'_f = \mu W' = 0.15 \times 250 \text{ lb} = 37.5 \text{ lb}$$

then,
$$F'_a = 590 \text{ lb} - 37.5 \text{ lb}$$
$$= 552.5 \text{ lb}$$

But, since
$$F'_a = m'a' = 250 \text{ lb}/(32.2 \text{ ft/sec}^2) \times a'$$

Therefore,
$$a' = 66 \text{ ft/sec}^2$$
Also, since
$$a' = v'_2/t'_1$$
Thus,
$$t'_1 = v'_2/a' = 7.27 \text{ ips}/12 (66 \text{ ft/sec}^2)$$
$$= 0.0092 \text{ sec.}$$

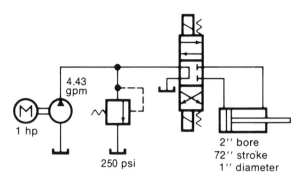

Fig. 4.3 Complete circuit indicates sizes of components as calculated in example.

Step 12. Having characterized the load cycle and plotted it, Figure 4.2, the designer can proceed with the selection of components and layout the circuit. For such a simple circuit the choice of components would likely be:
- fixed-displacement pump, probably gear type,
- 4-way, 3-position, spring-centered, open-center, and probably solenoid-operated directional control valve,
- direct-acting relief valve, and
- reservoir with a capacity of about 8 to 10 gal.

Assuming a pump efficiency, e, of about 75% the designer can now size the electric motor:

$$HP = pQ/1714e$$
$$= 250 \times 4.43/1714 \times 0.75 = 0.86$$

As a practical matter, he would specify a 1-hp electric motor. The complete circuit is shown in Figure 4.3.

Important Terms

Acceleration is an increasing change in velocity. Average acceleration over a period of time is $a = (v_2 - v_1)/t$. Instantaneous acceleration is $a = dv/dt = d^2s/dt^2$.

Deceleration is a decreasing change in velocity. The expressions for deceleration are the same as for acceleration except that the algebraic signs are negative rather than positive.

Velocity is the rate of transfer through a distance. Average velocity is $v = s/t$. Instantaneous velocity is $v = ds/dt$. Steady state velocity is $v = Q/Ap$ or $v = Q/Vm$.

REVIEW EXERCISES

1. What is the *first* step to consider in designing a fluid power circuit or system?

2. How does the *cycle profile* relate to Step 1?

3. Why should the designer always start at the "output end" of the circuit or system?

4. What are the names of the basic types of *loads*?

5. Discuss the basic criteria for each type of *load*.

6. What is the primary characteristic which defines the kind of *load* a designer is dealing with?

7. Is there ever a truly constant *load*? Discuss.

8. To what fundamental fluid power variable is *load* related?

9. To what fundamental fluid power variable is (load) *velocity* related?

10. Discuss the relationship between circuit actuator/motor velocity and load velocity.

11. What is the difference between load velocity and load acceleration/deceleration? Does it have any effect on performance characteristic(s)?

12. Referring to Fig. 4.1, discuss the relative characteristics of the three velocity profile plots shown for Methods 1, 2, and 3.

13. Referring to Fig. 4.1, discuss the shape of the force cycle plots as they relate to each of the velocity profile plots.

14. Referring to Fig. 4.1c, what is the meaning of the force curves crossing the axis in the cycle plot?

15. Referring to Fig. 4.1, which of the three methods illustrated 1, 2, and 3, would require the highest flow rate? Why?

16. Referring to Fig. 4.1, which of the three methods illustrated would require the highest system pressure? Why?

17. Discuss how Newton's Second Law of motion is applied in an analysis of a *load* such as that illustrated in Fig. 4.1.

18. Discuss the difference between average velocity and steady state velocity. On what fundamental parameter is each based?

19. Sketch a qualitative velocity profile of the type labeled Method 1, Fig. 4.1. Show qualitatively, the curve for steady state velocity and that for average velocity.

20. Discuss the concept of "breakaway" force as applied to an actuator.

21. What are the effects of static friction and dynamic friction on circuit performance? Is there a difference? If so, which is the greater?

22. Discuss why the *designer* must decide at what design pressure the system should operate.

23. Discuss the difference(s), if any, between design and actual system pressure level.

24. Relate the discussions of exercise questions 22 and 23 to the statement, "positive displacement" pumps do *not* generate pressure.

25. Rework the example problem shown in Chapter 4, Fig. 4.1, using Method 2. Use the same parameters except that *total* time is 15 sec and acceleration/deceleration periods are now 0.5 × time. Make necessary calculations and draw the cycle profile.

26. Rework the example problem of Fig. 4.1, using Method 3. Make necessary calculations and draw the cycle profile.

CHAPTER 5

ANALYZING OVERUNNING
AND INERTIAL LOADS

OVERRUNNING LOADS

Overrunning loads are characterized by the *load* reaction acting in the same direction as powered motion of the circuit output device. In Figure 5.1, the cable pull on the piston rod acts in the *same* direction as the incoming oil pushes the piston and rod.

Another overrunning load is illustrated in a milling machine. During the "climb milling" part of the work cycle, the cutter produces a load reaction which is in the same direction as the motion of the piston rod. A 50-lb casting is resting on a machine table weighing 400 lb; an additional 15-lb of clamps and other fastening devices hold the casting in place.

The horizontal distance the table travels is 18 in. The casting is 9 in. long, and let's assume that it is placed centrally on the machine table. Thus, the machine table traverses rapidly a distance of 4.5 in before it reaches the point where the cutter contacts the workpiece, 9 in. of feed travel while the cut is being made, and 13 1/2 in. of rapid return. The coefficient of friction for the machine ways and the table is about 0.1.

Step 1. The acceleration and rapid-traverse phases of the cycle are analyzed the same way as we did in the example of Chapter 4. The analysis is not repeated here.

Step 2. At the point where the workpiece contacts the cutter, the velocity must change to match the

desired feed rate, as shown in the velocity plot, Figure 5.2. The conventional method of achieving velocity change is to shift a directional control valve to bring the flow control valve into the circuit to act in a meter-out function.

Feed rate and piston velocity are determined from the machining characteristics of the material. As far as the fluid power circuit designer is concerned, this is a matter of methods engineering, and is an independent variable.

Step 3. The size of the overrunning load can be calculated from the size of the cutter and the horsepower of the motor that drives it. Assume that the cutter is 6 in. in diameter and that a 5-hp electric motor is driving it at 450 rpm.

First, calculate the torque from the equation

$$\text{HP} = TN/63,024$$
$$T = (63,024 \times \text{HP})/N$$
$$= (63,024 \times 5)/450$$
$$= 700 \text{ lb-in.}$$

The tangential force on the cutter which would produce this torque is found from the equation

$$T = F_t r$$
$$F_t = T/r = 700 \text{ lb-in}/3 \text{ in} = 233 \text{ lb}$$

The total load on the cylinder during the feed part of the cycle consists of the cutter force less the friction force resisting motion. Note that this is a *negative* force, that is, *opposite* in sense to the normal pressure force on the cylinder. A backpressure must be developed on the head end of the piston to hold it back. This is why the meter-out circuit is preferable. If a meter-in circuit were used, flow rate could be matched to feed requirements, but the cylinder would lose control of the overrunning load.

Step 4. The direction of motion must be reversed during the rapid-return phase of the work cycle to return the table to its home position. The method of analysis is the same as that used in the example of Chapter 4. Figure 5.2 shows how the velocity, flow, force, and pressure plots would look.

The circuit of Fig. 5.3 is designed to perform the work cycle for this application. The pump is sized on the basis of maximum flow rate calculated from the

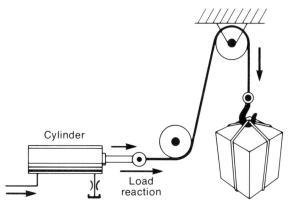

Fig. 5.1. Typical overrunning load: load reaction is in the same direction as powered actuator.

Cylinder

Load reaction

maximum piston velocity and piston area:

$$Q = A_p v_p e_v$$

The directional control valve is selected on the basis of manufacturers' specifications which relate flow rate to acceptable pressure drop across the valve. The cylinder is sized as in the example of Chapter 4. The cam-operated, 2-way valve directs flow to the flow control valve at the point where feed is to begin. Limit switch, LS-1, actuates the main directional control valve to reverse flow to the cylinder to retract the worktable. Limit switch, LS-2, de-energizes the directional control valve solenoids when the cylinder is fully retracted. This action neutralizes the 4-way, spring-centered valve, stopping the process until it is recycled externally.

The circuit in Figure 5.4 illustrates how the same functions might be achieved using a pressure compensated variable-displacement pump. All functions are the same as in Figure 5.3 except the feed part of the cycle. Whereas in Figure 5.3 a cam-operated, 2-way valve and a feed valve are used to regulate flow, in Figure 5.4 the compensator characteristics

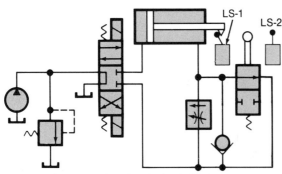

Fig. 5.3. Circuit equipped with fixed displacement pump. Cam-operated, 2-way valve regulates flow out of cylinder.

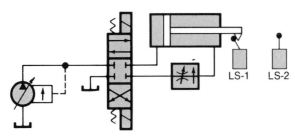

Fig. 5.4. Circuit equipped with pressure compensated variable displacement pump performs same functions as circuit illustrated in Fig. 5.3.

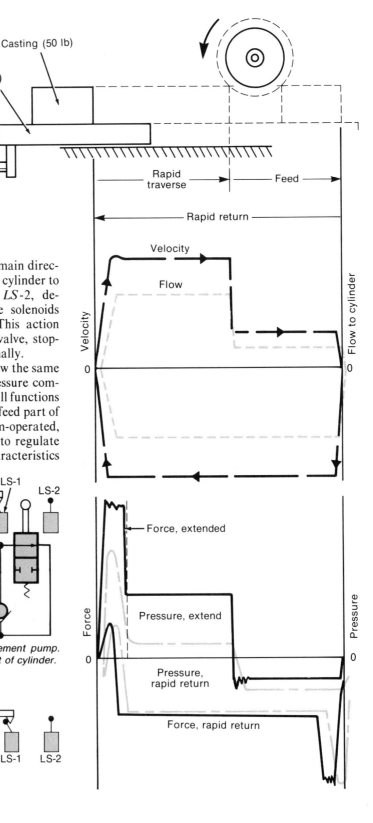

Fig. 5.2. Typical profile diagram of the work cycle of an overrunning load.

26

...ch the hydraulic motor to the operating cycle
l let acceleration take care of itself.

Step 2. Assume that the flywheel in the example has an outside diameter of 3 ft, an inside diameter of 2 ft and is 1 ft thick. Let's further assume that it is made of cast iron and that it weighs 1738 lb.

The moment of inertia of a ring, such as the rim a flywheel, is expressed in the equation

$$J_m = \int r^2 dm,$$

where

$$dm = \rho h \times 2\pi r\, dr$$
$$J_m = 2\pi\rho h \int_{R_2}^{R_1} r^3\, dr$$
$$= [(2\pi\rho h)/4]\,(R_1^4 - R_2^4).$$

But since

$$m = \text{total mass of flywheel rim}$$
$$= \pi\rho h(R_1^2 - R_2^2).$$

Therefore,

$$J_m = m \times \left[2\pi\rho h\,(R_1^2 + R_2^2)(R_1^2 - R_2^2) \right] / 4\pi\rho h(R_1^2 - R_2^2)$$
$$= \tfrac{1}{2}m(R_1^2 + R_2^2)$$
$$= \tfrac{1}{2}\left[1738\ \text{lb} / (32.2\ \text{ft/sec}^2) \right]\left[(9+4)/4 \right]$$
$$= 87\ \text{lb-ft-sec}^2.$$

Step 3. Assume that the flywheel rotates at 1000 rpm. Since 1 rev = 2 rad, the angular velocity is

$$\omega = 2\pi N = 2000\ \pi\ \text{rad/min}$$
$$= 33.3\ \pi\ \text{rad/sec.}$$

The average angular acceleration, then, is

$$\alpha = (\omega_2 - \omega_1)/t$$

Since α_1 is zero at start up,

$$\alpha = \omega_2/t.$$

Because there are no process parameters to define this calculation, let's see how torque would vary as a function of time, Figure 5.6

For $t_1 = 1$ sec, the average angular acceleration $\alpha_1 = 33.3\ \pi/1 = 33.3\ \pi\ \text{rad/sec}^2$. Then

cide how fast the flywheel...
a decision he will normally base on the application s operating parameters. The usual procedure is to

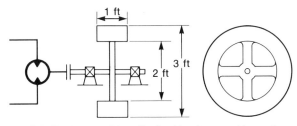

Fig. 5.5. Fluid motor driven flywheel is often used in applications such as centrifuges, roll stand drives where the load on the motor is in essence a flywheel.

Table 1. Corresponding equations for linear and angular motion

	Linear	Angular
Velocity	$v = s/t$	$\omega = \theta/t$
Acceleration	$a = v/t$	$\alpha = \omega/t$
Uniformly accelerated motion	$v_2 - v_1 = at$ $s = v_1 t + 1/2\ at^2$ $v_2^2 - v_1^2 = 2as$	$\omega_2 - \omega_1 = \alpha t$ $\theta = \omega_1 t + 1/2\ \alpha t^2$ $\omega_2^2 - \omega_1^2 = 2\alpha\omega$
Newton's Second Law	$F = ma$	$T = J\alpha$
Momentum	$M = mv$	Angular momentum $= J\omega$
Work	$W = Fs$	$W = T\theta$
Power	$P = Fv$	$P = T\omega$
Kinetic energy	$KE = 1/2\ mv^2$	$KE = 1/2\ J\omega^2$

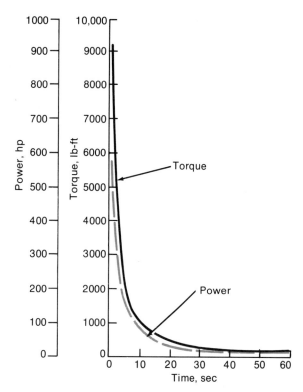

Fig. 5.6. Curves show how torque and power vary as a function of time.

$$T_1 = J_m\alpha_1 = 87 \times 33.3\pi$$
$$= 9100 \text{ lb-ft.}$$

If we let $t_2 = 5$ sec, then $\alpha_2 = 33.3\pi/5$
$$= 6.66\pi \text{ rad/sec}^2$$
and
$$T_2 = J_m\alpha_2 = 87 \times 6.66\pi$$
$$= 1825 \text{ lb-ft.}$$

If $t_3 = 10$ sec.; then $\alpha_3 = 33.3\pi/10 = 3.33\pi$ rad/sec^2 and
$$T_3 = Jm\alpha_3 = 87 \times 3.33\pi$$
$$= 910 \text{ lb-ft.}$$

If $t_4 = 1$ min $= 60$ sec; then $\alpha_4 = 33.3\pi/60$
$= 1.74\pi$ rad/sec^2 and
$$T_4 = J_m\alpha_4 = 87 \times 1.74$$
$$= 151.5 \text{ lb-ft.}$$

Step 4. To estimate the power requirements for these various angular accelerations, let's calculate the requirements for the two end values α_1 *and* α_4.

For $t_1 = 1$ sec, torque $T_1 = 9100$ lb-ft. The power requirement can be obtained from the expression

$$T_1\theta_1/t_1,$$

where
$$\theta_1 = \tfrac{1}{2}\alpha_1 t_1^2 = \tfrac{1}{2} \times 33.3\pi \times 1 = 16.65\pi \text{ rad.}$$

Thus,
$$T_1\theta_1/t_1 = (9100 \times 16.65\pi)1$$
$$= 47.5 \times 10^4 \text{ lb-ft/sec.}$$

The horsepower requirement, then, is

$$HP_1 = (947.5 \times 10^4)/550 = 864 \text{ hp.}$$

For $t_4 = 60$ sec, torque $T_4 = 151.5$ lb-ft. The value of θ_4 *is*

$$\theta4 = \tfrac{1}{2}\alpha_4 t_4^2 = \tfrac{1}{2} \times 1.74 \times 3600 = 3130 \text{ rad.}$$

The power requirement is thus

$$T_4\theta_4/t_4 = (151.5 \times 3130)/60 = 8100 \text{ lb-ft/sec}$$

or

$$HP_4 = 8100/550 = 14.72 \text{ hp.}$$

When specifying the hydraulic motor drive for this application, the designer must be sure to select one with adequate *torque* rating. The horsepower rating alone does not reflect the ability of a motor to deliver the required torque at low speeds.

Step 5. If a fixed-displacement hydraulic pump (output is relatively constant, *i.e.*, $Q = K$) is used for this application, part of the pump's output bypasses over the relief valve during acceleration, as shown in the cycle plot of Figure 5.7. The pump must be sized to supply enough oil to run the process at design speed. During acceleration the pump will supply more oil than the hydraulic motor can absorb, because the motor does not reach design operating speed until the end of the acceleration period. This type of application is highly suitable for a pressure-compensated, variable-displacement pump. Such a pump will adjust its output to that required by the system, as a function of system pressure.

Step 6. Consider now the situation where the process is running at the set design speed of 1000 rpm, but a change in speed is called for. The speed change may be either an increase or decrease in velocity. If an increase in rotational velocity is required, then an increase in torque, ΔT, will be needed:

$$\Delta T = J_m\Delta\alpha.$$

Still using the same system as an example, let's assume that a speed change of 100 rpm is required. The increase in torque will then be

$$\Delta T = 87(\omega_2 - \omega_1)/t$$
$$= (87 \times 200\pi)/60 \ t = 910/t \text{ lb-ft.}$$

There are two possible approaches to the problem of increasing the velocity:
a. Determine the fastest possible response with available maximum torque. Because the running torque will be less than the torque required for acceleration, there will be an *excess* of torque available for speed change. Assuming that the system is 80 percent efficient, a certain torque will be required just to keep the system moving at fixed velocity. Let's use the torque value, $T_4 = 151.5$ lb-ft, calculated in Step 3 for $t_4 = 1$ min. With 80 percent efficiency, $151.5/0.80 = 190$ lb-ft will be required

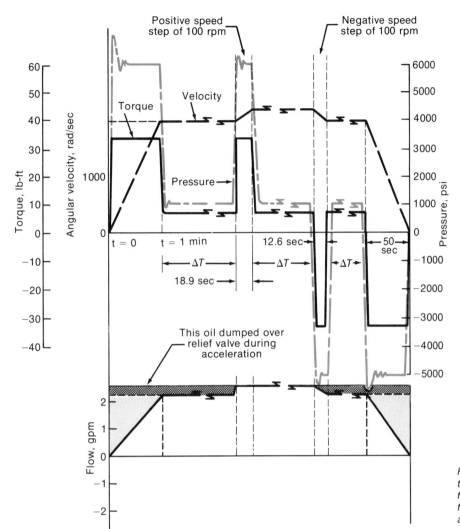

Fig. 5.7. Cycle plot illustrates that a portion of output of fixed displacement pump flows over relief valve during acceleration.

to accelerate in 1 min. The friction torque is $T_f = 190 - 151.5 = 38.5$ lb-ft at constant speed. Thus we have 151.5 lb-ft available, within system capability, to accomplish the speed change. Substituting the appropriate values in the equation

$$T = J_m\alpha,$$

we obtain,

$$151.5 = 87(200\pi/60t) = 910/t$$
$$t = 910/151.5 = 6 \text{ sec}.$$

b. Determine the torque required to achieve the change in a given time interval. Assuming that the speed change must be made in 10 seconds to accommodate some process requirement, the torque required for the change is

$$\Delta T = J_m\alpha = (87 \times 200\pi)/(60 \times 10)$$
$$= 91 \text{ lb-ft}$$

Step 7. Consider the second example where the speed change is a *deceleration* in rotational velocity rather than acceleration. In this case the system will be able to *absorb* energy rather than supply it. Again, using a speed change of 100 rpm, as in Step

6, the reduction will be -200π rad/sec. Let's also assume that the same total torque is available at 80 percent efficiency: namely, 190 lb-ft.

As in the case of deceleration of a linear system, frictional losses help slow the load. If the hydraulic motor can deliver 151.5 lb-ft of torque at design pressure, it will also be able to absorb that much. In addition, the friction torque of 38.5 lb-ft will *contribute* to the deceleration of the flywheel. Thus, total torque available for deceleration is 190 lb-ft. Now, we can calculate time, t:

$$t = (87 \times 200\pi)/(190 \times 60) = 4.8 \text{ sec}.$$

Thus, deceleration occurs 20 percent *faster* than did the acceleration with identical parameters.

It is important to remember that the circuit *must be designed* to absorb the excess energy during a period of deceleration. Unless the energy can be used regeneratively somewhere in the system, the usual procedure is to "convert" the motor to a pump during the slowdown period. The system's pump is then driven as a motor, and backpressure fluid flows over a relief valve to dissipate the energy as heat.

29

Figure 5.8 offers one solution to the problem of absorbing energy during deceleration. A variable-displacement pump driven by an electric motor supplies a fixed-displacement hydraulic motor. Return flow from the hydraulic motor to tank is through a solenoid-operated, spring returned 3-way 2-position valve. The normally open port of the three-way valve, A, ports return flow directly to tank, the other port from the directional control valve is connected to a relief valve, B, set at a pressure level that enables the system to develop the desired deceleration torque. A tachometer measures load speed in an open loop manner; that is, it displays speed on a dial which the operator can read. In this open-loop application it is the operator who exercises control. He uses one electric pushbutton switch to increase pump displacement and thus motor speed; he uses another pushbutton switch to decrease pump displacement to slow the hydraulic motor.

A further refinement is required because this is an open circuit hydrostatic transmission — that is, the pump draws oil from the tank and the hydraulic motor returns oil to tank. The second pushbutton, the one used to decrease pump displacement, also energizes the solenoid actuated 3-way valve, A, which ports fluid through relief valve, B, to provide decelerating backpressure on the motor. Obviously, the rate of change of pump displacement must match the rate of deceleration of the motor to prevent cavitation of the motor or dumping of excess oil over relief valve, C. However, this is difficult to achieve in an open loop system.

The circuit shown in Figure 5.9 is a closed circuit hydrostatic transmission, but still operates in an open loop fashion. Note that this is not a feedback system. A variable displacement pump, A, drives the fixed-displacement hydraulic motor, B, over a preset range of speeds. A low-pressure makeup pump, C, is needed to prevent cavitation caused by leakage from the closed system. The makeup pump supplies fluid to the low pressure part of the circuit through appropriate back-to-back check valves D and E, no matter what the direction of rotation.

Crossover relief valves, F and G, are provided within the closed circuit to guard against damage to the system due to inertial load. If a safe pressure is exceeded, the appropriate crossover relief valve will automatically bypass oil from the high pressure line to the low pressure line. As in the circuit shown in Figure 5.8, the operator still controls this system in an open loop manner.

Step 8. The next step in designing a circuit for an inertial load is to select the operating pressure level which will determine pump displacement, the size of the hydraulic motor, flow rate, line sizes, and all other components within the system.

Let's again assume that the hydraulic motor can generate torques to 190 lb-ft and will operate at

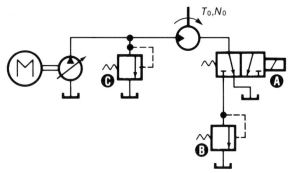

Fig. 5.8. Open circuit shows one possible design to absorb energy during deceleration.

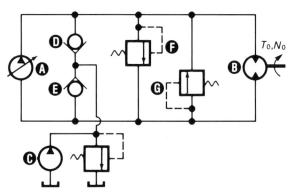

Fig. 5.9. Closed circuit operates in open loop fashion to absorb energy during deceleration.

80-percent efficiency. We can equate the formula for hydraulic horsepower,

$$HP = pQ/1714,$$

to the formula which expresses horsepower in terms of torque and rotational speed:

$$HP = TN/63,024.$$

Thus,

$$pQ/1714 = TN/63,024,$$

where $Q = V_dN/231$ (in this expression, V_d is the motor displacement in in^3/rev). Hence,

$$(pV_dN)/(231 \times 1714) = TN/63,024$$
$$T = 0.159pV_d.$$

Once we know the required torque, we can calculate hydraulic motor displacement for any operating pressure level. The current practice, and with the type of equipment we are using here, is to specify pressures in the range of 3000 to 5000 psi. Let's select 5000 psi as an acceptable pressure level. Then

$$\begin{aligned} V_d &= T/0.159p \\ &= (190 \times 12)/(0.159 \times 5000) \\ &= 2.86 \text{ in}^3/\text{rev.} \end{aligned}$$

The necessary pump output is

$$\begin{aligned} Q &= V_dN \\ &= 2.86 \text{ in}^3/\text{rev} \times 1000 \text{ rpm} \\ &= 2860 \text{ in}^3/\text{min} = 12.4 \text{ gpm.} \end{aligned}$$

Calculating the horsepower required for this system, we get

$$HP = PQ/1714$$
$$= (5000 \times 12.4)/1714$$
$$= 36.2 \text{ hp}$$

If the pump were 85 percent efficient, we would specify an electric motor rated at $36.2/0.85 = 42.5$ hp.

Having determined pressure level and flow rate, we can now select line sizes, control valves, relief valves and all other components. Because this is likely to be a continuous-duty application, the lines must be sized to provide laminar (not turbulent) flow. Such a procedure will minimize heat generation usually caused by turbulent flow in conductors.

The Reynolds number is the criterion which tells whether flow will be laminar or turbulent*:

$$N_R = vD/\nu$$

where v is velocity in fps, D is pipe diameter in ft, and ν is kinematic viscosity in ft2/sec. It is generally accepted that when the Reynolds number is less than 2000, flow is considered to be laminar; when greater than 2000, flow is turbulent.

*See Russell W. Henke, Introduction to Fluid Mechanics, Addison-Wesley, 1966, p. 136.

In the system we are analyzing,

$$D = 4Q/2000\pi\nu.$$

Let's assume the oil has a kinematic viscosity ν of 1.078×10^{-3} ft²/sec. Then,

$$D = (4 \times 4.93 \times 10^{-3})/(2000 \pi \times 1.078 \times 10^{-3})$$
$$= 0.00288 \text{ ft.}$$

Clearly, flow will be laminar.

Important Terms

Moment of inertia of a ring is the sum of the products obtained by multiplying each elemental area of the ring by the square of its radius: $J_m = \int r^2 \, dm$. It is useful for calculating the relation between torque and angular acceleration: $T = J_m\alpha$.

Angular velocity is the rate of transfer about an axis of rotation. Average angular velocity over a period of time is $\omega = (\theta_2 - \theta_1)/t$, where θ is angular displacement. Instantaneous angular velocity is $\omega = d\theta/dt$.

Angular acceleration is an increasing change in angular velocity. Average angular acceleration is $\alpha = (\omega_2 - \omega_1)/t$. Instantaneous angular acceleration is $\alpha = d\omega/dt = d^2\theta/dt^2$.

Reynolds number is an index of laminar vs turbulent flow: $N_R = vD/\nu$. Values below 2000 indicate laminar flow; above 3000 turbulent flow.

REVIEW EXERCISES

1. What is the dominant characteristic of an *overrunning load*?

2. How does an *overrunning load* differ from a *resistive load*?

3. Discuss why and how machine load cycles are made up of combinations of resistive and overrunning loads.

4. What is the dominant characteristic of an *inertia load*?

5. Are *inertia loads* always found in linear motion applications? Only in rotational motion? Or in both linear and rotational motion? Discuss.

6. Discuss how *inertia loads* fit into machine load cycles primarily made up of resistive and/or overrunning load components.

7. When constructing a machine cycle profile, why is it important to define each *load* component (or type) which exists during the machine cycle; and at what time each occurs during the cycle?

8. Discuss the reasons behind the statement, ". . . fluid power systems are *load* dominated systems."

9. Referring to Fig. 1.2, discuss how *load* type and machine cycle profile affect each of the three "active" sections of a fluid power Energy Transmission Systems.

10. Referring to Fig. 1.4, discuss how the *load* type and machine cycle profile affect the shape and position of the "energy level" curve for a typical fluid power system or branch circuit.

11. Explain why it is stated that, ". . . the effect of a varying load reaction is to shift the load-curve up and down the energy level (pressure) scale," as shown in the plots of Fig. 1.4.

12. What is the effect of flow rate on the energy level curve(s) of Fig. 1.4? Explain the relationship of flow rate to load analysis and the machine cycle profile.

13. What are the components of "total load" reacting on a cylinder (piston/rod) when a load is started from a stopped or zero velocity condition?

14. In the cycle profile plots of Fig. 5.2 relate the following:
   a. velocity profile to flow profile
   b. force (load reaction magnitude) to pressure
   c. flow to pressure.

15. Explain the high force/pressure peaks of short duration at each end of the cycle profile plots of Fig. 5.2.

16. Referring to Fig. 5.2, what is the implication of the force/pressure curves crossing the horizontal axis in the cycle plot?

17. Referring to Fig. 5.7, explain why the small change in flywheel speed (100 rpm) requires such a large torque input.

18. Are there any basic differences between load types, inertia effects, etc. in linear and rotational motion other than the use of linear or rotational motion equations? Explain.

19. Referring to Example Overrunning Load problem in text; Fig. 5.2.: Use the same data but change the basic cycle profile for machine element velocity to Method 2, as illustrated in Fig. 4.1*b*. Make related calculations and plot the new cycle profile.

20. Refering to Fig. 5.2, use example problem calculations from text: Calculate the power loss and related heat generation during the "feed" portion of the machine cycle, using the circuit of Fig. 5.3.

21. Optional Exercise: Rework the example *overrunning load* problem using SI metric units instead of CU.

22. Optional Exercise: Rework the example *inertia load* problem from the text using SI metric units instead of CU.

CHAPTER 6

CONSTANT FLOW CIRCUITS

As discussed in Chapter 2, fluid power circuits and systems are broadly categorized as open-loop or closed-loop. Open-loop circuits are further subdivided as open-center and closed-center.

Current usage characterizes an **open-center** circuit as one in which pump output bypasses to tank when the tandem-center directional control valve is in the neutral position. Figure 6.1 illustrates this principle in a simple circuit that has only one directional control valve; Figure 6.2 illustrates this for a multiple- or stack-valve installation. Note that the circuit in Figure 6.2 returns pump fluid directly to tank only when **both** valves are in neutral position. If either valve is shifted, normal 4-way valve directional control will start. Open center circuits are better characterized functionally as **constant flow** circuits.

PUMP DISCHARGE PRESSURE

In constant flow circuits, the pressure at which the pump discharges fluid is a function of load

resistance encountered by and reflected across the actuator. The system operating pressure required by the load is a function of the actuator geometry and/or speed requirement. If the prime mover can satisfy the energy demand, it will do so. If not, the prime mover will stall or, as is more likely to happen in actual practice, the relief valve will open to bypass fluid to tank; this wastes energy.

RELATION OF PUMP DISCHARGE TO ACTUATOR SPEED

In constant flow circuits, pump output is **not** determined by the actuator's instantaneous speed requirements. Here is why: a constant flow design technique most commonly calls for a fixed-displacement pump. The discharge rate of this

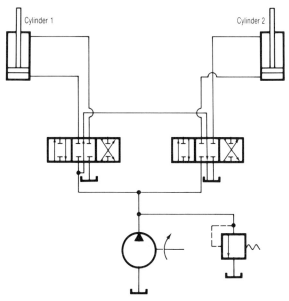

Fig. 6.2. Open center, multiple valve system. Pump output bypasses to tank only when **both** directional valves are in neutral position.

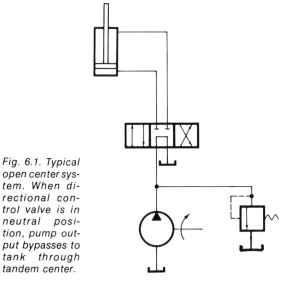

Fig. 6.1. Typical open center system. When directional control valve is in neutral position, pump output bypasses to tank through tandem center.

pump is a function of pump displacement and its speed of rotation. Pump output and actuator displacement jointly determine a steady-state speed, according to the equation:

$$v = Q_p/A_p \ ,$$

where v is speed, Q_p is pump output, and A_p is actuator area.

Load inertia may preclude rapid acceleration to this steady-state speed; if it does, excess flow

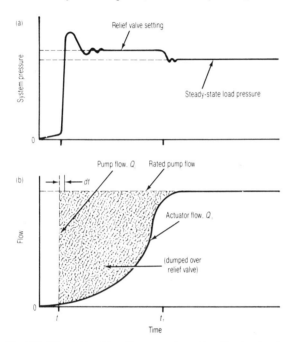

Fig. 6.3. Should load inertia prevent acceleration to steady state speed, excess flow from the pump returns to tank through the relief valve.

from the pump must return to tank through the relief valve, Figure 6.3. At time t_0 the control valve shifts, porting pressure fluid to the actuator. There is a slight time lag caused by such factors as the compressibility of the oil in the system and throttling while the valve spool is shifting. Pump flow, Q_p, then increases to full rated output, see vertical dotted line, Figure 6.3(b).

At time t_0 actuator velocity is zero. At time $t_0 + dt_0$ (the time that corresponds to full buildup of pump output), the actuator has not yet started to move. Therefore, actuator flow, Q_p, is zero at that instant. It could be demonstrated mathematically that for these conditions of finite pump output, Q_p, and zero actuator flow, Q_a, to coexist, the instantaneous acceleration of the actuator would have to be infinite. An infinitely powerful driving force would be required for this.

If we examine the pressure plot in Figure 6.3(a) and compare it with the flow plot of Figure 6.3(b), we see that fluid pressure rises rapidly and peaks at some level above the relief valve setting. This

level depends primarily on the response time of the relief valve; in addition, it also depends on the internal slip in the pump, valve leakage, and actuator slip. Once the relief valve opens, fluid pressure in the system levels out at the relief valve setting.

Now, consider the plot of the actuator flow rate Q_a. In any well-designed system consisting of one pump and one actuator, pump output just matches the actuator input requirement at design speed; thus, under steady-state conditions,

$$Q_p = Q_a \ .$$

At time dt_0, however, Q_p is equal to rated flow and Q_a is zero.

Actuator and load must accelerate from zero to design velocity. This takes a finite interval of time, from t_0 to t_1. During this interval, Q_a increases along a curve until $Q_a = Q_p$ at time t_1, which is the time when the actuator reaches design speed. Note that at that time, system pressure drops to the steady-state design level and the relief valve closes. The shaded area between the two flow curves, Figure 6.3(b), represents the volume of oil returned to tank through the relief valve during the acceleration period.

Because this complex sequence of events takes place in a fraction of a second, it is difficult to observe under normal operating conditions. And, in most constant flow circuit applications it is not even a matter for consideration. The designer would analyze this sequence only when dealing with applications that have high performance requirements, or if an operating malfunction could not otherwise be explained. Such a malfunction might occur if the pump's output flow rate and the actuator flow rate were badly matched.

For this reason, the designer must make sure that these two quantities are properly matched, especially when designing multi-branched circuits. If a pump must be sized for multi-branched circuit operation, as it frequently must, the designer should choose a pump with a capacity that equals peak flow requirements. Note that the capacity of such a pump exceeds the fluid needs of a single actuator.

Sizing the actuator

In constant flow circuits, the designer tries to size actuators to meet speed requirements as a function of pump output. For example, a cylinder might be selected so that

$$A_pS/t = Q_p,$$

where A_p is piston area, S is cylinder stroke, t is time, and Q_p is pump flow rate. In some instances, this formula may call for a cylinder with a capacity larger than that required for force output alone. The designer would ordinarily select a fluid motor

34

with a capacity (at desired operating speed) equal to rated pump output:

$$Q_p = V_a N.$$

Unloading the pump

In a constant flow circuit, the directional control valve unloads the pump when the valve is in its neutral position. This is an advantage in that auxiliary controls are not required to unload the pump. By unloading the pump, the designer reduces unnecessary energy dissipation during passive intervals in the cycle, thus minimizing the generation of heat. Care must be taken to insure that the directional control valve selected has enough capacity to bypass the *full* pump output *without* causing excessive pressure drop.

Output speed control

One way to control actuator speed in a constant flow circuit, is by restricting flow with a metering or flow control device. The most common metering approach uses one of the many types of flow control valves in combination with one of the basic methods of flow control described in Chapter 2. Another approach takes advantage of the throttling characteristics of the directional control valve. This approach is frequently adapted in circuits equipped with manually-operated and proportional control valves. The designer must remember that any flow control method that uses throttling is apt to create energy losses with attendant heat generation.

Application problem

Let's consider a typical example of constant flow analysis. As discussed in Chapter 2, a thorough analysis of system objectives is fundamental to good circuit design. The cycle-profile technique was suggested as one approach to orderly design; the designer will remember that this approach divides the circuit into sections, Figure 6.4. Note that the load is primarily a resistive one. Therefore, under steady state conditions,

$$F_a = ma = (W/g) \, [v2 - v1)/t],$$

where:

F_a — force required to accelerate load
t — time
v_1 — initial velocity
v_2 — final velocity, and
W — weight of load, actuator elements, machine tool carriage, etc.

Since, at start-up, $v_2 = 0$,

$$F_a = (W v_2)/(gt).$$

The equation

$$F_R = p_i A_p$$

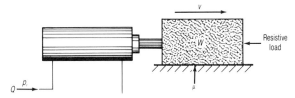

Fig. 6.4. Examples of typical resistive load system.

states a relationship between the resistive force F_R required to overcome the resistive load, the cylinder piston area A_p, and an initial system pressure p_i. However, the equation is not complete, because we must consider two other factors:

1. The frictional component of the resistive load given by

$$F_f = \mu N,$$

where μ is the coefficient of friction and N is the normal force. Since

$$N = W + L_N,$$

where W is the weight of the load, actuator elements, etc., and L_N is the normal component of any applied force (such as cable tension or cutter reaction), we may rewrite $F_f = \mu N$ as

$$F_f = \mu(W + L_N).$$

2. Breakaway and running frictions also enter into this relationship. We must distinguish between these two quantities because μ varies between the static condition μ_s and the dynamic condition μ_d, so that $\mu_s > \mu_d$

The breakaway friction is

$$F_{fb} = \mu_s \, (W + L_N),$$

and the running friction is

$$F_{fr} = \mu_d \, (W + L_N).$$

Note that breakaway friction force F_{fb} may vary during the cycle because of a variable normal component force, L_N. (There is another frequently neglected component of the total resistance energy requirement which, in some cases, cannot be overlooked. This is the energy needed to accelerate the mass of the oil within the system. We shall not discuss this component here, since it is beyond the scope of this presentation.)

Thus, the total resistive force at *breakaway* is

$$F_{Rb} = p_i A_p + \mu_s \, (W + L_N),$$

and the total resistive force at *running speed* is

$$F_{Rr} = p_i A_p + \mu_d \, (W + L_N).$$

We can now complete the equations for the total load reflected at the actuator. We distinguish three cases:

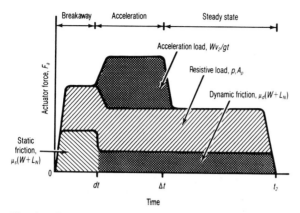

Fig. 6.5. Typical load cycle plot for system illustrated in Figure 6.4.

a) **load at breakaway,**

$$F_{ab} = (Wv_2/gt) + (p_iA_p) + \mu_s (W + L_N),$$

b) **load while running,** and while the system is accelerating to constant speed,

$$F_{ar} = (Wv_2/gt) + (p_iA_p) + \mu_d (W + L_N),$$

c) **load while running at the steady-state velocity,**

$$F_{ar} = (p_iA_p) + \mu_d (W + L_N).$$

Figure 6.5 shows a typical load cycle plot for the application of Figure 6.4. Note that $0 < \text{time} < dt$ represents the short interval during which breakaway from zero-velocity takes place. This is a transient state and would be difficult to plot without use of an analytical instrument such as an oscilloscope.

Qualitatively, however, load components are functions of static friction and the resistive load itself. In the interval $dt < \text{time} < \Delta t$, (also of short duration), the load and actuator masses are accelerated. Again, this is a transient state. The components are dynamic friction, resistive load, and the load due to the acceleration of a mass. Beyond $\Delta t < \text{time}$, acceleration of the load is essentially a steady-state; at least we usually assume this, even

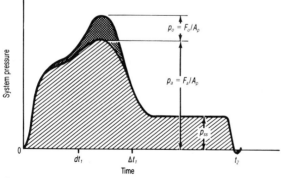

Fig. 6.6. Shape of typical pressure plot determined from load cycle plot shown in Figure 6.5. Note that highest pressures appear in the interval $0 < dt_1 < \Delta t_1$.

if it is not quite true in actual practice. In this time interval, the important components are resistive load and dynamic friction.

Figure 6.6 shows the shape of a typical system pressure plot determined from the load cycle plot shown in Figure 6.5. Note that the highest pressures appear when $0 < dt_1 < \Delta t$. These are the familiar transients, frequently seen on oscilloscopes, caused by the breakaway phenomenon and the superimposition of acceleration forces on normal load resistance. Figure 6.6 also shows that a steady-state pressure, p_{ss}, is achieved when load speed corresponds to actuator design speed.

The relief valve setting at this point is ordinarily between p_{ss} and $p_a + p_o$. If Δt_1 is brief in comparison with t_2, the relief valve setting can be close to p_{ss}, because the pressure transient will be so short that the relief valve cannot respond — or even if it could, the relatively small quantity of oil bypassed would not affect circuit operation significantly. If, on the other hand, Δt_1, is large in comparison with t_2, the relief valve will have to be set higher.

When interpreting such pressure plots, the student should bear in mind that the system will develop a fluid pressure p_o caused by the acceleration of the oil column in the line that connects pump and actuator. This pressure is superimposed on the other pressures reflected by the load at the actuator; this relationship develops because p_o is *not* load-reflective and occurs only in the oil in the line to the actuator.

Characteristics of constant flow

In light of this discussion, remember these characteristics of constant flow circuits:
- Pump discharge pressure is a function of load resistance and must build from zero
- Pump output is not determined by actuator speed requirements
- Actuators are sized to meet speed requirements as a function of pump output.

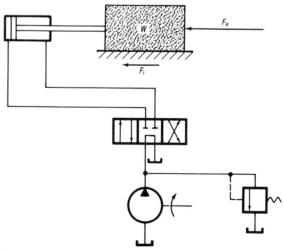

Fig. 6.7. Basic circuit for application illustrated in Fig. 6.4.

36

Statements 2 and 3 make sense only if we assume that the pump in a multi-branched circuit is sized to accommodate maximum system demand, no matter when or where it occurs. During parts of the cycle when demand is not at its peak, pump output will exceed that required by one actuator. In the simple example of Figure 6.4, pump and actuator displacements would have to be matched. Let us analyze the basic circuit Figure 6.7, required for the application shown in Figure 6.4.

Assume that the load resistance of the circuit calls for a piston area A_p for a design pressure p_i, and that the load must be moved through a stroke S; the cylinder will displace a volume

$$V_a = A_p S.$$

If the job to be done requires that the load be moved in t sec, then the necessary flow rate to the cylinder is

$$V_d/t = A_p S/t = Q \ in^3/sec.$$

At this point in the analysis the designer must check the columnar strength of the piston rod, which may turn out to be the critical factor. If a larger rod is needed, the cylinder bore would then have to be increased accordingly. Such a change would, in turn, require adjustment of the pump displacement calculation.

Assuming that we have satisfactorily calculated required pump output, Q_p, we can complete the input segment of the circuit we are using as an example, Figure 6.7. By the very nature of this circuit, we must use the tandem-center 4-way valve shown. Also, a constant flow circuit we must always use a relief valve with a fixed-displacement pump.

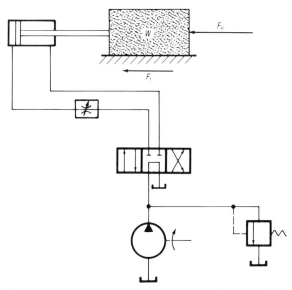

Fig. 6.8. Flow control valve in meter-in-type circuit provides speed control for circuit in Figure 6.7.

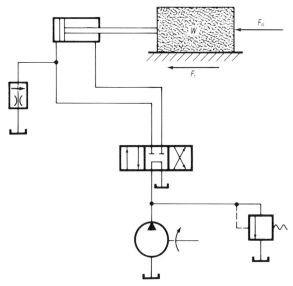

Fig. 6.9. Bleed off circuit could be used to control flow to cap end of cylinder, but meter-in circuit is preferred for fine adjustments.

The main functional element still missing from the simple circuit is a method for speed control. Since it was indicated that speed control could be accomplished only by throttling, the manually operated directional control or proportional valve can be used to throttle flow. In this example the pressure drop across the valve has the effect of reducing the pressure available at the actuator. Consequently, the force available to accelerate the load and overcome friction is reduced.

A flow control valve used in a meter-in circuit, Figure 6.8, would have essentially the same effect, unless it were a bypass valve. In this case, flow to the cylinder would actually be reduced. One could use a bleed-off circuit, Figure 6.9 for minor speed adjustment but a valve in meter-in circuit would be preferred for adjustment over a wide flow range. A meter-out circuit could be used, but since the load in this example is a resistive one, this alternative would have little advantage over a meter-in circuit.

Important Terms

Open-center circuit is one in which a tandem-center directional control valve unloads the pump when in neutral position.

Closed-center circuit is one that uses a closed-center directional control valve.

Breakaway force is encountered when starting a cylinder or fluid motor. Forces are greater during start-up than when the actuator is operating.

Transient condition is any condition of short duration which is incidental to the design.

Steady-state condition is one that persists for long periods and is essential to the design.

Review Exercises

6.1. What is meant by the term open-center circuit?

6.2. Why are these circuits better described functionally as constant flow circuits?

6.3. What are the essential hardware characteristics of constant flow circuits?

6.4. Referring to Figure 2.4: what class of circuit is represented? Why?

6.5. Referring to Figures 2.14 and 2.15: what class of circuit is represented? Why?

6.6. In constant flow circuits, what determines pump output? Explain.

6.7. In constant flow circuits, what determines pump discharge pressure? Explain.

6.8. Discuss the idea that in a constant flow circuit, pump delivery is not determined by the instantaneous speed of the actuator.

6.9. If the concept of question 6.8 is valid, what relationship is there between pump output and actuator instantaneous input flow? Where does the flow differential go?

6.10. What considerations must be given to sizing a pump to supply a multi-branch circuit?

6.11. Referring to Figure 3.7: what problems could be anticipated if a constant flow circuit was used for the application shown? Why is it important that the circuit designer anticipate these problems?

6.12. In constant flow circuits, how are actuators sized?

6.13. Why is it desirable to unload the pump during standby periods? How is this done in constant flow circuits?

6.14. How is speed of an actuator controlled in a constant flow circuit? What adverse effect is inherent in this kind of control?

6.15. The basic law of fluid mechanics describing the flow rate vs pressure differential characteristic for orifices* is: $Q = C_d A_o \sqrt{2g \Delta p/\gamma}$. Discuss the relationship to speed control of actuators in constant flow circuits.

6.16. Discuss inertia effects in constant flow circuits.

6.17. Discuss friction effects in constant flow circuits. How are friction effects in actuators and fluid motors usually accounted for in selecting components?

6.18. Discuss breakaway considerations in constant flow circuits. What are the force components of breakaway?

6.19. What is the relationship between breakaway pressure and steady state pressure? What are the implications as far as circuit design is concerned?

6.20. What causes the drop in pressure at the end of the acceleration period in an actuator cycle?

6.21. Why does excess pump delivery bypass over the relief valve during the transient stage of a

constant flow circuit cycle? Does this contribute to heat generation in the circuits? Why?

6.22. Discuss the idea that pump discharge must build from zero toward load (system) pressure when the directional control valve is shifted. What effect would this have on the response of the system?

6.23. Discuss the idea that two criteria are used for sizing fluid power actuators: one, hydraulic, the other, structural. How does one affect the other? Why do structural criteria sometimes dominate?

6.24. Referring to Figure 6.9: given the following data: $W = 20,000$ lb; $\mu_s = 0.4$; $\mu_d = 0.15$; mechanical efficiency of cylinder, $\eta_m = 85\%$; actuator stroke = 4 ft; time, t, to complete stroke = 0.8 min; acceleration and deceleration times are each estimated to be 0.1 minute. Make the necessary calculations to plot the cycle profile for the actuator stroke.

6.25. Based on the calculations of problem 6.24, what are the steady state and average load velocities? Is the differencenif any, significant?

6.26. Based on the above calculations what is the maximum pump delivery required?

6.27. The flow control valve is sized with a pressure drop $\Delta p = 150$ psi at the flow rate calculated in problem 6.26. The pressure drop, Δp through the directional control valve = 45 psi to port A at the same flow rate. What is the pump discharge pressure? Assuming a pump volumetric efficiency of 90% and a prime mover speed of 1750 rpm, what pump displacement is required?

6.28. The directional control valve pressure drop information is refined so that pressure drops are: p_s to port A = 45 psi; port B to tank, T = 50 psi; p_s to port B = 45 psi; port A to T = 48 psi and p_f to T = 60 psi, all at the calculated flow rate of question 6.26. Assuming that the diameter of the piston rod diameter is 2″, what is the return flow rate during retraction? What is the pressure drop, Δp, in the directional control valve? in the line from A to T during retraction? What is pump output pressure during retraction based on above calculations?

6.29. Using the data of problem 6.28, make the necessary calculations and plot the retract cycle profile. Compare it with the extend cycle profile. Are there any significant differences? If so, to what factors are they attributable?

6.30. Referring to problem 6.7, determine what effect backpressure on the head end side of the piston would have on circuit characteristics. Is it significant enough to require adjusting the pump discharge pressure calculated in problem 6.27?

6.31. Assume that the load pressure as the cylinder extends is high enough to intrude into the cracking range of the relief valve, so 50% of pump output bypasses over the relief valve. What effect, if any, will this have on circuit performance? If so, how can this problem be corrected?

6.32. Optional exercises: Repeat the calculations of problems 24-31, using SI metric units.

---

*Introduction to Fluid Mechanics, pp 75-85, R.W. Henke, Addison Wesley Publishing Co., Reading, MA.

CHAPTER 7

DEMAND
FLOW CIRCUITS

As previously discussed, a closed-center circuit is one in which the port from the pump to the directional control valve is blocked when the valve is in its neutral position, Figure 7.1. This simple circuit includes a fixed displacement pump, a 4-way, 3-position directional control valve, an actuator, and a valve that bypasses pump flow to tank when the directional control valve is in its neutral position. Such a configuration does not represent the optimal application of this class of circuit; typically, closed-center circuits are equipped with a fixed-displacement pump and an accumulator, Figure 7.2, or a variable displacement, pressure-compensated pump, Figure 7.3. Closed center circuits are more accurately characterized as demand flow circuits.

Fixed displacement pump circuits

In demand flow circuits that use a fixed-displacement pump and an accumulator, fluid pressure from the pump is not directly determined by actuator force requirements. As Figure 7.2 illustrates, the pump charges the accumulator to design pressure when the directional control valve is centered.

Design pressure in the circuits is controlled by the spring setting of an unloading valve. When this setting is reached, the valve opens and bypasses oil to tank, at low pressure. Note that the pilot signal to the relief valve is sensed downstream of a check valve placed between the pump and the accumulator. The check valve prevents the un-

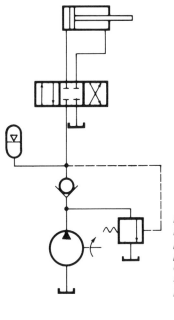

Fig. 7.2. In typical demand flow circuit powered by fixed displacement pump, accumulator is added to supply full design pressure immediately.

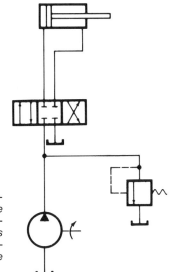

Fig. 7.1. In simple, demand flow circuit, line from fixed displacement pump to valve is blocked when directional control valve is in neutral position.

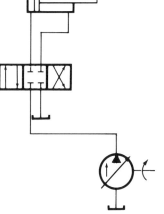

Fig. 7.3. Variable displacement, pressure compensated pump supplies pressure fluid to this demand flow circuit. Note absence of relief valve.

loading of the accumulator, as well as the pump.

When the directional control valve is shifted so that it ports oil to the actuator, the full design pressure (as stored in the accumulator) is immediately available to the system. As the cylinder moves, oil is forced from the accumulator by the compressed gas charge behind the oil. After a time interval, system pressure drops because of the expansion of the gas charge in the accumulator.

At some pressure level for which it has been designed, the unloading valve closes and causes output from the pump to reenter the system rather than bypass to tank. At this time, the pump will either

• add its output to that from the accumulator at the lower pressure level, or

• recharge the accumulator to a higher pressure. Which event occurs is a function of many other factors.

Some accumulator circuits are designed so that the accumulator supplies all the oil used during the active part of the cycle. It cannot do so at constant pressure, because the pressure of the gas charge drops as the gas expands when oil flows out of the accumulator. The load cycle must be designed so the system can still function at the lowest pressure level delivered by the accumulator. This design feature is used where the active or work segment of the cycle is rather short and is followed by a relatively long passive or dwell segment during which the pump recharges the accumulator. In such circuits, the pump is sized to charge the accumulator during the work cycle dwell segment, Figure 7.4.

Application problem 1

Assume a circuit similar to that in Figure 7.2, in which an accumulator supplies 924 in³ of oil to the circuit in 10 sec. What is the required pump output rate if the dwell time between work periods is 50 seconds.

Solution. Required pump discharge rate is

Q = 924 in³/50 sec

 = 18.5 in³/sec × 60 (sec/min) / 231 (in³/gal)

 = 4.8 gpm.

The horsepower required to drive the pump is:

 $HP_1 = pQ/1714$
   = (1000 × 4.8)/1714 = 2.8 hp.

In circuits that differ from the one illustrated in this example, the accumulator is frequently used to supplement the pump during brief periods when high-rate flows are needed. Thus, if the design calls for a high flow rate for a short time interval in the active part of the work cycle, the engineer can use a smaller pump in conjunction with an accumulator which it charges during the passive part of the work cycle. When the operator shifts the

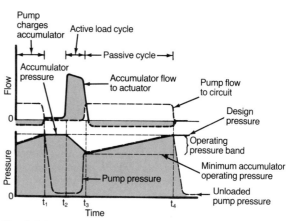

Fig. 7.4. In systems with cycles that have short work segments and long dwell segments, pump is sized to charge accumulator during dwell.

directional control valve, accumulator output flow is *added* to pump flow. Note that the combined flows may exceed several times the output of the pump alone. However, this condition will exist for only a very short period of time. In designs where a peak flow of short duration may be desirable, this configuration may be much more economical than one that relies on one big pump, Figure 7.5.

Application problem 2

Assume that a pump is used instead of an accumulator to supply the required oil in application problem 1. If the operating pressure is 1000 psi, what is the difference in horsepower required to drive the pump in these two examples?

Solution. Total flow to the system is

$Q_t = Q_p + Q_a$
 = 4.8 gpm + [(924 in³/10 sec) (60/231)]
 = 28.8 gpm.

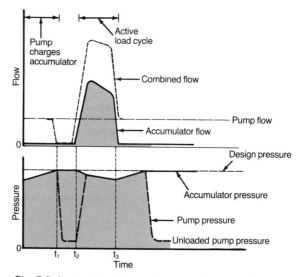

Fig. 7.5. In systems where short duration peak flows are needed, accumulator can often supplement pump output during short periods of high flow needs.

The horsepower required to drive the pump in application problem 1 was 2.8 hp. Power required in this problem is:

$$HP_2 = pQ/1714$$
$$= (1000 \times 28.8)/1714 = 16.8 \text{ hp}.$$

Therefore, using a pump instead of an accumulator to supply the required short-duration, high-volume flows increases the horsepower requirement 600 percent.

In these types of circuits, actuators are sized to meet the force requirements based on load cycle analysis. Frequently actuators, particularly cylinders, can be sized smaller than in comparable, constant flow circuits. This is true because in constant flow circuits the cylinders must be sized to provide the required speed based on available pump output. In demand circuits, on the other hand, a given force is available that accelerates the load at a rate proportional to the mass. Thus, the cylinder demands oil from the accumulator in proportion to its instantaneous velocity. The accumulator delivers only on demand because, unlike a pump, it is not a positive-displacement device.

PRESSURE-COMPENSATED PUMPS

We discussed the simplest form of pressure compensated pump in a demand flow circuit, Figure 7.3. If the demand flow circuit uses a pressure-compensated pump*, then the compensator setting determines maximum circuit pressure, Figure 7.6. Pump output is constant until the system reaches a given pressure, called **cutoff pressure**. At this point the force acting on the compensator begins to exceed the force of the control spring that holds the pump on stroke.

Now, as pressure increases, the pump starts to move off stroke to reduce displacement. The slope of the curve of this decreasing displacement is controlled to some extent by the spring rate of the compensator spring. Thus, the designer can specify a sharp or gradual cutoff, whichever the application requires. When fluid pressure in the system reaches the level known as **deadhead pressure**, pump output flow is zero. The only power consumed by the pump at deadhead is the relatively small amount required to overcome me-

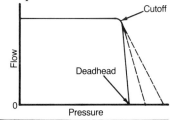

Fig. 7.6. In demand flow circuit equipped with pressure compensated, variable displacement pump, compensator setting determines maximum circuit pressure.

*See Chapter 15, Energy Conservation System, for additional types of pressure compensated pumps.

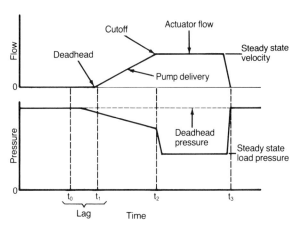

Fig. 7.7. In demand flow circuit equipped with pressure compensated pump, pump output is related to actuator speed requirements.

chanical losses and compensate for internal leakage. The pump maintains full deadhead pressure in the system at this low power input.

As indicated, the compensator setting determines the upper limit of system pressure. Up to its maximum capability, pump output is a function of the ability of the actuator and load to respond to the force exerted on both.

In our discussion of load response in systems equipped with a fixed-displacement pump, Chapter 4, it was stated that it would require infinite acceleration for the load to absorb the entire pump output the instant it delivers fluid to the actuator. With a pressure compensated pump, full force can act on the actuator and load, but there will be no flow until the load starts to accelerate. Thus, a system that uses a pressure compensated pump is a demand system, as was the case with an accumulator.

A pressure compensated pump functions as its own relief valve, shifting to deadhead conditions if and when an excessive load is applied. If a designer decides to use a relief valve for fail-safe protection, its pressure setting must be approximately 250-300 psi higher than the pressure at which the pump deadheads to minimize system instability. A rupture disc can also be used to provide fail-safe protection.

In a demand flow circuit equipped with a pressure compensated pump, pump delivery is related to actuator speed requirement, as illustrated in Figure 7.7. From time zero to time t_0 the control valve is in neutral position and the pump is deadheading — that is, maintaining maximum pressure at zero delivery. At time t_0 the control valve shifts porting pressure oil to the actuator, Figure 7.3. Thus, full deadhead pressure acts on the actuator.

Because the actuator cannot accelerate instantaneously, pump output remains at zero for a short time interval $t_0 < t < t_1$, Figure 7.7. During this interval the actuator begins to move. The pressure drops to some level — required to accelerate the load below the deadhead level. Simultaneously, the pump moves on stroke.

If the acceleration force requires a pressure greater than the cutoff pressure, the pump will compensate by reducing its output flow rate. This new output flow rate will be lower than that corresponding to the cutoff pressure, but higher than the flow rate corresponding to deadhead pressure. In this sense a demand flow circuit with a pressure-compensated pump is a self-regulating system.

Between times t_1 and t_2, Figure 7.7, the load accelerates to steady state speed. By time t_2, the pump has been stroked to full displacement, the load stops accelerating, and system pressure drops to some value corresponding to the steady-state resistive load. At time t_3 the actuator hits a mechanical stop, or the end of its stroke, and fluid pressure rises immediately. The pump is destroked and its output drops to zero; it deadheads until the control valve shifts to retract the cylinder. In this circuit no pressurized oil flows over a relief valve; the pump supplies precisely what the system demands.

Figure 7.8 illustrates a pressure-compensated variable-volume vane pump; Figure 7.9 a pressure-compensated variable-displacement piston pump.

Flow-compensated pumps

The simplest form of a flow-compensated pump is shown schematically in Figure 7.10. In these pumps a control orifice senses the flow rate, the pressure drop across the orifice being proportional to flow rate, according to equation*

$$Q = C_d A_o \sqrt{2g\Delta_p/\gamma}$$

where C_d is the discharge coefficient, A_o is the cross-sectional area of the orifice opening, g is acceleration due to gravity, Δp is pressure differential and γ is the specific weight of the fluid. This equation indicates that pressure drop is a function of the square of the flow. The induced pressure drop is felt by the compensator control piston which adjusts pump output in proportion to flow.

Figure 7.11 illustrates a flow-rate and pressure-compensating control. This configuration also uses a fixed orifice, A, to sense flow rate. In addition, it has a second fixed orifice, B, in the line to the spring end of the compensator. A pressure control valve regulates the pressure in the spring chamber end of the compensator. When pressure in this chamber matches that of the valve setting, the valve opens and bypasses oil to tank, creating a pressure drop across orifice B. Thus the total

*See Russell W. Henke, Introduction to Fluid Mechanics (Addison-Wesley, 1966), pp. 75 ff.

Courtesy Continental Hydraulics

Fig. 7.8. Pressure compensated, variable displacement vane pump.

Courtesy Sperry Vickers

Fig. 7.9. Pressure compensated, variable displacement piston pump.

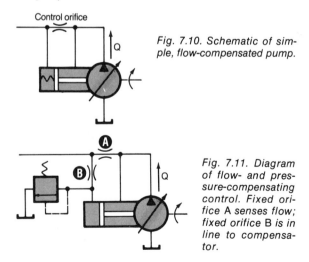

Fig. 7.10. Schematic of simple, flow-compensated pump.

Fig. 7.11. Diagram of flow- and pressure-compensating control. Fixed orifice A senses flow; fixed orifice B is in line to compensator.

pressure differential imposed across the compensator piston is the sum of the two pressure drops. This value will exceed the pressure drop induced across orifice A by flow alone.

CONSTANT VS DEMAND FLOW
A COMPARISON

Classical views of constant and demand flow hydraulic systems which focus on valves divert attention from more significant differences in system pressure, flow, and energy transfer. The following comparisons will be useful in evaluating constant and demand flow systems.

How system pressure characteristics compare

One of the key functional differences between contant-flow (open-center) and demand-flow (closed-center) systems lies in their pressure characteristics. In constant-flow systems, load pressure is approached as pressure **rises** from a minimum value that depends on small pressure drops through the valve and related lines. In demand flow systems, load pressure is approached as pressure **drops** from deadhead pressure, Figure 7.12.

When the directional control valve in a constant flow system is in neutral, pump flow bypasses to reservoir. At some time, t_1, the valve starts to shift, pressure rises slowly at first because the bypass orifice must close before pressure can build. As the metering orifice comes into play, system pressure rises toward load pressure.

When pressures match, fluid flows to the actuator port. By time, t_3, system pressure equals load pressure, transients have been damped out, and the pump delivers fluid to the actuator at a constant rate.

By contrast, maximum pressure in a demand flow system depends on deadhead pressure, which is maintained until the valve starts to shift at time, t_1. In closed center valves there is no bypass orifice, so metering notches come into play much sooner.

Pressure is throttled across the spool, and tends to drop toward steady-state load pressure, matching load pressure at time, t_2. Actually, the situation is more complex than is shown in Figure 7.12 because pressure depends on the dynamics of the load and on the supply characteristics, which are different for accumulator-supplied and pressure-compensated pumps.

How system flow characteristics compare

As their names imply, constant and demand flow systems deliver flows quite differently. It is this difference that makes demand flow systems so readily responsive to load conditions.

Theoretically, in a constant flow system, load pressure should make no difference to flow. But as a practical matter, even the best fixed displacement pumps have some slip, so the curve slopes downward slightly.

In demand flow systems with pressure-compensated pumps, the flow vs. pressure curve is the same as that for a fixed displacement pump up to the cutoff pressure, Figure 7.13. The curve is slightly displaced here for the sake of clarity.

At cutoff pressure the variable displacement mechanism starts to destroke the pump to reduce output flow. As system pressure rises, flow is further reduced, reaching zero flow at deadhead pressure.

System pressure cannot exceed deadhead pressure, so the pressure-compensated pump acts as a relief valve. Because flow is controlled by pressure, the pumps are responsive to load. They can also be made flow responsive, controlling power

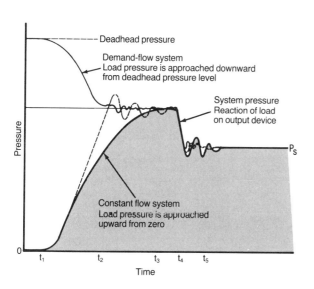

Fig. 7.12. In demand flow system, load pressure is approached as pressure drops from deadhead pressure.

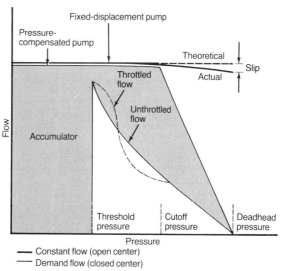

Fig. 7.13. In demand flow system equipped with pressure compensated pump, flow vs. pressure curve is same as for fixed displacement pump up to cutoff pressure.

delivered to the system. In a sense they perform like accumulators of infinite capacities.

Demand flow systems can also be based on the use of accumulators, which have different flow characteristics from either fixed-displacement or pressure-compensated pumps. Accumulator power sources are more difficult to characterize than pump sources because an accumulator can only deliver a finite volume of fluid to the system. Furthermore, because the gas charge in the accumulator expands, system pressure decreases as the accumulator releases fluid. As a result, demand flow from the accumulator is a function not only of accumulator characteristics, but of all the dynamic interactions in the system.

These variations in flow characteristics are represented in Figure 7.13 by a curve for throttled flow and another for unthrottled flow. Actually, an infinite number of characteristic curves would be needed to describe all possible operating conditions for an accumulator system.

Note that the accumulator curves stop at threshold pressure. This is actually the residual pressure in the accumulator when all of the useful volume of fluid has been withdrawn. It must be remembered that in systems equipped with accumulators, load pressure cannot exceed threshold pressure before the work cycle has been completed. Should load pressure exceed

threshold pressure, the system will stall because the accumulator cannot deliver any more fluid.

Differences between open and closed-center valves

By definition, open- and closed-center hydraulic systems depend on the characteristics of their directional control valves. The distinguishing characteristic usually featured is the ability of the valve to either block or unload the pump. But more critical for energy control is the ability of the valve to meter pump flow.

The open-center directional control valve has a bypass orifice in neutral position. Added to this is a metering notch, and finally a seal land that reduces leakage. This construction results in a relatively long deadband and a relatively small metering range.

To understand how open-center valves operate, Figure 7.14 bottom, consider the sequence of events when the valve is shifted from neutral with a load pressure of 1250 psi:

1. Signal input moves spool
2. Spool crosses bypass opening and closes bypass orifice
3. Metering orifice contacts land in valve body; flow is throttled through metering notches; pressure rises. As one set of metering notches closes the bypass opening, another set of notches opens

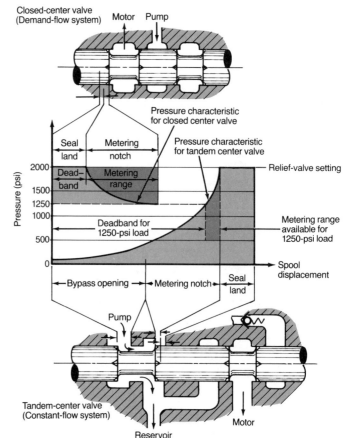

Fig. 7.14. For open center valves (bottom) deadband is relatively large, metering characteristics poor. Closed-center valves (top) reduce deadband by eliminating bypass orifice when valve is in neutral position.

44

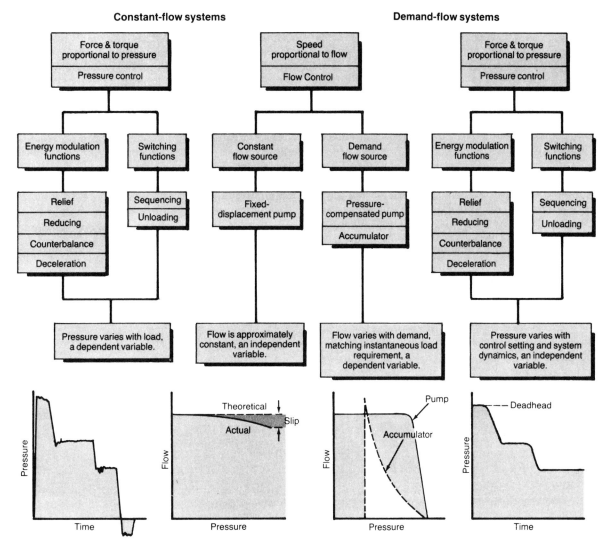

Fig. 7.15. Schematic guide to hydraulic systems.

the motor port. However, there is no flow until throttled fluid pressure equals required load pressure. At this point, some fluid flows to the actuator, although some is still bypassing to reservoir.

4. Spool reaches end of travel, closing the metering orifice at the bypass and completely opening the fluid actuator port; full pump output flows to motor.

With this sequence of events, the metering range extends from load pressure to relief valve setting. The sum of the spool motion required to close the bypass orifice and the length of the metering orifice required to achieve 1250 psi pressure level constitutes the deadband of the valve. The remaining spool motion is the metering range for a 1250 psi load pressure. Deadband and metering range change with load pressure.

For an open-center valve, Figure 7.14, bottom deadband is relatively large, so its metering characteristics are poor, particularly at high pres-

sure levels. The lower the load pressure, the better the metering characteristics.

Closed-center valves, Figure 7.14 top, reduce deadband by eliminating the bypass orifice in the neutral position. They have only a seal land and metering orifice, so the deadband is only the length of the seal land. The sequence of events from neutral to ON becomes:

1. Signal input moves spool

2. Metering notches move to edge of seal land

3. Metering notches start to open. Flow is throttled across metering notches starting at maximum pressure and decreasing toward load pressure. Since there is an excess of pressure fluid, further movement of the spool accelerates the load and instantaneous flow increases. Alternately, the metering notches can be held partly open to throttle flow and control motor speed

4. Metering notch is completely opened

5. Spool reaches end of travel, fully opening the motor port.

SUMMARY COMPARISON

A frequently overlooked fact is that the pressure level and flow rate are independent at steady-state conditions. While pressure losses *are* a function of flow velocity, at constant velocity, pressure losses throughout a system are the same regardless of load pressure. Thus, pressure losses constitute a tare* for the system.

Important Terms

Closed-center circuit is one characterized by a closed-center directional control valve that blocks all ports when it is in the neutral position.

Accumulator is a device that stores energy by compressing a confined gas.

Pressure-compensated pump is a variable-displacement pump which is self-regulating as a function of discharge pressure.

Flow-compensated pump is one which is self-regulating as a function of discharge flow rate.

Cutoff pressure is the pressure level at which a pressure compensated pump starts to regulate flow.

Deadhead pressure is the pressure level at which the discharge flow rate for a pressure-compensated pump becomes zero.

Demand system is one in which the flow rate is a function of the instantaneous velocity of the actuator.

---

*tare *is a means for measuring systems where constant losses produce an offset in the instrument's output.*

Review Exercises

7.1. What is a closed center circuit?

7.2. Why are these circuits better described functionally as demand flow circuits?

7.3. What are the essential hardware characteristics of demand flow circuits?

7.4. Referring to Figure 2.15: What class of circuit is represented? Why?

7.5. In demand flow circuits, what determines pump/accumulator delivery? Explain. How does this compare to constant/flow circuits?

7.6. In demand flow circuits, what determines maximum system pressure? What determines system pressure? How do these relate to design pressure? How do these compare to pressure in constant flow circuits?

7.7. Why is there no bypass flow over a relief valve in a demand flow system? Is this important? Why?

7.8. Referring to Figure 3.7, would a demand-flow system have any advantages over a constant flow system for this application? Discuss.

7.9. In demand flow systems how are actuators sized?

7.10. Discuss the relationship of unloading to deadheading during standby periods, in constant flow and demand flow systems?

7.11. How is speed of an actuator controlled in a demand/flow system? Compare to constant flow system.

7.12. What happens to the energy represented by pressure drops when throttling a fluid to control flow rate in a system? Is this considered a bad characteristic? Explain.

7.13. Discuss inertia effects in a demand flow system. How do they compare with those in a constant flow system?

7.14. Are there any significant differences in the way friction effects influence performance between constant and demand flow circuits? Explain.

7.15. Discuss "breakaway" considerations in a demand flow circuit. Are they different than in a constant flow circuit? Explain.

7.16. Discuss the pressure characteristics of demand flow circuits compared to constant flow circuits. What are the implications for performance of each type of circuit in actual applications?

CHAPTER 8

PRESSURE CONTROL FUNDAMENTALS

The two control factors which affect energy transfer are pressure and flow. Pressure control affects the potential energy level of the fluid in the system. Flow control regulates the quantity of fluid passing a reference point per unit of time. The product of pressure and flow rate is the power transferred by the fluid in the circuit.

Two pressure control modes are used in fluid power circuits:

1. **direct control** of the pressure level, such as:
   - *relief valves*, to control maximum pressure,
   - *reducing valves*, to control pressure at some level *below* maximum system pressure and,
   - *pressure-compensated variable-displacement pumps*.

2. **secondary control,** exercised when a given pressure level is reached, such as:
   - *sequence valves*, to switch flow to a secondary circuit when fluid pressure in the primary circuit has reached a preset level, and
   - *unloading valves*, to bypass pump flow to reservoir after system pressure has reached a preset level.

DIRECT CONTROL OF PRESSURE LEVEL

Control of Maximum Pressure

In its simplest form, control of maximum fluid pressure can be achieved with an orifice, Figure 8.1. For control to be uniform, this method requires constant load resistance, constant temperature, and a fixed-displacement pump. A sharp edged orifice has the advantage that it is virtually viscosity insensitive[1], that is, its performance is

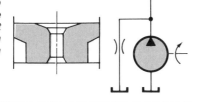

Fig. 8.1. Sharp edged, fixed orifice provides simplest form of maximum pressure control in a system.

[1]*Introduction to Fluid Mechanics*, R.W. Henke, Addison-Wesley Publishing Co., Reading, MA, 1968, pp. 75-80

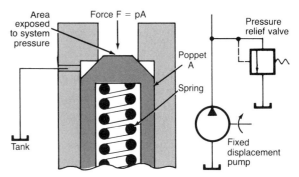

Fig. 8.2. Direct-acting relief valve is most commonly used means for controlling maximum system pressure.

not affected by changes in fluid temperature. Orifices offer the most economical type of control — and minimum performance.

1. **Direct-acting relief valves.** A relief valve is the most commonly used means to control maximum pressure in a system. It consists basically of a moving element, such as a poppet, A, which is exposed to primary circuit pressure, Figure 8.2. A *hydraulic* force pA, (pressure × area acted upon by the fluid), is opposed by the *mechanical* force exerted by a spring. When system pressure reaches the preset level, pA overcomes the spring force, the relief valve unseats and allows fluid to bypass to tank. The pressure drop across the valve is equal to primary system pressure. Note that the relief valve poppet and its seat form an annular orifice. The more the relief valve opens, the greater the area of this annular orifice.

Flow, Q, through an orifice is expressed by the equation[2]

$$Q = CA \sqrt{(2g\Delta p)/\gamma}$$

where C is a coefficient characteristic of the orifice, A_o is the orifice area; Δp is the pressure drop across the orifice, expressed in psi; γ is specific weight of the fluid and g is acceleration due to gravity. This expression indicates that flow is a function of the square root of the pressure differential across the valve. As Δp approaches the

[2]Ibid: pp. 76-77

preset pressure, the valve will open partially. Therefore only part of pump output will pass through the valve.

A direct-acting relief valve operates over a pressure band, rather than at one specific pressure. At some pressure level, called the *cracking pressure,* the valve opens slightly to allow a small percentage of total flow to bypass to tank. In effect, it *bleeds off* some of the pump's output and reduces the flow rate to the circuit by that amount. As the pressure level increases, the valve opens wider and more fluid is bypassed to tank. At its *rated pressure setting,* the valve opens enough to bypass all pump output to tank.

Thus the relief valve protects circuits and other components in the system from excessive pressure. To properly design a circuit with a relief valve, the designer must know the cracking characteristics of the particular valve.

2. Piloted relief valve. A two-stage relief valve overcomes the disadvantages of the direct-acting relief valve and is called a *pilot-operated valve,* Figure 8.3. A small *pilot piston* is held on its seat by a relatively long, low gradient spring. Because the pilot piston has a small diameter, the hydraulic force acting on it is also small. This minimizes the cracking effects commonly noticeable in direct-acting relief valves.

The *main poppet* is held on its seat by the force exerted by hydraulic pressure fluid acting on differential areas, A and a. When the pilot valve opens, some of the fluid acting on A of the main poppet flows to tank. A temporary pressure imbalance is created, lifting the main poppet off its seat. This happens so fast that the cracking range of the main poppet is greatly reduced.

The pilot-operated relief valve is much more stable than the direct-acting type. In addition, it can be vented remotely to unload the pump, giving the circuit designer a means of ensuring greater stability and closer control, and provides the added versatility of remote control.

3. Hydraulic fuse. The hydraulic fuse, Figure 8.4, is akin to an electric fuse. It consists of a rupture disc which blows out at a preset pressure level,

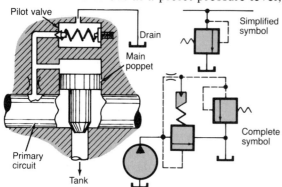

Fig. 8.3. Pilot operated, 2-stage relief valve overcomes drawbacks of direct acting relief valve.

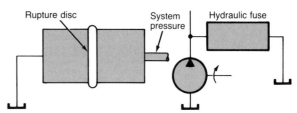

Fig. 8.4. Hydraulic fuse consists of a rupture disc which bursts instantly at a preset pressure.

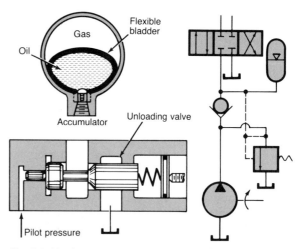

Fig. 8.5. Maximum system pressure can also be controlled with an accumulator and an unloading valve.

releasing system oil to tank. It is used where the rate of pressure rise is very high, 150,000 psi/sec for example, and pressure relief must, for all intents and purposes, be *instantaneous.* This reaction rate is too fast for a conventional relief valve to respond in the necessary time. Like an electric fuse, the hydraulic fuse must be replaced, (it cannot be reset), and the system remains inoperative until the fuse is replaced.

4. Shock suppressor valve. This is a special valve designed to open on a signal it receives when the rate of pressure rise reaches a preset level. It clips off shock waves before they reach their maximum potential amplitude.

5. Accumulator control. Maximum system pressure can be controlled with an accumulator and an unloading valve, Figure 8.5. In this configuration, system pressure is a function of the gas precharge and the volume of fluid in the accumulator. Maximum pressure depends on the setting of the unloading valve. When a preset pressure is reached, the unloading valve opens and bypasses pump output to tank. A check valve in the line prevents the accumulator from being unloaded at the same time.

6. Pump control. Pump control of maximum pressure involves the use of a pressure-compensated variable displacement pump, Figure 8.6. Functionally, a pressure compensator control is a hydraulic cylinder which varies the position of the pumping elements. Opposing this cylinder is a

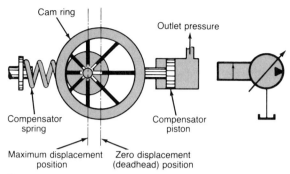

Fig. 8.6. In schematic of pressure compensated, variable displacement vane pump, small cylinder alters position of cam ring, thus varying pump displacement.

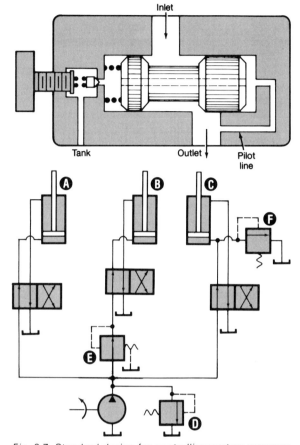

Fig. 8.7. Standard design for controlling system pressure with pressure reducing valve.

spring, Figure 8.6. A compensator spring acting on a cam ring holds the pumping elements in the maximum displacement position, e, as shown.

When system pressure reaches a preset level, called the *cutoff* pressure, the force exerted by the compensator cylinder exceeds that of the spring and starts to shift the cam ring to the left, toward neutral position. The higher the pressure, the greater the hydraulic force and the farther it shifts the cam ring toward neutral. At some point, called the *deadhead* pressure, the cylinder force is high enough to shift the cam to full neutral position. Thus, while the rotor and vanes still rotate, no oil is being delivered to the system.

A pressure-compensated pump can function as a system relief valve. Because no oil is being throttled across the valve, less energy is lost through heat generation, making the pressure-compensated pump more efficient than a relief valve. In most cases, it is not desirable to use a pressure-compensated pump *and* a relief valve in the same circuit because of hydraulic feedback signals between them. If a relief valve *is* used, it should be set 200-300 psi higher than pump deadhead setting, to avoid instability of the system.

PRESSURE CONTROL IN CIRCUIT BRANCHES

1. Pressure reducing valves. This normally-open, 2-way valve senses system pressure *downstream* from the valve inlet. There are two basic types. One maintains *fixed* reduced pressure in a circuit branch regardless of the pressure in the balance of the system, Figure 8.7; the other maintains a fixed pressure differential to provide *varying* reduced pressure with change in system pressure, Figure 8.8.

Like relief valves, pressure reducing valves can be either direct-acting or pilot-operated. The circuit in Figure 8.7 illustrates several design features. When cylinder, A, extends, fluid pressure in cylinder A is controlled by system relief valve,

D. Fluid pressure in cylinder B is controlled by pressure reducing valve, E, within the maximum pressure range controlled by relief valve D. If fluid pressure in cylinder B is low, then, relief valve, D, controls overall system pressure; fluid pressure to cylinder C is controlled by relief valve, F, on the extend stroke; by relief valve D on retract stroke. If fluid pressure in cylinder A drops below the setting of relief valve, F, then cylinder C will operate at the same pressure as cylinder A.

On their retract strokes, cylinders A and C are controlled by relief valve, D, while cylinder B is controlled by pressure reducing valve, E.

To ensure proper functioning, pressure reducing valves should be drained to tank. This prevents downstream pressure buildup (backpressure) due to leakage, in normal return lines.

Another application suitable for some types of reducing valves, is shown in Figure 8.8. Here, a reducing valve, G, supplies a secondary branch at a pressure level below that in the primary circuit.

2. Sequence valves. A sequence valve is a normally-closed (usually) internally-piloted valve which remains closed until pressure in the primary circuit reaches the preset pressure level of the valve. When this occurs, sequence valve, *H*, Figure 8.9, opens to provide output flow into the secondary circuit. As illustrated, this type of control is frequently used to switch flow to a secondary circuit after the actuator in the primary circuit has reached the end of its stroke and pressure starts to rise. This design eliminates the need for a directional control valve to sequence flows.

Note that in the circuit in Figure 8.9, sequence valve, *H*, will close again when the directional control valve in Branch 1 (not shown) is shifted to retract cylinder *A*. To prevent premature operation, design operating pressure to cylinder *A* in Branch 1 must be *below* the setting of sequence valve, *H*.

3. Counterbalance valve. Figure 8.10 illustrates a typical application of a counterbalance valve, *J*. It is a normally-closed, 2-way valve with internal pilot, internal drain, and (usually) a built-in, free-flow check valve for reverse flow. It is used to prevent free fall of a load held up by a cylinder or fluid motor, or to provide controlled resistance in a line. Overcenter valves are counterbalance valves with external piloting to accommodate load reversals on actuators. Brake valves are special counterbalance valves used with hydraulic motors, Figure 8.11.

4. Pressure switch. A pressure switch, Figure 8.12, is an electrical device operated by a pressure-sensitive element such as a bourdon tube or a bellows. It can actuate a solenoid-controlled valve when a preset pressure is reached. This valve might unload a pump, switch to a secondary circuit, or reverse an actuator.

5. Pump unloading. Though not a pressure control technique in the strictest sense, pump unloading is

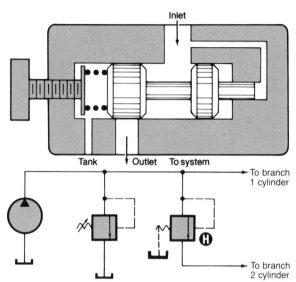

Fig. 8.9. Sequence valve controls fluid pressure in hydraulic circuit branches.

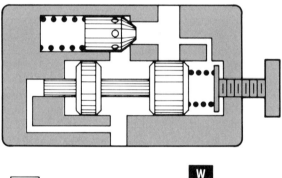

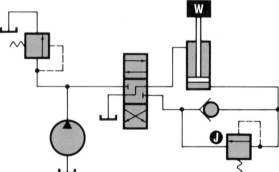

Fig. 8.10. Counterbalance valve controls fluid pressure in a hydraulic circuit branch.

of considerable importance in some circuit designs because it reduces power consumption during idle periods in the cycle. By eliminating the need to bypass oil over a relief valve, an unloaded pump reduces the amount of heat a system generates.

We have already discussed the use of the unloading valve. Here are some additional useful pressure control techniques.

a) *Control-valve unloading*. Figure 8.13 shows a circuit using a 2-way, normally-closed, directional control valve, *K*, which vents system

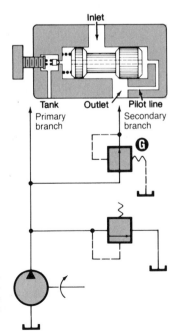

Fig. 8.8. Pressure reducing valve supplies a secondary branch at a pressure below that of primary circuit.

relief valve, L, to unload the pump. The solenoid in valve, K, is actuated by a limit switch or some other signalling device. Note that in this application, the normally-closed directional control valves *must* be centered to unload the pump.

b) *Accumulator*. As illustrated in Figure 8.14, an accumulator maintains a preset system pressure when the closed-center directional control valve is in neutral. A pressure switch, M, energizes the solenoid of 2-way valve, N, which shifts to bypass pump flow to tank.

c) *Relief-valve unloading*. A low-pressure relief valve, P, Figure 8.15, connected in parallel with the cylinder's head end, is set just high enough to retract the cylinder. When the cylinder is fully retracted, low-pressure relief valve, P, unloads the pump. With this type of circuit, the machine operator does not need to hold a spring-centered direction control valve shifted until the cylinder is fully retracted.

d) *Multiple-cylinder unloading*. If 3-position, 2-way, normally-open valves are arranged in series with each main directional control valve, Figure 8.16, the system relief valve will be vented when all directional control valves are in neutral. However, if any one of the main directional control valves is shifted, the vent line will be blocked. The number of venting valves that can be put in series is limited by the backpressure across each valve.

SYSTEM PRESSURE DROP CONSIDERATIONS

Pressure drop[3] is a reduction in pressure between two consecutive points in a fluid power system.

---

[3]Ibid: pp 77, 79, 86-100, 150-176

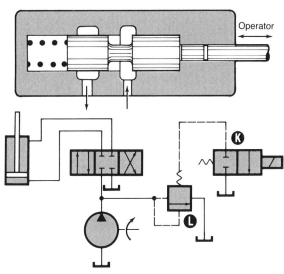

Fig. 8.13. *Two-way, NC directional control valve vents system relief valve to unload pump.*

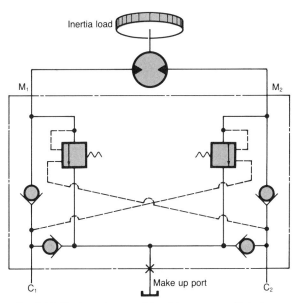

Fig. 8.11. *Brake valve consists of two, cross-piloted counterbalance valves which apply backpressure to decelerate the fluid motor under overrunning conditions caused by an inertia load. The check valves cross feed return oil to minimize motor cavitation.*

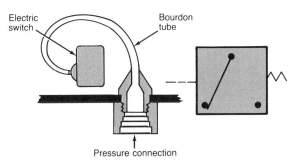

Fig. 8.12. *Pressure sensing, electrical pressure switch actuates solenoid-controlled valve when preset pressure level is reached.*

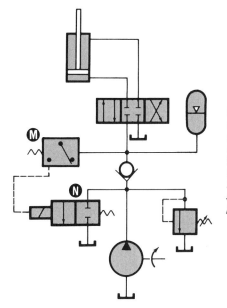

Fig. 8.14. *Accumulator and closed-center directional control valve maintain preset system pressure.*

Pressure drop happens because some energy in the system is required to do work to maintain fluid flow against a resistance. This resistance can be internal fluid friction, orifice-like restrictions in the flow paths, or external load resistance.

A pressure drop between a pump and motor represents a loss in energy which manifests itself as heat. The pressure drop across the motor reflects the energy being transferred to the external load. Motor efficiency is an indication of internal losses which reduce the actual energy of the motor and the energy available for transfer.

The pressure drop across a given valve varies as the ratio of the specific gravity of the fluid. If, for instance, we know the pressure differential, Δp_1, for a fluid with a specific gravity Sg_1, then we can approximate the value of Δp_2 for a second fluid from the expression:

$$\Delta p_2 = \Delta p_1 \, (S_{g2}/S_{g1}).$$

Similarly, the pressure drop varies as the square of flow rate:

$$\Delta p_2 = \Delta p_1 \, (Q_2/Q_1)^2.$$

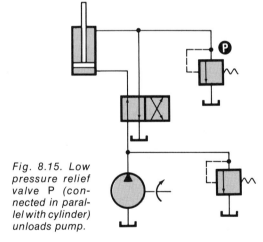

Fig. 8.15. Low pressure relief valve P (connected in parallel with cylinder) unloads pump.

Application problem 1

Assume that flow rate through a valve is 1.2 gpm at a pressure drop of 50 psi. What would be the pressure drop at a flow rate of 8 gpm?

First, determine the ratio of the flow rates: 8/1.2 = 6.66:1. The square of this ratio is $6.66^2 = 44$. Thus the pressure drop at 8 gpm would be

$$\Delta p_2 = 50 \times 44 = 2200 \text{ psi.}$$

The designer must be alert to the dramatic increase in pressure drops which can occur with seemingly small increases in flow rate. One such place is in the return line from a cylinder. If pump flow to the head end is reflected across the area differential of the piston, the result can be a return flow several times greater than pump rate.

Application problem 2

Assume a cylinder with a 5-in bore and 3-in diameter rod. A pump supplies fluid to the cylinder at a rate of 10 gpm. Determine the piston velocity during extension and retraction strokes. What will be the flow rate of the returning oil during the retraction stroke? If the directional control valve experiences a pressure drop of 20 psi at 10 gpm, what will be the pressure drop during return flow?

Piston velocity during the extension stroke is
$v_e = Q/A_p = [(10 \text{ gpm} \times 231 \text{ in}^3 \text{ gal)]} /19.6 \text{ in}^2$
$= 118 \text{ ipm.}$
During the retraction stroke, return velocity of the fluid is
$v_r = Q/A_p - A_r$
$= [(10 \text{ gpm} \times 231 \text{ in}^3/\text{gal)]} /(19.6\text{-}7.1 \text{ in}^2)$
$= 185 \text{ ipm.}$

Flow rate during the retraction stroke is:
$Q_r = A_p v_r$
$= 19.6 \text{ in}^2 \times 185 \text{ ipm}$
$= 3626 \text{ in}^3 /\text{min}$
$= 15.7 \text{ gpm}$
Another way to calculate piston velocity is:

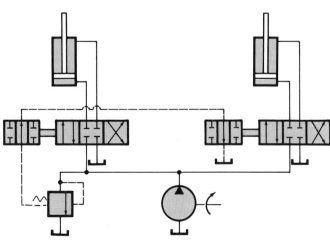

Fig. 8.16. If NO valves are arranged in series with each main directional valve, system relief valve is vented when all directional valves are in neutral.

$Q_r = QA_p/(A_p - A_r)$
   $= [(10 \text{ gpm} \times 19.6 \text{ in}^2)]/12.5 \text{ in}^2$
   $= 15.7 \text{ gpm}.$

Hence, the pressure drop during return flow will be:

$\Delta p_2 = [\Delta p_1 \ (Q_2/Q_1)^2]$
   $= 20 \times (15.7 \text{ gpm}/10)^2$
   $= 49.2 \text{ psi}.$

The Force-Balance Concept

A review of pressure controls reveals that control valves work on the principle of a hydraulic force acting against a mechanical spring. This is known as the *Force-Balance* concept, Figure 8.17. It is essential to understand and remember that when working with pressure controls, and, for that matter, all fluid power components, we are dealing with mechanical devices. They all work on the FORCE-BALANCE principle.

A hydraulic force can be developed on one side of a control element (interface), as for example the poppet in a relief valve, the spool in a reduicng valve or in a sequence valve. The magnitude of the hydraulic force equals the product of the pressure differential across the element (*not* just inlet pressure) and the effective area of the element on which the pressure fluid acts. This relationship is expressed by

$$F_H = \Delta p A_e.$$

If this hydraulic force were unopposed, the element would shift to wide-open position and fluid would flow through the control valve with very low pressure drop — just the equivalent orifice drop across the valve flow path. To achieve any degree of control, a method must be provided to regulate the opening of the valve control orifice by limiting the motion of the control element, *i.e.*, poppet or spool. This is accomplished by opposing the hydraulic force with a spring force, Figure 8.17. The force exerted by a compression spring is expressed by the equation,

$$F_s = K_s x_s,$$

where K_s is the spring constant in lb/in, x_s is the amount of spring compression in inches, and F_s is the force in lb.

When designing hydraulic controls, the common practice is to provide some initial spring compression, x_i, to establish a minimum force level in the control system. This relationship translates to a minimum pressure drop, Δp, across the control element to bring the hydraulic force into equilibrium with the spring force. In a relief valve this force roughly corresponds to the cracking pressure. As the control element moves off its seat during normal valve operation, the spring compresses more, as shown by Δx_s, Figure 8.17. This action establishes a new equilibrium posi-

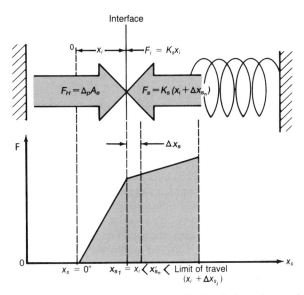

Fig. 8.17. Force-balance concept. Hydraulic force is equal to sum of product of pressure differential across the element and effective area of element on which the pressurized fluid acts.

tion based on the relationship:

$$\Delta p \cdot A_e = F_H = F_s = K_s \ (x_i + \Delta x_s).$$

In this manner, a new equilibrium position is established for each pressure generated in the fluid power system. This relationship is plotted as the curve in Figure 8.18.

A second consideration, of particular importance when designing with energy-modulating-type controls, is the effect of the orifice flow Δp characteristic, discussed on page 53. With respect to the force-balance principle, it is important to recognize that the pressure referred to is actually the pressure differential, Δp across the control element at a flow-rate that is equal to the amount of fluid actually passing through the valve. The relationship is expressed roughly as

$$\Delta p = K_o Q^2,$$

and is represented by the curve shown in Figure 8.18. This curve is typically characteristic for a relief valve, which illustrates the point under discussion. In a force-balance system using a spring, such as is commonly used in fluid power controls, it is impossible for any reaction to happen instantaneously.

A finite amount of movement is always required for the valve to reestablish new equilibrium points along the curve. Such movement, along with the changes in control orifice area and by-passed flow rate associated with it, require some increment of time, no matter how little. Thus, relief valves do *not* exhibit a step-change characteristic relating pressure level and bypass flow rate; rather they display an exponential characteristic, Figure 8.18. At any system pressure below the cracking pressure, p_c, the valve remains closed; bypass flow rate, $Q_o = 0$.

In the pressure range between valve cracking and setting, $p_e < p_s < p_{max}$, bypass flow rate will also vary, $0 < Q_{Bp} < Q_{max}$. When full pump output, $Q_{max} = 100\% \; Q_o$ is bypassing to tank, system pressure is at maximum, p_{set}. These concepts apply in general, to all pressure *and* flow controls used in fluid power systems.

We have extended the force-balance concept to its application to pressure compensated pumps, Figure 8.19. Shown schematically are a vane pump and an axial-piston, variable-displacement, pressure-compensated pump. The *spring force* for the compensator control is represented at left, the *hydraulic force* at right. Force relationships are plotted as typical curves below the pump representations. The principal difference between the pressure-compensated pump and the relief valve previously discussed is that pump pressure equals system pressure; the relief valve works with a pressure drop across the relief valve poppet.

Pressure compensator

Compensator spring initial conditions are illustrated at upper left, Figure 8.19. Spring free length is shown, and initial compression is labeled x_i. With a spring constant, k_s, this results in an initial force of $F_s = k_s x_i$, which is plotted on the spring force curve at left center.

At right center of Figure 8.19 is a plot of the hydraulic compensator piston force. The point on the spring force curve corresponding to initial compression is projected across to the hydraulic force curve. Initial pressure, p_i would be system pressure which would just balance the spring force under initial conditions.

If initial pressure, p_i, is established as the cut-off pressure for the pressure compensated pump, x_i is the amount of precompression required to

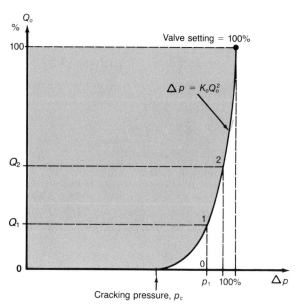

Fig. 8.18. In force-balance concept, fluid pressure is actually the pressure differential across the control element at a flow rate equal to the amount of fluid actually passing through the valve.

determine cut-off. Any pressure below cut-off will not affect pump displacement. Pressures between cut-off and deadhead will result in new equilibrium points being established by additional spring compression. Simultaneously, the displacement mechanism is adjusted to reduce pump delivery. The limit is deadhead pressure. At this point the pump stops delivering fluid to the system although maximum pressure is maintained.

Steps I through V in Figure 8.19, illustrate the algebraic equations relating spring force and hydraulic compensator force. The characteristic curve at right is the typical pressure compensated pump curve and includes indication of displacement conditions for each part of the curve.

The above describes direct acting compensator controls. Chapters 14 and 15 discuss compensators which use modulating valves for control.

Review Exercises

8.1. What two types of control relate to energy transfer in fluid power systems?

8.2. Which of the two system parameters relating to the controls referred to in exercise 8.1 deals with the potential energy level of the fluid in the system?

8.3. To what parameter does the product of pressure (psi) and weight flow rate (lb/time) relate? What are the relationships in SI units?

8.4. What are the two basic modes of pressure control?

8.5 List the basic kinds of pressure control valves used in fluid power systems. Define their functions briefly. Illustrate with ANSI graphic symbols.

8.6. What is the primary function of a pressure relief valve in a fluid power system?

8.7. How is a relief valve sized for a circuit?

8.8. Discuss the differences between a direct-

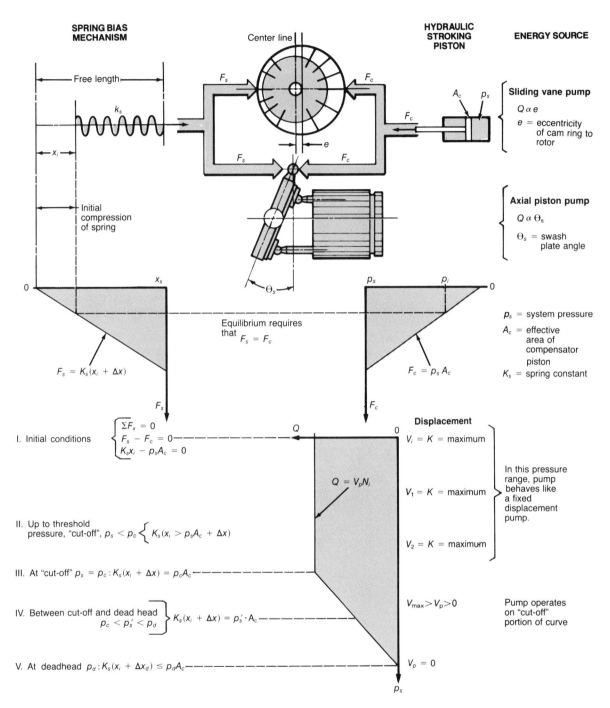

Fig. 8.19. Schematic of vane and axial piston variable displacment, pressure compensated pumps. Spring force for compensator control is at left, hydraulic force at right.

acting and a pilot-operated relief valve. What are the advantages and disadvantages of each? Draw the ANSI symbols for each.

8.9. Discuss "cracking band" of relief valves and its significance in circuit applications.

8.10. What techniques are available to minimize shock pressures in a circuit?

8.11. Discuss the concept of valve control of pressure vs. pump control of pressure.

8.12. What is meant by the "force-balance" concept? How does it apply in fluid power controls?

8.13. Discuss the difference in application of "force-balance" in a "modulating" pressure control vs. a "switching" type pressure control.

8.14. Why is it erroneous to talk about "instantaneous" actions in a fluid power system?

8.15. What is the function of a reducing valve? Is it an energy "modulating" or "switching" type of pressure control? Draw its ANSI symbol.

8.16. What is/are the difference(s) between the two types of reducing valves?

8.17. What is the function of a sequence valve? Is it an energy "modulating" or "switching" type of pressure control? Draw the ANSI symbol for the sequence valve.

8.18. Once a sequence valve has "sequenced", what is the relationship between the pressure level in the primary and secondary circuits?

8.19. Typically a manufacturer of a sequence valve may specify the "reset" pressure level of his valve as 85% of its actuation pressure. Discuss what this means and its implications in a circuit application.

8.20. What is the function of a counterbalance valve in a circuit? Is it a "modulating" or "switching" type valve? Draw its ANSI symbol.

8.21. What is the function of an unloading valve? Is it a "modulating" or "switching" type of valve? Draw its ANSI symbol.

8.22. What is the function of a pressure switch? Draw its ANSI symbol.

8.23. Explain how venting a relief valve can unload a circuit. Draw a venting circuit using ANSI symbols.

8.24. Which types of pressure control valves must have external drain lines connected to tank?

8.25. Discuss the effect of pressure differential(s) across controls in a circuit on:
   a. pump discharge pressure relative to load pressure;
   b. efficiency of a circuit.

8.26. Is it possible to achieve a measure of pressure control with a directional control valve by modulating spool position? Explain.

CHAPTER 9

PRESSURE CONTROL CIRCUITS

In previous chapters, we discussed pressure optimization and means for achieving pressure control. In this chapter we consider typical circuits that provide the systems designer with various modes of pressure control.

CIRCUITS FOR LIMITING MAXIMUM PRESSURE

Figure 9.1 illustrates a basic pressure limiting circuit: a relief valve connected in parallel with the main pressure line. When system pressure reaches the relief valve setting, pump output flow bypasses to reservoir at full system pressure. During this period, all the energy input to the system is converted to heat.

The circuit of Figure 9.2 is functionally similar to the action of a relief valve circuit, except that it uses a hydraulic fuse. This is a one-shot device: when the rupture disc blows out it must be replaced to reset the circuit. This design arrangement would be used primarily with pressure-compensated pumps to give positive and instantaneous overload protection in case the compensator control on the pump failed to operate.

A pressure-compensated pump limits maximum system pressure, Figure 9.3. The maximum attainable pressure corresponds to the **deadhead** pressure setting of the pump control.

Unloading circuits

Unloading circuits differ from circuits that limit maximum pressure primarily in the pressure drop across the control device: unloading circuits bypass pump flow at a lower pressure drop across the control device. This arrangement minimizes heat generation during bypass.

Figure 9.4 shows a simplified unloading valve circuit equipped with a fixed-displacement pump.

The unloading valve opens when the cylinder bottoms out at the end of its stroke in either direction. Shifting the directional control valve to reverse the direction of the piston rod causes a pressure drop in the circuit, allowing the unloading valve to reset.

A balanced relief valve which can be vented

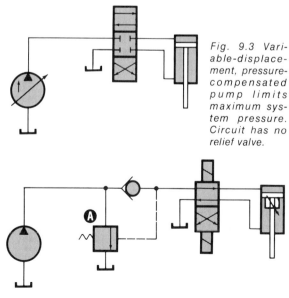

Fig. 9.3 Variable-displacement, pressure-compensated pump limits maximum system pressure. Circuit has no relief valve.

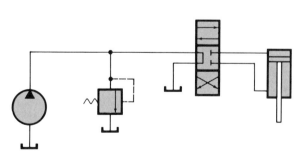

Fig. 9.1. In basic pressure limiting circuit, relief valve is connected between pump and valve, in parallel with main pressure line.

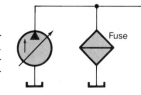

Fig. 9.2. Power portion of circuit resembles that of Fig. 9.1, but hydraulic fuse replaces relief valve for instantaneous overload protection.

Fig. 9.4. Unloading valve, **A,** opens when cylinder bottoms at the end of stroke.

through the main directional control valve is shown in Figure 9.5. Note that this configuration requires a special directional control valve with a fifth port to vent the circuit.

Figure 9.6 illustrates a circuit with a solenoid-operated, normally closed, 2-way valve, A, to unload the pump. Limit switches at each end of the piston stroke signal the valve to shift. These limit switches are wired in series with a switch operated by shifting the manual valve operator.

A typical pressure-switch control is shown in the circuit of Figure 9.7. When system pressure reaches a preset level, the pressure switch is actuated, energizing the solenoid operator of a normally closed, 2-way valve. The pump is unloaded when this 2-way valve opens.

Pumps can be unloaded by means of bypass ports built into the cylinder, Figure 9.8. In this

circuit, a single bypass port is placed in the head end of the cylinder. When the piston passes over this port, the port opens to the cap end, permitting incoming fluid to bypass to tank. Dual bypass ports are illustrated in Figure 9.9.

Hi-lo circuits

Hi-lo circuits provide two output forces at two different operating pressures, Figure 9.10. Usually such a system delivers low torque (or force) and high actuator speed, and then, on signal, shifts to high torque (or force) and slow actuator speed by unloading the high-flow, low-pressure pump.

Figure 9.10 illustrates a basic hi-lo circuit using two fixed-displacement pumps. The unloading valve unloads the high-flow, low-pressure pump when the system reaches a preset pressure. Prior

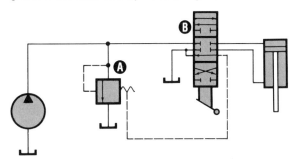

Fig. 9.5. Balanced relief valve, **A,** vents through main directional control valve **B.**

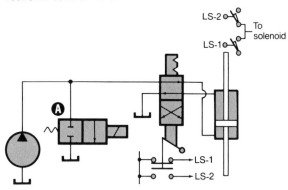

Fig. 9.6. Solenoid operated, NC, 2-way valve, **A,** unloads fixed-displacement pump. Limit switch signals valve **A.**

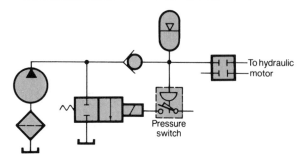

Fig. 9.7. When system pressure reaches preset level, pressure switch **A** is made, signalling NC, 2-way valve **B** to shift to unload the fixed-displacement pump.

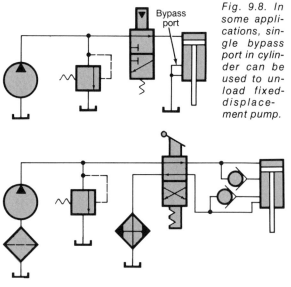

Fig. 9.8. In some applications, single bypass port in cylinder can be used to unload fixed-displacement pump.

Fig. 9.9. Dual bypass ports can also be used to bypass pump output to tank.

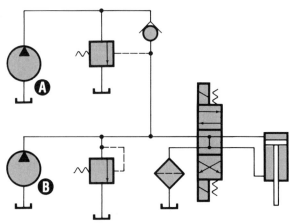

Fig. 9.10. In Hi-Lo circuit, each of two fixed-displacement pumps is protected by a separate relief valve. One pump provides high flow at low pressure, the other low flow at high pressure.

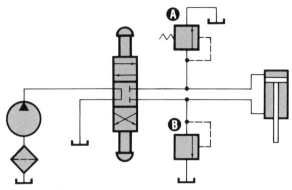

Fig. 9.11. Circuit provides different pressures in each end of the cylinder.

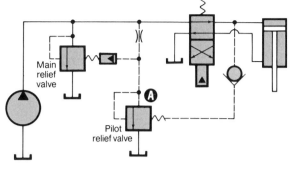

Fig. 9.12. Piloted relief valve provides high pressure when cylinder extends, low pressure when it retracts.

to this point, both pumps supply fluid to the circuit. After the low-pressure pump, A, is unloaded, only the high-pressure pump, B, supplies fluid to the circuit. This type of circuit is frequently used in applications requiring a rapid traverse (feed) cycle as in machine tools, or for a rapid approach cycle on presses. Observe that in these circuits the check valve separates the primary and the secondary pumps. If the check valve were omitted, both pumps would be unloaded, not just the secondary one.

CIRCUITS FOR
CONTROLLING CYLINDER PRESSURE

Most circuits described in this chapter provide pressure control under specific conditions. Figure 9.11 illustrates a technique for obtaining two different controlled pressures in a cylinder, one in the cap end, another in the head end. Relief valve A, connected to the line from the directional control valve to the cylinder's cap end is set to open at one pressure. Relief valve B, to the cylinder head end is set to open at another.

Note that placing a control valve *upstream* of the directional control valve would affect both actuator lines. However, placing a control valve **downstream** from the directional control valve affects only the line to which it is connected. If, in Figure 9.11 relief valve A, had been placed upstream of the directional control valve, it would have exercised priority control over the pressure level in **both** cylinder lines. Relief valve, B, would have been effective only if its setting were below that of relief valve A, and then only affect the line from the head end of the cylinder.

Figure 9.12 illustrates a circuit where a piloted relief valve, A, provides **high pressure** control during cylinder extension and low pressure control during retraction. The pilot line is connected in parallel with the line to the cap end of the cylinder. When the cylinder cap end is pressurized, pressure fluid in the pilot line holds the pilot relief valve closed. The pilot relief valve, in turn, holds the main relief valve closed against the high pres-

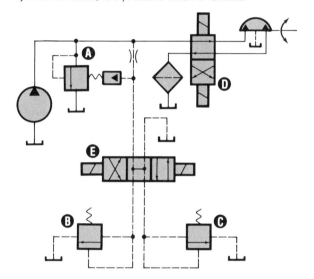

Fig. 9.13. In 3-pressure level circuit, either piloted relief valve (bottom) can vent main relief valve.

sure level. When the directional control valve is shifted to retract the cylinder, fluid pressure in the pilot line drops to the pressure level of the return line. This enables the pilot relief valve to control the main relief valve at whatever pressure the pilot valve was set to operate.

Figure 9.13 illustrates a 3-pressure circuit in which main relief valve, A, or either of the two pilot relief valves, B or C can set the limiting pressure. Auxiliary directional control valve, E, determines which of the two pilot valves, B or C, will vent main relief valve, A. When directional control valve, E, is in neutral position, neither pilot valve, B or C, is active and main relief valve, A controls system pressure. Main directional control valve, D, controls the direction of actuator motion.

In the multibranched circuit, Figure 9.14, three 4-way 3-position main directional control valves are connected mechanically to three auxiliary 2-way 3-position valves so main and auxiliary valves shift simultaneously.

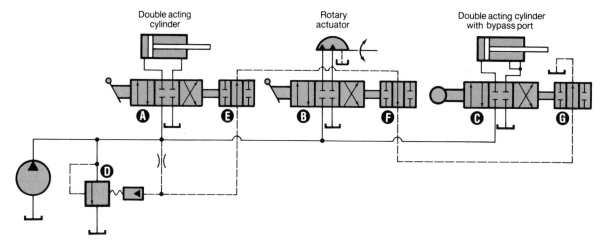

Fig. 9.14. In multibranch circuit, 4-way, 3-position directional control valves are linked mechanically to auxiliary 2-way, 3-position valves which vent main relief valve.

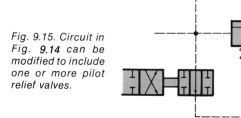

Fig. 9.15. Circuit in Fig. 9.14 can be modified to include one or more pilot relief valves.

relief valve *D* vents through the normally open ports of 2-way, auxiliary directional control valves, *E*, *F*, and *G*. The pump unloads through open relief valve, *D*. If anyone of the directional control valves is shifted, its mating, auxiliary 2-way valve also shifts, blocking that vent line from the relief valve. Relief valve, *D*, now controls system pressure at the desired setting.

The basic circuit shown in Figure 9.14 can be modified as in Figure 9.15. The addition of a pilot relief valve to a branch of the pilot or venting circuit enables the designer to control a system with different pressure levels at each branch.

In the multibranch circuit in Figure 9.16, a pressure-reducing valve, *A*, controls the reduced pressure in a secondary branch of the circuit. The pressure in the primary branch supplying pressure fluid to cylinder *B* is controlled by the setting of main system relief valve, *C*. The pressure in the secondary branch to cylinder *D* is controlled by the setting of pressure reducing valve, *A*, providing the pressure level in the secondary branch is *lower* than that of the primary branch.

ACCUMULATOR CIRCUITS

Accumulators are fluid power components that store potential energy and return it to the circuit on demand. Accumulators are used in fluid power circuits for two purposes, to
a) store energy and provide pressurized fluid to a circuit, and

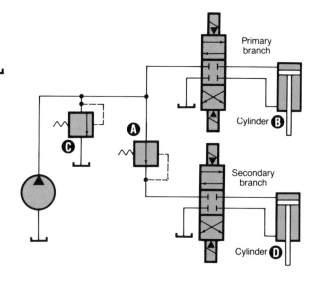

Fig. 9.16. Pressure reducing valve, **A**, controls reduced pressure level in secondary branch of circuit.

b) act as surge suppressors and reduce pressure shocks in a system.

The circuit in Figure 9.17 illustrates how an accumulator is used as a primary source of pressurized fluid. The variable-displacement, pressure-compensated pump supplies pressure fluid to the gas charged accumulator during non-working or dwell periods in the work cycle. An unloading valve opens when the desired maximum pressure is reached, bypassing pump output flow to tank at low pressure. When the cam-operated, spring-returned directional control valve is shifted, the accumulator delivers pressurized fluid into the circuit.

Figure 9.18 shows a circuit in which the accumulator maintains a constant pressure in the system. This circuit appears to be identical to that

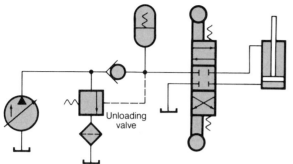

Fig. 9.17. Spring-loaded accumulator acts as auxiliary source of pressurized fluid to cylinder.

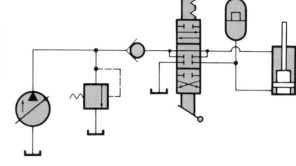

Fig. 9.19. In modified pressure-holding circuit, weighted accumulator is connected to cylinder line downstream of directional control valve, maintaining pressure only in cap end of cushioned cylinder.

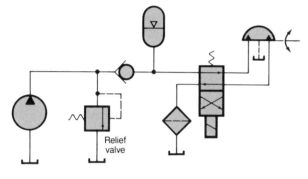

Fig. 9.18. Gas-loaded accumulator maintains constant pressure on both sides of rotary actuator.

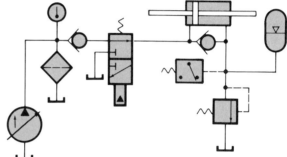

Fig. 9.20. In fail-safe-retract circuit, gas-loaded accumulator provides pressurized fluid to retract cushioned cylinder, should pump stop.

of Figure 9.17 except that a relief valve is used instead of an unloading valve. This type circuit would be used where it is necessary to maintain a certain pressure, yet it may also be desirable at times to stop the pump.

Figure 9.19 is a modification of the basic pressure-holding circuit: the weighted accumulator is connected to the cylinder line **downstream** of the directional control valve. When a control device is so placed, it controls only that line. Thus, the accumulator in Figure 9.19 **only** pressurizes the cap end of the cylinder; the accumulator in Figure 9.18 holds pressure in **both** lines to the rotary actuator.

Figure 9.20 shows an accumulator used in a failsafe-retract mode. Should the pump fail, the accumulator would provide the pressurized fluid needed to retract the cylinder. There are many applications in which this safety feature is desirable.

Accumulators may also be used where electric power failure may create a hazardous situation, Figure 9.21. Here, loss of electric power would deenergize the solenoid operators of main directional control valve, A, allowing it to center. Should this happen, secondary directional control valve, B, could then be shifted manually to control

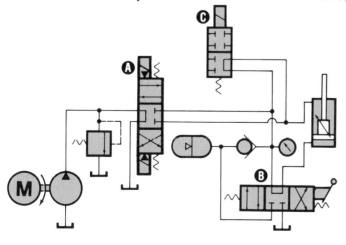

Fig. 9.21. In another fail-safe-retract circuit, gas-loaded accumulator will retract adjustable cushioned cylinder in case of electric power failure.

the cylinder, using pressurized fluid stored in the accumulator. Auxiliary directional control valve, C, provides the necessary flow paths during emergency operation.

Figure 9.22 illustrates an application where the accumulator reduces pump pressure surges. All positive-displacement pumps exhibit a pulsating output characteristic due to the cyclic mechanical input to the pumping mechanism. In some applications these pulsations must be damped out with an accumulator.

Figure 9.23 is an application similar to that illustrated in Figure 9.22. Here, the accumulator reduces any shock that might be generated in the circuit by impact loading on the cylinder piston rod. A resistive-type impact on the cylinder rod could momentarily convert the cylinder into a pump and send a pressure shock back into the system. An overrunning type load impact would cause cavitation on the cap end of the cylinder, and fluid rushing in to fill the void could create a pressure shock. The accumulator damps out the pressure shock in either case.

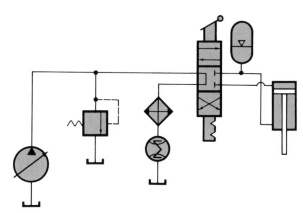

Fig. 9.23. In another shock-suppressing circuit, accumulator is mounted downstream of 4-way, 3-position directional control valve.

These examples are but a few of the unlimited varieties of circuits which can be used to solve fluid power design problems.

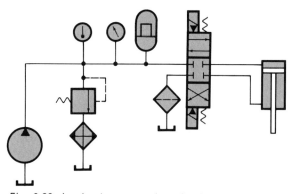

Fig. 9.22. In shock suppressing circuit, accumulator is connected upstream of directional control valve to reduce pump pressure surges.

Important Terms

Pressure-limiting circuit is the basic relief valve circuit, which limits the maximum pressure which a circuit can develop.

Unloading circuit is designed to unload — that is, reduce the pressure of the pump during non-work portions of a load cycle.

Hi-lo circuit is one in which two pumps provide two flow rates to the circuit at different pressures during different parts of the work cycle.

Accumulator circuit is one in which an accumulator acts as an energy storage device or damps out fluid-induced shocks and pulsations in the circuit.

Review Exercises

9.1. What are the principle techniques for limiting maximum system pressure? Which is most commonly used?

9.2. Is it permissible to use a relief valve in a system with a pressure compensated pump? If so, explain what precautions should be taken to insure proper system performance? What would happen if such precautions were not taken?

9.3. Explain the difference between a maximum pressure limiting circuit and an unloading circuit. Why would each be used?

9.4. What techniques are available for unloading a pump(s) in a hydraulic circuit(s)?

9.5 Why is a check valve placed in the supply line of some types of unloading circuits? What would be the consequences if the check valve were omitted from the circuit?

9.6. What is meant by "venting" a relief valve? Is it an important technique? Explain.

9.7. Referring to Fig. 9.1: Explain how the "cracking characteristic" of the relief valve might affect circuit performance.

9.8. Discuss the operation of an unloading circuit using an accumulator, as shown in Fig. 9.7. How could an unloading valve be used in place of the components shown?

9.9. In the circuit shown in Figure 9.8, how is the piston rod retracted?

9.10. In the circuit diagram of Fig. 9.9, what component is symbolized in the return line to tank connected to the directional control valve?

9.11. Referring to Fig. 9.9, explain why the check valves are required at the cylinder ports.

9.12. Discuss the operation of the Hi-Lo circuit

shown in Fig. 9.10.

9.13. Referring to Fig. 9.11, what is the effect of connecting the relief valves to cylinder lines as shown? Are there any differences or advantages to placing them as shown compared to placing the relief valve at the pump? Explain.

9.14. Referring to Fig. 9.13, discuss how remote electrical control of relief valves might be used as an alternative to this design for multiple pressure level control. Discuss how programmable control might be used.

9.15. In Fig. 9.16, what is the function of the pressure reducing valve? Why is an external drain line shown from the spring end of the symbol?

9.16. What is the difference in function of the accumulator as shown in Fig. 9.17 and 9.18? What kind of pressure control is used in each circuit?

9.17. In Fig. 9.18, what kind of actuator is symbolized?

9.18. Referring to Figs. 9.17, 9.18 and 9.19: what kind of accumulator is indicated by the symbol used in each?

9.19. Discuss the effect of accumulator positioning in the circuits illustrated in Figure 9.19 and Figure 9.20.

9.20. Draw a circuit diagram using ANSI or ISO symbols for a circuit incorporating a counterbalance valve to hold a load on a cylinder (piston rod). Discuss performance of counterbalance valves compared to pilot operated check valves or "lock" valves.

9.21. Draw a circuit diagram using ANSI or ISO symbols for a circuit incorporating a sequence valve to control motion of two cylinders. Show how the circuit could be modified to give sequencing in both the extend and retract direction.

9.22. Explain how reset pressure of a sequence valve can affect circuit performance.

9.23. Discuss the idea that the performance curves for a control valve represent a graphic picture of how the valve actually performs in a circuit.

9.24. Using ANSI or ISO symbols, draw a circuit diagram showing use of a reducing valve to control pressure in the cap end of a hydraulic cylinder.

9.25. Discuss the practicality of using reducing valves for branch isolation in multibranched circuits. Compare with use of pressure compensated flow control valves for the same purpose.

CHAPTER 10

FLOW CONTROL FUNDAMENTALS

Flow control deals with the rate of energy transfer which, in turn, is related to the rate of fluid flow. There are three types of fluid flow rates:

1. *Volumetric Flow Rate, Q_v,* is expressed in units of in^3/sec or min. or cc/sec or min. Volumetric flow rate must be used to calculate the *speed* of travel of piston rods or motor shafts.

2. *Weight Flow Rate, Q_w,* (using CU measure) is expressed in units of lb/sec or min. Weight flow rate must be used to calculate *power* using CU units of measure.

3. *Mass Flow Rate, Q_g,* is expressed in units of slugs/sec or min. (in CU measure) or Kg/sec-min. in SI metric measure. Mass flow rate must be used in calculating *inertia forces* during acceleration and deceleration periods. Refer to Chapters 4 and 5 on load analysis.

The same control valves are used for all three types of flow rates since they control the quantity of fluid that flows through the valve per unit of time.

VALVE CONTROL OF FLOW RATE

There are eight types of flow control valves.

1. Orifice. A simple orifice in the line, Figure 10.1*a*, is the most elementary method of controlling flow. Remember that this is also a basic pressure control device, Figure 8.1. When used for flow control, the valve is placed in **series** with the pump. An orifice can be a drilled hole in a fitting, in which case it is a fixed orifice; or it may be a calibrated needle valve, in which case it functions as a variable orifice, Figure 10.1*b*. Both types are also known as non-compensated flow control devices.

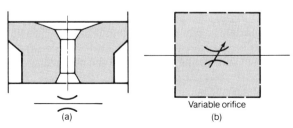

(a)   (b)   Variable orifice

*Fig. 10.1. Simple fixed orifice (**a**) and variable orifice (**b**).*

2. Flow regulator. A flow regulator, Figure 10.2, is slightly more sophisticated than the fixed orifice. A flow regulator consists of an orifice which senses flow rate, as a pressure drop across the orifice, and a compensating piston which adjusts to variations in inlet and outlet pressures. This compensating ability provides closer control of flow rate under varying pressure conditions. Control accuracy may be ± 5 percent, possibly less with specially calibrated valves which operate around a given flow-rate point.

3. Bypass flow regulator. In this flow regulator, flow in excess of set flow rate returns to reservoir through a bypass port, Figure 10.3. Flow rate is controlled by throttling fluid across a variable orifice regulated by the compensator piston. The bypass flow regulator creates lower energy losses in a system.

4. Pressure-compensated, variable flow. This class

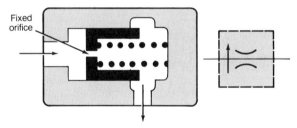

Fixed orifice

Fig. 10.2. Flow regulator adjusts to variations in inlet and outlet pressures.

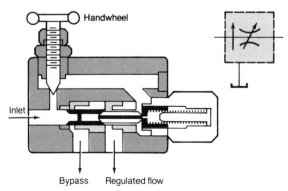

Handwheel

Inlet

Bypass   Regulated flow

Fig. 10.3. Bypass flow regulator returns excess flow from pump to tank.

of flow controls is equipped with an adjustable, variable orifice placed in series with a compensator. The compensator automatically adjusts to varying inlet and load pressures, maintaining essentially constant flow rate under these operating conditions to accuracies of :5%, Figure 10.4. Pressure-compensated, variable flow control valves can be obtained with integral free-reverse flow check valves and integral overload relief valves.

5. Pressure-compensated, temperature-compensated, variable flow. Since viscosity varies with temperature, as does the clearance between valve parts, output of a flow control valve may tend to drift with temperature changes. An attempt has been made to compensate for such temperature variations, as well as for varying pressure Figure 10.5. Temperature compensators adjust the control orifice setting to offset the effects of viscosity changes caused by temperature fluctuations of the fluid.

6. Demand-compensated flow control. Flow controls are available to bypass excess system flow to a secondary circuit, Figure 10.6. Controlled flow rate goes to the primary circuit. The bypassed fluid can be used for work functions in secondary circuits without affecting the primary one. There must be a flow into the primary circuit for this type

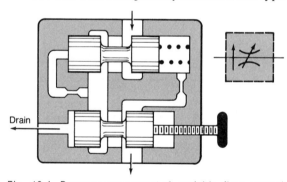

Fig. 10.4. Pressure-compensated, variable flow control valve adjusts to varying inlet and load pressures.

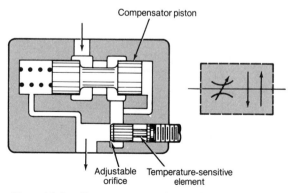

Fig. 10.5. Pressure-compensated, temperature-compensated, variable flow control valve adjusts control orifice settings to offset effects of viscosity changes.

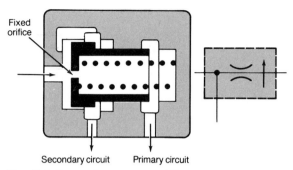

Fig. 10.6. Demand-compensated flow control bypass full pump output to tank during idle portion of work cycle.

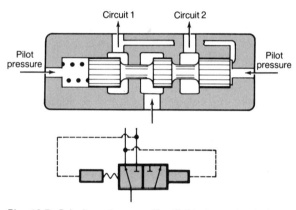

Fig. 10.7. Priority valve supplies fluid at a set rate to a primary circuit.

of valve to function. If the primary circuit is blocked, the valve will cut off the secondary circuit.

7. Priority valve. A priority valve, Figure 10.7, is essentially a flow control valve which supplies fluid at a set flow rate to the primary circuit, thus functioning like a pressure-compensated flow control valve. Flow in excess of that required by the primary circuit bypasses to a secondary circuit at a pressure somewhat below that in the primary circuit. Should inlet or load pressure (or both) vary, the primary circuit has priority over the secondary as far as supplying the design flow rate is concerned.

8. Deceleration valve. A deceleration valve, Figure 10.8, is a modified 2-way, spring-offset, cam-actuated valve used for decelerating a load driven by a cylinder. A cam attached to the cylinder or load gradually closes the valve. This provides a variable orifice which gradually increases backpressure in the cylinder as the valve closes. Some deceleration valves are pressure-compensated.

The force-balance concept of control function, discussed in Chapter 8, also applies to flow rate control valves.

Methods of valve control

1. Meter-in control. The circuit in Figure 10.9 illustrates meter-in control. The flow control valve (shaded) is placed *in series* with the directional control valve and the cylinder. Thus the flow control function is exercised on the fluid flowing to the cylinder. This type of control is best suited for **resistive** loads, where it is essential to control the speed at which a cylinder extends.

2. Meter-out control. The flow control valve is placed in the cylinder return line, Figure 10.10. The valve controls the rate of fluid flow from the cylinder to tank and is best used with *overrunning* loads. Because the valve controls the rate at which fluid leaves the head end of the cylinder, it thus controls the speed of the piston rod and load. Also, because it is placed in the return line, the overrunning load cannot force the piston rod to move at higher inertia than that set by the flow control valve.

3. Bleed-off control. The flow control device is placed *in parallel* with the cylinder, bypassing a part of pump output flow to tank over the flow control valve. The flow control valve can be sized to handle bleed-off flow rather than the entire pump output. In addition, a bleed-off flow control valve does not introduce a pressure drop into the active part of the circuit, because it is in parallel,

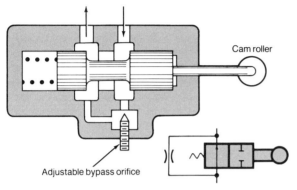

Fig. 10.8. Deceleration valve slows load by being gradually closed by action of cam mounted on cylinder or load.

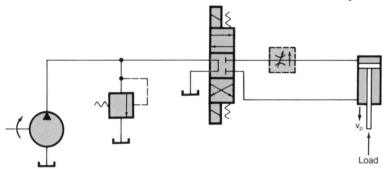

*Fig. 10.9. In meter-in control circuit, flow control valve is connected **in series** with directional flow control valve.*

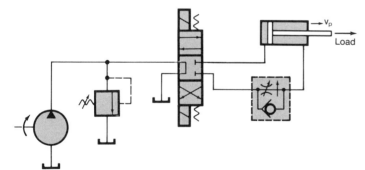

*Fig. 10.10. In meter-out control circuit, flow control valve is installed in cylinder **return** line.*

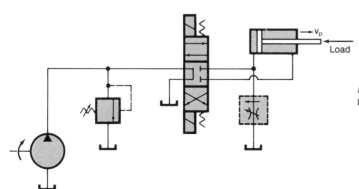

*Fig. 10.11. In bleed-off control circuits, flow control valve is mounted **in parallel** with cylinders.*

not in series, with the active elements. Inlet pressure will be actual load pressure rather than the pressure of the relief valve setting. Figure 10.11 illustrates how a typical bleed-off circuit might be installed.

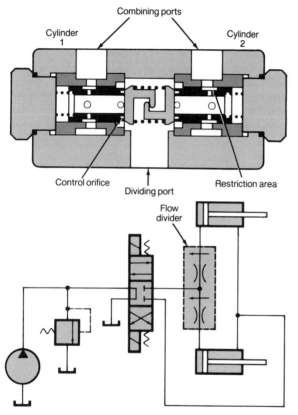

Fig. 10.12. Linear type flow divider splits input flow into two output flows.

Fig. 10.13. Flow dividers can be cascaded in series to control multiple actuator circuits.

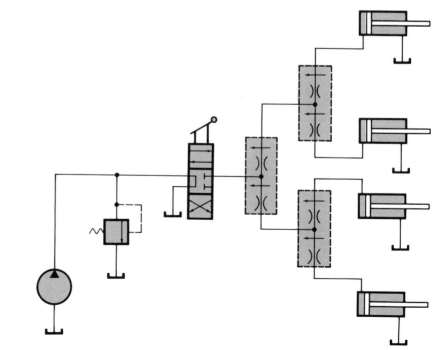

Flow-dividers

A flow-divider valve is a form of pressure-compensated flow control valve which receives **one input** flow and splits it into **two output** flows. The valve can deliver equal flow rates in each stream or a predetermined ratio of flow rates. Figure 10.12 shows how a flow divider could be used to roughly synchronize two cylinders in a meter-in circuit. It should be pointed out that flow dividers, like all pressure- and flow-control devices, operate over a narrow bandwidth rather than at one set point. Thus, there will be a variation of flow rates in the secondary branches, and precise synchronization cannot be achieved with a flow-divider valve alone.

Flow dividers can also be used in meter-out circuit configurations. Bleed-off does not affect a flow divider valves. They can also be "cascaded," *i.e.*, connected in series, to control multiple actuator circuits, Figure 10.13.

Rotary flow dividers

Another technique for dividing one input flow into proportional, multiple-branch output flows is the rotary flow divider, Figure 10.14. A rotary flow divider consists of several hydraulic motors connected together in *parallel* by a common shaft. One input fluid stream is split into as many output streams as there are motor sections in the flow divider. Since all motor sections turn at the same speed, output stream flow rates are porportional to the sum of displacements of the motor sections. Rotary flow dividers usually have larger capacities than available flow divider valves.

The pressure drop across each motor section is

68

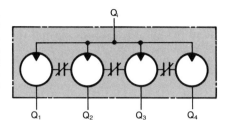

Fig. 10.14. Rotary flow divider consists of several fluid motors connected in parallel.

Q_1 Q_2 Q_3 Q_4

relatively small because no energy is delivered to an external load, as is usually the case with a hydraulic motor. However, the designer cannot overlook pressure intensification generated by a rotary flow divider. If, for any reason, the load pressure in one or more branches drops to some lower level or to zero, full differential pressure will be felt across the motor section(s) in the particular branch(es). The sections thus pressurized will act as hydraulic motors and drive the remaining section(s) as pump(s). This results in an elevated (intensified) pressure in these circuit branches. Caution must be exercised in applying rotary flow dividers to minimize the potential for pressure intensification. Rotary flow dividers can also integrate multiple branch return flows into a single return flow.

Pump control of flow rate

Pump control of flow rate presupposes the use of a variable-displacement pump. Of the three basic types of pumps most commonly used in fluid power applications — gear, vane and piston — only the vane and piston types are currently made in variable designs.

Nonpressure-compensated pumps require an auxiliary control to shift the pumping element to vary the pump's displacement. These auxiliary controls are available in hydraulic, pneumatic, mechanical, and electrical versions to match the needs of most control applications, see Chapter 15. Though pressure-compensated pumps are usually considered to be pressure control devices, the designer must remember that control is achieved by reducing the displacement of the pump when a set pressure level is reached. Thus, a change in flow rate is involved. If this change occurs while the actuator is still in motion, it is reflected as a change in actuator speed.

The purpose of flow control is speed control.

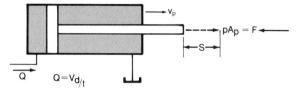

Fig. 10.15. Actuator speed determines rate of speed transfer which is a function of flow rate. Cylinder displacement V_d is equal to piston area, A_p, multiplied by the cylinder stroke S. Flow rate, Q, is equal to cylinder displacement, V_d, divided by time, t (per stroke).

All the devices discussed in this chapter control the speed of the actuator by controlling the rate of flow to it. Flow rate also determines rate of energy transfer at any given pressure. The two are related in that the actuator force multiplied by the distance through which it moves (stroke) equals the work done on the load. The energy transferred must also equal the work done. The speed of the actuator determines the rate of energy transfer (*i.e.*, horsepower), and speed is thus a function of flow rate, Figure 10.15.

A note on direction control

The third basic control area in fluid power technology is directional control. Directional control does not deal primarily with energy control, but rather with directing the energy transfer stream to the proper place in the system at the proper time. Directional control valves can be thought of as fluid switches which make the desired "contacts," that is, they direct the high-energy input stream to the actuator inlet, and provide a return path for the lower-energy oil.

That this is an important function can be inferred from the scores of different directional control valve configurations available in the marketplace. Moreover, it is of little consequence to control the energy transfer of the system via pressure and flow controls, if the flow stream does not arrive at the right place at the right time. Thus a secondary function of direction control devices might be defined as the timing of cycle events. Since fluid flow can be throttled in a directional control valve, some measure of flow rate or pressure control can also be achieved with these valves.

Review Exercises

10.1. Which of the two system parameters relating to energy transmission deals with controlling *speed* of a system output component?

10.2. Write the basic algebraic expression relating flow rate, piston area, and piston rod velocity for a cylinder.

10.3. Write the basic algebraic expression relating flow rate, displacement, and output speed for a fluid motor.

10.4. Explain why a simple orifice, Fig. 10.1, does not give acceptable flow rate control as load pressure changes. Explain the effects of temperature change.

10.5. Explain the purpose of pressure-compensation in a flow control valve.

10.6. What is the essential difference between a *flow regulator* and a *pressure compensated flow control valve*? Draw the ISO symbols for each.

10.7. What is the difference between a *straight pressure compensated* flow rate control and a *by-pass compensated* flow rate control valve? Draw the ISO symbol for each.

10.8. Discuss the implications of applying the *straight* pressure compensated flow control valve or the *by-pass compensated* flow control valve in circuits.

10.9. What is the difference between a *straight pressure compensated* flow rate control and a *demand compensated* flow control valve. Draw the ISO symbol for each type.

10.10. Discuss the difference in application considerations between *by-pass compensated* and *demand compensated* flow rate controls.

10.11. What is a *priority* valve? Draw the ISO symbol.

10.12. What is the primary purpose of a *deceleration* valve? How does it work in a circuit?

10.13. Can deceleration valves be pressure compensated? Explain.

10.14. What are the three classic flow rate control circuits?

10.15. Discuss which types of flow control valves can be used in each of the three types of flow rate control circuits; which cannot? Why?

10.16. Discuss the relationship between type of load (Chapters 3, 4, and 5) and the type of flow rate control circuit used. Discuss how the cycle profile provides insights into how to apply these flow rate control circuits.

10.17. Discuss the relationship between *pressure-compensated flow regulators* and *flow divider* valves. Is it possible to use flow regulators instead of a flow divider? If so, explain how.

10.18. Discuss the differences between *flow divider valves* and *rotary flow dividers*. What are the advantages and disadvantages of each?

10.19. What is meant by *cascading* flow dividers in a multibranch circuit? When is this technique used?

10.20. Can *directional control valves* ever be used to control flow? Explain.

10.21. Can flow dividers be used *in reverse* to integrate, or combine, multiple branch return flows into a single return flow? Explain.

10.22. How are flow controls sized for circuit applications?

10.23. What is the effect of a pressure drop across a flow control on system pressure level? Explain why this pressure differential (Δp) is unavoidable.

10.24. Explain what is meant by *pump-control* of flow rate? Compare this technique to valve control.

10.25. In their literature, some manufacturers use the term *volume control* when referring to flow rate controls. Explain why this is technically incorrect. Discuss the difference between *volume* and *flow rate* and their relationships to speed control.

As was pointed out in Chapter 10, fluid power flow control circuits are really methods for speed control. The circuits in this chapter are representative of flow control in fluid power. The student can extend the principles outlined to an almost unlimited variety of circuits and applications.

METER-IN CIRCUITS

When a flow control valve is placed in the line connecting the controlled output port of a directional control valve to, for example, the cap end of the cylinder, Figure 11.1, the flow control valve controls the rate of flow into the cylinder and thus the **output** velocity of the piston rod. This technique is best used with **resistive** loads.

Control of a load with a fluid power circuit depends on controlling the output member of the circuit. In this example, the output member is the combination of piston and its rod. Together they can be thought of as a mechanical interface between the load reaction and the energy-charged fluid. The load is under control when this interface is locked between a load reaction and the

pressurized fluid. Whenever this locked condition is lost, control of the load is lost. For example, it may be lost when the load reverses from resistive to overrunning.

Unless a bypass type of flow control valve is used, in a meter-in circuit the pump works against relief valve pressure setting.

METER-OUT CIRCUIT

When the flow control is placed in the line connected to the **return** flow port of the actuator, such as the cylinder head end, Figure 11.2, a meter-out circuit is formed. The output velocity of the piston rod is controlled by limiting the rate at which fluid leaves the cylinder.

This control technique is used with **overrunning** loads. The pump operates against a relatively constant pressure which consists of the sum of the load reaction and the flow control backpressure. This type of circuit is rather inefficient, because at low load levels or with overrunning load cycles, valve backpressure can exceed pump pressure because of the area differential across the piston.

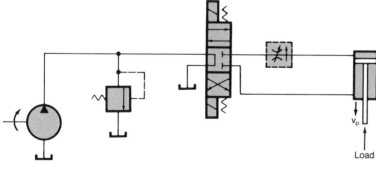

Fig. 11.1. In meter-in speed control circuit, flow control valve is mounted in pressure line series between directional control valve and cylinder cap end.

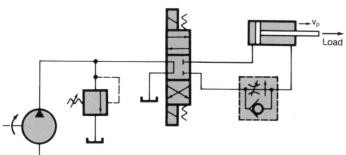

Fig.11.2 In meter-out speed control circuit, flow control valve is mounted in return line from actuator to tank.

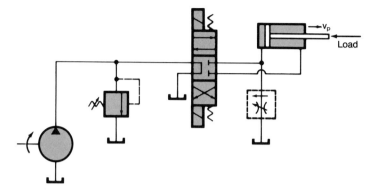

Fig. 11.3. In bleed-off circuit, portion of pump output bypasses to tank at system pressure.

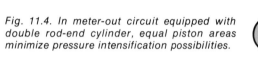

Fig. 11.4. In meter-out circuit equipped with double rod-end cylinder, equal piston areas minimize pressure intensification possibilities.

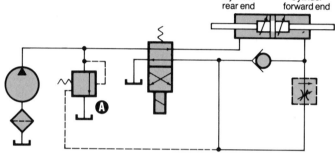

Cylinder rear end   Cylinder forward end

This area differential produces an intensifier effect.

The circuit in Figure 11.4 illustrates a **meter-out** control. Intensification is virtually eliminated if the piston areas are balanced.

The use of the differential relief valve allows the forward pressure to vary with load reaction. The relief valve setting is a function of the backpressure on the forward end of the cylinder. This backpressure reflects the overrunning load reaction. At maximum load, the relief valve is open and pump pressure is zero.

BLEED-OFF CIRCUITS

In this type of flow control circuit, part of pump output is bypassed to tank at system pressure, Figure 11.3. This arrangement provides speed adjustment around some average value. It does not, however, allow speed control over the entire range. Another disadvantage is that it does not provide positive load control, as discussed under **meter-in** and **meter-out** circuits.

REGENERATIVE CIRCUIT

In a regenerative circuit, sometimes called the differential circuit, Figure 11.5, a directional control valve, A, connects both cylinder ports in parallel to the supply port. Pressure is applied equally to the cap and head ends of the cylinder. Such a procedure would appear to lock the piston hydraulically. However, an analysis of the hydraulic forces on both sides of the piston shows that this is not the case.

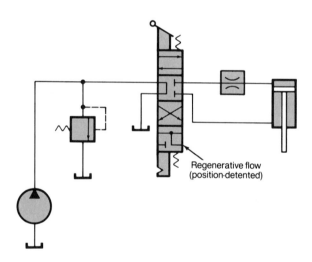

Regenerative flow (position-detented)

Fig. 11.5. Regenerative circuit using directional control with detended 4th position.

Example

First, we calculate the sum of the forces acting on the cylinder piston. Let the pressure force on the cap end be

$$F_1 = pA_1$$

and on the head end,

$$F_2 = -pA_2$$

The latter term carries a negative sign because F_2 acts in a direction opposite to F_1.

The other force we must consider is the load reaction, F_L. Its sign will be positive or negative, depending on whether the load is resistive or overrunning. Hence,

$$F = F_1 + F_2 + F_L.$$

It has been shown that the effective area in a regenerative cylinder is the area of the piston rod, A_p. The net force developed by the cylinder to overcome a resistive load is

$$F_c = pA_p.$$

As long as p is below the relief setting, the cylinder piston will extend against the load reaction. That is, if

$$p = F_L/A_p < P_r$$

the cylinder will move.

When the cylinder extends, fluid in the head end is displaced. Normally, this fluid would return to reservoir through the 4-way directional control valve. However, in a regenerative circuit the fluid is *recycled*: it bypasses the reservoir and flows directly to the cap end of the cylinder. Thus the would-be return fluid is added to the pump delivery. If, for example, the ratio of the area of the cap end to that of the head end is 2:1, the piston velocity will be the same in both directions.

INTERMITTENT FEED CONTROL
Meter-in and *meter-out* circuits can be converted to intermittent control circuits by adding a cam-operated or limit-switch-controlled, solenoid-operated, 2-way valve, Figure 11.6. Return flow bypasses through the normally open,

2-way valve, A, during those parts of the cycle when no flow control is needed. The bypass valve closes at the proper time during the work cycle. Return flow must then pass through the flow control valve. When flow control is no longer required, the 2-way valve reopens, again taking the flow control valve out of the circuit.

DECELERATION CONTROL
A specially designed, cam-operated 2-way valve can be used to decelerate a high-speed cylinder or heavy load. The deceleration control device can be thought of as a variable orifice which is gradually closed by the action of the cam. As the orifice closes, backpressure builds, slowing the cylinder, Figure 11.7.

Some deceleration valves are pressure-compensated to provide constant backpressure, regardless of changes in flow rate. The integral check valve allows free-flow bypassing through the deceleration valve when the cylinder is reversed.

MULTIPLE-AREA CONTROL AND COMPOUND CYLINDERS
The double-area cylinder shown in Figure 11.8 provides extension at low speed and high force, and retraction at high speed and low force.

Another version of the double-area cylinder, Figure 11.9, is the compound cylinder. During the rapid, low-force traverse frequently needed to advance a tool and bring it into contact with a work piece, the small piston area is used. Since piston velocity $v_p = Q/A_p$, the smaller the area the greater the speed for a given input flow rate Q.

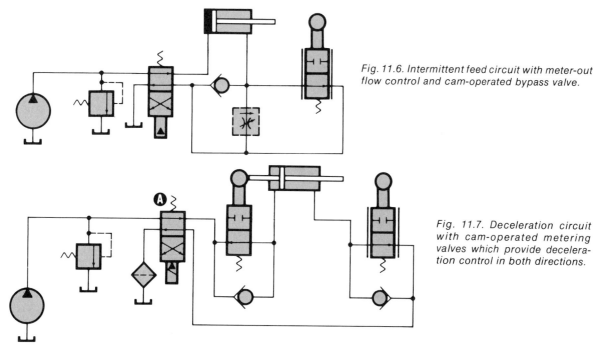

Fig. 11.6. Intermittent feed circuit with meter-out flow control and cam-operated bypass valve.

Fig. 11.7. Deceleration circuit with cam-operated metering valves which provide deceleration control in both directions.

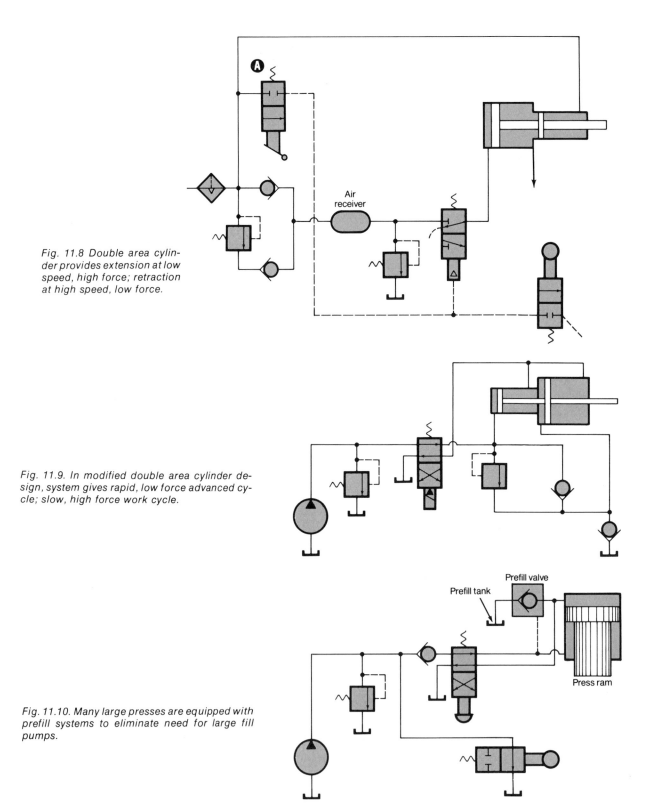

Fig. 11.8 Double area cylinder provides extension at low speed, high force; retraction at high speed, low force.

Fig. 11.9. In modified double area cylinder design, system gives rapid, low force advanced cycle; slow, high force work cycle.

Fig. 11.10. Many large presses are equipped with prefill systems to eliminate need for large fill pumps.

Once the tool contacts the work piece, a high force at very low speed is needed to retract the cylinder. The large piston area is then pressurized to generate maximum force at system pressure.

PREFILL SYSTEMS

Many large press circuits use prefill systems to eliminate the need for very large pumps. The design concept of a prefill system is illustrated in

Figure 11.10. The large press ram — sometimes up to 36 to 48 in. in diameter — would require a high capacity pump to supply fluid during its extension stroke. After contact with the work piece, most of this fluid would have to be dumped over the relief valve. In the circuit shown in Figure 11.10, the ram free-falls because of the acceleration due to gravity when the 4-way, 2-position directional control valve is shifted to bypass fluid from the head end to tank. Simultaneously, pressure in the pilot line to the prefill valve is released and the prefill valve opens.

Since a vacuum is produced by the falling piston, fluid flows into the cap end of the cylinder through the prefill valve. After the ram or tool has made contact with the workpiece, the manually operated, push button directional control valve is shifted to port pressurized oil to the top of the ram and the cam-operated bypass valve closes. Note that the cam must be long enough to accommodate the required stroke of the piston. Once the cam rides off the valve operator, the valve opens and bypasses pump output to tank.

In many presses, friction is so great that the ram will not "free-fall"; instead, it must be driven down by kicker cylinders. Kicker cylinders are usually small-diameter cylinders which generate enough force to overcome friction in the ram, Figure 11.11. The circuit uses a prefill valve to minimize pump size. In addition, a 4-way, 3-position valve is added to control cylinder direction. Since this valve has an open-center configuration, a counterbalance valve is added to prevent uncontrolled descent of the cylinders. A sequence valve switches the flow from the kicker cylinders to the main ram once contact has been made with the workpiece and pressure starts to build up.

Where space does not permit the use of external kicker cylinders, one may be built into the main ram, Figure 11.12. The rest of the circuit is similar to that of Figure 11.11.

FLOW-DIVIDER CIRCUITS

A flow divider may be thought of as a fluid bridge circuit; it splits a single input into two out-

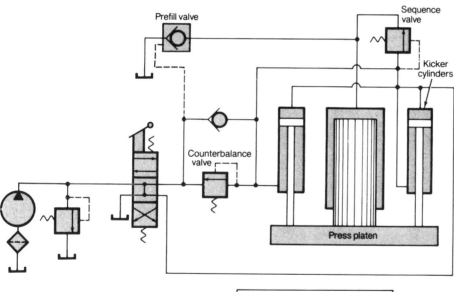

Fig. 11.11. In some presses, kicker cylinders are used to overcome high ram friction.

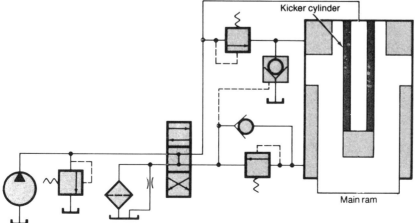

Fig. 11.12. Where there is no external space for quicker cylinders, one may be made an integral part of the ram.

puts. These outputs may be, though not necessarily, equal.

The basic flow divider circuit was shown in Figure 10.12. A single input is split between two branches of a cylinder output circuit. Usually the designer intends to synchronize the motions of two cylinders. For a single stroke or over a small number of cycles, this method provides approximate synchronization. However, if a larger number of repeat cycles is required, this method of synchronization is not accurate enough.

To synchronize actuators in an open-loop circuit, it is necessary to abut them against mechanical stops to realign them. Otherwise, the only positive way of maintaining synchronization is to use a servo system.

Figure 11.13 shows a flow-divider circuit for synchronizing fluid motors. It is subject to the same problems just described for cylinders. Figure 11.13(a) illustrates a meter-in circuit; Figure 11.13(b) a meter-out circuit.

Figure 10.13 illustrated cascading flow dividers to control four linear actuators. The first divider splits pump output into two flows, each of which was delivered to a branch of the circuit. A flow divider in each branch subdivides the flow once again. Within limitations imposed by the pressure drop across the valves and by their accuracy, any number of such branches could be cascaded.

SPECIAL APPLICATIONS

Figure 11.14 illustrates an unusual arrangement: a pressure reducing valve and a variable orifice connected in series. Since the pressure

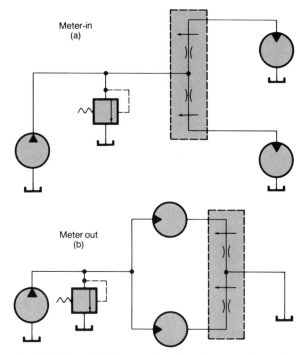

Fig 11.13. Flow dividers synchronize fluid motors in meter-in and meter-out applications.

reducing valve maintains approximately constant output pressure, it will control the pressure drop across the variable orifice. If the pressure drop across the orifice is constant, flow rate through it will also be constant. However, this is not the case when $\Delta p_o = \Delta p_r$, that is, when the pressure drop across the orifice equals that across the reducing valve. When this is the case, Δp_o becomes the

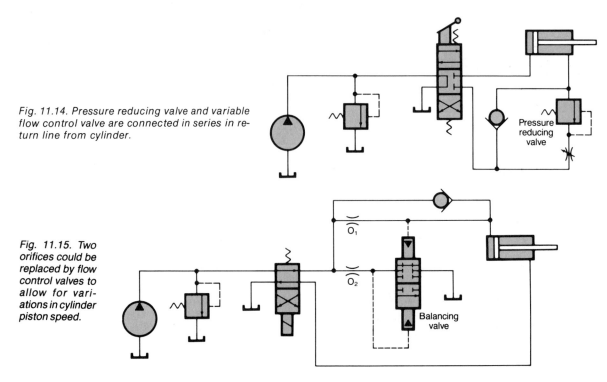

Fig. 11.14. Pressure reducing valve and variable flow control valve are connected in series in return line from cylinder.

Fig. 11.15. Two orifices could be replaced by flow control valves to allow for variations in cylinder piston speed.

controlling factor and the reducing valve is effectively eliminated from the circuit.

The circuit of Figure 11.15 shows the use of a balancing valve. Pump output, Q, flows into two parallel circuit branches: one has a simple orifice O_1; the other has an orifice, O_2, in addition to the balancing valve. Flow rate to the cylinder is a function of the relationship:

$$Q_c = QR_1/(R_1 + R_2)$$

where R_1 and R_2 are the resistances of orifices O_1 and O_2, respectively. The balancing valve modulates bypass flow as a function of pressure in the cylinder line and the pressure downstream from orifice O_2. Some engineers claim that this circuit is more efficient than one with a compensated flow control valve because cylinder flow, Q_c, passes through only one orifice, O_1.

In the circuit of Figure 11.15, the two fixed orifices could be replaced by flow control valves to allow for variations in piston speed. In addition, either meter-in or meter-out modes can be used.

An endless variety of circuits can be made from various combinations of components. The examples show in this chapter are typical of what can be accomplished with a little imagination and thorough understanding of the basic principles of fluid power.

Review Exercises

11.1. Discuss the relationship between type of load (referring to Chapters 2, 3 and 4) and type of flow control circuit. How does the cycle profile assist the circuit designer in choosing a circuit?

11.2. Discuss the relationship between placing the flow control upstream or downstream of the directional control valve and the control's effect on the actuator.

11.3. Referring to Figure 11.2, what kind of flow control circuit is this? Given: pump delivery is 30 gpm; flow control is set so flow rate to the cylinder is controlled at 20 gpm; relief valve is set at 1500 psi. How much horsepower example of problem 11.3?

11.5. Discuss the concept of "locking-up" the interface member of an output device in controlling a fluid power system.

11.6. Referring to Figures 11.1 and 11.2, discuss the effects on meter-out flow control of using a differential cylinder, as in Figure 11.2, and a balanced cylinder, as in Figure 11.4.

11.7. Referring to Figure 11.5, what kind of a circuit is this? Given: pump output is 20 gpm; cylinder cap end area of 30 in²; a head end piston area of 15 in². Discuss the relationship of extend and retract piston rod velocities in this circuit. What would be the effect, if the head end area were 10 in²?

11.8 Referring to Figure 11.6, what is the effect on the circuit of adding the 2-way, 2-position directional control valve to the basic meter-out circuit?

11.9 Discuss the function of a deceleration valve in a circuit. What techniques other than a deceleration valve might be used for the same purpose? How do they compare?

11.10 Describe the function of prefill valves in press circuits using large bore rams. How does it prevent cavitation in the system?

11.11. Referring to Figure 11.13, discuss the functional difference of the flow control between the meter-in and meter-out applications. Could the same component be used in both instances?

11.12. Redraw the circuit of Figure 11.13 using a rotary flow divider.

11.13. Discuss the possibility of using a rotary flow divider in the circuit of Figure 11.15.

11.14. Rework examples 11.3 and 11.4 using SI metric units.

11.15. Discuss the reasons why only resistive pressure compensated flow control valves can be used for meter-out and bleed-off circuits, while resistive pressure compensated by-pass compensated and demand compensated flow controls can all be used for meter-in circuits. What are the implications relative to system efficiency for the three types of flow control circuits?

11.16. What kind of flow control valve would a designer want in a system where one branch is a steering circuit? Why would you choose this type of valve?

11.17. Referring to Figure 11.9, what kind of a flow control circuit is this? Given: a resistive load on the piston rod of 60,074 lb; desired piston rod velocity of 2.72 in/sec; mechanical cylinder efficiency of 85%; pressure in the cap end of the cylinder: 2500 psi. Pump delivery is 30 gpm.

  a. at what pressure level should the relief valve be set to prevent by-passing over the relief valve?

  b. assuming the relief valve is set for 3000 psi, calculate the energy loss in the system due to flow control.

  c. given: the pressure drop across the directional control valve at the controlled flow rate is 45 psi. Calculate the efficiency of the directional control valve in the circuit.

  d. given the sum of the flow losses in the piping

as a pressure drop of 100 psi, calculate the efficiency of the piping.

f. assuming that the area ratio across the cylinder piston is 2:1, calculate the return flow from the head of the cylinder.

g. from step f above, estimate the pressure drop across the directional control valve due to return flow. Will this materially affect system performance? Why?

h. assume that the directional control valve is shifted to retract the cylinder. Discuss the effect on the circuit as drawn in Figure 11.9. If this were a problem, how would you modify the circuit to eliminate it?

11.18. Rework problem 11.17 using SI metric units.

CHAPTER 12

DIRECTIONAL CONTROLS

In Chapter 2, we mentioned the three types of control functions which are basic to fluid power systems. Pressure controls were described in Chapters 8 and 9; flow controls in Chapters 10 and 11. This chapter deals with directional controls.

Directional control valves can be used in one of two modes:

• **discrete position** in which the valve switches a stream of fluid toward the proper flow path in a circuit at the proper time of a machine cycle. The ISO symbol, for example, for a 4-way, 3-position, spring centered valve is shown in Figure 12.1(*a*).

• **proportional position,** in which the valve element which controls direction of flow can assume any of an infinite number of positions between the valve's minimum and maximum limits. Proportional directional control valves behave as multi-function controls in which *switching andpressure* or *flow* control are combined in one component. A typical valve is symbolized in Figure 12.1(*b*). Figure 12.1(*c*) illustrates a typical application of a directional control valve in a circuit.

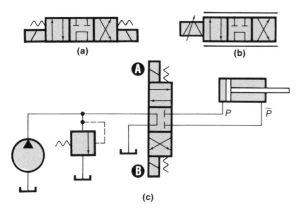

Fig. 12.1(a). ISO symbol of typical 4-way, 3-position, spring centered directional control; (b) ISO symbol of typical electro-hydraulic servovalve; (c) in simple circuit, 4-way, 3-position, solenoid actuated valve is connected to double acting cylinder.

SWITCHING THEORY

The theory, based on algebra developed by George Boole, concerns itself with any variable which can exist in one of two states. If, for example, we are dealing with electrical switches, the switch can be either open or closed. If the switch is **open**, the electrical circuit is *not* conducting beyond the switch; if **closed**, the electrical circuit is conducting.

A 2-way valve can be likened to a fluid switch. In one position, when the control element blocks the passage of fluid through the valve, the circuit is **closed**: there is no fluid flow downstream from the valve. In the **open** position, the valve control element ports fluid through the valve, the circuit is "made," and there is fluid flow downstream.

Boolean algebra

In the language of Boolean algebra, when a circuit is made, it is designated by a 1; when not made, by a 0. Since this convention applies to the state of one port in any one valve, these two states are mutually exclusive; that is, they both cannot exist at the same time. It stands to reason that a valve port can be open or closed, but not both. These states are said to be complementary.

The switching theory *is not* concerned with the level of the signal, but only that *it be* high enough to perform a switching operation. The signal (pressure, for example) is ON when it is present at any level at or above the threshold, *i.e.*, the *minimum* necessary to perform the operation. It is OFF when it is either *not present* or *below* that threshold level.

In Table 12.1, let, *P*, stand for the pressure signal in the line downstream from a 2-way valve; *A* stands for one state of the valve. For example, in a normally closed (NC), 2-way valve, the state is 0 (*i.e.*, the port is *blocked*) when the valve has received no actuating signal.

To obtain an output, *P*, the valve must first receive an actuating signal. Thus, the equation $P = A$,

79

Table 12.1 Examples of Boolean equations and their meanings

Function	Device or circuit	Boolean equation
(a) Normally closed, 2-way valve		$P = A$
(b) Normally open, 2-way valve		$P = \overline{A}$
(c) Normally closed, 2-way valve		$P = A$
(d) Normally open 3-way valve		$P = \overline{A}$
(e) 3-position, 4-way, spring-centered open-center valve		$P_1 = A\overline{B}$ $P_2 = \overline{A}B$ $\overline{P_1}\overline{P_2} = \overline{AB}$
(f) 2-position, 4-way valve		$P_1 = A\overline{B} +$ $P_1\overline{B} + P_1A$ $P_2 = B\overline{A} +$ $P_2\overline{A} + P_2B$

Table 12.1(*a*) or the expression: *P corresponds to A* describes the valve function. The = sign does not connote equality, as in conventional algebra. Here, it is read as *corresponds to,* and denotes that the term on the left-hand side of the equation is an entity with the term on the right-hand side. When the valve receives an operating signal, there will be pressure at the outlet port.

Let us now consider the normally open (NO), 2-way valve in Table 12.1(*b*). Here, there is a pressure output, *P*, at the valve port when there is no actuation of the valve. That is, when *A* is OFF, or when $A = 0$. The equation for this condition is $P = \overline{A}$, in which the dash over the *A* means *"not A."* Thus this equation is read: *P corresponds to "not A."* The equation tells us that although no signal is applied to the valve operator, there will be pressure fluid at the outlet port.

Both equations tell us, in essence, what we must do to get pressure fluid at the outlet port of the valve: in (*a*) we must apply a signal; in (*b*) we do nothing. The balance of Table 12.1 illustrates this process for 3-way and representative 4-way valves.

Consider the 4-way, 3-position, spring-centered, open-center valve, Table 12.1(*e*). The first equation,

$$P_1 = A\overline{B},$$

shows that there will be a pressure output, P_1, when solenoid *A* is energized and solenoid *B* is not. The second equation,

$$P_2 = \overline{A}B,$$

tells us that there will be a pressure output, P_2, when solenoid *B* is energized and *A* is not. The third,

$$\overline{P_1}\overline{P_2} = \overline{AB},$$

shows that there will be no output at either P_1 or P_2 when neither of the two solenoids *A* and *B* is energized.

A 4-way, 2-position valve is shown in Table 12.1(*f*). It is known as a "maintain position" valve, that is, the spool remains in its last position until it receives a signal to shift to the opposite position. This type of valve is sometimes called a "memory" element, because it "remembers" where the last signal came from. In this sequence, the first equation,

$$P_1 = A\overline{B} + P_1\overline{B} + P_1A,$$

shows that there will
● be a pressure output, P_1, when solenoid *A* is energized and *B* is not ($A\overline{B}$),
● continued to be a pressure output no matter what happens to *A*, as long as *B* is not energized ($P_1\overline{B}$), and
● continue to be a pressure output P_1 no matter what happens to *B*, as long as *A* is ON (P_1A). The second and third terms of this equation are somewhat ambiguous when divorced from the actuator to which the pressure ports would normally be connected.

Figure 12.1(*c*) shows a 4-way, 3-position valve connected to a cylinder. A refinement in symbology is labeling pressure to the cap end of the cylinder as *P*, and that to the head end as $\overline{P}$. This can be done as long as the valve controls nothing but one cylinder, because *P* and $\overline{P}$ are complementary and switch simultaneously when the valve is shifted. Thus, we can write the equation to extend the cylinder as:

$$P = A\overline{B} + P\overline{B} + PA,$$

and to retract:

$$\overline{P} = B\overline{A} + \overline{P}B + \overline{P}B.$$

Figure 12.2 shows the next development: the use of limit valves (or switches) to control the end positions (extended and retracted) of the cylinder. For purposes of illustration only, cam-operated, NC, 2-way valves are shown. The Boolean equations for extension and retraction can be written in the same way as in Figure 12.1(*c*). Note, however, that now signal *C* corresponds to the retracted position; that is, we have

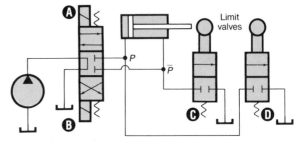

Fig. 12.2. Two limit valves control end-of-stroke positions of cylinder.

80

C ("not C") for all conditions other than cylinder retraction. Similarly, D corresponds to the extend position of the cylinder; and we have $\overline{D}$ ("not D") for all other conditions. Thus, we might say that $D = P$ and $C = \overline{P}$. We can then rewrite our equations strictly in terms of switching signals:

$$p = D + A\overline{B} + D\overline{B} + DA,$$

and

$$\overline{p} = C = B\overline{A} + C\overline{A} + CB.$$

It is possible to simplify these equations. However, before proceeding further, we must consider other aspects of the switching theory.

Graphical representation of logical functions

We must find a technique to represent the variables encountered in the design of a switching circuit (we consider the term "switching circuit" synonomous with "fluid power circuit"). The object is to design the most economical circuit to perform the desired functions.

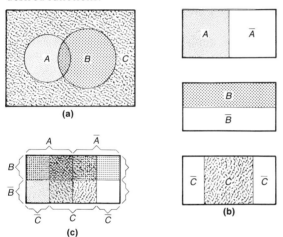

Fig. 12.3(a). Venn diagram is used in a graphic representation of logical functions; (b) three functional areas of Venn diagram; (c) three areas of 12.3(b) are shown superimposed.

Figure 12.3(a) is called a *Venn diagram* and is used in the graphic representation of logical functions. We introduce it here to illustrate the evolution of the *Veitch* diagram.

Based on our discussion of Boolean terminology, we can determine from the Venn diagram the Boolean functions: ABC, $\overline{A}BC$, $A\overline{B}C$, $AB\overline{C}$, and ABC.

These functional areas are shown in rectangular form in Figure 12.3(b). In Figure 12.3(c), the three areas of Figure 12.3(b) are superimposed. Thus, the square labeled 1 represents ABC, the square labeled 2 represents ABC, the square labeled 3 represents ABC, etc. Figure 12.3 (c) is the Veitch diagram for the three variables: each square of the Veitch diagram represents an AND term.

When the Veitch diagram is used in circuit analysis, the variables represent the signals within the

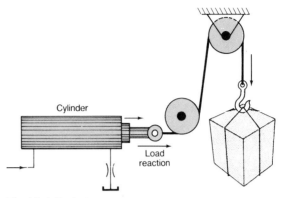

Fig. 12. 4. Typical overrunning load.

circuit, or the states of each valve producing the signals. Both a sequence and the equations of its switching circuit may be superimposed on one Veitch diagram. Before we can develop this technique further, we must examine one more concept.

Switching action

In Chapters 4 and 5, we discussed the Cycle Profile techniques used to describe the load cycle. Refer to Cycle Profile, Figure 5.2, page 26*. This plot represents what we want the load to do, but it does not show what the circuit components can or will do.

The circuit of Figure 5.3 is a possible solution to the problem in Figure 5.2. Let us consider only the cam-operated 2-way valve. This meter-out valve reduces the flow rate from maximum, which occurs during rapid traverse, to that desired for the feed cycle. The valve accomplishes this by blocking the bypass path to reservoir and by forcing oil to flow from the head end of the cylinder through the flow control valve. The time it takes to accomplish this change depends on the time required to shift the cam-operated valve, and on some interaction effects (called transients) between the cam-operated and flow control valves.

The plot of Figure 12.5 illustrates what might actually happen while this change takes place in the circuit function. The input signal in this case is the physical contact between the cam roller and the cam. The reader might be able to visualize the chain of events easier if the valve were operated by a limit switch or pilot valve.

Contact is made at time t_1, Figure 12.5. From t_1 to t_3 the cam forces the roller down, closing the valve so fluid can flow through it. At t_3 the signal is fully ON. At some time, t_2, the spool begins to respond to the fluid flowing through it, and by time t_6, the flow control valve has the flow fully under control. There is a time delay, Δt, from the time the signal is fully ON, t_3, until the flow control valve fully controls output flow, t_6. The interval Δt represents a transient state during the operation of the circuit. Conditions

See Figure 5.2, and discussion of cycle profile, Chapter 5, starting on page 25.

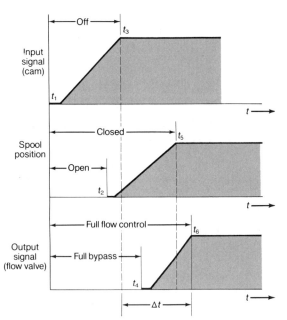

Fig. 12.5. Change in variable component in circuit causes at least one unstable step before next stable condition is reached.

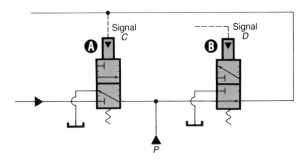

Fig. 12.6. Signal C shifts valve A to port pressure fluid to valve B.

Function	Signal	1	2	3	4	5	6	1
Initiate	C		▨	▨				
Terminate	D					▨	▨	
Output	P			▨	▨	▨	▨	

Fig. 12.7. Sequence diagram charts events in circuit of Fig. 12.6.

of instability occur during such transient periods.

To summarize: switching theory deals with sequential events. It presumes that:

- only one variable may change during each step
- the sequence is cyclic, and
- each step of the sequence is unique.

A sequential circuit functioning in a steady-state condition is considered to be stable. Whenever a variable changes the state of a component, there will be at least one unstable step before the next stable condition is reached, Figure 12.5. Thus, the circuit of Figure 5.3 will be in stable condition after the directional control valve is shifted during rapid traverse. An unstable condition occurs when the cam valve is actuated. This, in turn, is followed by a stable condition when the flow control valves control flow during the feed part of the cycle.

It is interesting to note that if a transient state or the change in a variable disappears too soon, the circuit will revert to the previous stable state. If, on the other hand, the duration of the variation is long enough, the system will move on to the next state in the sequence.

SEQUENCE DIAGRAMS

We can now discuss a method for representing the steps in a sequence graphically.* Consider, for instance, the subcircuit of Figure 12.6. In this type memory circuit, the initiating signal, C, shifts 3-way valve A, porting pressure supply fluid to its output connection.

Connected in parallel with the subcircuits of valve

See Figure 22.3 which shows use of sequence diagram in circuit design.

A is the subcircuit containing valve B. Here, the NO, 3-way valve transmits the output flow P, back to the operator of valve A to hold valve A in its open position. When a signal D, shifts valve B, it blocks the feedback signal from P, and valve A closes, blocking flow to the output port.

The sequence diagram of Figure 12.7 illustrates these events. The horizontal bars in the diagram represent the ON condition of the respective signals and outputs. During those steps through which a given bar does not pass, the corresponding signal is in the OFF condition. The sequence diagram is based on the premise that to determine the condition of the circuit, the designer must know only the signal state.

Veitch diagram

We can now combine the idea of sequencing and the representation of variables by a Veitch diagram into a method for determining the Boolean equations for a switching circuit. The one limitation of the method we are about to discuss is that the exact sequence for the cycle must be known. There are no generally accepted rules for selecting the best sequence, though in this instance the cycle-profile technique will prove to be a valuable tool. To choose the best sequence for a cycle, the designer must also know and understand components.

The Veitch diagram for the sequence of Figure 12.7 is shown in Figure 12.8. This diagram was constructed in the manner illustrated in Figure 12.3 for three variables. The three rules for laying out the Veitch diagram are:

- the sequence path follows adjacent squares
- only one step is allotted to each square, and
- the first and lasts steps must be adjacent.

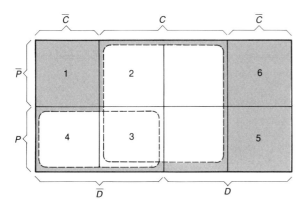

Fig. 12.8. Veitch diagram of sequence of events shown in Fig. 12.7.

By adjacent squares we mean either.
• any two squares lying next to one another, or
• the squares at the opposite ends of a row or column. In the simple Veitch diagram of Figure 12.8, squares 1 and 2, 2 and 3, and 3 and 4 are adjacent. However, note that squares 4 and 5, and 1 and 6 are also adjacent.

We can use the diagram to determine the switching equations. A switching equation is required for each output signal; although in this simple example there is only one output signal. We start by summarizing the sequence as follows:

Output	Initiate	Hold	Terminate
P	2	3, 4	5

First, we mark the *initiate* and *hold steps* on the Veitch diagram. For the sequence to proceed, we must go sequentially from step 2 to step 3 to step 4. Thus, the two adjacent squares 2 and 3 are a set of steps in the sequence, as are squares 3 and 4. These are called *tie sets* and are identified by the dotted lines encircling them on the Veitch diagram. In a sequential circuit they overlap, as shown. Each tie set represents an AND function (a "minterm," giving the minimum number of inputs to produce an output) and is a term in the switching equation. Thus

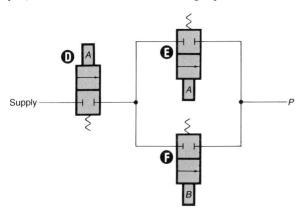

Fig. 12.9. Analysis of events in simple circuit.

the set 2-3 represents the term C, while the set 3-4 represents the term PB. The switching equation is

$$P = C + \bar{P}D.$$

Although we have used a very simple example, this technique for determining switching equations is also applicable to more complex circuits.

Application example

Assume that in a multi-cylinder circuit, cylinder A must remain *extended*, while positions of cylinders B, C, and D can vary. Now suppose that the table below, where 1 = extended and 0 = retracted, represents these conditions:

A	B	C	D
1	1	1	0
1	0	1	0
1	1	1	1
1	1	0	1

The switching equation can then be written:

$$A = BC\bar{D} + \bar{B}C\bar{D} + BCD + B\bar{C}D.$$

The first two terms reduce to

$$C\bar{D}(B + \bar{B}) = CD\cdot1 = C\bar{D}.$$

The last two terms become

$$BD(C + \bar{C}) = BD\cdot1 = BD.$$

Then,

$$A = C\bar{D} + BD.$$

Table 12.2 is a logic table which helps in this type of analysis. Consider the circuit of Figure 12.9: the function $P = A(A + B)$ is true because the operator would have to energize valve D and either valve E and F to complete the path. However, valve E is also energized by the same signal which energizes valve D. Therefore, valve F is, in fact, not needed. The logic theorem, $A(A + B) = A$, tells us this. The technique of switching algebra can provide a systematic approach to logical design of fluid power circuits, previously unattainable. They do not, however, preclude the necessity for a basic knowledge of fluid power technology and of the components used in the solution of problems which arise in practical circuit design.

Proportional directional control valves

The second of the two basic directional control valve operating modes is proportional control. Theoretical characteristic of a *proportional* directional control valve spool is compared to that of a *discrete* position spool in Figure 12.10. In the discrete position valve only one level of input signal, I_s, is admissible: fully ON. The spool shifts fully and cannot stop at any intermediate position between neutral and

Table 12.2 Basic fluid power devices or circuits

Function	Device or circuit	Boolean equation
Open valve or clear conductor	Supply ————————— P	$P = 1$
Closed port or blocked conductor	Supply ———$\dashv\vdash$——— P	$P = 0$
Normally closed, 3-way valve (signal causes output)	Supply ———[A]——— P	$P = A$
Normally open, 3-way valve (signal stops output)	Supply ———[A]——— P	$P = \overline{A}$
AND (all signals must be ON to obtain output)	Supply —[A]—[B]—[C]— P	$P = ABC$
OR (any one signal ON will give output)	Supply —[A][B][C]— P	$P = A + B + C$
NOT (NOR) (all signals must be OFF to obtain output)	Supply —[A]—[B]—[C]— P	$P = \overline{ABC}$
NAND (any signal ON causes loss of output)	Supply —[A]—[B]—[C]— P	$P = \overline{A} + \overline{B} + \overline{C} = (ABC)'$
AND NOT (Inhibit) (A must be ON and B must be OFF to obtain an output)	Supply —[A]—[B]— P	$P = A\overline{B}$
OR NOT (A must be OFF or B must be ON to obtain an output)	Supply —[A][B]— P	$P = \overline{A} + B$
Spool-valve memory Maintain-position spool Nonspring or pilot offset	Supply ———[A / B]——— P	$P = A\overline{B} + P\overline{B} + AP$ $= (A + P)\overline{B} + AP$ $= A\overline{B} + P(\overline{B} + A)$

maximum travel. Except for a short transient condition, while the valve spool is shifting, the discrete position directional control valve is either ON or OFF.

On the other hand, the proportional directional control valve element can assume any intermediate position on the ramp characteristic proportional to

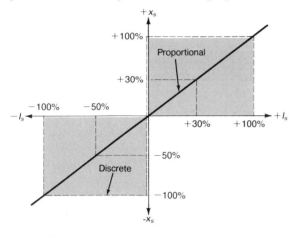

Fig. 12.10. Comparison of theoretical characteristic of proportional directional control valve spool to that of discrete position spool.

the magnitude of the input signal, I_s, such as, the 30% or 50% positions illustrated in Figure 12.10.

Proportional valve types

There are two classes of proportional valves:
- *remote control,* for open loop circuits*
- *servovalves* for closed loop (feedback) systems.

Of the two classes, servovalves are well known and have a long history of development and applications, originally in aerospace and specialized industrial machinery requiring high levels of precision and response. While feedback in servovalves can be mechanical, penumatic, hydraulic and electrical, the most common is the electrohydraulic servo system.

Remote, proportional directional control valves represent a still emerging segment of fluid power control technology. Proportional controls evolved from older, manually-operated directional control valves. The operator controlled a machine function by shifting a valve lever, a method sometimes called "feathering." He was actually changing the magnitude of the input signal, I_s — lever angle. The result was simultaneous control of both switching

See Chapter 2 for definitions of open and closed loop systems.

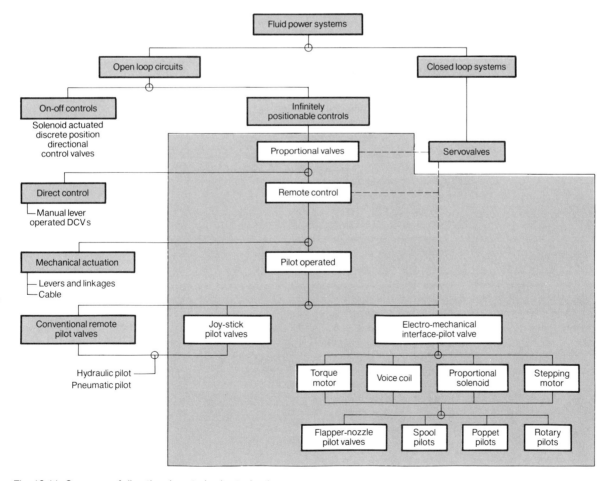

Fig. 12.11. Summary of directional control valve technology.

and flow control functions. Figure 7.14 illustrates this point. When lever-operated power-valves were moved from the operator's work station, an alternate solution for transmitting a "feathering" signal from the machine operator to the now remote power directional control valve had to be found. Remote, proportional directional control valve technology provided that solution. Figure 12.11 summarizes directional control valve technology. The shaded area is the proportional valve technology.

A proportional valve is infinitely positionable, making orifices in the valve infinitely variable. This provides flow rate control as a function of pressure differential over the entire range of the valve, Figure 7.14. Input signals must be ramp type to provide infinite positioning of the power valve spool.

Proportional valves fulfill two simultaneous control functions:

• **directional control** by routing the fluid stream to the appropriate ports to control direction of actuator motion, and

• **flow-rate control** by regulating valve orifice sizes to control the velocity of the actuator.

However, proportional valves perform still another function in multi-branched parallel circuits: that of balancing the circuit. A typical parallel circuit is illustrated in Figure 12.12(a). Because load reactions are not equal, *i.e.*, $F_1 \neq F_2$, it follows that load pressures in the branches are not equal either, *i.e.*, $p_1 \neq p_2$.

If discrete position valves were used, all fluid supplied to the circuit would flow to the branch with the lowest load pressure requirement; none would flow to the branch with the higher load pressure. This is a classic problem in parallel circuits. Figure 12.12(b) shows an equivalent circuit to that shown in Figure

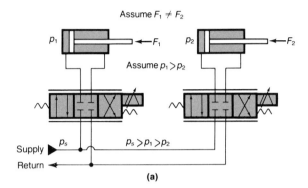

(a)

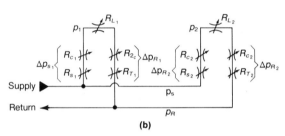

(b)

Branch 1: $p_s - p_R = \Delta p_{s_1} + \Delta p_{L_1} + \Delta p_{R_1}$
Branch 2: $p_s - p_R = \Delta p_{s_2} + \Delta p_{L_2} + \Delta p_{R_2}$
Circuit: $\Delta p_{L_1} - \Delta p_{L_2} = (\Delta p_{s_2} + \Delta p_{R_2}) - (\Delta p_{s_1} + \Delta p_{R_1})$
where $\Delta p_{L_1} \neq \Delta p_{L_2}$

Fig. 12.12. In typical parallel circuit, because load reactions are not equal, therefore load pressures are not equal.

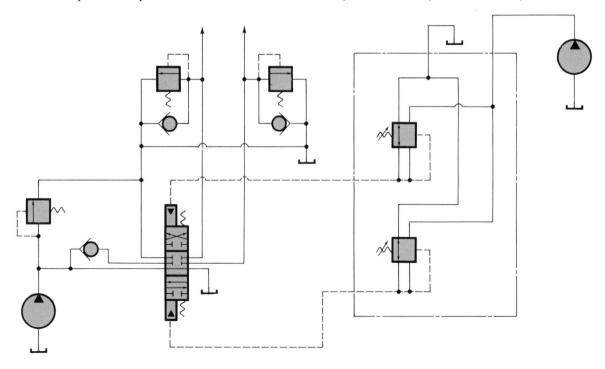

Fig. 12.13. Hydraulic circuit for one-axis control.

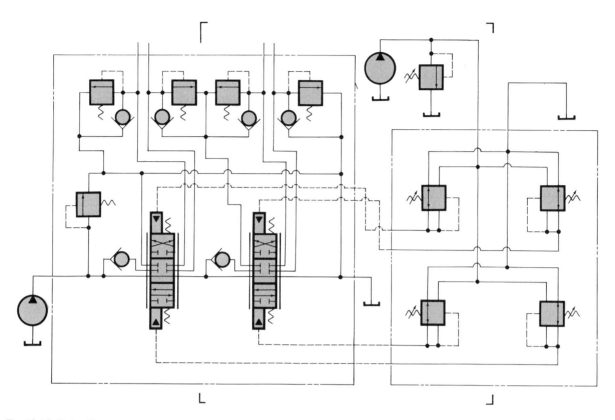

Fig. 12.14. Hydraulic circuit for two-axis control.

12.12(a); here orifices are used to represent the valves and loads in place of ISO graphic symbols.

To operate both branches simultaneously, the sum of the pressure drops around each branch loop must equal the pressure differential from supply to return lines, $\Delta p = p_S - p_R$. Because of varying load pressures caused by unequal loads, the only way to balance the circuit is to introduce pressure differentials across the directional control valves by throttling flow. Proportional valves provide this balancing.

How proportional valves work

In the past, manually-operated, lever-actuated directional control valves were used in hydraulic systems to perform the proportional valve function. However, because horsepowers transmitted have increased substantially, power valves on machines were moved to more convenient, efficient locations, usually away from the operator's station. To meet these requirements, it became necessary to provide remote, proportional control for the directional control valve spool. Refer to Figure 12.11 for a summary of techniques used.

Remote control evolved into proportional control along two paths. As summarized in Figure 12.11 these are hydraulic or pneumatic pilot controls and electrohydraulic controls. Both use joystick control levers instead of manual lever-operators, mounted directly on the directional valve.

Types of levers

Joystick lever controls come in one- and two-axis designs. Figure 12.13 illustrates the hydraulic circuit for a single axis control; Figure 12.14 a two-axis control. Figure 12.15 illustrates a typical joystick lever controller.

Joystick controls provide an input signal to the directional control valve proportional to lever movement from neutral position. The command signal is a differential pressure applied to the ends of the power spool, shifting it against centering springs. Figure 12.16 shows a joystick pilot control valve and the proportional directional valve it controls. In some systems, an electro-mechanical stage may be required to provide enough fluid pressure to shift the power valve spool.

One type of electrical lever control adjusts potentiometers to provide a voltage signal proportional to lever motion. Another type, uses linear variable differential transformers instead of potentiometers. Figure 12.17 compares state-of-the-art technology and relates the pilot stage and interface to the bridge circuit equivalent of typical proportional valves.

Electro-mechanical interfaces

The simplest electro-mechanical interface can be a direct-acting solenoid, if:
● shifting of the solenoid armature could be made proportional to voltage signal, and

87

Fig. 12.15. Typical joystick type directional control valve.

Fig. 12.16. Remote joystick pilot control valve (foreground) and proportional directional control valve it controls (background).

● the solenoid could generate enough force to shift the valve spool.

DC proportional solenoids are available to satisfy item 1 above but are presently limited to smaller valve sizes for item 2. However, the potential is there for proportional solenoids with greater force outputs if market demand could support development costs. Figure 12.18 illustrates an application of DC proportional solenoids for direct valve spool actuation in a directional control valve.

Figure 12.19 compares force vs. stroke characteristics for a closing air-gap solenoid, A, as typically used in ON-OFF solenoid operated valves, and a proportional solenoid B. The A solenoid shows a continuously increasing force as the air gap closes; B solenoid shows an increasing force over the initial closure of the air gap becoming almost constant over the second half of the armature stroke.

Figure 12.20 shows force vs. stroke at three different duty cycles: continuous, ½ and ¼. Continuous duty cycle is defined as the wattage, which, when applied to a solenoid, causes its temperature to rise and saturate at 105 C in an ambience of 20 C, without a heat sink or use of any cooling device. The ½ duty cycle rating is twice and ¼ duty cycle rating is four times the continuous duty wattage. When higher power levels are used, heat sinks or some means of cooling may be required to prevent coil over-heating.

Fig. 12.18. Directional control valve with DC proportional solenoid controls.

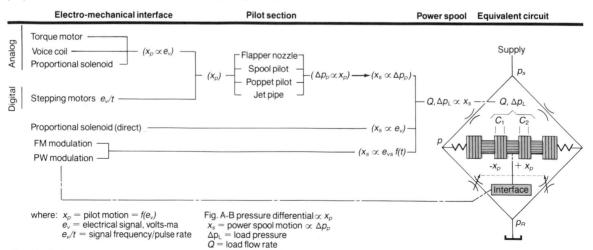

where: x_p = pilot motion = $f(e_v)$
e_v = electrical signal, volts-ma
e_v/t = signal frequency/pulse rate

Fig. A-B pressure differential $\propto x_p$
x_s = power spool motion $\propto \Delta p_p$
Δp_L = load pressure
Q = load flow rate

Fig. 12.17. Comparison of state-of-the-art technology of pilot stage and interface to bridge circuit equivalent of typical proportional valves.

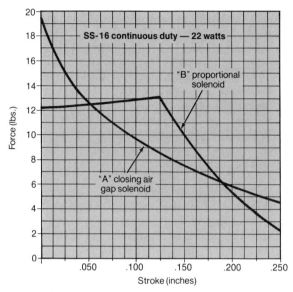

Fig. 12.19. Force vs. stroke curves of proportional and closing air-gap solenoids.

The approach zone of the curve is required when two servo solenoids are used to control a spool valve. If this is not required, use only the control zone which is that segment of the stroke which can be controlled proportionally.

Flapper-nozzle torque motor

The torque-motor, flapper nozzle pilot is a second type of proportional valve. The design, Figure 12.21, is similar to servovalve pilot stages. The first stage is an electro-mechanical device in which an armature is positioned between two permanent magnets. Windings are wrapped around the armature. When a current flows through the windings, magnetic forces swing the armature through a slight angle, proportional to input current.

Since the flapper is at the midpoint of the armature, angular deflections are transmitted to the flap-

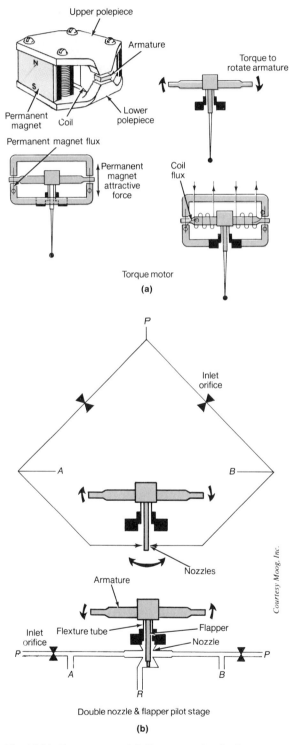

Fig. 12.21. Torque-motor, (a), flapper nozzle pilot in proportional valve is similar to servovalve pilot stage, (b). Nozzle-flapper provides variable orifice in bridge circuit.

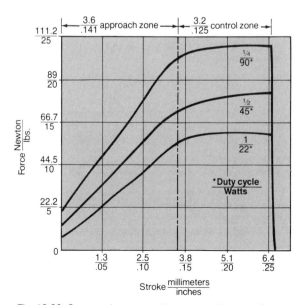

Fig. 12.20. Curves relate proportional solenoid output force to stroke for continuous, ½, and ¼ duty cycle.

per. In the double nozzle pilot stage illustrated, a differential pressure results as the flapper moves closer to one nozzle and away from the other. This differential pressure can be impressed across the power spool, shifting it proportionally against centering springs. The nozzle-flapper provides the variable orifices in the bridge circuit.

The power valve in Figure 12.22 is available with many of the standard options available with similar mobile equipment directional control valves, *i.e.,* work port relief valves, cross-over relief valves, anti-cavitation check valves, lever override, pressure-beyond, and several mid-inlet options for stack valves.

Proportional valves are made to commercial rather than servovalve standards. Typically, the power valve design is similar to that used in manually-actuated directional control valves. Commercial grade spools have significant overlap, resulting in larger deadbands. Response times are slower than those required of servovalves. Typical performance characteristics are shown in Figure 12.23.

Mobile and industrial valves

Principal differences between mobile and industrial type proportional control valves center on historical divergences of technology in the two market areas. One is in the configuration of the power valve body spool. Mobile valves historically have been single-stage, multiple spool designs, with many options available to structure a control valve for a specific application. Typically, mobile valves have not been manifold or subplate mounted. Before proportional control valves arrived, mobile valves were usually lever operated. Development of mobile proportional control valves have followed a path of replacing the function of the lever operator with the remote operator.

Industrial controls have historically been solenoid-operated, discrete-position, manifold- or subplate-mounted valves. Very few options have been incorporated into the basic valve, having been added into the circuit in the form of packages which could be "sandwiched" between the directional control valve and subplate.

Electric command first applied (spool will move to left)

Final condition after spool moves

Courtesy Moog, Inc.

Fig. 12.22. Power valves come with choice of many operating options.

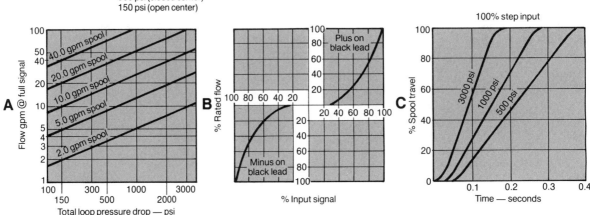

System requirements	Technical Data

Filtration — 25 micron absolute (10 nominal)
Operating fluid — petroleum base hydraulic oil
Operating temperature — 0° to 180° F
Operating pressures –
  Pressure port: 3000 psi maximum
  Cylinder port: 3000 psi, 5000 psi surge
  Return port: 50 psi maximum
  Minimum operating pressure:
    500 psi (closed center)
    150 psi (open center)
	Deadband — 30% of full signal
	Internal flow — 0.5 gpm maximum @ 3000 psi
	Coil — 50 ohms, 0 to ± 4 VDC @ ± 80 MA
	Response time — (see curve below)
	Flow rating — (see curve below)
	  Flow rated at 150 psi total loop pressure drop
	  (See curve below)

Fig. 12.23 Typical performance of proportional valves: (a) curves for valve sizing, (b) load flow metering characteristics and (c) valve response to step inputs.

Alternately, discrete-pressure or flow-control valves were piped into the circuit outside the envelope. Industrial directional control valves with ports larger than ¼ in, are generally of the two-stage, or "piggyback" type. A small solenoid operated pilot valve is mounted directly on top of the pilot-operated main power valve. One form of industrial proportional valves follows this general configuration, merely substituting the proportional electrical interface for the standard ON-OFF solenoid operator used in standard piggy-back valves. A typical directional control valve of this design is illustrated in Figure 12.24. Not all similiar designs use flow feedback as illustrated.

Another trend evident in European industrial valves is the use of modular valves—directional, pressure and flow control—which are mounted on four sides of a central manifold which effectively results in a hydraulic "integrated circuit" without external piping, except for connections to actuators and motors. Proportional control of all three func-

tions can easily be substituted for ON-OFF controls, Figure 12.25.

Cartridge valves

A development in European proportional control is the cartridge valve which actually bears no relationship to the cartridge valves used in the United States. The European cartridge valve is a binary device consisting of a poppet and seat arrangement, Figure 12.26. Poppet position is controlled by pilot pressure on top of the poppet. If the fluid on top of the poppet is vented, the poppet will open wide. If pilot pressure is modulated, as by a pilot control valve mounted on top of the main poppet valve, position of the poppet can be controlled. These valves can provide switching plus flow or pressure control.

Cartridge valves, European style, have been primarily used in press-type circuits, including injection molding machines circuits, etc. Their appearance in the U.S.A. has been primarily on imported equipment. Marketing here has so far been minimal.

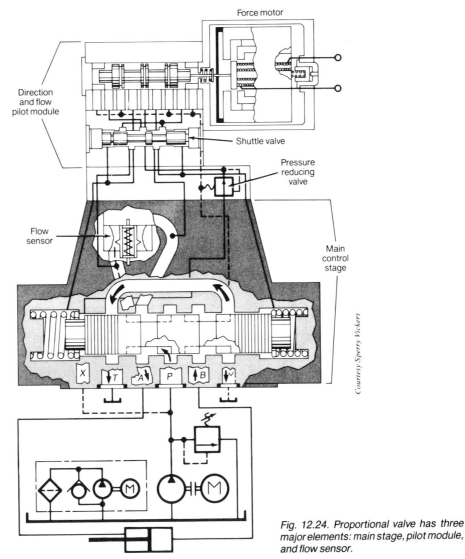

Fig. 12.24. Proportional valve has three major elements: main stage, pilot module, and flow sensor.

91

Fig. 12.25. Example of industrial modular valves clustered on four sides of central manifold.

Fig. 12.26. Exploded view of cartridge valve.

It appears that the principal form of electro-mechanical interface used on European proportional valves has been proportional solenoids. Pulse width modulation and frequency modulation are alternate techniques. While discussion has centered on proportional directional control valves, pressure- and flow-control valves can also be remote, proportionally controlled, Figure 12.27(*a*).

Such valves introduce the possibility for pressure or flow programming an injection molding machine; Figure 12.27(*b*) illustrates an electrical program analogous to the machine pressure profile. This electrical program, when fed into the pilot section of the proportional relief valve, would adjust relief valve setting to match the pressure profile. A simple switching circuit, a programmable controller or microprocessor could provide the electrical commands to match the profile. One of the principal reasons for the emphasis on electrohydraulic types of controls, as opposed to oil-to-oil or air-to-oil remote pilot control, is rapidly expanding emphasis on microprocessor and microcomputer control of hydraulic and pneumatic power systems.

Pressure compensated directional control valves

These are another sub-class of directional control valves. They combine the switching functions of directional control valves with the flow control characteristics of pressure compensated flow control, Figure 10.4. In pressure compensated directional control valves, the orifice defined by the land on the spool and port in the valve body, performs a dual function; it

- routes fluid to the proper port, and
- acts like a variable orifice in the flow control. The

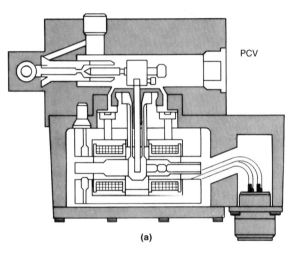

(a)

Multiple pressure control

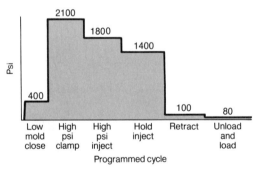

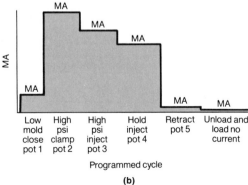

(b)

Fig. 12.27. Electrohydraulic pressure control valve: (a) for injection molding machine, (b) electrical program analogous to machine pressure profile.

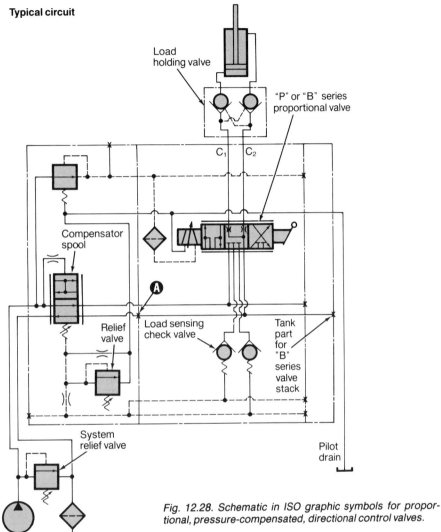

Load holding valve

"P" or "B" series proportional valve

C_1 C_2

Compensator spool

A

Relief valve

Load sensing check valve

Tank part for "B" series valve stack

System relief valve

Pilot drain

Fig. 12.28. Schematic in ISO graphic symbols for proportional, pressure-compensated, directional control valves.

pressure drop across the spool orifice is impressed across the compensator as in a flow control valve.

There are two types of pressure compensated directional control valves.
● one compensator is shared by several spools in series in a multiple spool valve. Only one circuit branch can be actuated at one time, and
● each spool in a multiple spool valve has its own, independent compensator. These pressure compensated directional control valves can be used in parallel because each circuit branch is isolated from the other by the independent branch compensators.

Pressure compensated directional control valves were originally developed to reduce spool shifting

forces and to improve metering characteristics for speed control with manually-operated mobile equipment valves. The added advantage of branch isolation simplified problems during simultaneous operation of a number of circuit branches.

The reduced spool shifting forces and superior metering characteristic of pressure-compensated directional control valves can also be used to improve the performance of proportional control valves. Figure 12.28 shows the schematic in ISO graphic symbols for a proportional, pressure-compensated, directional control valves.

Chapter 15 discusses the further evolution of directional control valves for use in load-sensing and other energy conserving systems.

Important Terms

Boolean algebra is the algebra of logic systems.

Complementary conditions are those in which two variables exist simultaneously in opposite states; one variable is ON while the other is OFF.

Discrete position is a single, stable position of a fluid power control element.

Electro-mechanical interface is a device which provides a mechanical output proportional to an electrical input signal.

Memory is the ability of a control device to remain in the last position according to the signal it has received.

Pilot valves are small fluid valves which produce a pressure differential output proportional to a mechanical input.

Pressure compensated directional control valve is a control which combines the hardware and functions of a directional control and pressure compensated flow control valve into one component.

Proportional control is remote control of a valve element using proportional positioning techniques.

Proportional control valve is a directional control valve designed to commercial performance standards which includes interfacing and pilot stages resulting in proportional control characteristics.

Proportional positioning refers to infinitely variable positioning of a control element in a defined relationship to an input signal.

Ramp function is defined as an input-output characteristic which is a straight line with a constant slope.

Remote control is the ability to control position of a valve element from a location at a significant distance from the valve.

Sequence diagram is a graphical representation of events which occur in a switching system.

Sequential system is one in which a series of events occurs in discrete steps of predetermined order.

Servovalve is a proportional valve designed and manufactured to a degree of precision and high response characteristics that meets performance requirements of closed loop systems.

Step function is an input characteristic where the signal level rises almost instantaneously after which it remains constant at its maximum level.

Switching theory provides the basis for applying Boolean algebra to the design of logic systems for control.

Threshold signal level is the magnitude of a signal which will bring about an incipient change of condition.

Veitch diagram is a graphical means of simplifying logical systems to arrive at the simplest Boolean equations for the system.

Venn diagram is a graphical representation of logical relationships.

Review Exercises

Fig. 12.1. Define *discrete position* and explain how it is applied to conventional directional control valves.

12.2. Draw the ISO graphic symbol for a solenoid operated spring centered directional control valve.

12.3. Discuss the term *proportional position* and how it applies to proportional directional control valves.

12.4. Draw the ISO graphic symbol for a 4-way, 3-position proportional control valve. Describe how it varies from the symbol drawn for example 12.2. What kind of valve operator is symbolized? Is it possible to determine from the operator symbol whether electrical, mechanical, pneumatic or oil pilot control is used? Discuss.

12.5. In Boolean rotation, what does a 1 mean; what does a 0 mean?

12.6. Discuss the relationship of an ON signal and the level of the signal.

12.7. Does the inverse relationship apply to an OFF signal? Explain.

12.8. In a Boolean expression, what is the significance of the = sign?

12.9. Referring to Table 12.1: discuss how the Boolean equation $P = A$ applies to the normally closed, 2-way directional control valve.

12.10. Why does the same Boolean expression describe the action of the normally closed 3-way directional control valve?

12.11. Referring to Figure 12.1, discuss the relationship of the Boolean equation for piston rod extension to the circuit function.

12.12. Discuss how the Veitch diagram of Fig. 12.3(c) was evolved from the Venn diagram of Figure 12.3(a). What is represented on a Veitch diagram?

12.13. Referring to Figure 12.5, discuss the condition necessary for transition to a new stable condition from a previous one.

12.14. What is a sequence diagram?

12.15. How is a sequence diagram used in circuit design?

12.16. In the sequence diagram represented in Figure 12.7, which events are sequential and which are concurrent?

12.17. Referring to Table 12.2, what is the significance of the AND circuit shown? What other term might be applied to an AND circuit?

12.18. Referring to Table 12.2, what is the significance of the OR circuit shown? What other term might be applied to an OR circuit?

12.19. Discrete position directional control valves are sometimes referred to as bang-bang valves. Discuss the implications of this "jargon" as applied to directional control valves.

12.20. Discuss the differences in control signals and resulting outputs between discrete position and proportional direction control valves.

12.21. What two classes of proportional control valves are there? How do they differ?

12.22. Why do we think of proportional control valves as multi-function valves? Compare the multi-function pressure compensated valves with the function of a bang-bang directional control valve.

12.23. Referring to Figure 12.11: discuss the differences between *open loop* and *closed loop* systems.

12.24. Compare directly controlled with remote controlled proportional valves.

12.25. Referring to Figure 12.11: what types of electromechanical interfaces are used with proportional directional control valves. What is their function?

12.26. What types of pilot valves are used with proportional directional control valves? What is the function of the pilot valve?

12.27. Describe what is meant by "using proportional directional control valves to balance pressure in a parallel circuit." Why is this necessary?

12.28. Discuss how *pressure compensated* directional control valves function to balance loads in parallel circuits. What is another function of pressure compensation in a directional control valve?

12.29. What basic condition must be met to achieve balance in a parallel circuit?

12.30. Is there a difference between *remote* and *proportional* control? Discuss.

12.31. What is a joystick pilot valve? What is its function? How does it work?

12.32. What kinds of joystick remote controls are there? Describe the function of each briefly.

12.33. Why are electromechanical interfacing devices receiving so much attention?

12.34. Discuss the differences between a bang-bang solenoid and proportional solenoids.

12.35. What is a *torque motor*? How does it function?

12.36. What is a *voice coil* (sometimes called a force motor)?

12.37. What one characteristic do all electromechanical interface devices have in common? Hint: refer to Figure 12.17. How is this common characteristic utilized in proportional control valves.

12.38. What is a *flapper nozzle* pilot valve? How does it function?

12.39. What is a *spool* pilot valve? How does it function?

12.40. What is a *poppet* pilot valve? How does it function?

12.41. What is a *jet pipe* pilot valve? How does it function?

12.42. What characteristic do all the pilot valves have in common? How is this common characteristic utilized in proportional control valves?

12.43. Referring to Figure 8.7, discuss how the force-balance principle is used in proportional control valves.

12.44. Discuss the characteristic curves for the two types of solenoids illustrated in Figure 12.19.

12.45. In general terms, what would be the major differences between a proportional control valve and true servovalve characteristics? Discuss how the characteristics of a proportional valve would affect its suitability for use in closed loop systems.

12.46. Discuss some of the differences in the evolution of mobile equipment proportional valves and those intended for industrial applications.

12.47. What types of pressure compensated directional control valves are available?

12.48. What are the primary advantages of pressure compensated directional control valves over non-compensated type?

12.49. What characteristics of pressure compensated directional control valves make them attractive as proportional control valves? Discuss.

CHAPTER 13

HYDRAULIC CIRCUITS

In earlier chapters we discussed examples of circuits classified as flow control, pressure control, and so on. Some circuits, however, are combinations of several techniques and do not lend themselves to such simple classifications.

SEQUENCING CIRCUITS

In this typical cylinder sequencing circuit, Figure 13.1, two cylinders are operated sequentially. Cylinder 1 strokes first, then cylinder 2. The main directional control valve determines whether the cylinders extend or retract. A sequence valve connected in parallel with the cap end of cylinder 1, has its outlet port connected to the cap end of cylinder 2.

When cylinder 1 has completed its stroke, fluid pressure builds in the line. This increase in pressure,

above that needed to extend cylinder 1, opens the sequence valve porting fluid to cylinder 2. This type circuit is frequently used with a machine tool as in a *clamp-work* sequence, where cylinder 1 operates the clamping mechanism and cylinder 2 the work mechanism. The circuit in Figure 13.1 provides positive sequencing during cylinder extension, but cylinder retraction is random; that is, there is no control over the retraction stroke of either cylinder.

If the machine requires retraction sequencing, the circuit of Figure 13.2 will serve the purpose. Note the addition of a second sequence valve in the line to the head-end of cylinder 1. With this design, cylinder 2 retracts first, followed by cylinder 1. Note that this is the reverse of the extension sequence.

Figure 13.3 shows an adaptation of the sequence

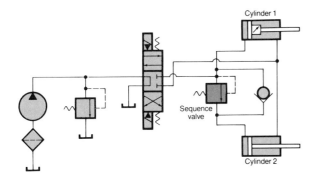

Fig. 13.1 In typical cylinder sequencing circuit, sequence valve insures that cylinder 1 extends before cylinder 2. Retraction is at random.

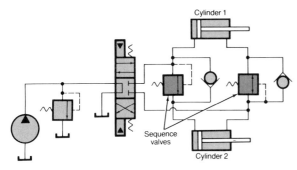

Fig. 13.2. Addition of second sequence valve insures that cylinders will extend and retract in proper sequence.

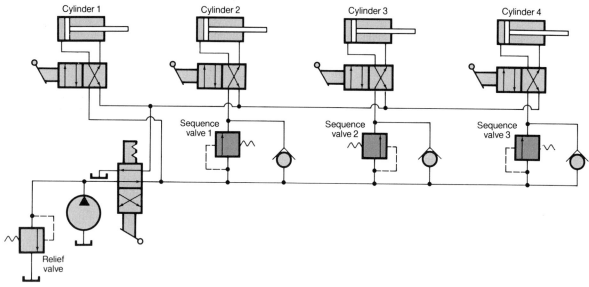

Fig. 13.3. Adaptation of sequencing control technique in multi-branch circuit.

valve control technique to a multi-branched circuit. As illustrated, cylinder 1 will extend first, followed by cylinders 2, 3, and 4. As in the circuit of Figure 13.1, cylinder retractions will be random.

CIRCUITS FOR SYNCHRONIZING ACTUATORS AND MOTORS

Figure 13.4 illustrates one of the most deceptive circuit diagrams in fluid power technology. It appears to show that two cylinders (or fluid motors) of equal displacement can be synchronized merely by connecting them in parallel and using a pump of sufficient displacement. Nothing could be further from the truth.

Even if the two actuators of Figure 13.4 could be made identical — which, as a practical matter is not possible — the loads on the two cylinder piston rods would also have to be identical for the two cylinders to be perfectly synchronized. If the loads differ (however slightly), the cylinder with the lowest load reaction would extend first, because it would require the lower operating pressure to move it. Only after that cylinder completed its stroke, thus satisfying its load requirements, would the second start to move — and then only after system pressure built to a new,

higher level as required by the larger load reaction.

In addition to these obvious problems, the designer must also consider the more subtle random variations in characteristics of the two actuators. No two cylinders are identical because of differences in seals friction; clearances; internal leakage; and machining tolerances. The net result is that two cylinders which started out synchronized would soon get out of phase. While in many applications, lack of synchronization is merely an inconvenience; in others it could be downright dangerous.

Only one method can ensure absolute synchronization, namely use of a servo system.

The circuit of Figure 13.5 shows a useful open-loop circuit technique for synchronizing two or more cylinders. Note that cylinders 1 and 2 are connected in series. From the pump, fluid flows to the cap end of cylinder 1 through directional control valve port C_1. Fluid then flows from the head end of cylinder 1 to the cap-end of cylinder 2; the head-end of cylinder 2 is connected to the C_2 port of the directional control valve. For the two cylinders to be approximately synchronized, the head-end displacement of cylinder 1 must equal the cap-end displacement of cylinder 2. In addition, the pump must be capable of developing

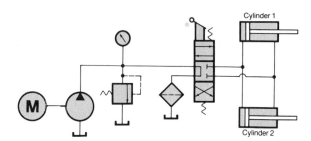

Fig. 13.4. Two cylinders connected in parallel will not necessarily be synchronized. The cylinder moving the lighter load will go first.

98

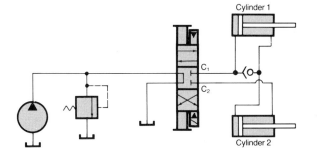

Fig. 13.5. Open loop circuit technique can be used to synchronize two or more cylinders connected in series.

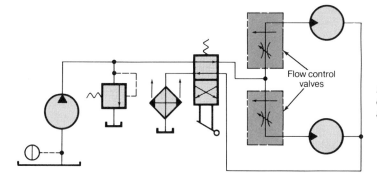

Fig. 13.6. Flow control valves can be used to synchronize fluid motors, depending on tolerances and allowable deviations.

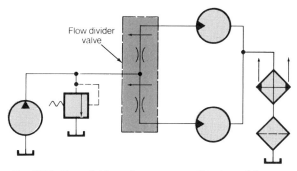

Fig. 13.7. Flow divider valves are sometimes used for synchronizing fluid motors. They are subject to the same limitations as flow control valves, Figure 13.6.

a pressure equal to the sum of the pressure differentials across both pistons. Note that the fluid pressure in the cap end of cylinder 2 becomes the head-end (back) pressure of cylinder 1.

Even the circuit method of Figure 13.5 will not guarantee cylinder synchronization over a large number of cycles because of the differentials in leakage of the two cylinders. Where this type circuit has been used successfully, some provision has been made to resynchronize the cylinders periodically. This is usually done by providing:

• a mechanical stop for both pistons or rods, and
• a method for replenishing system fluid which has leaked while both pistons are against their stops.

This synchronization method will not work with rotary motors, because slip (internal leakage) varies from motor to motor. Assume, for example, that the volumetric efficiency of one piston motor is 96 percent, while that of a second is 97 percent. It would

take only a few minutes of operation for the two motors to get several revolutions out of synchronization.

Attempts are made frequently to synchronize motors with flow control valves, Figure 13.6. The success of this technique depends on the tolerances applied to the performance of the flow control valves, and on the allowable deviation from synchronization. It has been established that cylinders or motors cannot be synchronized precisely by means of open-loop control over a large number of cycles of operation under varying load conditions. Fortunately, in many applications there is enough performance latitude to enable flow control valves to provide satisfactory synchronization. However, each case must be considered on its own merits.

Flow-divider valves are sometimes used for synchronizing fluid motors, Figure 13.7. They are subject to the same limitations as flow control valves.

FAIL-SAFE CIRCUITS

Fail-safe circuits protect the operator and the machine against such eventualities as power failure, overload, carelessness, and other unexpected and potentially dangerous events. These circuits are usually designed to return the load to some safe condition, should one of these unscheduled events occur.

Figure 13.8 illustrates an overload-reversal circuit. It is designed so that an overload on the piston rod will generate excessive pressure to automatically open the sequence valve. Output flow from the sequence valve provides a hydraulic pilot signal to shift 2-way, 2-position directional control valve, B. Valve B now vents pilot fluid from directional valve, A, to

99

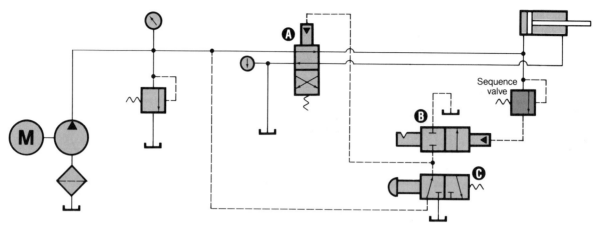

Fig. 13.8. Overload reversal circuit is designed so overload reaction on cylinder piston will raise fluid pressure to shift sequence valve.

tank, allowing the spring to shift main directional control valve A to its spring position. When valve A shifts, it causes the cylinder to retract. The system may be overridden manually with manually-operated directional control valve, C.

Cylinders are often used to lift a load. One possible hazard in such an application is that the load might drop, should anything reduce the pressure of the fluid acting on the piston. A load could suddenly drop because of power or pump failure, a broken line, inadvertent shifting of the wrong control valve, or valve failure. To avoid these events, a load-locking circuit, Figure 13.9, uses pilot-operated check valves placed as close to the actuator as possible.

When neither cylinder line is pressurized, the check valves remain seated to positively lock the hydraulic circuit. If either cylinder line is pressurized, a pilot connection unseats the check element in the opposite line to allow return flow through the valve. The area ratio between a pilot piston and the check element determines the level of pilot pressure needed to open the check valve against a given back pressure.

Some designs incorporate load checks in the cylinder itself. Directional control valves are commercially available with built-in load checks. However, they have the disadvantage of not protecting against failure of any component other than the directional control valve. Their offsetting advantage is that such valves are easier to pipe into the system.

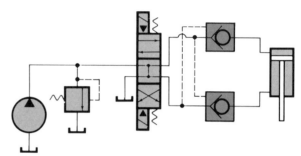

Fig. 13.9. Pilot operated check valves in load locking circuit prevent inadvertent cylinder actuation in case of hydraulic component failure.

The circuit in Figure 13.10 provides control over piston motion in case of sudden load removal or reversal. If a resistive load were suddenly removed or changed to an overrunning load, the cylinder piston would tend to lunge. Counterbalance valve, A, connected in the return line from the cylinder prevents this lunge by providing a controlled back pressure on the piston.

The circuit of Figure 13.11 is similar in function to that of Figure 13.10, except that pilot pressure to the counterbalance valve comes from the input or cap end of the cylinder, rather than from the head end. There must be a positive pressure in the cap end of the cylinder before the counterbalance valve can open and bypass return fluid. This circuit provides positive control of an overrunning load.

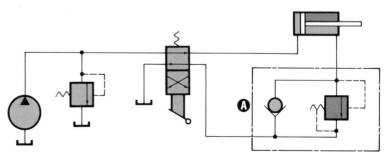

Fig. 13.10. Circuit provides control piston movement in case of sudden load removal or reversal.

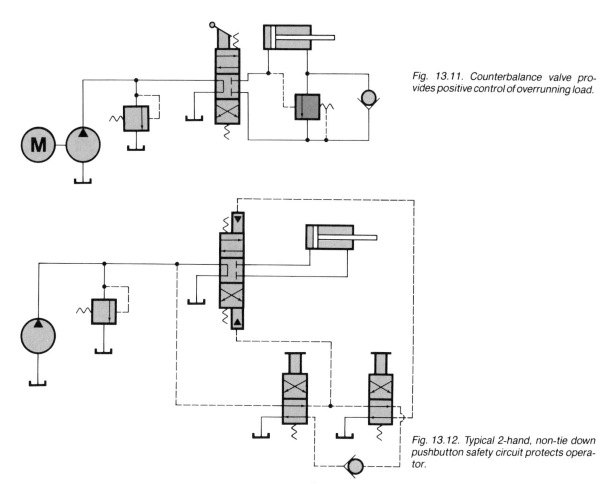

Fig. 13.11. Counterbalance valve provides positive control of overrunning load.

Fig. 13.12. Typical 2-hand, non-tie down pushbutton safety circuit protects operator.

The circuit of Figure 13.12 illustrates a typical two-hand or pushbutton type safety circuit, designed to protect the operator from injury. The operator must depress both manual valve pushbuttons on the 4-way, 2-position directional control valves *simultaneously* for the circuit to function. He cannot tie down one of the pushbuttons because both must be released to retract the cylinder. Actuation of the two manual directional control valves initiates operation of the main pilot-operated directional control valve.

This chapter discussed several, typical examples of fluid power circuits designed to perform specific functions. The designer can expand and amplify these basic concepts.

Important Terms

Sequencing circuits provide automatic operation of two or more actuators, sequentially one after the other.

Actuator synchronization is the technique which moves two or more cylinders or hydraulic motors in such a way that the positions or velocities of their output elements are precisely the same, or bear some fixed relationship to each other.

Fail-safe circuits protect the operator, or the machine, or both, in case of power failure, overload, component failure, carelessness, or any other undesirable occurrence.

Load locking circuits maintain load position until a control action is initiated which releases the locking device, allowing load motion.

Exercises

13.1. In the circuit of Figure 13.1, the sequence valve is set to open at 1250 psi. A plot of load pressure in cylinders 1 and 2 is shown in the diagram.

    a. Discuss the pressure relationship between points 0-1;

    b. Discuss what occurs at point 2;

    c. Discuss the pressure relationship between points 1-3;

    d. Between points 2 and 3, load pressure in cylinder 2 rises to 2000 psi; what happens to the pressure in branch 1?

    e. At point 4, load pressure in branch 2 drops to 1000 psi. What happens to branch 2?

13.2. Referring to Figures 13.1 and 13.3, discuss the implications of the different locations of the sequence valves in the two circuits.

13.3. Discuss the problems attendant to synchronizing cylinders or fluid motors in a system.

13.4. What is the effect of varying piston seal and rod seal friction on synchronizing cylinders? Also, what is the effect of pressure level on this friction? How does this friction affect the mechanical efficiency of a cylinder?

13.5. How do varying cylinder leakage rates affect cylinder synchronization?

13.6. Referring to Figure 13.4, assume the cylinders are loaded identically and seal friction forces are identical. Cylinder 1 has a stroke of 24 in; cylinder 2 stroke is 24 in; cycle rate = 10 cycles per minute; cylinder bores are 5 in. Cylinder 1 leaks at the rate of 5 in^3/cycle; cylinder 2 leaks at the rate of 10 in^3/cycle. Calculate how many cycles would be required to desynchronize the cylinder strokes by 10%? What could be done to minimize this desynchronization effect?

13.7. Using the data of problem 13.6, what would be the effect of a load differential of 15% between cylinders 1 and 2?

13.8. Referring to Figure 13.5, discuss the considerations for synchronizing two cylinders in series as shown.

    a. What are the pressure relationships in the cylinders?

    b. What are the effects of varying loads on the two cylinders?

    c. What would be the effect of cavitation in the trapped volume between the two cylinders? What can be done to offset this effect?

13.9. Referring to Figure 13.5, cylinder 1 has a bore of 6 in, a rod diameter of 2 in, and a stroke of 12 in; cylinder 2 has a stroke of 12 in. The load on cylinder 1 is 5000 lb; on cylinder 2 it is 16,500 lb. Piston rod velocity of cylinder 2 is 120 fpm.

    a. Neglecting the pressure drop across the directional control valve, what is pump discharge pressure?

    b. What are the specifications for cylinder 2?

    c. What pump delivery is required?

    d. Assuming a leakage rate of 1% of the volume trapped between the two cylinders, how long would it take to desynchronize the cylinder strokes by 10%?

    e. Discuss the implications of inverting cylinder 2 relative to cylinder 1, that is, turning cylinder 2 around so the rod is fixed and the cylinder barrel moves along with the rod of cylinder 1.

13.10. Rework example 13.9 using SI metric units.

13.11. Referring to the circuit of Figure 13.5, assume the two cylinders are interconnected by a plastic hose having a compliance equivalent to 25% of the volume displaced by cylinder 1 to cylinder 2. What would be the effect on synchronizing the strokes of the two cylinder piston rods?

13.12. Flow dividers are sometimes used for synchronizing cylinders and motors. Accuracy of control for most commercial flow dividers is about ±5 to ±10% of full range. Discuss the implication of accuracies of this order on cylinder/motor synchronization.

13.13. Referring to Figure 13.9, it has been observed that load locks (pilot operated check valves) used in relatively massive systems involving heavy, gravity-type, resistive loads result in jerky lowering of the load as it drops. Analyze the circuit of Figure 13.9, and discuss what might cause this chatter motion. (Hint: consider pressure variations in the supply lines as energy exchanges between the load and hydraulic system).

13.14. Discuss the difference between the load holding circuits of Figures 13.10 and 13.11.

CHAPTER 14

PNEUMATIC POWER CIRCUITS

The technology of fluid power deals with the transmission of energy using a compressed fluid as the transmission medium. The fluid can be either a liquid or a gas. Up to this point, most of the illustrative examples we have discussed dealt with hydraulic circuitry.

This chapter discusses the differences between pneumatic and hydraulic systems. Functionally, the two are similar. Therefore, what was said about the functional design of hydraulic systems is also valid for pneumatic systems. The differences lie in the handling of the fluid medium — a liquid in one case, a gas in the other.

DIFFERENCES IN FLUID CHARACTERISTICS

The primary difference between a liquid and a gas is their relative degree of compressibility.
1. A **fluid**[1] is a substance which has definite mass and volume, but no definite shape; a fluid cannot sustain a shear stress under equilibrium conditions.
- A **liquid**[2] is a fluid which has definite volume for a given mass, and is relatively incompressible.
- A **gas**[3] is a fluid which is highly compressible and whose volume varies to fill the vessel containing it.

Compressibility

For all but the most critical fluid power applications, it is common practice to consider a liquid, for all intents and purposes, as being incompressible. Remember, however that as a practical matter no fluid is perfectly incompressible. Typical hydraulic oils exhibit a compressibility of about 0.5 percent by volume per 1000 psi over the normal range of pressures encountered in hydraulic systems.

In addition, liquids have a characteristic coefficient of expansion which is a function of change in temperature. Though the change in volume with temperature is relatively small for these fluids, it is

big enough to cause extreme pressures to build in closed systems which are subject to large temperature increases.

In contrast to liquids, gases are completely elastic. Their volumes change inversely with tbe pressure exerted on them (Boyle's Law)[4]; that is, as pressure increases, the volume of a given mass of gas decreases. The volume of a gas also increases proportionately with its temperature (Charles' Law)[5]; that is, as the temperature of a gas increases (at constant pressure), its volume increases. Conversely, the pressure of a gas is directly proportional to temperature if the volume is held constant. Thus, if the temperature of a gas increases, the pressure within its container will increase proportionately.

Other differences

There are also some secondary differences between liquids and gases which affect their relative performance in a system:
1. Viscosity[6] is the measure of a fluid's resistance to shearing stress. Under conditions most frequently encountered in fluid power systems, liquids exhibit much higher viscosity than do gases.
2. Mass, m is the measure of the resistance of a quantity of a substance to change in velocity (acceleration or deceleration). The weight, W, of a substance is a measure of the force acting on the substance as a result of the accelerating effect of gravity, g. Thus: $W = mg$.
a) It is obvious that the mass of liquids exceeds the mass of gases.
b) The mass of a fluid affects its performance in a system in accordance with Newton's Second Law; Force, F, equals the product of mass, m, and acceleration, a, $F = ma$.
3. Other characteristics. Chemical characteristics of hydraulic fluids can affect their performance in a fluid power system. A detailed discussion of these is beyond the scope of this book.[7]

EFFECT OF FLUID CHARACTERISTICS ON MOTOR PERFORMANCE

The performance of the fluid in a hydraulic or pneumatic system is related primarily to compressibility. Figure 14.1 illustrates this point.

The load cycle plot of Figure 14.1(*a*) is identical for hydraulic and pneumatic systems. The pressure plot of Figure 14.1(*a*) is determined from the load plot. If the hydraulic actuator, such as a cylinder, is driven by a *fixed-displacement* pump, volumetric flow rate to the actuator is constant, as shown by the horizontal flow curve, Figure 14.1(*b*). Also, refer to Chapter 6.

A constant flow to the cylinder results in a constant velocity of the piston rod. Because of the relative incompressibility of hydraulic fluid, fairly accurate velocity control is possible.

Comparing liquids and gases

In a pneumatic system, Figure 14.1(*c*), the pressure plot has the same form as for the hydraulic system because the same load cycle is involved. At this point the similarity between the systems ends.

It is difficult to determine what the air flow rate to the cylinder really is. For instance, an initial load pressure of p_1 results in a corresponding initial flow

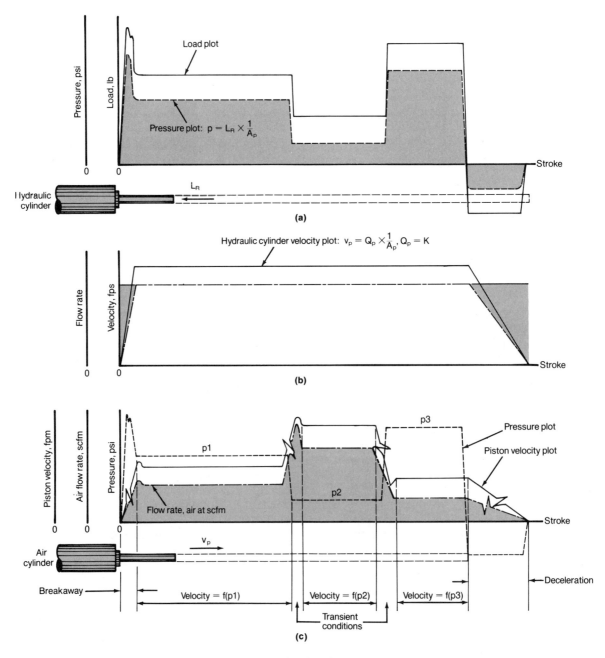

Fig. 14.1. Performance comparison of liquids and gases. Load cycle plot which controls pressure plot (a) is identical for both. Volumetric fluid rate (b) is constant.

rate of air. The density of the air is a function of pressure, p_1, and temperature T_1. The source of the compressed air is the central compressor; the air is delivered through a pressure regulators, which is a throttling device.

If it is assumed that the compressor can deliver an unlimited quantity of compressed air to a cylinder, the factors which limit flow rate to the cylinder include load, resistance to flow inside the piping valve orifices, the regulator, etc. It is important to remember that ALL of these factors contribute some pressure drops, and that every change in pressure results in a corresponding change in the volume of the gas.

Consider the change in load pressure from p_1 to p_2, Figure 14.1(c). This pressure difference is caused by a change in the load reaction on the piston rod, not by a change in the pressure of the air inside the cylinder. At the instant the load pressure drops to p_2, there results a force imbalance in the cylinder. This imbalance occurs because the air in the cylinder is at pressure p_1. The gas does the only thing it can — it expands until it reaches a new equilibrium at pressure, p_2. The piston rod tends to jerk as the gas expands in the cylinder.

The load pressure curve of Figure 14.1(c) indicates that a pressure increase from p_2 to p_3 will follow. The reverse of the process just described now takes place: the piston rod slows down or may even stop momentarily, to allow incoming air to re-compress the gas already in the cylinder to the new equilibrium pressure, p_3.

In a pneumatic system these momentary changes in piston rod velocity occur every time there is a change in load pressure. Thus, we cannot speak in terms of a flow rate to the actuator in the same sense as in a hydraulic system. Instead, we must deal with *instantaneous* piston velocities.

The designer of a pneumatic system must remember that it is difficult to obtain controlled output velocities with pneumatic systems. The compressibility of the gas also makes it difficult to main-

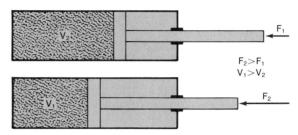

Fig. 14.2. In a pneumatic system, as the load increases from F_1 to F_2, air pressure in the cylinder increases and air volume decreases from V_2 to V_1.

tain accurate position, Figure 14.2. As the load changes from F_1 to F_2, the air volume in the cylinder decreases, altering the position of the cylinder piston rod.

These characteristics of liquids and gases explain why hydraulic systems are often preferred over pneumatic systems in applications requiring accurate control of position or velocity. Until recently, pneumatic systems have been used mostly for sequential types of applications where the end conditions are those of prime importance: *i.e.*, circuits in which the important factor is whether the rod is fully extended or fully retracted. Transfer, clamping, and press circuits are typical illustrations.

Where the economics of the situation warrant the use of a pneumatic power system, yet where control requirements are also greater than those attainable with an all-pneumatic system, the designer should consider using an air-oil system. In air-oil systems*, compressed air provides the source of potential energy, while hydraulic oil provides the incompressible fluid characteristics necessary to achieve the desired degree of control. Figure 14.3 illustrates two types of air-oil systems.

The first, Figure 14.3(a) uses a tandem cylinder. A large bore pneumatic cylinder is connected in series with a hydraulic cylinder. When the pneumatic cylinder is pressurized, it generates the force

---

*See *Introduction to Fluid Mechanics,* Chapter 17.

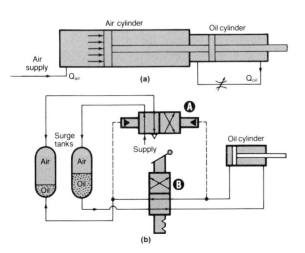

Fig. 14.3. Where required actuating forces permit, air-over-oil system combines the economic advantages of pneumatics with the fine controls of hydraulics.

required to overcome the external load and to displace oil from one end of the hydraulic cylinder, through an adjustable flow control orifice into the other end. Velocity is controlled by adjusting the orifice in the bypass flow path.

An alternate approach is shown in Figure 14.3(*b*). Air-over-oil surge tanks are used in place of tandem cylinders. Compressed air is ported alternately to one tank or the other by a pilot operated, 4-way pneumatic valve, *A*. The pilot valve, in turn is operated by pilot signals from cylinder supply lines as the operator shifts lever-operated directional control valve, *B*.

When air pressure flows into one of the surge tanks, oil is forced out of the tank into the hydraulic circuit. The hydraulic cylinder responds to the directional control valve and return oil flows into the other surge tank which had been evacuated. Surge tank volumes must balance cylinder displacements to avoid forcing oil into the pneumatic system.

EFFECT OF FLUID CHARACTERISTICS ON CONTROL VALVE PERFORMANCE

The compressibility of air makes performance prediction for pneumatic valves more difficult than for their hydraulic counterparts. The function of pneumatic directional control valves is very similar to that of hydraulic valves. Thus, the functional designations — 2-way, 3-way, 4-way, etc. — are applicable to both.

A major difference in the design and construction of pneumatic and hydraulic components reflects the vast difference between their operating pressure levels. Hydraulic valves, which operate at pressures ranging from 500 to 10,000 psi, are made from heavy castings or bar stock. On the other hand, pneumatic valves are seldom exposed to pressures over 150 psi. For this reason, they can be die-cast or otherwise fabricated from aluminum, brass, or even zinc alloys.

Valve operators

The types and functions of the valve operators are the same as those previously discussed for hydraulic valves.* That is, pneumatic valves can be actuated with solenoids, pilot controls, manually, by foot, cam, or palm buttons, etc. The major differences between hydraulic and pneumatic valve operators reflects the lower operating pressures of the pneumatic valves. Since lower forces are encountered, the operators are usually smaller.

Pneumatic valves respond faster than do hydraulic valves. For example, a pneumatic valve of a given size will probably shift from three to four times faster than its hydraulic counterpart. A solenoid-operated hydraulic valve of a given size might shift in 30 to 40 ms (1 ms = $\frac{1}{1000}$ sec). A pneumatic valve of the same size might require 5 to 10 ms.

Another major differences between pneumatic

*See *Introduction to Fluid Mechanics*, Chapter 18.

and hydraulic valves clearly shows that one is designed to handle "incompressible" fluids (hydraulic), the other "compressible" fluids (pneumatic). It can be said that hydraulic valves perform roughly according to the relationship[8]

$$Q = K \sqrt{2g\Delta p_l},$$

where Δp is the pressure drop across the valve and K is a valve constant. This form of the relationship is valid only for incompressible fluids. Under these conditions, the thermodynamic effects of fluid flow through the valve can be ignored. That is, we can assume constant fluid density without introducing significant error into the calculation of flow rate.

In the case of a pneumatic valve, since we are dealing with a compressible fluid, the pressure drop across the valve affects the flow rate. As pressure decreases, the air volume expands and the density (mass per unit volume) decreases. Air expansion also causes variations in flow velocity within the valve.

The C_v factor

To attempt to take all these factors into consideration every time a designer wants to specify a valve would require a prohibitive amount of time. Fortunately, manufacturers of air valves have devised a means for rating valves with a universally accepted method. It is called the C_v factor, which enables a user to estimate the flow capacity of a valve under certain conditions of inlet and outlet pressure. Refer to Chapter 24 for a detailed discussion on valve selection criteria.

The C_v factor approach to selecting a pneumatic valve works "backwards" — from required conditions of flow rate and pressure at the actuator, to a valve size which will satisfy these requirements.

This discussion emphasized the major differences between hydraulic and pneumatic systems from the designer's point of view. The student should consult additional sources for more detailed discussion of the individual components and their characteristics.*

EXAMPLES OF PNEUMATIC POWER CIRCUITS

A basic directional control circuit for a single-acting cylinder, Figure 14.4, illustrates some of the differences between pneumatics and hydraulics. For instance, note the absence of an input device such as a pump. Most pneumatic circuits use plant compressors as their source of energy. To provide the input to the circuit, you simply plug into an air manifold at a convenient location. An individual air compressor may also be used at the machine. Conversely, for most hydraulic systems, use of individual power units does not preclude use of a central system.

A typical component used in pneumatic circuits is a filter-regulator-lubricator combination (FRL) at

*See *Introduction to Fluid Mechanics*, Chapter 18.

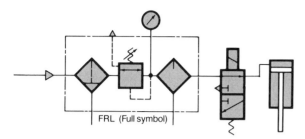

Fig. 14.4. Basic directional control pneumatic circuit for single acting cylinder. Exhaust port symbol indicates that exhaust to atmosphere is through plain, unconnectable orifice.

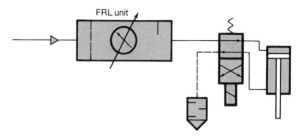

Fig. 14.5. Basic directional control pneumatic circuit for double acting cylinder. Exhaust port symbol indicates that exhaust to atmosphere is through silencer (muffler).

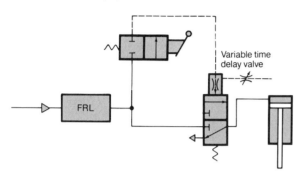

Fig. 14.6. Time delay control creates a time lag between the instant a control signal is applied and the instant the valve reacts. Time delay valve retards slightly pilot signal to 3-way directional control valve. Exhaust port shows threaded (connectable) port.

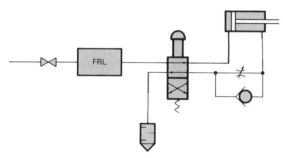

Fig. 14.7. Variable orifice (free return) flow control valve regulates speed at which cylinder extends.

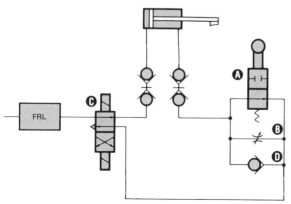

Fig. 14.8. In deceleration circuit, cam shifts 2-way valve, A, diverting some air through variable flow control valve B, decelerating the cylinder. When valve C is shifted, pressure air flows through check valve D, retracting the cylinder at full speed.

the source or point where the plant air manifold is tapped. The FRL provides clean air at regulated pressure, and adds enough lubricant to the air to minimize wear of downstream components.

Note that there is no return line to tank in the circuit diagram of Figure 14.4. The small triangle at the exhaust port of the control valve indicates that the air exhausts to atmosphere.

Figure 14.5 shows a basic directional control circuit for a double-acting cylinder with a muffler connected to the directional control valve.

A single-acting cylinder control valve is shown in Figure 14.6. The time-delay control creates a predetermined, usually adjustable, time lag between the instant when the actuation signal is applied to the circuit and the instant the control valve responds. In most cases the time-delay control is variable so the lag can be varied over a given range.

The manual or solenoid operator for the directional control valve can be replaced by a mechanical operator, such as a cam actuator.

Accurate flow control under conditions of varying load is difficult to obtain with a pneumatic circuit. However, when the load does not vary excessively, pneumatic flow controls are available and can be used successfully. A typical meter-out flow control circuit is illustrated in Figure 14.7.

A deceleration circuit is shown in Figure 14.8. In this application, a cam mounted on the cylinder rod shifts a 2-position, 2-way normally open directional valve at the proper point in the stroke to decelerate the cylinder piston. As shown, all exhaust air flows through valve A to atmosphere — no speed control. As the cam begins to close valve A, some air is throttled through variable flow control valve B, to atmosphere through valve C. When C is shifted, incoming air flows through check valve D *directly* to retract cylinder.

A basic pneumatic sequence circuit is illustrated in Figure 14.9. It is essentially the same as its hydraulic counterpart discussed in Chapter 8. Figure 14.10 illustrates a multi-branched pneumatic circuit using cam-operated limit switches to control a sequencing mode. The limit switches can be used to operate relays which, in turn, initiate secondary motions such as, for example, reversing directional control valves.

Figure 14.11 shows a circuit designed to achieve multiple speeds of one actuator. In this circuit, a shaped cam connected to the piston rod operates four limit switches, two for extend and two for retract. The limit switches signal the solenoid operators of directional control valve A. Each port of valve A, is connected to a variable flow control valve. One valve is set for high speed, the other for low speed to control the flow of air out of the cylinder and thus the speed of the piston rod in both directions.

A pneumatic dual pressure control circuit with two pressure regulators is shown in Figure 14.12. Each regulator supplies air to one port of a 2-position, 4-way 5-ported directional control valve,

C. When valve C is shifted to its (a) position, regulator B supplies air to retract the cylinder. When valve C is shifted to its (b) position, regulator A supplies air to extend the cylinder. The two regulators, can be set at different pressures to correspond to various circuit operation requirements. For example, they can be set to provide the same force in both directions even though different piston areas are involved.

Figure 14.13 illustrates a modification of the dual pressure circuit: two pressure regulators are used to supply a single input to the circuit through a selector valve. Thus, the circuit can be fed at either of two input pressure levels.

The pneumatic equivalent of the hydraulic closed-center circuit is shown in Figure 14.14. This type of pneumatic circuit does not have the same stiffness as its hydraulic counterpart.

The circuit illustrated in Figure 14.15 is the pneumatic equivalent of a hydraulic "float" circuit. Note that both cylinder ports exhaust to atmosphere when the directional control valve is in neutral position.

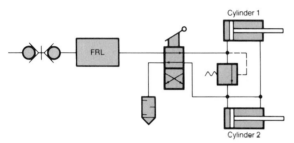

Fig. 14.9. In basic sequence circuit, Cylinder 2 sequence valve will not allow cylinder 2 to extend until after cylinder 1 has completed its stroke.

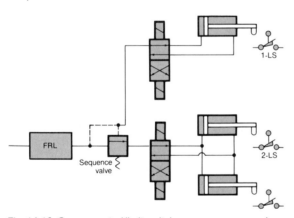

Fig. 14.10. Cam-operated limit switches can sequence various cylinder motions in multibranched pneumatic circuit. Sequence valve insures that cylinder at top is actuated before the other two.

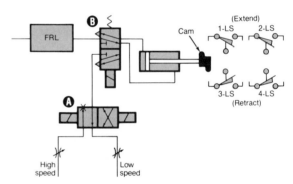

Fig. 14.11. Pneumatic cylinder can be operated at multiple speeds.

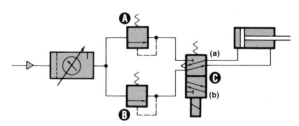

Fig. 14.12. Pneumatic dual pressure control circuit.

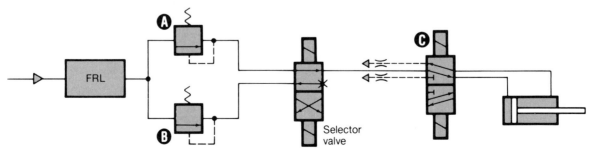

Fig. 14.13. Modified dual pressure circuit. Two pressure regulators supply cylinder through selector valve.

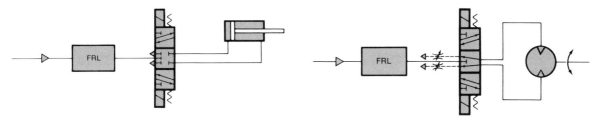

Fig. 14.14. Pneumatic equivalent of hydraulic closed center circuit.

Fig. 14.15. Pneumatic equivalent of hydraulic float circuit.

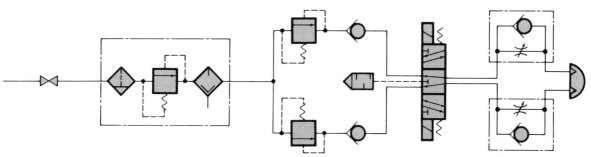

Fig. 14.16. Pneumatic locking circuit.

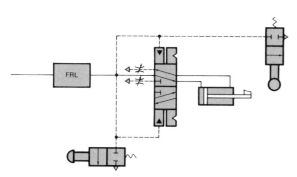

Fig. 14.17. Manual or cam-operated venting of pilot circuit.

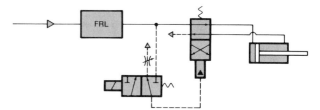

Fig. 14.18. Pilot circuit with built-in time-delay control.

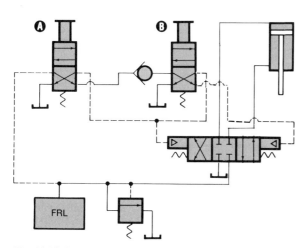

Fig. 14.19. In pneumatic safety circuit, valves A and B MUST be depressed simultaneously to extend cylinder.

The circuit shown in Figure 14.16 is the opposite of that shown in Figure 14.15. It provides positive locking (without the capability of the compressible fluid to sustain a load) when the directional control valve is in neutral. In addition, the circuit also has dual pressure capability. Individual flow control is provided in each of the lines to the oscillator.

A circuit that provides manual or cam-operated venting of the pilot circuit is shown in Figure 14.17. Ths circuit uses 2-way, 2-position pilot valves. The circuit of Figure 14.18 shows a pilot circuit with a built-in time-delay control.

A pneumatic safety circuit is illustrated in Figure 14.19. Both pushbutton-operated pilot valves, A and B, MUST be actuated to extend the cylinder. Both pilot valves MUST be released to retract.

Another safety circuit is shown in Figure 14.20. For the cylinder to extend pilot valves A and B MUST be depressed simultaneously and pilot valves C and D MUST be released. To retract the piston rod, pilot valves A and B MUST be released, while pilot valves C and D MUST be depressed.

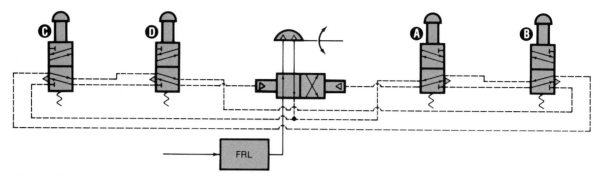

Fig. 14.20. In pneumatic safety circuit, valves A and B must be depressed simultaneously and valves C and D released simultaneously to operate pneumatic oscillator.

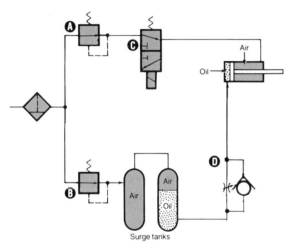

Fig. 14.21. In combination feed circuit, compressed air provides the power, oil the controls.

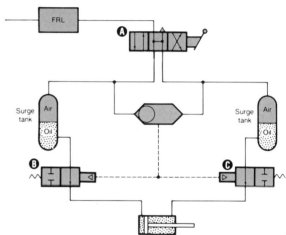

Fig. 14.22. Compressed air powers cylinder in both directions: directly to retract; through air-over-oil surge tanks to extend.

EXAMPLES OF AIR-OIL CIRCUITS

Combination circuits using both air and oil have been designed to take advantage of the best features of both media. Figure 14.21 shows a feed circuit. Shop air supplies the required energy; oil provides the control capability. Pressure reducing valve A is set at a higher pressure than pressure reducing valve B. When directional control valve C is shifted to vent the head end of the cylinder, air pressure in the surge tanks forces oil out of the tank and through valve D to the cap end of the cylinder. When directional control valve C is shifted again, it ports air to the head end of the cylinder. The cylinder retracts, forcing the oil back into the surge tank.

The circuit of Figure 14.22 illustrates a method for air-powering a hydraulic cylinder and locking the cylinder at any point during its stroke. Two surge tanks provide the air-oil interface and storage space for the oil. The air is supplied through an open-center directional control valve, A. When valve A is in its center position, this valve bleeds both surge tanks to atmosphere, thus removing air pressure from the oil system.

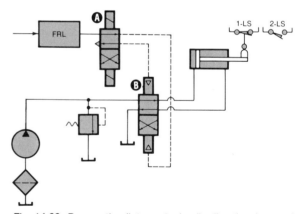

Fig. 14.23. Pneumatic pilots on hydraulic directional control valve insure faster cycling time of cylinder.

Shifting directional control valve A pressurizes one of the surge tanks, the shuttle valve, and both air pilots of hydraulic 2-way, 2-position control valves B and C. Oil is forced out of the pressurized surge tank into the cylinder; return oil is forced into the unpressurized surge tank. Centering 4-way directional control valve A bleeds off all air pressure: air pilot-operated hydraulic control valves B and C shift to

110

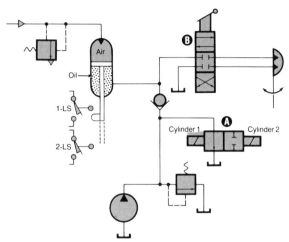

Fig. 14.24. Compressed air can be used to continually charge hydro-pneumatic accumulator.

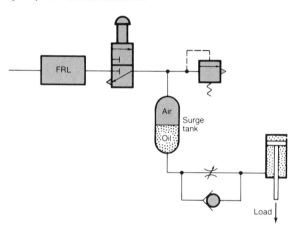

Fig. 14.25. Counterbalance system is designed with air-over-oil circuit.

the accumulator. When the accumulator is charged, *LS*-1 shifts valve *A* to unload the pump. Working fluid is taken from the accumulator when the operator shifts manually controlled, 4-way directional control valve, *B*.

Figure 14.25 shows a counterbalance system using an air-oil circuit. Shop air pressurizes the surge tank. Oil is delivered to the cylinder through a combination check valve and orifice. When the control valve is shifted to vent air from the surge tank, the orifice provides controlled return flow of the oil.

Important Terms

Boyle's Law: a gas law which relates pressure and volume, while temperature is held constant.

Charles Law: a gas law which relates pressure, temperature and volume of a gas as a function of temperature.

Fluid is a substance which cannot sustain a shear stress under equilibrium conditions.

Gas is a fluid whose volume, for a given mass, is proportional to temperature and inversely proportional to absolute pressure. A gas is a compressible fluid.

Liquid is a fluid which has a definite volume for a given mass. A liquid is considered incompressible.

Mass is the measure of the resistance of a quantity of substance to change in velocity (acceleration) under action of an unbalanced force.

Viscosity is a measure of fluid's resistance to shear stress under non-equilibrium conditions.

---

1 — Introduction to Fluid Mechanics, *Russell W. Henke, Addison-Wesley Publg., Reading, MA, p. 2.*

2 — Ibid, p. 2

3 — Ibid, p. 3

4 — Ibid, pp. 179, 180, 184, 192

5 — Ibid, pp. 179, 192

6 — Ibid, pp. 136-142; pp. 218-220

7 — Ibid, p. 179

8 — Ref. Chapter 24, Selecting Control Valves

their spring positions, locking the cylinder in position.

The circuit of Figure 14.23 shows a method for obtaining faster cycling time in a hydraulic circuit by air-piloting the main directional control valve. Solenoid operated air pilots controlled by valve *A* shift hydraulic valve *B* faster than could be done with hydraulic pilots.

Shop air can be used to charge an accumulator, Figure 14.24. Pressurized shop air is forced into the top of the piston accumulator. Limit switches, *LS*-1 and *LS*-2, control solenoid-operated, 2-position, 2-way unloading valve *A*. When the accumulator has reached the end of its active stroke, it makes *LS*-2, closing valve *A*, allowing the pump to deliver oil to

Review Exercises

14.1. Define a fluid.

14.2. What is the difference between a liquid and a gas?

14.3. What is the typical compressibility of a hydraulic fluid in terms of % of volume? What effect does entrained air have on compressibility?

14.4. Discuss the difference between the thermal coefficient of expansion of a hydraulic fluid (liquid) and thermal effect on a gas.

14.5. Why does a moderate increase in temperature in a trapped volume of liquid result in very high pressures?

14.6. Discuss what the effect would be on a trapped volume of gas undergoing the same moderate increase in temperature.

14.7. Discuss the idea that the transfer medium in fluid power systems — liquid in a hydraulic, gas in a pneumatic system — is or is not foreign to the ament environment. What implications does this have on fluid power systems design?

14.8. Discuss how the relative compressibility of hydraulic fluids and gases affects their performance in a fluid power system.

14.9. What would be the differences, if any, between the load cycle plot for the same machine load cycle if it was to be powered by a pneumatic system or a hydraulic system?

14.10. Given the load cycle plot of question 14.9 (Ref. Fig. 14.1): if the same bore cylinder was to be used, would there be any difference in pressure for the hydraulic or pneumatic systems? Explain.

14.11. Referring to Fig. 14.1(b): discuss the relationship between the flow rate plot and the velocity plot shown. What is the significance of the shaded portions under the flow rate plot?

14.12. Referring to Figure 14.1(c): how does the pressure plot relate to the load cycle plot?

14.13. Referring to Fig. 14.1(c): discuss the piston velocity plot and its relationship to the pressure cycle plot. Why does piston velocity vary as load varies? What effect does this have on air flow rate?

14.14. Referring to Fig 14.1(c): why is there no shaded area under the flow rate curve during acceleration and deceleration periods in the load cycle?

14.15. If pressure p_2, as shown in Fig. 14.1(c), dropped below $0.53 p_s$ — where p_s is inlet pressure to the control valve — what would happen to air flow through the valve? Would this affect the ability of the valve to control the cylinder?

14.16. Referring to Fig. 14.2: discuss the effect of an increase in load reaction on a static pneumatic cylinder. Explain.

14.17. Discuss the "air-over-oil" systems illustrated

in Fig. 14.3. What is the intent of such systems?

14.18. Discuss general effects of liquid or gas characteristics on control valve design and performance.

14.19. What is the purpose of the C_v factor? How is it applied?

14.20. What are the functions of an FRL in a pneumatic system?

14.21. Discuss the function of the time delay control shown in Fig. 14.6. How is the time delay accomplished?

14.22. Referring to Fig. 14.8: discuss the relative performance of the deceleration circuit illustrated when used in a hydraulic or pneumatic system. Discuss why piston rod "kick-back" is sometimes observed in the pneumatic version of this deceleration circuit.

14.23. Referring to Fig. 14.9: assume the load pressure in cylinder 2 is lower than in cylinder 1. Discuss potential interactions between the two cylinders which might occur when the sequence valve opens.

14.24. Continue the discussion of question 14.23, to apply to the circuit shown in Fig. 14.10.

14.25. Discuss the operation of the dual pressure system shown in Fig. 14.12.

14.26. Compare anticipated performance of the pneumatic closed center circuit illustrated in Fig. 15.14, with its hydraulic counterpart as discussed in Chapter 7.

14.27. What is the purpose of the "float" circuit shown in Fig. 14.15?

14.28. Discuss the relative performance capabilities of the pneumatic circuit shown in Fig. 14.16, and its hydraulic counterpart.

14.29. Referring to Fig. 14.19, trace the pilot signal through the two-level safety circuit shown and discuss how it operates.

14.30. Referring to Fig. 14.20, discuss the operation of this safety circuit. Trace the pilot signals controlling the system directional control valve.

14.31. Discuss the operation of the air-over-oil circuit shown in Fig. 14.21.

14.32. In the circuit in Fig. 14.22, what is the purpose of the shuttle valve?

14.33. Referring to Fig. 14.24, discuss the difference(s) in the performance of the accumulator pressurized by regulated shop air pressure, as shown, and an equivalent accumulator charged with pressurized nitrogen gas.

14.34. Discuss the difference(s) in performance between the air-oil counterbalance system shown in Fig. 14.25, and conventional hydraulic systems using a counterbalance valve.

CHAPTER 15

CONSERVING ENERGY

As with other power transmitting technologies, designing fluid power systems to use less energy and do more work is a major consideration. Designs range from conventional circuits to special systems for conserving energy like load sensing, regeneration, stored energy, and many others.

In Chapter 1, we discussed the fundamental concepts of energy transmission and control. The key points relating to energy conservation are:

1. Determine every condition that the system will be required to meet. The Cycle Profile plotting technique, Chapters 3, 4, and 5, outlined a logical approach to establish hydraulic system performance requirements.

2. Bear in mind that only two variables are involved in the process of energy transmission and control: pressure and flow rate.

3. Remember that hydraulic system pressure is a function of the load reacting on the system's output component. The pressure is, in fact, an output variable, *not* an input variable. Refer to Figure 1.4.

4. Recognize that energy losses in a hydraulic system are a function of flow rate, not pressure level. Energy loss in a hydraulic system is caused by a fluid flowing at a given rate through a pressure drop, while no work is done. Thus:

$$U = K_s (Q \times \Delta p)$$

To reduce energy losses in a hydraulic system, minimize the conditions in the above equation. If at all possible, avoid passing any flow rate, Q, through a pressure drop Δp.

If this is unavoidable, take every precaution to minimize the pressure drop and flow rate if possible.

Many factors contribute to energy losses in a hydraulic system. The designer should recognize what they are and use good judgment and ingenuity to avoid them. Some of these factors include use of unnecessarily large numbers of fittings, conduits with small inside diameters, unnecessary flow through relief valves, indiscriminate use of flow controls, excessive slip in pumps and motors, undersized directional control valves, excessive leakage past cylinder piston seals, etc. Refer to Chapters 23, 24, and 25 for additional considerations.

Techniques which remove or dissipate heat generated in a hydraulic system have no relation to heat generation itself. Oil cooling is an after-the-fact event. Providing heat exchangers or adequate radiator convective heat dissipation capacity to reduce oil temperature does not imply that the system designer did, in fact, design the best energy conservation systems. Chapter 18 provides additional information on heat generation and control in hydraulic systems.

Other heat generating factors

Other factors contribute to heat generation over which the designer has *no* control, *i.e.*, internal friction, both Coulomb and viscous; compression-decompression cycles caused by pulsations associated with positive displacement pumps and motors, and related to system requirements; transient by-passing over control valves during load acceleration and deceleration, (Chapters 3 and 6); quiescent control flow in certain types of control valves, (Chapters 8 and 10); and similar factors frequently overlooked in the steady-state design of hydraulic circuits.

ENERGY CONSERVATION IN CONVENTIONAL HYDRAULIC CIRCUITS

Constant flow systems

Chapter 6 defined a *constant flow* system as one supplied by a fixed-displacement pump, whose output bypasses to tank through an open- or tandem-center directional control valve.

Figure 15.1 is based on the elementary constant flow system used for Figure 1.4 and defines the areas

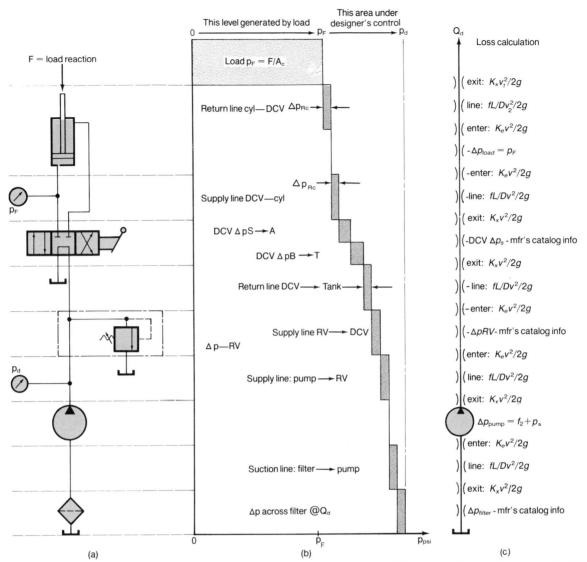

Fig. 15.1. *Simple constant flow systems:* a) *drawn with ISO fluid power symbols;* (b) *pressure drops and levels across each flow element in system shown at* (a)*; and* (c) *graphic technique for evaluating pressure drops throughout system based on empirical expressions of fluid mechanics.*

in which a circuit designer HAS control in his attempt to minimize energy losses. Figure 15.1(*a*) represents the circuit using ISO fluid power symbols; Figure 15.1(*b*) pressure drops and levels across each flow element in the entire system; Figure 15.1(*c*) illustrates a graphic technique for evaluating pressure drops throughout an entire system based on empirical expressions used in fluid mechanics.

Energy level, as evidenced by hydrostatic pressure, (see Figure 1.4), is represented along the X-axis; the elements which make up the circuit along the Y-axis. Pressure drop through each element is represented by the width of the shaded bars in the manner of a sequence diagram suggesting that differential pressures in series in a hydraulic system add algebraically.

Note that return line effects are also included. Thus, the sum of the losses in the system is:

$$\Delta p = p_d - p_F,$$

where:

p_d — pump discharge pressure, psi, and
p_F — load pressure, psi.

The only way to reduce energy losses in a system is to minimize opportunities for any flow rate, Q, to pass through a pressure differential, Δp, without doing work on the load. Since Q is determined by required load velocities, (see Chapters 4 and 5) the designer can do little to change flow rate, Q. The remaining possibility is to minimize pressure drops.

Two fundamental rules of fluid mechanics govern

114

undesirable pressure drops as a function of fluid flow rate:

1. The orifice equation:

$$Q = C_d A_o \sqrt{2g\Delta p/\gamma}, \qquad (15.1)$$

in which two factors are important:

- $\Delta p \propto Q^2$, which provides the square or square root relationship governing all turbulent flow devices, and
- $Q \propto A_o$, which states that for a given differential pressure, Δp, flow rate is proportional to the cross sectional area of the flow path.

These two relationships are the only ones the system designer can use to reduce pressure drop in a hydraulic circuit. Either he must reduce the flow rate through the orifice or increase the size of the orifice.

2. The Darcy-Weisbach equation:

$$h = f(L/D)(v^2/2g), \qquad (15.2)$$

where:

h — head loss (which can be convected to $\Delta p = \gamma h$

f — an empirical friction factor; refer Moody diagram, Appendix D.

L — length of flow path

D — diameter of flow path

$v^2/2g$ — velocity head, v being the average flow velocity and equal to Q/A.

The Darcy-Weisbach equation is used to estimate head losses in conductors where length L substantially exceeds diameter D. In fluid power technology, the rule of thumb is to keep flow velocities in the *supply* line between 15 and 25 fps; in the *inlet* line at a maximum of 5 fps with petroleum oils and 2.5 fps with fire resistant fluids.

When using the technique shown in Figure 15.1(c) to estimate pressure losses in a system, it is imperative that the velocity head be calculated for the *actual* cross sectional area, A_o, for *each* circuit element. Use of nominal sizes will introduce substantial errors. Here is the procedure to follow:

1. Analyze the circuit diagram accurately to identify *all* flow elements in series in the circuit or branch.

2. Remember that flow elements include:

- all fittings, such as elbows, tees, couplings, etc.
- *entrance* and *exit* ports for all major components, such as pumps, motors, valves, cylinders, filters, manifold blocks, etc. These components appear "like fittings" to the fluid and have characteristic K constants.
- pipe, use actual — not nominal — ID sizes for American Standard pipe corresponding to schedule numbers, (see Chapter 25).
- hydraulic tubing, and
- hose, etc.

3. Construct a series element diagram, representing each element with an orifice symbol as shown in Figure 15.1(c).

4. Write the appropriate expression for head/pressure loss opposite each element.

5. Find the appropriate K factor or the friction factor on the Moody diagram. Note that the f factor is plotted as a function of the Reynolds Number, which takes into account fluid viscosity. Typically, there would be a different friction factor for each type conductor.

6. Calculate velocity head, $v^2/2g$, for the flow velocity associated with each flow element; g is the acceleration due to gravity.

7. Substitute numerical values of K, $v^2/2g$, f, L, and D into Equation 15.2 and calculate the estimated head loss, h, for each.

8. Sum all head losses and convert to pressure drop, if required.

9. Note that this method is based on $Q = K$, as in a constant flow system. Variable flow rates require a number of iterations from which a curve relating Δp to Q can be plotted, or a computer solution can be used.

While the above method is detailed, it actually is not as laborious as it might appear. If energy conservation is the way of the future, designers will have to pay attention to the all-too-long-ignored elements.

Demand flow systems

In Chapter 7, we defined *demand flow* systems as those which use fluid sources which are responsive to the spontaneous flow rate demand of output devices and use closed-center directional control valves. Examples of fluid sources are:

- accumulators, charged by fixed-displacement pumps which are bypassed through an unloading valve during standby periods, or
- pressure-compensated variable-displacement pumps which deadhead during standby or overload conditions.

The concepts for energy conservation previously discussed for *constant flow* systems apply *equally* to *demand flow* systems. The difficulty arises in providing a simple representation like that in Figure 15.1 because Δp vs. Q characteristics change constantly.

Component sizing for a *demand flow* system should be made at maximum flow rates. The circuit designer may treat it as a constant flow system, with $Q_c = Q_{max}$ for sizing purposes, knowing that energy losses will be smaller for lower flow rates. If peak flow demand is of short duration, it may be more economical to size for lower flows.

Rethink the circuit

Some system designers tend to follow a "cookbook" approach based on examples of existing circuits, as illustrated in Chapters 9, 11, 13 and 14. The danger is that these so called "typical" circuits may not properly match the requirements of the application cycle profile. Damaging inefficiencies can result. A hot-running system is the common consequence of circuit-to-load mismatches.

If analysis of the application indicates widely varying loads, the designer should be alert to watch for excessive inefficiencies. Within the framework of the techniques discussed in Chapters 3, 4, and 5, the design sequence can be summarized as follows:

1. Perform the load analysis 2. Produce the cycle profile of the application	**LOAD ORIENTED.** Not discretionary — depends on machine cycle
3. Select *design* pressure 4. From force/torque profiles, size cylinder or motor 5. From velocity profile, calculate flow rates using calculated cylinder and/or motor sizes	**HYDRAULIC CIRCUIT ORIENTED.** It is here that the designer can control circuit parameters which affect efficiency. Discretionary
6. Calculate power profile based on $P = K(Qp)/e_{so}$; where e_{so} is system overall efficiency	**POWER CYCLE.** Not discretionary, depends on flow rate and pressure.

Clearly, selection of system *design pressure P_d* is of prime importance because it virtually predetermines all other circuit design parameters.

Note: *design pressure* differs from component *rated pressure*. Design pressure is the acceptable pressure at the actuator corresponding to the maximum load reaction, and would correspond to p_F in the diagram in Figure 15.1. To this value must be added the sum of the losses Δp_s around the complete circuit which corresponds to the summation of differential pressure losses ($\Sigma \Delta p$ losses) shown in Figure 15.1.

When selecting a component for a system (refer to Chapters 23, 24, and 25), rated pressure p_R, must be equal to or greater than design pressure p_d. The final decision is whether to use continuous rated pressure p_{Rc} or intermittent rated pressure, p_{Ri}. The decision will depend on the nature of the load, *i.e.*, whether it is steady, rapidly changing, high shock, etc.

Generally, the only discretionary decision left to the hydraulic system designer is the selection of system design pressure. Virtually, all other design decisions are compromises in the attempt to optimize dependent variables. If the circuit designer is also the machine designer, or has inputs into the machine cycle design, he may have an opportunity to manipulate machine functions which yield a hydraulic system profile which will optimize energy efficiency.

For example, it may be possible to modify a machine cycle so that high velocities (which need higher *flow rates*) do not occur simultaneously with high load reactions (which need high *pressures*). Many machine performance specifications are arbitrary and may not be necessary.

Values for machine parameters are frequently "picked out of thin air" and can totally distort hydraulic circuit requirements. The cycle profile plotting technique helps emphasize these distortions, and define legitimate machine functions.

What to look for

Here are warning signs the system designer should be alert to:

1. *Excessive flow rates* caused by
● excessive velocities or speeds related to unrealistic (or unnecessarily fast) time cycles. (Refer to Chapter 5).
● oversized cylinders or motors due to low *design pressure* selected.

2. *Excessive pressures* caused by
● undersized cylinders or motors for the machine's load reactions
● failure to account for loads caused by inertia which occur during changes in velocity. (Refer to Chapters 3, 4, and 5).
● failure to adequately account for friction in hydraulic output devices and in machine loads
● intermittent shock loading as a function of machine cycle.

3. *Incompatibilities between circuit branch requirements*
● flow rate matching problems with branches con-

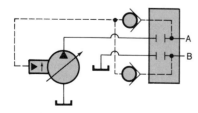

Fig. 15.2. ISO representation for pressure-sensing pump controls.

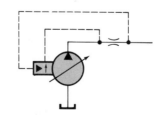

Fig. 15.3. ISO representation for pressure- and flow-sensing pump controls.

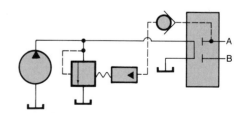

Fig. 15.4. ISO representation for valve controls.

nected in parallel, (see Figure 3.7)
• branch pressure variations caused by non-uniform loading and/or different size output devices to match available flow rate to velocity requirements
• pressure variations caused by use of flow or pressure control valves in circuit branches, especially in meter-out or counterbalance modes
• load changes from resistive (Chapter 4) to overrunning (Chapter 5) during work cycle.

Load sensing systems

A special class of hydraulic systems has evolved to improve the efficiency of transmitting power from the prime mover to the load. They are called **load sensing** systems.

There are two basic methods of sensing load: with pump controls and valve controls. Most commercial load-sensing systems use pump controls. The control signal cometimes consists of only a load pressure signal, but often the load-pressure signal is combined with a flow signal.

Load-sensing pump-control systems resemble those used in pressure-compensated pumps with one significant difference. Control pressures for pressure-compensated pumps are sensed *inside* the pump and reflect *all* system pressure variations.

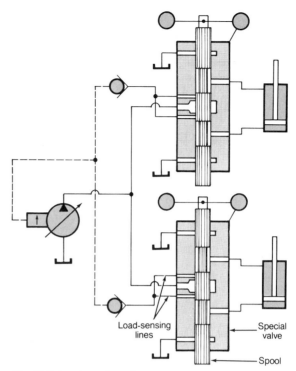

Fig. 15.6. Load-sensing valve arrangement.

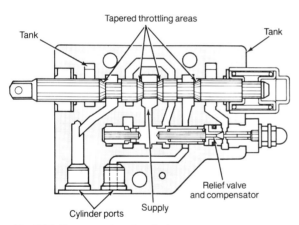

Fig. 15.5. Cross section of typical pressure-compensated directional control valve.

Control pressures for load-sensing systems are sensed *close to* the load, reflecting only variations in that *specific load*. These load pressures are usually sensed at the motor port of the directional control valve or at a motor or actuator inlet port, Figure 15.2. Differential pressures reflecting flow are usually measured in the pump or in the control valve, Figure 15.3. (Refer also to Figure 7.10).

In load-sensing valve-control systems, sensed pressure is used to adjust the setting of a control valve. Most valve-control systems use the pressure signal to adjust the relief-valve setting, but it would be possible to apply the technique to flow control, as is done in pressure-compensated directional-control valves, Figure 15.4.

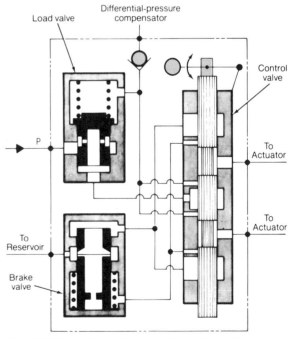

Fig. 15.7. Prepackaged load sensing unit combines load-sensing directional control valve, brake valve, and load valve.

Difference between valves

There is a fundamental difference between load-sensing and pressure-compensated directional control valves. Load-sensing valves are used for external pilot control, so *piloting is external* and has no direct effect on the valves themselves. Instead, the external

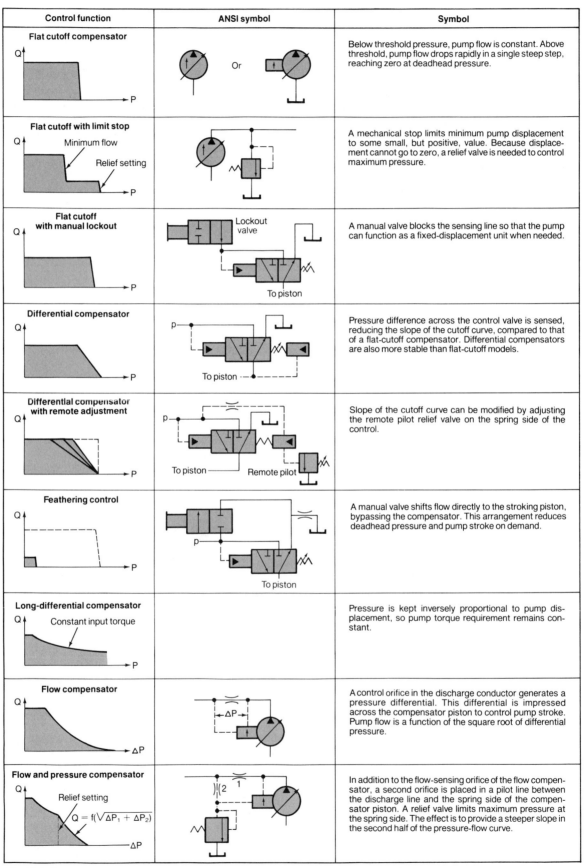

Control function	ANSI symbol	Symbol
Flat cutoff compensator	Or	Below threshold pressure, pump flow is constant. Above threshold, pump flow drops rapidly in a single steep step, reaching zero at deadhead pressure.
Flat cutoff with limit stop (Minimum flow, Relief setting)		A mechanical stop limits minimum pump displacement to some small, but positive, value. Because displacement cannot go to zero, a relief valve is needed to control maximum pressure.
Flat cutoff with manual lockout (Lockout valve, To piston)		A manual valve blocks the sensing line so that the pump can function as a fixed-displacement unit when needed.
Differential compensator (To piston)		Pressure difference across the control valve is sensed, reducing the slope of the cutoff curve, compared to that of a flat-cutoff compensator. Differential compensators are also more stable than flat-cutoff models.
Differential compensator with remote adjustment (To piston, Remote pilot)		Slope of the cutoff curve can be modified by adjusting the remote pilot relief valve on the spring side of the control.
Feathering control (To piston)		A manual valve shifts flow directly to the stroking piston, bypassing the compensator. This arrangement reduces deadhead pressure and pump stroke on demand.
Long-differential compensator (Constant input torque)		Pressure is kept inversely proportional to pump displacement, so pump torque requirement remains constant.
Flow compensator (ΔP)		A control orifice in the discharge conductor generates a pressure differential. This differential is impressed across the compensator piston to control pump stroke. Pump flow is a function of the square root of differential pressure.
Flow and pressure compensator (Relief setting, $Q = f(\sqrt{\Delta P_1 + \Delta P_2})$)		In addition to the flow-sensing orifice of the flow compensator, a second orifice is placed in a pilot line between the discharge line and the spring side of the compensator piston. A relief valve limits maximum pressure at the spring side. The effect is to provide a steeper slope in the second half of the pressure-flow curve.

Fig. 15.8. Summary of controls for pressure-compensated pumps.

pilot control sends load signals to the pump or valve control.

On the other hand, pressure-compensated valves are self-contained; *piloting is internal*, helping to reduce flow forces acting on the spool, Figure 15.5.

Shifting the spool of a load-sensing valve opens the correct sensing passage, simultaneously blocking the other, as system flow is directed to the proper actuator port, Figure 15.6. Load-sensing pilot lines can be connected directly to a compensator, but most commonly are connected to other controls within a packaged control unit.

One common packaged unit, Figure 15.7, combines a load-sensing directional-control valve with a brake valve and a load valve. The brake valve accommodates overrunning loads, while the load valve provides improved metering characteristics and isolation for simultaneous operation of multiple branched circuits.

In a pressure-compensated directional-control valve, the spool-land orifice is used as a control orifice in series with the pressure-compensated variable orifice. This confines the major portion or the pressure differential across the valve to the compensator, and keeps fluid pressure differential across the spool low, resulting in low shifting forces. Depending on the application, the metering orifice can be formed with tapered throttling areas on the spool, as shown in Figure 15.7, tapered grooves in the spool, or semicircular orifices in combination with tapered lands in the valve body.

Here are some functional combinations for pressure-compensated load-sensing valves:

1. Inlet compensated, load sensing with or without return flow — regeneration capability.

2. Outlet compensation (brake valve) with or without flow regeneration.

3. Variations on inlet or outlet compensators to allow straight load-pressure sensing, differential-pressure sensing, etc.

The second major component used in load-sensing systems is the pressure-compensated, variable-displacement pump. Chapter 7 briefly considered the simplest form of pressure-compensated pumps. Figure 15.8 summarizes other types of pressure-compensated pump controls which offer versatility in matching pumps to energy conservation systems.

More complex

Here are some illustrations which show increasing complexities of control hardware as designers require more sophisticated controls and the correlation of power relationships for pumps equipped with these controls.

Figure 15.9 illustrates proportional, pressure-compensated pump controls. Figure 15.9(*b*) shows the reduction in power loss over a fixed-displacement pump. Note, however, that the prime mover must still be able to provide required corner horsepower.

If the pump supplies fluid to more than one load, a throttling device, such as a flow-control valve or a pressure-reducing valve, is typically installed between the pump and one or more of the loads. The power loss occurs at these throttling devices.

Performance characteristics of the proportional pressure compensator control can be improved with a two-stage, or pilot-operated, compensator, Figure 15.10(*a*).

Here, pilot fluid at load pressure is admitted to one end of the main-stage spool. Fluid flows through a small orifice in the spool, creating a relatively small pressure drop. The resulting force is opposed by a spring. Pilot flow then returns to reservoir through a small relief valve.

The relief-valve setting determines maximum pump pressure. In this design, Figure 15.10(*b*) the main spool starts opening earlier in response to a sudden decrease in flow demand. This anticipation results in less pressure overshoot than typically produced by a single-stage compensator control.

To obtain better dynamic-performance characteristics, the control piston of the single-stage propor-

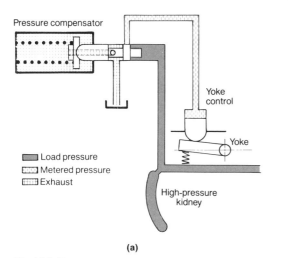

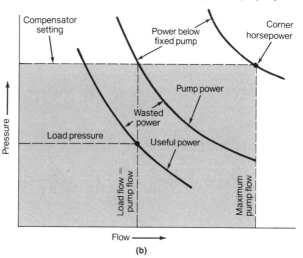

Fig. 15.9. Pump proportional, pressure compensator, (a), provides least complex controls; (b) performance characteristics.

119

tional compensator is supplemented with a bias-control piston.

Load sensing, or power matching, control can be provided by a relatively simple variation of the single-stage proportional pressure compensator, Figure 15.11(a). Here, the spring chamber is connected to the downstream side of a variable orifice. When the pressure drop across the orifice matches the spring setting, the spool achieves equilibrium. If the circuit is arranged so the variable orifice is a manually operated valve, the result is a load-matched flow-control arrangement.

When the valve opens, flow increases proportionately because the pressure drop is constant across the orifice, which keeps increasing in size. The flow is at a pressure only slightly above load pressure; wasted power is very low, Figure 15.11(b).

However, if load flow drops to zero, as when an actuator reaches the end of its stroke, for example, the pressure drop across the orifice also drops to zero. Then, the spring drives the spool to vent the control piston to reservoir, and the pump is stroked to full displacement. Thus, a relief valve must be included to protect the pump. In this design, full pump output returns to reservoir over the relief valve and the prime mover is loaded to corner horsepower.

The undesirable waste of power over a relief valve in a load-sensing system can be avoided by adding a pressure-limiting control. With this combination, Figure 15.12(a), the load-sensing portion controls the pump until load pressure reaches that of the compensator setting. Then the pressure-limiting portion overrides the load-sensing portion and destrokes the pump. Even with this arrangement, the prime mover must be able to provide corner horsepower, Figure 15.12(b).

A two-stage pressure-compensator control, Figure 15.13, can be combined with the load-sensing control to reduce pressure overshoot, just as with the two-stage pressure compensator alone.

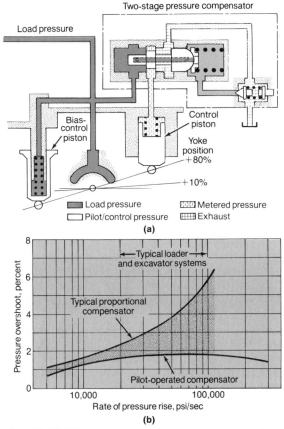

Fig. 15.10. Pilot-operated pump compensator (a) reduces overshoot in pump output pressure. Curves (b) compare performance with that of typical single stage compensator.

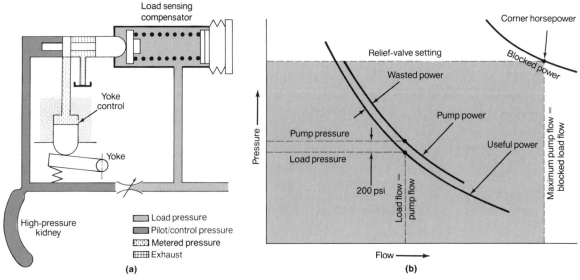

Fig. 15.11. Pressure drop across variable orifice, a) combines with control spring preload to provide load sensing control arrangement; b) performance characteristics for normally operating system.

Bypassing corner horsepower

The corner horsepower requirement can be avoided with the design in Figure 15.14. Here, a feedback spool, positioned by the movement of a bias-control piston, meters a portion of the output pressure fluid to provide a feedback signal which, in turn, provides an additional input to control the pressure-compensator spool.

At low pump displacement, feedback pressure is only a fraction of pump discharge pressure because of the long path to the feedback pressure passage. As pump stroke increases, feedback pressure becomes a larger percentage of pump discharge pressure. Because the feedback is a function of pump discharge pressure and pump displacement, the signal becomes a function of pump torque. Thus, the control is torque limiting. The pressure-flow characteristics are shown in Figure 15.14(b).

This arrangement permits the user to derive maximum performance from the prime mover. At low load levels, the control provides high pump displace-

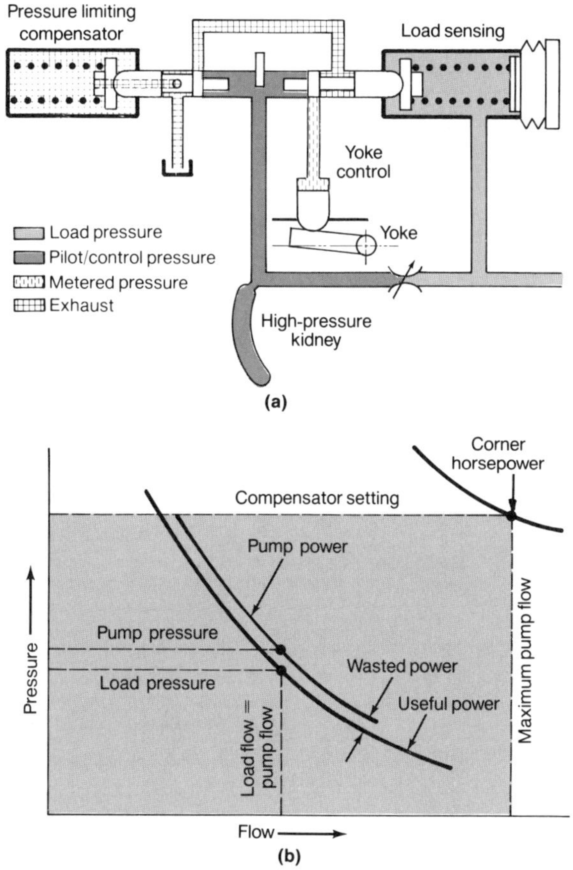

Fig. 15.12. Pressure-limiting control plus load-sensing control (a) avoids power waste over relief valve when load flow drops to zero. Curves (b) show maximum pump flow controlled by pressure limiting pump control.

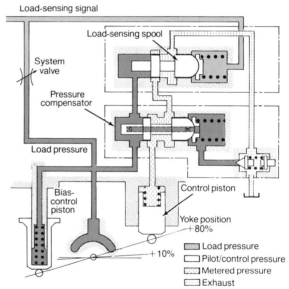

Fig. 15.13. Pilot-operated compensator reduces pressure overshoot when combined with load-sensing control.

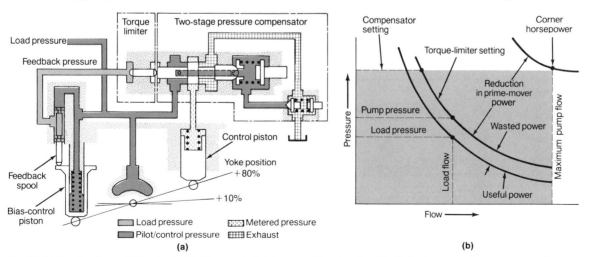

Fig. 15.14. Feedback spool (a) actuated by bias-control piston, provides signal which eliminates corner horsepower requirements; (b) shows effect of load pressure changes on torque load on prime mover.

ment and, therefore, high load speeds. Conversely, at heavy loads, maximum speed decreases, preventing the prime-mover from stalling.

This torque-limiting feature can also be added to the load-sensing/pressure-limiting control arrangement previously described.

If two or more pumps are driven by the same prime mover, a torque summer, Figure 15.15 can be added to accept a feedback pressure signal from the second pump. In this arrangement, the second pump has first call on engine output, and will destroke the first pump to prevent prime-mover overload.

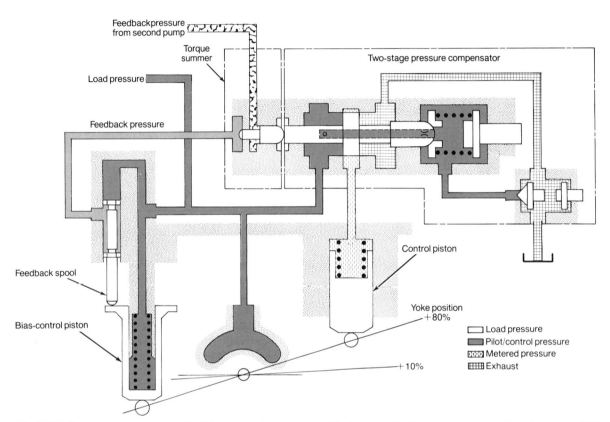

Fig. 15.15. Torque summer accepts signal from second pump to provide dual control when two pumps are driven by same prime mover.

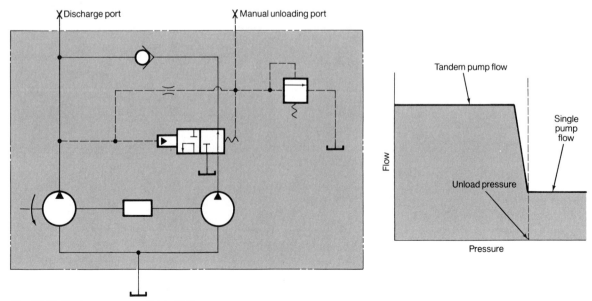

Fig. 15.16. Basic power summing system.

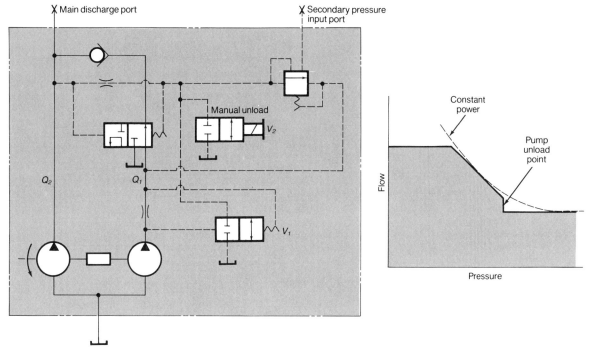

Fig. 15.17. Constant power summing system.

Power summation for fixed-displacement pumps

In addition to energy saving circuits using pressure compensated pumps, successful systems have also been designed for fixed displacement pumps. Systems designed around fixed-displacement pumps take a different approach than those designed with variable-displacement pumps. The basic idea is to package two fixed-displacement pumps with an unloading-valve subsystem to limit hydraulic power, and thus the power demand on the prime mover.

At pressures below the setting of the unloading-valve, both pumps deliver fluid to the system. At pressures above the setting of the unloading-valve, flow from one pump returns to tank, while flow from the other delivers fluid to the system. The result is a **step** change in flow, rather than the continuous variations available from variable-displacement pumps, Figure 15.16.

However, this method can also be used to approximate the constant-power characteristics of variable-displacement systems. An orifice in the output line of one of the pumps monitors pump flow. As long as flow Q_1, Figure 15.17, is low enough, valve V_1, remains closed and system pressure is controlled by the main unloading valve, as in the simple system described above.

When flow Q_1 rises, generating a larger pressure drop across the orifice, valve V_1 opens, bypassing the pilot system and shifting the main unloading valve to unload the second pump. A secondary relief valve, keeps pressure in the pilot system low, so the un-loading valve cannot close again at high system pressure and high prime-mover speed.

Summary

In review, here is how load-sensing hydraulics can help save energy.

The big advantage of load-sensing hydraulic systems is that they supply only slightly more flow and pressure than required to move the load. Accordingly, these systems save large amounts of power compared to conventional constant flow and demand flow hydraulic systems. For example, consider a circuit in which 10 gpm and system pressure of 1500 psi are needed to extend a cylinder at a metered flow rate. Other elements in the same circuit may require flows to 30 gpm at pressures to 2500 psi, but not at the same time as the cylinder.

A constant flow circuit, Figure 15.18(a), must have a fixed-displacement pump capable of delivering 30 gpm, with relief valves set at 2500 psi. Because circuit pressure is determined by load resistance, the pump drives the cylinder at 1500 psi. The energy not required by the actuator is wasted, as shown by the cross-hatched area.

When no flow is required, a constant flow circuit delivers full flow at low pressure — the backpressure through the lines and across the spool of the control valve. The pump wears, full flow passes through filters and heat exchangers, and considerable energy is lost.

A demand flow circuit, Figure 15.18(b), must have a pressure-compensated variable-displacement

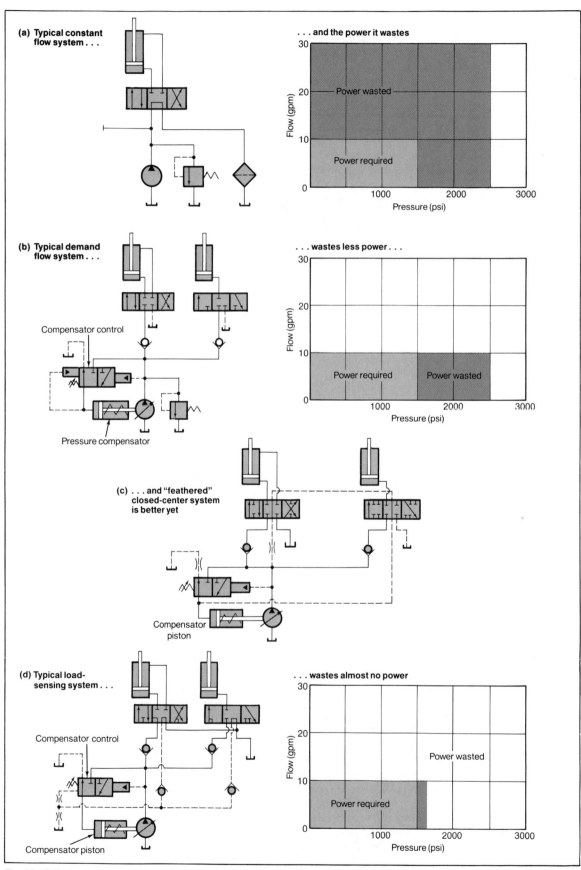

Fig. 15.18. Typical hydraulic systems: (a) open center; (b) closed center; (c) feathered closed center and (d) load sensing.

124

System type	Metering capability					Power utilization				
	Cost	Pump life	Max load	Min load	Standby no demand	100% pressure 100% flow	100% pressure no flow	25% pressure 75% flow	75% pressure 75% flow	25% pressure 25% flow
Open center	Low	Low	Poor	Poor	Fair	Good	Very poor	Good	Fair	Poor
Constant pressure closed center	Medium	Moderate	Good	Poor	Fair	Good	Good	Poor	Fair	Fair
Feathered closed center	Higher	Long	Good	Poor	Good	Good	Good	Poor	Fair	Fair
Load sensing closed center	Highest	Extra long	Good	Good	Good	Good	Good	Good	Good	Good

Fig. 15.19. Comparison of load sensing systems with other hydraulic systems.

pump capable of delivering 30 gpm, with the compensator set to destroke the pump at 2500 psi. Since the pump provides only the 10 gpm metered into the cylinder, waste is substantially less than with the open center circuit.

When no flow is needed, demand flow circuits deliver just enough fluid to make up internal leakage. Flow losses are small, but the pump operates at full pressure. Extended intervals in this mode can cause localized fluid heating near the pump. Even though flow is small, energy loss in this mode is significant, since the pump operates at full pressure.

A load sensing circuit, Figure 15.18(d), provides only the flow and pressure required to meet load requirements. Almost no energy is wasted. The contrast is equally striking in a no-flow situation, when energy losses in conventional systems can be significant. When the actuator requires no flow, the main control valve is centered in neutral or "null" position.

Load sensing circuits deliver low flow at low pressure, resulting in minimum pump wear, flow losses, and energy losses. Only the "feathered" type of demand flow circuit, Figure 15.18(c), can approach the efficiency of a load sensing circuit and reduce pump wear and energy loss in the no flow mode. The chart, Figure 15.19 compares the performances of these circuits.

Important Terms

Corner horsepower is the horsepower calculated by multiplying maximum flow rate by maximum system pressure.

Flow regeneration is the technique of by-passing return flow from an actuator return port to its inlet port without going through the entire circuit.

Load sensing directional control valve is one in which internal passages connect to load ports in the valve so load pressures can be sensed.

Load sensing systems are hydraulic systems which automatically adjust to changes in load pressure to improve efficiency in energy transmission.

Pressure compensated directional control valve: See Chapter 12.

Pressure and flow sensing systems use pressure sensing pumps with the addition of a flow-sensing orifice in the discharge line to the system.

Pressure sensing systems use pressure compensated pumps when the pressure signal comes from the load port in the directional control valve.

Valve control load sensing systems use the load pressure pilot signal to adjust the setting of a control valve.

Much of the material in this Chapter is based on information supplied by Mr. Howard Sculthorpe, Sperry Vickers.

Review Exercises

15.1. Why is energy saving in hydraulic circuits of increasing importance?

15.2. What two variables are involved in energy transmission in a hydraulic system?

15.3. Which depends upon load reaction?

15.4. Which is related to load speed?

15.5. Of the two variables mentioned in review exercise 15.2, which is related to the principle losses in a system? Why?

15.6. What basic condition is necessary in a hydraulic system to cause significant energy losses? Discuss.

15.7. Discuss the statement: "The fact that a hydraulic system is operating at normal temperature does not mean it is also operating at optimum efficiency."

15.8. What factors, in addition to those discussed in review exercise 15.2, contribute to energy losses in a hydraulic system?

15.9. Referring to Figure 15.1: discuss the implications of the diagram in Figure 15(b) for evaluating energy losses in the hydraulic circuit of Figure 15(a).

15.10. In Figure 15.1(b), why are there two components of Δp across the directional control valve?

15.11. What would the effect be on the Δp diagram

of Figure 15.1(b), if the directional control valve spool were "feathered" as in a proportional valve?

15.12. Referring to Figure 15.1(c): What is the principle advantage to the technique shown for estimating flow losses in the circuit?

15.13. What two rules of fluid mechanics apply to calculating estimated Δp losses in a hydraulic system?

15.14. Given a flow rate of 50 gpm of mineral oil at 125 F through a ¾-in tee, calculate the estimated loss through the tee. What are the units of this loss as calculated?

15.15. Given the flow rate of review exercise 15.14, there are 50 ft. of ¾-in OD tubing connected on each side of the tee. Calculate the estimated Δp in the tubing.

15.16. Referring to problem 15.15: Recalculate the loss if ¾-in × schedule 40-pipe had been used instead of tubing.

15.17. Referring to Figure 15.1(a): What effect would by-passing part of the flow across the relief valve while operating in its cracking band (refer to Chapter 8) have on energy loss in the circuit? What corollary effect would this have on load velocity?

15.18. Given the circuit of Figure 15.1: What would be the effect on energy losses of inserting a pressure reducing valve (refer to Chapter 8) between the relief valve and the directional control valve?

15.19. In review exercise 15.18, what would be the effect if the reducing valve were placed between the directional control valve and the cylinder cap end port?

15.20. All controls consume energy in the normal performance of their function. True or False? Discuss.

15.21. All controls exhibiting the same Δp for a given flow rate, regardless of function, will have the same energy loss. True or False? Discuss.

15.22. Construct a qualitative diagram similar to Figure 15.1, for a demand flow circuit such as illustrated in Figure 7.3 and plotted in Figure 7.7.

15.23. Under what conditions might components in a circuit be sized for some flow rate other than maximum?

15.24. Discuss the statement that "a circuit designer can only exercise discretionary control over circuit parameters in the area of design pressure selection."

15.25. Discuss the difference between design pressure, rated pressure, and load pressure. Where do prime losses in a system fit into this picture?

15.26. How does selection of design pressure work to establish flow rate?

15.27. Discuss how machine cycle parameters can be varied to improve hydraulic system efficiency.

15.28. Circuit designers often get "into more trouble" by ignoring inertia loads during acceleration and deceleration periods than for any other reason. Discuss how this relates to energy saving practices.

15.29. Discuss factors which contribute to excessive pressures in a hydraulic system.

15.30. Define a *load sensing* system. What is the primary purpose of these systems?

15.31. What three classes of load sensing systems are there?

15.32. Discuss the differences between pressure-compensated directional control valves and load-sensing directional control valves. Is it possible for a directional control valve to be both pressure-compensated and load-sensing?

15.33. What effect does the addition of flow-sensing have on energy saving?

15.34. Discuss the differences between load-sensing pump control and valve control systems.

15.35. Compare the types of compensator controls for variable-displacement pumps summarized in Figure 15.8 as to energy saving capabilities and applications considerations.

15.36. Referring to Figure 15.9: To which type of control discussed in review exercise 15.35 does this compare? Discuss the "control power" shown in Figure 15.9(b).

15.37. Discuss the difference between performance of a straight proportional-type pressure-compensator and a pilot-operated compensator.

15.38. Why is a bias-control piston used in a single-stage compensator as shown in Figure 15.10?

15.39. Discuss how the addition of *flow-sensing* reduces energy waste in a system as shown in Figure 15.11.

15.40. Referring to Figure 15.11: Discuss the *flow-sensing* technique as it relates to a load-sensing directional control valve in the system.

15.41. Why must a relief valve be included in the system of Figure 15.11?

15.42. How does a *pressure-limiting* control avoid the problem discussed in review exercise 15.41?

15.43. Discuss the advantage of the two-stage pressure compensator shown in Figure 15.13 over single-stage compensators. What effect does adding load sensing have on wasted energy?

15.44. Referring to Figure 15.14: What is the effect of adding the *torque limiter* to the compensator control? Where does the feedback pressure come from?

15.45. In Figure 15.14, why is there a difference between load pressure and pump pressure? Is this true of all controls? Explain.

15.46. What factors contribute to the feedback pressure of Figure 15.14? Why is the signal proportional to pump input torque? How does this relate to prime mover requirements?

15.47. Referring to Figure 15.15: Discuss the effect of adding a pressure-feedback signal from a second pump. Under what conditions would this type of control be required?

15.48. Is it possible to achieve energy saving in circuits using fixed-displacement pumps?

15.49. Discuss the energy saving implications of the unloading circuit shown in Figure 15.16. What kind of flow change is used?

15.50. Referring to Figure 15.17: Discuss how the addition of a flow-sensing orifice in the discharge line of one pump changes flow control from step-variable to an approximation of proportional control.

15.51. At what cost in energy loss is the function of example 15.50 achieved? How does this compare with the power curves shown in Figure 15.12(b)?

15.52. Referring to Figure 15.18(a): Discuss the relationship between total input power, load power, and wasted power shown for the constant-flow system. Where in the system is the wasted power dissipated?

15.53. Referring to Figure 15.18(b): Explain why the power wasted in the demand-flow system is so much less than with the constant-flow system. Why would energy wasted be less for the feathered demand flow system?

15.54. Referring to Figure 15.18(c): Where does the small amount of power wasted go in the load-sensing system illustrated?

15.55. Which hardware costs are likely to be higher: those for a constant-flow system, those for a demand-flow system, or those for a load-sensing system? What economic justification is necessary for selecting one over the other for a given application?

CHAPTER 16
HYDROSTATIC TRANSMISSIONS

A hydrostatic transmission (HST) is a special case of energy transmission systems, (ETS) described in Figure 1.2. An HST consists of a rotary drive wherein the hydraulic energy input element is a pump and the output element a fluid motor. HST pumps and motors are designed and matched to optimize energy transmission.

What HSTs can do

Hydrostatic transmission offer many important operating features
• remain stalled and undamaged under full load with low power loss
• hold a preset speed accurately against driving or braking loads
• operate efficiently over a wide range of torque/speed ratios
• operate in reverse at controlled speed, within design limits, unaffected by output loads
• transmit high power per cubic inch displacement

with low inertia
• not creep at zero speed
• provide faster response than any other type transmission
• provide dynamic braking

Figure 16.1 summarizes the four basic HST configurations. It conforms with the terminology used in Chapter 2 and international controls technology usage. Specifically, this chapter attempts to help eliminate the confusion resulting from the ambiguous usage of the terms *open loop* and *closed loop*.

The terms **open circuit** and **closed circuit** describe how the hydraulic lines in the conducting circuit are connected. Thus in an **open circuit**, the flow path of fluid is not continuous, being interrupted by the reservoir, see Chapter 25. In a **closed circuit**, the flow path *is* uninterrupted: the hydraulic fluid flows in a continuous, uninterrupted path from the pump discharge port to the fluid motor inlet port and directly back to the pump.

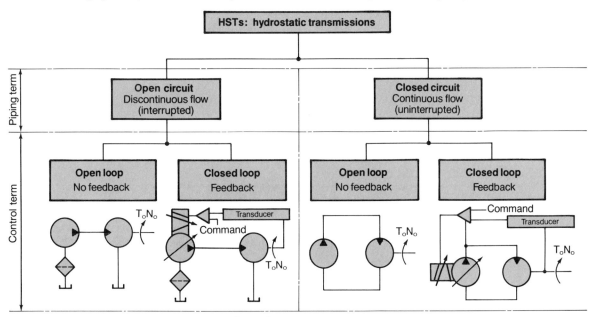

Fig. 16.1. Block diagram summarizes four basic HST configurations.

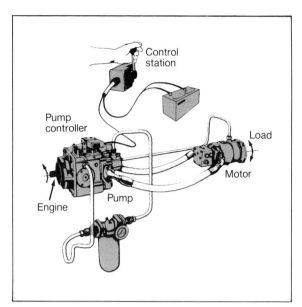

Fig. 16.2. In open loop, closed circuit hydrostatic control, simple connection of a potentiometer and battery to a hydraulic pump containing an electric controller gives remote velocity control for a hydraulic motor. Control is open-loop. If the engine slows, or if load builds, then the load velocity will change. Operator may "close the loop" by observing the output velocity and moving the control lever to compensate, but this is not automatic feedback control.

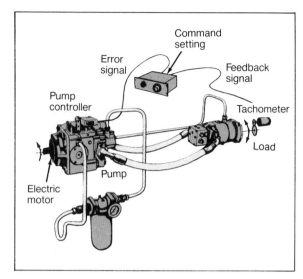

Fig. 16.3. In closed loop, closed circuit hydrostatic control, if a tachometer is attached to measure the speed of the hydraulic motor, then the tachometer signal can be fed back and compared with (subtracted from) the command signal. The resultant error signal is amplified and used to drive the pump controller. Best performance is achieved if the amplifier has integral control. In this case amplifier supplies a continuously increasing amount of current to the controller whenever a steady velocity error exists. This system is called a velocity servo.

Figure 16.2 shows a *closed circuit open loop* HST; Figure 16.3 shows a *closed circuit closed loop* HST.

Hydraulic technology has evolved from open circuit *constant flow* systems (refer to Chapter 6) to open circuit *demand flow* systems (refer to Chapter 7); and is now moving toward closed loop, electrohydraulic servo systems. Because HSTs have evolved as a definitive branch of fluid power technology, they first became commercially successful as *closed circuit* systems, followed by *open circuit* systems. The entire spectrum of HSTs shown in Figure 16.1 is now available commercially.

Why hydrostatic transmissions?

Reviewing Figures 1.1 and 1.2, we see that the primary job of any HST is to:
• accept energy input from a source, *i.e.* a prime mover with its own output characteristics
• transmit and modulate the energy within the ETS, and
• deliver an energy output to the load, which has its own set of characteristics, as defined by the cycle profile. Refer to Chapters 3, 4, and 5.

To fulfill its job, the ETS must have a set of characteristics which permits an optimum match

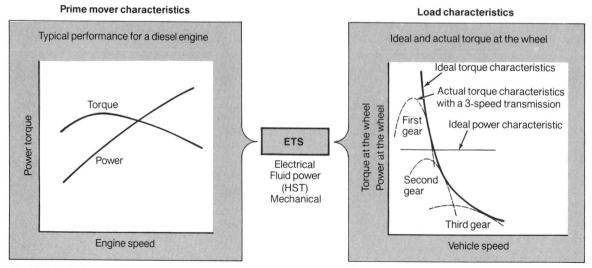

Fig. 16.4. Typical output characteristics for internal combustion engine and simple load.

130

between the prime mover and the load. Figure 16.4 illustrates a set of typical output characteristics for an internal combustion engine and a simple load.

The better the match between input and output characteristics, the more efficient the productive process. Ultimately, process efficiency in terms of either dollar-minutes per production unit or maximum production units per dollar become the only meaningful criteria for designing any system.

A comparison between a mechanical ETS, such as a 4-speed-gear box, and an ideal output torque curve which can be closely approximated by an HST is shown in Figure 16.5. The curves were plotted using dimensionless ratios. The dotted lines show the effect of power matching on gear shifting. The dotted lines become the actual torque-speed and power-speed characteristics during gear shifting.

Departure from the ideal curves is obvious. The effect on the production process is a series of interruptions in power flow between the prime mover and the load. In many applications, this translates into cyclic speed variations, which correspond to gear shift points.

A gear type transmission can provide ideal load torques at only four points over its speed range. However, an ideal ETS would deliver constant horsepower over full speed range; and torque which varies inversely with speed. Hydrostatic ETSs can be designed to approach these requirements. As this discussion on HSTs proceeds, remember that the primary difference between an HST and a hydraulic system equipped with hydraulic pumps and motors is that an HST is a whole unit in which pump and motor are specifically matched to work together. Also HST controls are designed to provide the functions which enable the transmission to perform specific tasks.

Pump/motor interaction

The most common way to characterize a fixed displacement pump is shown in Figure 16.6. Typically, we view this as a constant flow source where

$$Q_t = K = N_i V_p,$$

where:

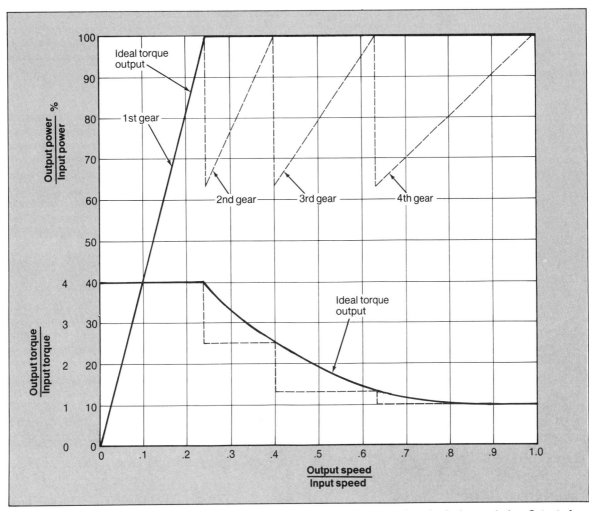

Fig. 16.5. Power and torque outputs drop sharply at each gear change in conventional mechanical transmission. Outputs from variable displacement hydrostatic transmissions closely follow ideal torque and power curves.

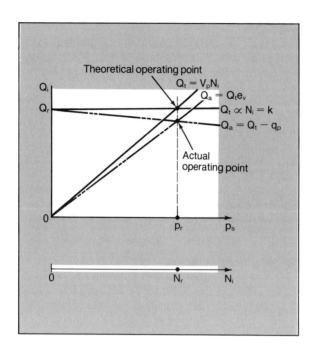

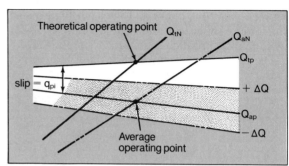

Fig. 16.7. Shaded area represents characteristic variances which can be expected because of manufacturing tolerances.

Fig. 16.6. Curves provide output vs speed characteristics of fixed displacement pump.

Q_t — theoretical output, gpm
K — constant
N_i — input speed, rpm
V_p — pump displacement

Characteristic flow as a function of system pressure is a straight line. The operating point at rated pressure, p_r, is also illustrated in Figure 16.6.

If we plot output, Q_t, as a function of input speed, N_i, the characteristic curve is a straight line starting at the origin and passing through the theoretical operating point when $N_i = N_r$ (rated speed). Unfortunately, sometimes, this is as far as designers pursue the selection process, often resulting in systems with mismatched components.

The next step is to account for internal leakage or slip flow q. Slip is a complex variable which depends on many parameters, but is principally related to discharge pressure, p_s, for a given pump. Actual delivery is

$$Q_a = Q_t - q_p$$

where:

Q_a — actual output, gpm
Q_t — theoretical output, gpm
q_p — pressure slip, gpm

and is generally determined by laboratory testing.

Component manufacturers frequently provide data on slip characteristics in the form of volumetric efficiency, usually given at rated pressure and speed. Another, and possibly a more accurate operating point or parameter, called *actual operating point*, which accounts for slip, is also illustrated in Figure 16.6.

Variable characteristics

Next, we consider the variance on the basic p_s vs Q_p or N_i vs Q_p characteristics which can be expected

in components because of variations in manufacturing tolerances. Figure 16.7 illustrates the area around the operating points of Figure 16.6. The flow characteristics labeled Q_{ap} is an average curve for the operating flow envelope,

$$Q_{ap} - \Delta Q_a < Q_{ap} + \Delta Q_a$$

In most applications this is a refinement hidden in the lumped parameters approach to selecting components. When an application requires precise speed control or speed matching, as when fluid motors must be synchronized (Chapter 12), the system designer must consider such variations carefully.

These design concepts can be applied to interpret pump/motor interactions in a hydraulic system. The simple circuit in Figure 1.4 illustrates this point in Figure 16.8.

During an initial approximation, we selected a hydraulic pump and motor for a hydraulic drive. Parameters were matched on the basis of *rated* values of pressure, flow rate as a function of rated speed, volumetric efficiency figures supplied by the manufacturers of components, etc. As may be inferred from the parameters of Figure 16.8, where precision and high performance are required, first level approximations are not fully satisfactory.

Referring to Figure 16.8, we note that:

1. It is assumed that input speed to the pump is constant, $N_i = K$. Otherwise, the result will be a change in slope of the speed related variables, but the general relationship will still hold true.

2. When $N_i = K$, theoretical output is

$$Q_t = K = N_i \times V_p$$

3. As pressure rises, pump slip increases $q_{e_1} = f(p_1)$, and actual output becomes $Q_{a_1} = Q_t - q_{e_1}$, see performance characteristics, Figure 16.8.

4. Pump output variables are:
$$p_1, Q_{a_1} = Q_t - Q_{e_1}$$
Losses in the conducting system and controls are shown simplified to
$$\Delta p'_x \text{ or } \Delta Q_x = \Sigma q_{e_2} + q_r.$$
If, in an actual application, such losses are negligible, they should be set equal to zero.

5. Motor input variables are shown as:

$$p_4 = p_1 + \Sigma \Delta p_{lm}$$

where:

p — load pressure
p_4 — inlet pressure to motor
p_1 — discharge pressure at pump

In the approximate method of component selection and application, designers often use $p_4 = p_1$. Such an assumption can introduce significant errors

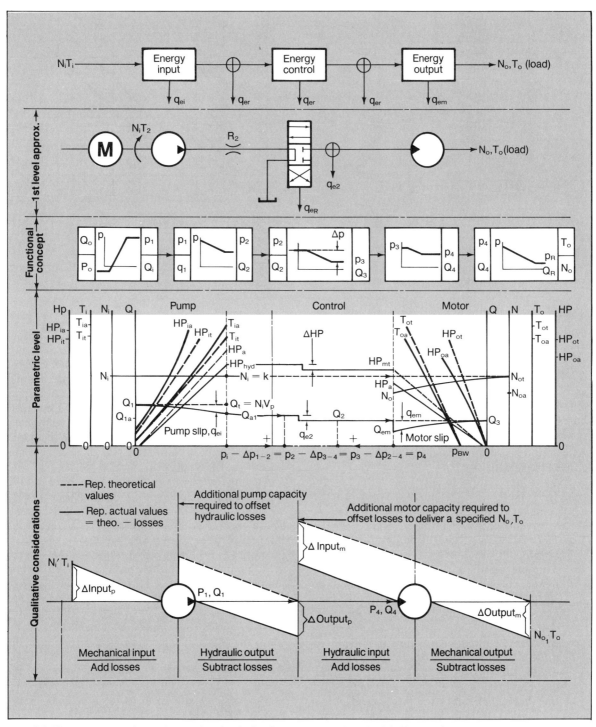

Fig. 16.8. Fluid power pump/motor interactions in a hydraulic system based on circuit in Figure 1.4.

133

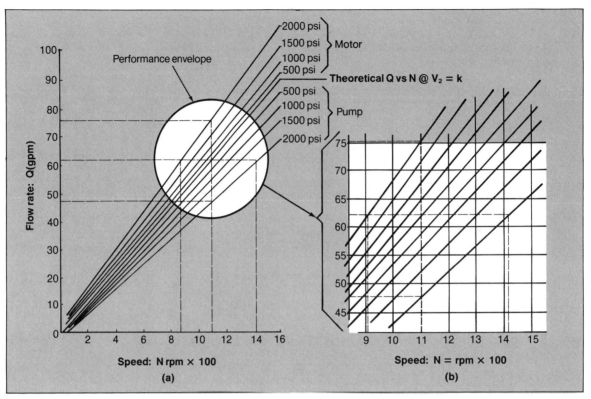

Fig. 16.9. Speed vs flow rate plots for a hydraulic pump and motor as illustrated in Figure 16.8. It is assumed that pump and motor have the same displacements so the I/O speed ratio is 1:1.

in the analysis of many hydraulic drive applications. And

$$Q_2 = Q_{a_1} - q_{e_2}$$

If Q_2 is used to calculate motor output speed, $N_0 = Q_2/V_m$, significant errors should be expected. Figure 16.8 shows that output speed is reduced as system pressure increases. Pump and motor slips combine to reduce the motor's effective input flow rate:

$$Q_{e_m} = Q_2 - (q_{e_p} + q_{e_m}).$$

As a result, speed droop could be double of that in either component alone.

6. Plots of input torque to pump and output torque from fluid motor as well as input and output horsepower emphasize another characteristic of these two classes of components.

   a. For input devices, such as pumps, *losses must be added* to the theoretical values of mechanical input variables, such as torque and horsepower, to obtain required values. However, *losses must be subtracted* from theoretical values of hydraulic output variables to obtain actual values.

   b. For output devices, such as fluid motors, *losses must be added* to the theoretical values of hydraulic input variables to obtain required values. However, *losses must be subtracted* from the theoretical values for mechanical output variables to get actual values for load parameters. Figure 16.8 summarizes these concepts.

Application example

Figure 16.9 illustrates the practical implications of the above discussion. It shows speed vs flow rate plots for a hydraulic pump and motor such as those represented in Figure 16.8. To simplify interactions, it is assumed that both components have the same displacement and the input-output (I/O) speed ratio is 1:1. The effects of pressure are introduced by using families of Q vs N curves for varying load pressures. Pump and motor characteristics share a common boundry at the theoretical curve.

Assume, for example, that desired speed is 1100 rpm. We find this value on the X-axis and read vertically (dotted line) until we intersect the appropriate theoretical flow rate curve (diagonal solid line), at 62 gpm. For an I/O speed ratio of 1:1, we theoretically need a pump which can deliver 62 gpm at an input speed of 1100 rpm. Also, we need a fluid motor with an output of 1100 rpm. Frequently, and unfortunately, this is as far as the selection process proceeds.

Now, consider the family of curves which represents the effect of changing system pressures on pump performance. These curves lie *below* the theoretical line, Figure 16.8. As output pressure at the pump *increases* to 2000 psi, Figure 16.9, note that pump output Q_1 *decreases* to 48 gpm. Thus, it supplies 22.5% *less* than needed.

A similar analysis of the fluid motor curves shows

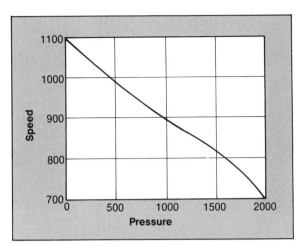

Fig. 16.10. Net effect of pump/motor interaction. Output speed N_0 is plotted as a function of load pressure.

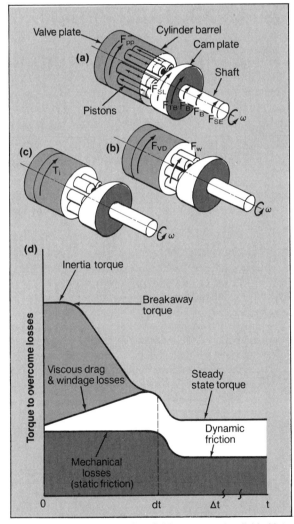

Fig. 16.11. Internal losses in a fluid motor can be divided into three components: (a) those related to Coulomb friction (that which occurs between dry surfaces); (b) those generated by viscous drag, also called windage losses; and (c) inertia which is not strictly a loss, but acts like one during breakaway and acceleration; (d) time period to breakaway and acceleration to steady state velocity.

that as load pressure increases to 2000 psi, input flow to motor, Q_4, would have to increase to 75 gpm to maintain the required, 1100-rpm output speed, an increase of 20.9%.

Assume we normalize the analysis to $Q = 62$ gpm $= K$. Looking at the pump curves, we see that to maintain anoutput of 62 gpm, pump speed would have to be increased to 1420 rpm as system pressure rises to 2000 psi. However, as load pressure increases to 2000 psi at the motor, output speed decreases to 910 rpm until $Q_4 = 62$ gpm $= K$. There is no way to offset this motor-slip generated speed droop in the drive represented in Figure 16.9.

The net effect of pump/motor interaction is shown in Figure 16.10: output speed N_0 is plotted as a function of load pressure. This speed regulation curve indicates a drop of output speed to 700 rpm at 2000 psi. It is typical of the effect component interactions have on system performance. It also suggests why designing with hydrostatic transmission systems is a more complex undertaking than when dealing with individual pumps and motors.

We must consider two more characteristics of fluid motors before discussing HSTs.

Fluid motor breakaway

It is essential that the designer be aware that each fluid motor exhibits its own particular set of characteristics when it must first start rotating then accelerate a load from zero to some steady state velocity, Figure 16.11.

Internal losses in a fluid motor consist of three components:
- **Coulomb friction**, (that which occurs between dry surfaces) Figure 16.11 (*a*)
- **viscous drag**, (also called windage losses) which are related to velocity, Figure 16.11 (*b*), and
- **inertial**, Figure 16.11 (*c*), which is not an actual loss, but acts like one during breakaway and acceleration because inertia torque adds to the load and friction torques. The algebraic sum of these three torque components must be supplied by the fluid motor manufacturer.

As Figure 16.11 (*d*) shows, the time interval from breakaway-and-accelerate to steady-state-velocity can be divided into three segments:

a. A very brief period, dt, during which Coulomb friction changes from a static to dynamic friction condition, see Figures 3.4, 4.1 (*c*), 4.2, 5.7, and 6.5 . From $0 < t_1 < dt$, static friction prevails. When $t_1 = dt$, the threshold velocity is reached when static effects yield to dynamic effects, and friction drops. Also present during this brief time interval are the inertia torque component and small viscous drag/windage losses. These are small because they are velocity sensitive and the rotational velocity is low when $t_1 = dt$.

b. A time interval $dt < t_2 < \Delta_t$ which occurs after the change in friction characteristic, and continues during the period of acceleration. During this time period, viscous losses increase because the velocity of the fluid motor is increasing.

c. When $t_3 \geq \Delta t_1$, steady state velocity is reached, and the inertial component vanishes. There remain only steady state viscous drag and friction torques in addition to load torque if the motor is expected to be able to start moving a load and accelerate it.

Motor stall torque characteristics

Figure 16.12 illustrates a typical set of hydraulic motor characteristics plotted as a function of output speed as the independent variable. Torque vs. speed characteristics are shown as a family of three curves at load pressures of 1000, 2000 and 3000 psi. Similar curves apply to all hydraulic motors.

The key factor to consider is the torque vs. speed characteristic at the **low speed end** of the scale. Note that motor output torque capability drops substantially, regardless of pressure, at speeds below 200-400 rpm. At speed $N_0 = 0$ rpm, torque reaches its minimum.

The implication of these $T_0 - N_0$ characteristics is that a hydraulic motor can handle less load at the low end of the speed range than under normal operating conditions. The parameter commonly used to express this condition is called *stall torque efficiency*, which is equal to the mechanical efficiency at $N_0 = 0$ rpm. It is equal to the ratio of output torque capability at zero speed to theoretical torque capability based on motor parameters. That is

$$T_t = \Delta p_m / 2\pi.$$

This equation suggests that only the pressure differential across the motor, Δp_m; and motor displacement, v_m, affect output torque. An operating mechanical efficiency, e_m, is applied for normal operating ranges to correct for mechanical losses. Thus,

$$T_{oa} = (\Delta p V_m / 2\pi) e_m$$

However, e_m should be matched to the actual motor operating point, whereas e_m is often given only for rated speed. To determine stall, (or breakaway) torque capability of a hydraulic motor, the designer must know its stall torque efficiency, e_{ms}. Depending on torque and size of motor, stall torque efficiencies can vary over a range from 10 to 25% *below* operating mechanical efficiencies. In addition, stall torque efficiencies are not necessarily consistent over a range of displacements in any one series of motors.

There appears to be a scaling effect: sample, axial piston, fixed displacement motors with an operating mechanical efficiency, e_m of about 92%, exhibit stall torque efficiencies ranging from 85% at the upper end of the scale to 55% at the lower. The net result of these considerations is that hydraulic motors must frequently be sized on the basis of *stall torque* rather than *operating torque* capabilities. This could force a designer to specify a hydraulic motor up to twice the size needed for normal operating conditions.

This peculiarity of conventional high speed, low torque fluid motors has led to the development of low

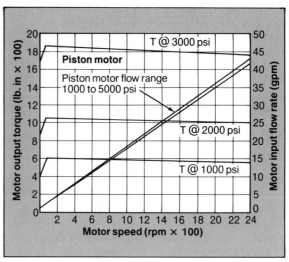

Fig. 16.12. Set of hydraulic motor characteristics plotted as a function of output speed as the independent variable.

speed high torque (LSHT) motors, in which the speed limitation shows up at the high end rather than at the low end of the scale. Conventional low speed, high torque (LSHT) motors are discussed later. Hydraulic motor selection criteria are discussed in Chapter 23.

A second reason for using LSHT motors is the erratic low speed characteristics of conventional high speed motors. A low end slip-stick phenomenon, called *cogging*, takes place at low speeds, making high speed motors unsatisfactory for low speed applications.

Motor volumetric efficiency

Typically, the volumetric efficiency of a motor e_{v_m} is given or for rated conditions. What are the implications of using rated e_{v_m} for other than rated speeds?

Assume, for example, an hydraulic motor with a displacement of 10 in³/rev, with a rated speed of 1200 rpm and a volumetric efficiency of 95%.

From these data we can calculate:

1. Flow rate: $Q_{r_t} = 10 \times 1200$
   $$= 12,000 \text{ in}^3/\text{min} = 51.95 \text{ gpm}$$
   $$= Q_4$$

2. Slip flow at $e_{v_m} = 95\%$
   $$q_m = Q_{r_t} e_{v_m}$$
   $$= 12,000 \times 0.05$$
   $$= 600 \text{ in}^3/\text{min}$$
   $$\text{or } 2.59 \text{ gpm}$$

3. Effective flow rate, $Q_{e_m} = Q_{r_t} - q_m$
   $$= 12,000 - 600$$
   $$= 11,400 \text{ in}^3/\text{min}$$

4. Speed @ $Q_{e_m} = N_0 = Q_e / V_m$
   $$= 11,400/10 = 1140 \text{ rpm}$$

which is the actual output speed adjusted for slip. Or, input flow rate could be adjusted to maintain $n_0 = 1200$ rpm:

$Q_4 = 12,000/0.95$
$= 12,631.58 \text{ in}^3/\text{min} = 54.68 \text{ gpm}.$

5. Assuming that the fluid motor *must* operate at 600 rpm instead of 1200 rpm, what is the motor's volumetric efficiency at this reduced speed? Slip is essentially constant for a given motor at a given pressure differential. While there may be some slight speed-sensitive changes in slip, it can be generally assumed that slip for this motor remains at

$$q_m \approx 600 \text{ in}^3/\text{min}.$$

Then: $Q_e = 600 \text{ rpm} \times 10 \text{ in}^3/\text{rev} - 600 \text{ in}^3/\text{min}$
$= 6000 - 600 = 5400 \text{ in}^3/\text{min}$

and,

$$e_{v_m} = (5400/6000) \, 100 = 90\%$$

6. Assuming that the motor used in this example has an acceptable lower operating speed of 300 rpm, what would be the volumetric efficiency at that speed? First, calculate the flow rate:

$$Q_e = (300 \times 10) - 600 = 2400 \text{ in}^3/\text{min}$$

then,

$$e_{v_m} = (2400/3000) \, 100 = 80\%$$

The effect of operating fluid motors at low speeds for significant segments of a work cycle on system efficiencies is obvious. Also refer to Chapter 15.

The emphasis has been on hydraulic motors because they are the ones which interface directly with a load. Thus the balance of the hydraulic system must be designed to interface with the motor's characteristics to accomplish what the system was designed to do. Whatever the motor is designed to do, it will. The remainder of the system must be able to compensate for any deficiency.

HYDROSTATIC TRANSMISSIONS— CLOSED CIRCUIT

Figure 16.1 classified HSTs based on type of circuit and controls.

Closed circuit HSTs come in two basic configurations:

1. *Integral* or *packaged*. Figure 16.13 resembles a

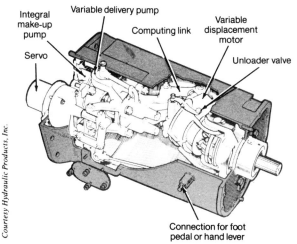

Fig. 16.13. Integral (packaged) hydrostatic transmission.

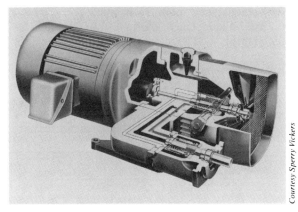

Fig. 16.14. Industrial type of integral HST.

Courtesy Sperry Vickers

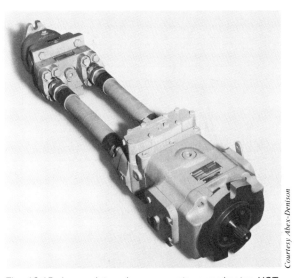

Fig. 16.15. In non-integral, or separate pump/motor HST, pump is coupled to prime mover and motor to load.

Courtesy Abex-Denison

gear transmission externally because the pump, motor, controls, conducting system, and all auxiliary components are enclosed in one housing. Generally, only the mounting surfaces and input/output shafts are visible.

Many integral HSTs are designed specifically for mobile drive applications, in which case mountings and shaft must meet SAE standards for direct-coupling to vehicle power trains. Other packaged HSTs are designed for industrial uses and consist of stand-alone systems, Figure 16.14.

2. *Separate pump and motor combinations* are the most common types of HSTs. The pump is coupled to the prime mover and the motor to the load or loads either directly or through a gearbox. Pump and motor are connected by appropriate hoses and/or tubing, Figure 16.15.

Figure 16.16 illustrates four types of hydrostatic transmissions based on the types of pumps and motors used, i.e. fixed or variable displacement with their corresponding output characteristics. Constant pressure and pump speed are assumed.

● **Fixed displacement pump and fixed displacement motor** — The simplest form of hydrostatic transmission, Figure 16.16(a) consists of a fixed displacement pump driving a fixed displacement motor. Although this transmission is inexpensive, its applications are limited. Because pump displacement is fixed it must be sized to drive the motor at a fixed speed under full load. When the pump accelerates its output bypasses to reservoir over the relief valve.

● **Variable displacement pump and fixed displacement motor** — This combination is called a constant torque transmission. Torque output is constant at any speed because torque depends only on fluid pressure and motor displacement. Power output is varied by adjusting pump displacement which changes motor speed. Typical performance curves

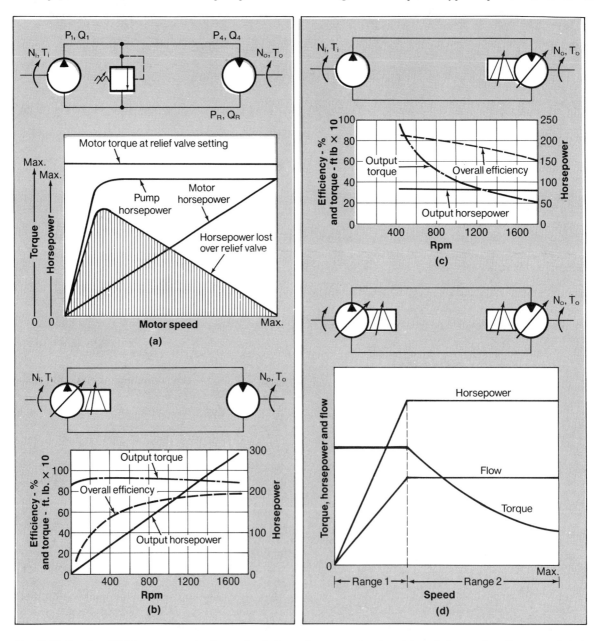

Fig. 16.16. *Functional HSTs are summarized according to types of pumps and motors. (a) wasted power from flow over relief valve during acceleration produces system heat. Power loss decreases as motor reaches design speed; (b) torque remains constant as speed and horsepower increase. These output curves are characteristic of a variable displacement pump powering a fixed displacement motor. Efficiency also increases with increasing speed; (c) efficiency and torque decrease and horsepower remains constant as speed increases in this transmission having a fixed displacement pump and a variable displacement motor; and (d) motor displacement is held at its maximum and pump displacement increases through range 1. Pump displacement is maximum at maximum horsepower and flow. Motor displacement decreases through range 2. Output has constant torque through range 1 and constant horsepower through range 2.*

are shown in Figure 16.16(b).

- **Fixed displacement pump and variable displacement motor** — If the pump has a fixed displacement and the motor a variable displacement, the transmission can deliver constant power. If flow to the motor is constant, and motor displacement is varied to maintain product of speed and torque constant, then, power delivered is constant. As motor speed is increased (by reducing its displacement) torque decreases, maintaining constant power. Typical performance curves for constant power transmissions are shown in Figure 16.16(c).

- **Variable displacement pump and variable displacement motor** — Varying the displacements of pump and motor provides infinite ratios of torque and power, Figure 16.16(d). When motor displacement is at maximum, varying pump output directly varies speed and horsepower output, while torque remains constant. Decreasing motor displacement at full pump displacement increases motor speed to its maximum, while torque varies inversely with speed: horsepower remains constant.

The curves in Figure 16.16(d) illustrate the two ranges of adjustment. In range 1, motor displacement is fixed at maximum; pump displacement increases from zero to maximum. Torque remains constant through this range while horsepower and speed increase.

Range 2 starts when the pump reaches maximum flow. Pump output is then held constant and motor displacement reduced. Through this range, torque decreases as speed increases; horsepower remains constant. Theoretically, motor speed could be increased infinitely, but from a practical standpoint, it is limited by the motor dynamics.

Although the combination of fixed displacement pump and fixed displacement motor, Figure 16.16(a), is used in many hydraulic applications, the system designer should be aware that this combination is not practical for closed circuit HSTs.

Application example

For example, assume that a 3116 lb-in-torque load must be driven at 1000 rpm. Horsepower required is determined from:

$$HP = TN/63,024$$
$$= (3116 \times 1000)/63,024 = 50 \text{ hp}$$

where:

T — torque, lb-in
N — speed, rpm

We choose a 2000-psi pump rated at 50 hp, which must deliver:

$$Q = 1714 \text{ hp}/p$$
$$= (1714 \times 50)/2000 = 43 \text{ gpm}$$

where:

p — pressure, psi
Q — flow, gpm

We then select a hydraulic motor with a displacement of 10 in³/rev to deliver 3116 lb-in of torque at

2000 psi or approximately 43 gpm at 1000 rpm. Figure 16.16(a) shows the power-torque-speed characteristics for the pump and motor assuming the pump operates at constant speed.

Pump flow is maximum at this operating speed, and the pump attempts to deliver this quantity of oil to the fixed displacement hydraulic motor. Load inertia makes it impossible to accelerate instantaneously to full speed, and part of the pump output flows over the relief valve, Figures 5.7 and 6.3. As motor speed increases, it absorbs more of the pump's output and less oil flows over the relief valve. At rated speed, all oil flows through the motor. Figure 16.16(a) also illustrates the power loss during acceleration.

Torque is constant because system pressure builds to relief valve setting immediately after the control valve shifts. Power lost over the relief valve is the difference between the constant horsepower delivered by the pump and the variable horsepower absorbed by the motor. The area under this curve represents the power wasted when the transmission starts or stops. It also shows the low efficiency for any operating speed below maximum. A fixed displacement transmission is not recommended for applications requiring frequent starts and stops.

Torque speed ratio

Theoretically, the maximum power a hydrostatic transmission can transmit is a function of flow and pressure. However, in constant power transmissions with variable output speeds, theoretical power is divided by the torque/speed ratio to determine actual power output. The highest constant horsepower which can be transmitted is determined by the lowest output speed at which this constant power must be transmitted. For instance, if the minimum speed

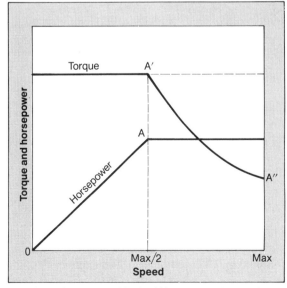

Fig. 16.17. Critical speed (point A) in a constant power transmission is the lowest speed at which maximum constant power can be transmitted.

139

represented by point A on the horsepower curve in Figure 16.17 is half maximum speed, the torque/speed ratio is 2:1. The maximum power which can be transmitted is the theoretical maximum divided by 2. At point A', corresponding to output speed, A, the torque curve drops off as speed increases. At maximum output speed it has dropped to A''.

At output speeds lower than $\frac{1}{2}$ maximum, torque remains constant at its maximum value, but horsepower drops off in proportion to speed. The speed at point A, Figure 16.17 is called the critical speed. Below critical speed, horsepower drops off linearly (with constant torque) to zero at zero rpm. Above the critical speed, torque drops off with increase in speed, providing constant horsepower. Critical speed is determined by the dynamics of the transmission components.

The general characteristics of HSTs are summarized in Figure 16.18.

Corner horsepower

Corner horsepower, CHP, is a numerical value which describes the capability range of a transmission, and is based on the product of maximum torque and maximum speed. However, the designer must remember that these two parameters generally do NOT occur simultaneously. Figure 16.19(a) shows that a much larger engine would be needed to meet CHP demand. Corner horsepower normally exceeds transmitted horsepower. Refer to Chapter 15, Figures 15.9 through 15.18 for pump controls relating to this subject.

The effect of adding a 2-speed gear box to the output shaft of an HST is illustrated in Figure 16.19(b). Engine horsepower required to equal corner horsepower is less than that required in Figure 16.19(a). There are only three points on the engine horsepower curve where the load horsepower coincides, namely at T_1, for low speed; at the shift point N_1 from low to high gear; and at, N_2, at maximum speed in high gear with low load torque. An HST may be thought of as a transmission with an infinite

Characteristics of hydrostatic transmissions				
Displacement		Transmission output		
Pump	Motor	Power	Torque	Speed
Fixed	Fixed	Constant	Constant	Constant
Variable	Fixed	Variable	Constant	Variable
Fixed	Variable	Constant	Variable	Variable
Variable	Variable	Variable	Variable	Variable

Fig. 16.18. General characteristics of four basic types of HSTs.

number of gear ratios with every "shift point" lying on the engine curve.

Practical closed circuit hydrostatic transmission

In the discussion relating to types of closed circuit hydrostatic transmissions, Figure 16.16 and summarized in Figure 16.18, we concentrated on parametric considerations only. It is necessary to provide additional functions to achieve a practical HST. To illustrate this point, consider, for example, the constant torque HST of Figure 16.16(b) since it is the most commonly used type.

Figure 16.20(a) shows the basic functional HST circuit of a servo controlled, variable displacement pump driving a fixed displacement fluid motor. Since this is a closed circuit HST, slip flow accumulates in the pump and motor cases and is removed through a case drain line, Figure 16.20(b). Typically, the motor case drain line is connected to the pump case where the two case drains combine. The case drain from the pump is connected to the reservoir via a heat exchanger, Figure 16.20(c).

One of the most important features of a closed circuit HST is the addition of a charge pump (generally an integral part of the main pump package), Figure 16.20(d). The charge pump performs two functions: (1) it prevents cavitation, by replenishing the closed system with fluid lost through pump and motor slip and (2) it provides control fluid required by the stroking mechanism of the variable displace-

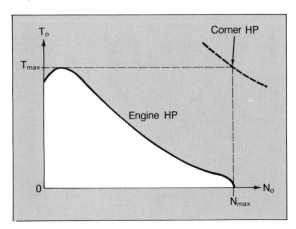

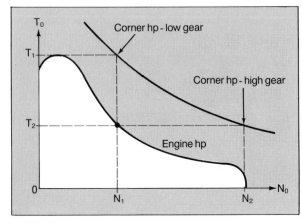

Fig. 16.19. (a) Calculated on the basis of maximum torque and speed, corner horsepower is normally greater than transmitted horsepower; (b) effect of 2-speed gear box on HST output.

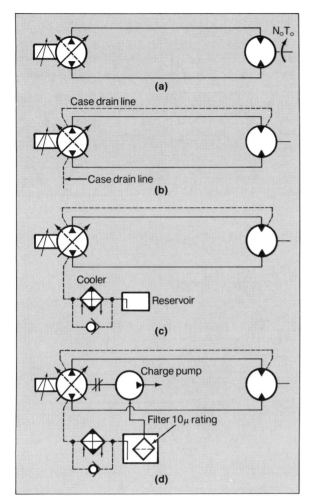

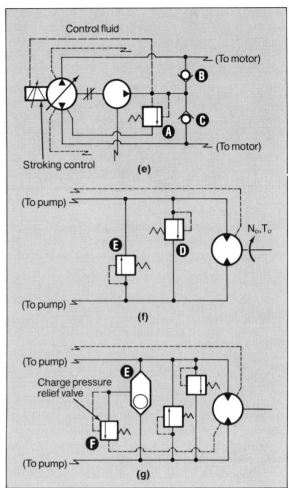

Fig. 16.20. Constant horsepower HST, with separate pump and motor; (a) basic functional circuit includes variable displacement pump and fixed motor; (b) case drain line interconnects pump and motor; (c) case drain line fluid flows through heat exchanger then into reservoir; (d) flow to charge pump, which is usually integral part of pump package, is filtered to 10 qm; (e) back-to-back replenishing check valves provide make up fluid to either line; (f) cross-over relief valves which are integral part of motor package, limit pressures in supply line; (g) shuttle valve is shifted by high pressure fluid, connecting low pressure line to bypass.

ment pump, Figure 16.20(d). Charge pump inlet flow normally passes through a 10-micrometre filter.

Control pressure is set by low pressure relief valve, A on the discharge side of the charge pump, Figure 16.20(e). While charge pressures vary from one manufacturer to another, they typically range from 250 to 300 psi. Back-to-back replenishing check valves, B and C supply make-up fluid to the appropriate low pressure line, Figure 16.20(e). This completes the necessary hardware at the pump end of the HST.

Motor end

A typical, closed circuit HST also requires crossover relief valves, D and E, Figure 16.20(f), which are integrated in the motor package. Relief valves D and E limit fluid pressure in either supply line due to shock load feedback through the motor, overrunning load conditions, etc. These relief valves perform the same function as a system relief valve in an open

circuit, but are located at the fluid motor end because this is where overpressures in a closed circuit HST originate. Two crossover relief valves are required because either line may be pressurized and bypassing fluid must flow to the low pressure line.

In addition to crossover relief valves, a shuttle valve E is also included, Figure 16.20(g). The shuttle valve is shifted by high pressure fluid, connecting the low pressure line to a low pressure relief valve F which bypasses excess charge pump flow to the motor case, via the drain line to the pump case and returns to the charge pump reservoir through the heat exchanger, Figure 16.20(d).

Combining the partial circuits of Figures 16.20(e) and 16.20(g), provides the circuit diagram for a basic, constant torque, closed circuit hydrostatic transmission. An alternate version is shown in Figure 16.21.

Principal differences include:

• pump and motor case drains are not connected.

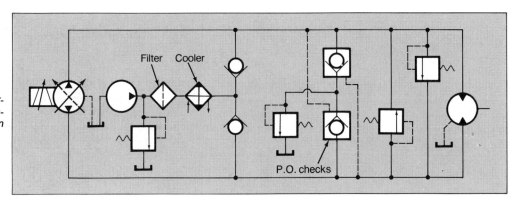

Fig. 16.21. Alternate circuit design to that in Figure 16.20.

Each drains directly to reservoir
• charge circuit filter and heat exchanger are on the discharge side of the charge pump so output flow from the charge pump is filtered and cooled continuously
• pilot operated check valves replace the shuttle valve at the motor end of the charge pressure relief valve.

Cavitation control

The stiffness of a HST depends on the compressibility of the fluid and the compliance of system components, i.e. piping and/or hoses. The influence of these components can be visualized as the effect an accumulator would have if piped in parallel with the supply line. Figure 16.22(a) represents an HST operating under a light load so the effective accumulator spring is compressed *lightly*.

In Figure 16.22(b), the HST is heavily loaded, the accumulator spring is *substantially* compressed and there is more fluid in the pressure side of the HST. This additional fluid volume must be supplied by the charge pump.

The critical factor is the rate-of-pressure rise in the system. If pressure rises too fast, the rate of volume increase on the supply side (so-called compressibility flow) may exceed the flow capacity of the charge pump, and the supply side may cavitate. Possibly the most serious danger is in circuits equipped with variable displacement pumps which have automatic controls. When the system cavitates, pressure drops or disappears altogether. The automatic controls attempt to respond, resulting in an unstable system.

Mathematically, the rate of pressure rise can be expressed as

$$dp/dt \text{ (psi/sec)} = B_e Q_{cp}/V$$

where:

B_e—Effective bulk modulus of the system, psi
V — Volume of fluid on pressure side, in^3
Q_{cp}—Charge pump output, in^3/sec

Application example

Assume that the HST of Figure 16.20 is connected with 2 ft of 1½ ID steel tubing. Neglecting

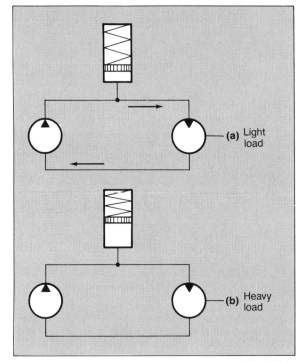

Fig. 16.22. Stiffness of HST depends on compressibility of fluid and compliance of system components: (a) light load: (b) heavy load.

the volumes of pump and motor, $V \approx 30$ in^3. For oil in steel tubing $B_e \approx 200,000$ psi. Assume the charge pump delivers 6 gpm ≈ 23.1 in^3/sec.

Rate of pressure rise is

$$dp/dt = 200,000 \times 23.1/30$$
$$\approx 154,000 \text{ psi/sec.}$$

Consider the effect of plumbing the system with 20 ft of 1½ in ID, 3-wire braid hose. Your hoses manufacturer or HST supplier would have to supply the cubic mean expansion coefficient in in^3/1000 psi to calculate the effective bulk modules, B_e which for this example $\approx 84,000$ psi.

Calculating the rate of pressure rise, $dp/dt = 84,000 \times 23.1/294.5 \approx 6588$ psi/sec.

The most effective way to offset the tendency of such a system to cavitate would be to increase the output of the charge pump. Alternately, if changes in the external load are not continuous, an accumulator

Courtesy Eaton Corp.

Fig. 16.23. Typical axial piston, slipper type pump (left) and motor (right).

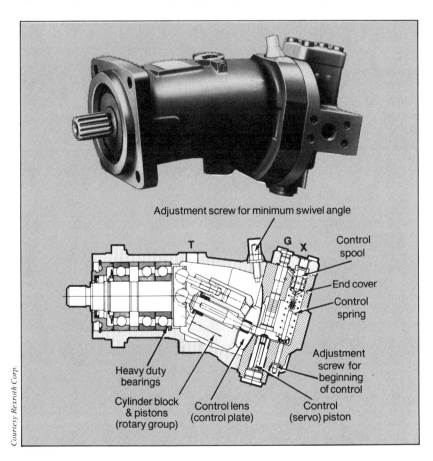

Adjustment screw for minimum swivel angle

T   G X

Control spool

End cover

Control spring

Adjustment screw for beginning of control

Heavy duty bearings

Cylinder block & pistons (rotary group)

Control lens (control plate)

Control (servo) piston

Courtesy Rexroth Corp.

Fig. 16.24. Bent axis, piston motor.

can be added to the charge circuit.

Some HST manufacturers provide a port to connect an accumulator to the charge circuit. If the stiffness of the HST is low and the HST is equipped with automatic controls, the HST should be started from neutral (zero displacement) position. In addition, acceleration of the displacement mechanism should be limited to prevent a jerky start which, in turn, would result in excessive rate of pressure change. Some HST manufacturers provide damping orifices in the stroking circuit for this very purpose.

This discussion shows that the purpose of the charge system is not simply for keeping the closed circuit HST "solid." System stiffness and control of rate of pressure rise may be the primary considerations which determine charge pump delivery, rather than pump slip and motor slip flows. It must be assumed that HST manufacturers consider these factors when supplying HST systems. However, the system user must also exercise good judgment in dealing with these factors when under his control. Refer to Figure 15.10, for an example of a variable

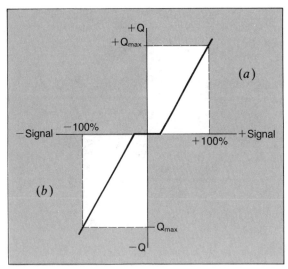

Fig. 16.25. Performance characteristics for (a) unidirectional, (a) and (b) bidirectional circuits.

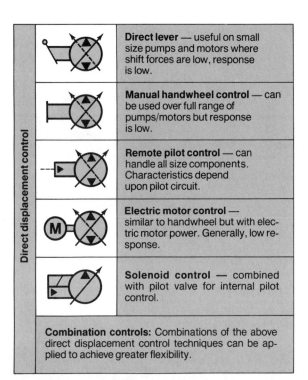

Fig. 16.26. Summary of types of displacement controls for HSTs.

displacement pump control designed to reduce rate-of-pressure-rise.

The cutaway of a typical axial piston pump for a hydrostatic transmission is illustrated in Figure 16.23, left; the cutaway of a compatible axial piston fluid motor is at right. A typical bent-axis variable displacement pump is shown in Figure 16.24, top; a cross-sectional view is shown below.

HST CONTROLS

Spurred on by escalating energy costs, the growth in variety and sophistication of HST controls during the 1970s has been remarkable as it all but eliminated the cost differential for higher performance HSTs, which can achieve the energy input/output match up illustrated in Figure 16.4. As we delve further into our discussion of HST controls, remember that they conform to the basic force-balance concept described in Chapter 8 and illustrated in Figure 8.17.

Pump/motor controls

A variety of straight displacement controls is available, all of which implement the characteristics illustrated in Figure 16.25. If the variable displacement control is unidirectional, only the right side of Figure 16.25 applies; if bidirectional, the complete characteristic describes the control performance.

There is usually a small deadband around neutral. The term *signal* means any control input which produces a change in displacement of the pump or motor. Figure 16.26 summarizes with ISO graphic symbols, the kinds of controls available for manual and non-servo stroker displacement applications.

Generally, direct displacement controls respond slower than servo types. Typically, their response times would be measured in fraction of a minute, sometimes even greater. By comparison, servo type

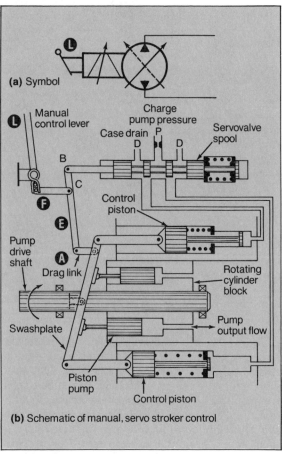

Fig. 16.27. Manually operated servo stroker: (a) ISO symbol, (b) cross sectional view.

controls respond in fractions of a second. The accuracy of direct displacement controls is also inferior to servo controls. Direct displacement controls require smaller actuating forces, especially the manual types.

Because of these limitations, direct displacement controls are generally used for lower power HSTs in

which high performance and precision are not a major consideration.

Servo-displacement controls

In a servo displacement (servo stroker) control, a servo system provides a level of performance not attainable with direct displacement controls. These servo systems can be mechanical, hydraulic, electrical, or electrohydraulic. As a practical matter, servo stroker controls for HSTs have resolved themselves to one or two basic types.

The first is the manually operated servo stroker, Figure 16.27, offered by all manufacturers. It encompasses the general principles illustrated, although the hardware is likely to vary from one manufacturer to another. For example, some use spool type servovalves, others rotary, etc.

The input signal to the servo stroker of Figure 16.27 is any motion of the manual control lever L. When the operator moves lever L, link E rotates about pivot point A by thrust of link F. As link E swings, it shifts the servovalve spool, porting fluid to the stroking pistons which rotate the pump swashplate. The swashplate provides a mechanical feedback signal through the drag link to reposition link E which rotates about pivot C.

This motion renulls the servovalve spool, blocks the flow of control fluid to the control pistons and stops the swashplate at the position commanded by the manual control lever. The system remains in this position until the control lever signals a new command. This type of mechanical position feedback system is also known as a follower servo.

To convert a manual servo controller to an electrohydraulic servo controller, the control lever and linkages are replaced with an electrohydraulic pilot stage and mechanical position sensing, using force feedback to the flapper in the pilot valve stage of the electrohydraulic servovalve, Figure 16.28. The technology is the same as described in Chapter 12, in the discussion of electrohydraulic and proportional valves.

Electrohydraulic stroker servos are designed to work open loop within the HST system. The servo functions primarily as a force amplifier, Figure 16.29, to enable low level commands to control high level loads, namely stroker forces required to move the swashplate or swing the cylinder barrel and yoke at high pressure. A second function is to stabilize the displacement mechanism in its commanded position against transient, disruptive forces which might tend to shift the mechanism.

The basic types of pressure actuated controls for hydrostatic transmissions were discussed at length in Chapter 15.

OPEN CIRCUIT HYDROSTATIC TRANSMISSIONS

In Figure 16.1, *open* circuit HSTs were defined and compared with *closed* circuit HSTs. The pri-

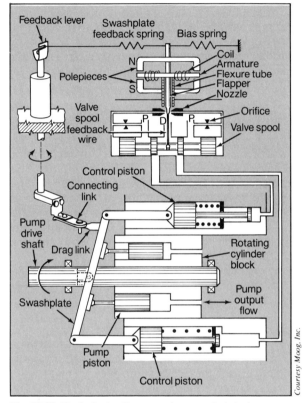

Fig. 16.28. Electrohydraulic servovalve operated stroker.

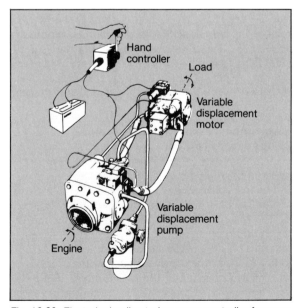

Fig. 16.29. Electrohydraulic stroker servo controller for open loop HST.

145

mary difference is that the reservoir introduces a flow discontinuity in the flow path of the fluid, enabling the reservoir to perform functions (see Chapter 25) which must be handled in other ways in a closed HST system. Refer to Figure 16.20.

Pumps/motors

One of the key factors the system designer must consider when specifying open circuit hydrostatic transmissions is the inlet conditions to the pump, see Figure 26.7. Open circuit pumps rely on atmospheric pressure to "push oil" into the pump inlet port, imposing limitations on pump *maximum speed*. Overspeeding causes pump cavitation, and as pump displacement increases, allowable speed decreases. Because these relationships are a function of pump design, manufacturers specify maximum speed ratios.

If an open circuit pump must be operated faster than rated maximum speeds, the pump must be *supercharged*. It is important to distinguish a *supercharge* pump from a *charge* or *make-up* pump in a closed circuit HST. Figure 16.30 illustrates the difference.

Figure 16.30(*a*) shows a **charge** pump which supplies to the main pump only a *fraction* of its output capacity. The size of the charge pump is normally based on the sum of the slip in the main pump and motor, transient control flow requirements, bypass flow through the shuttle valve, Figure 16.20(*g*), and compressibility flow requirements, Figure 16.22.

A **supercharge** pump must be larger than the main pump because it must be able to deliver *full* power pump output flow AND *slip* flow, Figure 16.30(*b*). In some designs a pressurized reservoir can replace a supercharge pump. However, this technique requires careful engineering and adherence to

sound safety practices. Designers must remember that a pressurized reservoir is in fact a low pressure vessel and it must be designed to withstand the structural loads imposed on the shell. Refer to Chapter 25.

Pumps and motors used in open circuit HSTs are fundamentally the same as those used in closed circuit systems. Much of the auxiliary hardware illustrated in Figure 16.20 is *not* required in open circuit applications. To minimize cavitation, open circuit pumps must be designed for optimum inlet characteristics. Some manufacturers design a full flow supercharge pump into the pump package, thus eliminating the need for a supercharge pump in the external circuit.

Controls and contamination control

The same control options discussed in Chapter 15 and for closed circuit HSTs are also available for open circuit HSTs. Figure 16.31 illustrates typical controls and applications. The major difference between closed and open circuit hydrostatic transmissions is that several motors can be used with open circuit pumps, while single actuators are generally used with closed circuit pumps. Open circuit pumps can be sized to deliver flows required by multiple outputs. Refer to Figure 3.7 and Chapter 22.

Contamination control in HSTs follows the guidelines discussed in Chapter 20. Historically, closed circuit HSTs have relied on filtration in the charge pump auxiliary circuit to remove from a system ingested and internally generated contamination. Typically, motor case drain has been connected to the pump case drain and the combined drain flows circulated through the charge pump circuit. This arrangement subjects pump and motor to system contamination.

Some authorities recommend that one filter be placed in the case drain between the pump and motor, Figure 16.32(*a*). Others suggest that a filter be placed in *each* of the legs of the main power circuit, Figure 16.32(*b*). Obviously, cost is apt to be a significant factor when high pressure filters are used in this manner. Open circuit hydrostatic transmissions can use the conventional filtration techniques outlined in Chapter 20.

Overrunning loads/dynamic braking in open circuit HSTs

The condition of load reversal from resistive to overrunning can be critical in open circuit drives. Refer to Figures 3.4, 3.10, 5.2 and 5.7. In a closed circuit, some dynamic braking is generally inherent in the system. Load reversal tends to override the hydraulic motor, functionally converting it into a pump. The HST pump can absorb energy and transmit it to the prime mover, which now functions as an energy absorber under these conditions. If the system was designed properly, a safe equilibrium speed will be established and overspeeding or runaway avoided.

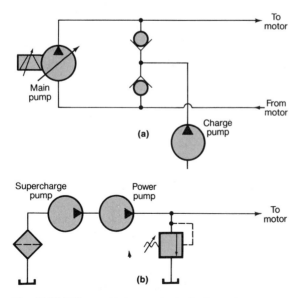

Fig. 16.30. Difference between circuits having a charge pump (a) and supercharge pump (b).

Type	Description	Schematic	Characteristics	Typical application
Servo Displacement Control	Sets flow rate zero to maximum flow proportional to lever position. Spring centered to zero displacement.	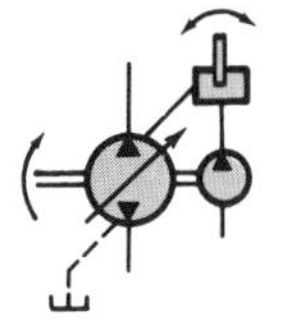	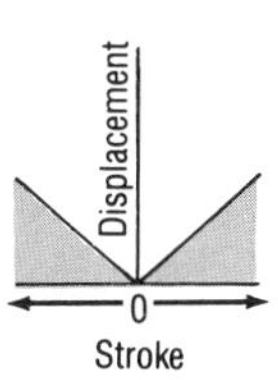 Displacement / Stroke / 0	Hydrostatic transmissions and other applications where pump flows must be varied by mechanical means. 
Constant Torque Control	Determines flow proportional to lever position. Spring centered to zero displacement in both directions. Mechanical input can be overridden as follows: The torque is limited at a constant value, the pump displacement is a function of a predetermined pressure curve, until it reaches the setting of the pressure compensator (flat cut-off). Signal can be externally overridden for emergency stop or brake action.	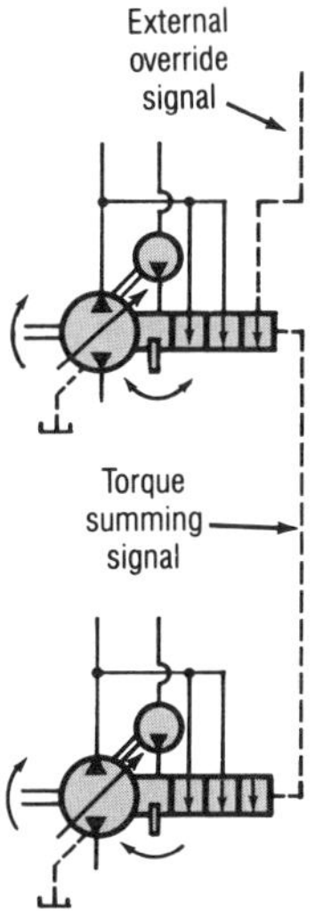 External override signal	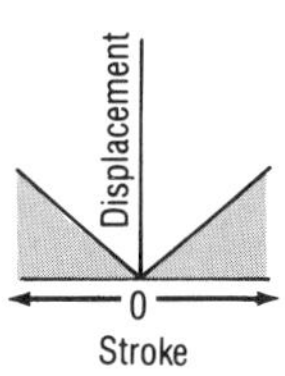 Displacement / Stroke / 0	Hydrostatic drives where an automatic variable speed torque range is desirable or essential. 
Constant Torque Control with torque summation.	Same as above. When pressure summation is used, both pump displacements simultaneously follow a function of the sum of the two system pressures.	Torque summing signal	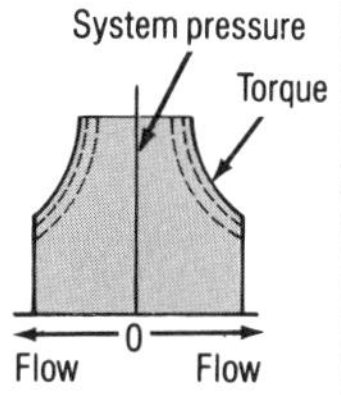 System pressure / Torque / Flow Flow / 0	Hydrostatic drives where equal traction speed from two drives is essential. 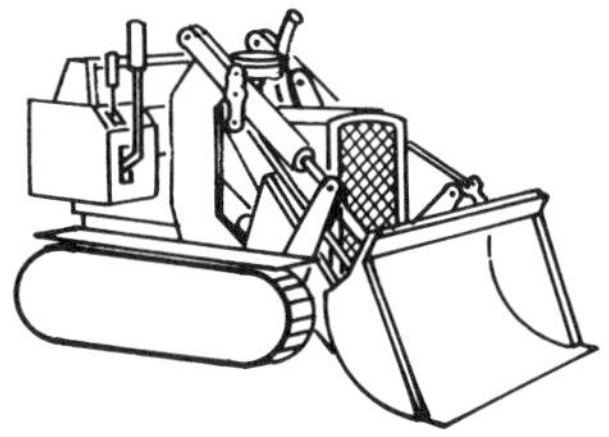
Acceleration Control	Acceleration control allows vehicle to gradually speed up or slow down.		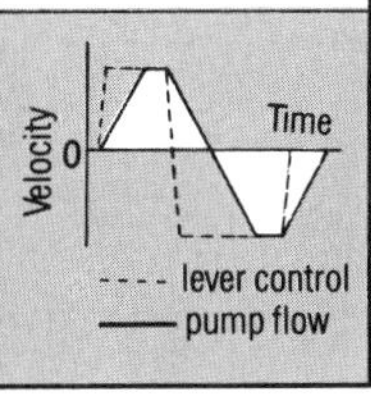 Velocity / Time / 0 / ---- lever control / —— pump flow	Hydrostatic drive, swing circuits, etc. 

Fig. 16.31. Typical hydrostatic transmission controls and applications.

The solution to the problem of overspeeding is not as easy to achieve in open circuit drives as in closed circuit drives because dynamic braking is not characteristic of such systems. In open circuit drives, the braking function must be introduced by means of controls. Figure 16.33 illustrates a typical solution. Figure 16.33(a) shows a typical load reversal situation for an HST traveling *downhill*. A more subtle case is to use the HST to slow a vehicle. Enough kinetic energy is stored in the vehicle to overrun the hydraulic motor. Figure 16.33(b) illustrates the load reversal as it would appear on a load plot. Refer to Figure 3.4. Use of a brake valve is illustrated in Figure 16.33(c). A brake valve is a special use of counterbalance valves (Chapter 8) combined with a check valve network to provide the required functions for controlled load deceleration.

Assume, for example, that when the directional control valve (not shown) is shifted, port V_1 is pressurized. Pressure fluid flows through V_1, CV_1, to junction point 2. Input flow, Q_4, could flow either through

counterbalance valve CB_1 or to hydraulic motor port I. Since counterbalance valve CB_1 is normally closed, output Q_4 flows to the hydraulic motor which propels

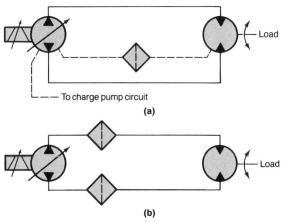

Fig. 16.32. Location alternatives for filters in hydrostatic transmission loop.

the vehicle up the grade, Figure 16.33(a).

Return fluid, Q_5, flows through fluid motor port R to junction point 3, but cannot continue to tank (*i.e.*, through port V_2) because check valve CV_2 is seated and blocks fluid flow. Instead, flow Q_5 must pass through counterbalance valve CB_2 to reach return port V_2. Under normal circumstances, the full pressure drop across counterbalance valve CB_2 would be added to the pressure drop across the motor, re-

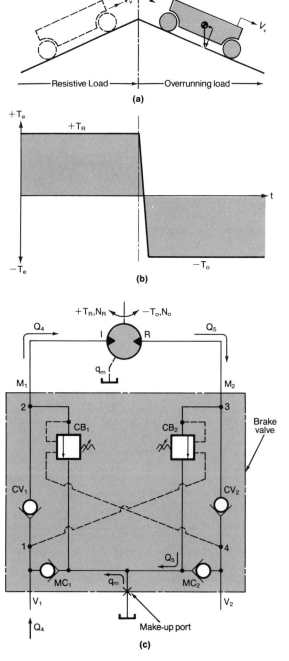

(a)

(b)

(c)

Fig. 16.33. Overspeeding situations: (a) typical HST load reversal in downhill operation; b) load reversal as it would appear on load plot; (c) with use of brake valve.

sulting in excessive system inefficiency and heat generation. Counterbalance valves CB_1 and CB_2 are cross-piloted from opposite passages in the brake valve body. When port V_1 is pressurized, full load pressure differential is transmitted to counterbalance valve CB_2 through its cross-pilot connection shifting it wide open. Flow Q_5 can now return to tank with a minimum of backpressure across counterbalance valve CB_2.

When load reversal occurs, port V_1 functions as the inlet line to motor port I and port V_2 becomes the discharge side of the motor, now being driven as a pump by the load. When fluid pressure drops to inlet pressure, cross-piloting to counterbalance valve CB_2 is lost, and it closes. Inlet pressure to counterbalance valve CB_2 at junction point 3 is sensed at the inlet to counterbalance valve CB_2 and it again functions as a conventional counterbalance valve. The backpressure introduced at port R by counterbalance valve CB_2 provides a decelerating torque to the load, resulting in dynamic braking.

Return flow Q_5 recirculates through make-up check valve MC_1 back to motor inlet port I. Theoretically, recirculation in this essentially closed circuit would provide all the fluid needed to prevent cavitation of the motor-turned-pump. It must be remembered that the motor will exhibit slip flow, q_m, whether it is driven hydraulically as a motor, or mechanically as a pump. Refer to the discussion of inversion of functions from pump to motor, Figure 16.8.

Slip, q_m is subtracted from flow Q_5 so there is danger of cavitation. A make-up port, which can be connected to tank, is included to provide a flow of fluid equivalent to the slip losses. Alternately, an accumulator could be used to supply make-up fluid and minimize cavitation effects.

Applications

Hydrostatic transmissions follow the general rules for fluid power circuit design outlined in Chapters 3 through 7. Load analysis techniques for HST vehicle drives rely mostly on empirical data which characterize vehicle performance. To apply this data, the designer must use the definitions and equations shown in Table 16.1.

Table 16.2 summarizes average coefficients of adhesion for various types of soils and other materials. Table 16.3 shows average values of rolling resistance, RR for various operating conditions for rubber tired and crawler vehicles.

Hydrostatic transmission manufacturers generally use a "cookbook" approach for sizing an HST for a particular application, reflecting the empirical nature of the data base on which the analysis is based. Before proceeding with an actual example, a typical "recipe" must be reviewed.

Vehicle corner limit

In Figure 16.19(a), corner *horsepower* was de-

TABLE 16.1 — Data for calculating vehicle performance

TERMS	
AC	Application coefficient
DB	Drawbar Pull (lb)
EFF	Efficiency (%)
FD	Final drive ratio
FLG	Full load governed
FPM	Speed (Feet per minute)
G	Grade (%)
GPM	Flow
GR	Grade Resistance
GVW	Gross Vehicle Weight (lb)
HP	Horsepower
LR	Loaded Drive Wheel Radius (in)
MLC	Machine corner limit, lb. mph
MPH	Speed (miles per hour)
MTE	Maximum Tractive Effort (lb)
N	Speed (rpm)
NLG	No load governed
e	Efficiency (%)
OVERALL EFF	Overall Efficiency (%)
π	3.1416
PSI	Pressure
Δ PSI	Differential Pressure
Q	Flow
R	Gear Reduction (Ratio: 1)
RPM	Speed
RR	Rolling Resistance
ST	Wheelslip torque (in.- lb)
T	Torque (in. - lb)
TE	Tractive effort (lb)
U	Coefficient of Adhesion
V	Volume
VAC	Vacuum (in. of Hg.)
VOL. EFF.	Volumetric Efficiency (%)
WD	Weight on Drive Wheel (lb)
V_p	Displacement

FORMULAS	
DB	Drawbar Pull (lbs) DB = (T) + (LR) + (RR)
DISP	Displacement (in³ per rev) Disp. for Motor = (T) (2π) ÷ (Δpsi) (Overall Eff.) Disp. for Pump = (gpm) (231) ÷ (rpm) (Vol. Eff.)
FPM	Speed (ft. per min.) FPM = (mph) (88)
G	Grade (%) G = [(Vertical Rise in Ft.) ÷ (100 ft. of horizontal)] (100) G Max. = [(1200) (T) ÷ (LR) (GVW)] ÷ (GVW) (R)
GPM	Flow GPM for Motor = (disp) (rpm) ÷ (231) (vol. eff.) GPM for Pump = (disp) (rpm) (vol. eff.) ÷ (231)
GR	Grade Resistance GR = (0.1) (GVW) (G)
HP	Horsepower HP for Motor = (T) (rpm) ÷ (63025) HP for Pump = (Δ psi) (gpm) (000583) ÷ (Overall Eff.) HP = (T) (N) (Constant)

Table 16.2: Average Coefficients of Adhesion = U

Surface	For rubber tires	For crawlers
Concrete & asphalt	.80/1.00	.45
Dry Clay loam	.50/.70	.90
Wet Clay loam	.40/.50	.70
Damp Sand & gravel	.30/.40	.35
Loose sand	.20/.35	.30
Firm earth	.50/.60	.90
Loose earth	.40/.50	.60

Table 16.3: Average Rolling Resistance Coefficient = C_R (% of Vehicle Wt.)

Surface	RR = Coefficient For rubber tire vehicles	RR = Coefficient For crawler vehicles
Concrete & asphalt	.02 (GVW)	.04 (GVW)
Smooth hard dry dirt & gravel, well maintained, free of loose material	.025 (GVW)	.04 (GVW)
Dry dirt & gravel—not firmly packed—some loose material	.04 (GVW)	—
Soft unplowed dirt, poorly maintained	.05 (GVW)	.08 (GVW)
Wet muddy surface on firm base	.05 (GVW)	—
Snow—packed 4″ loose	.03 (GVW) .05 (GVW)	—
Soft plowed dirt or unpacked dirt fills	.09 (GVW)	—
Loose sand or gravel	.10 (GVW)	.10 (GVW)
Muddy, deeply rutted, or soft spongy base	.17 (GVW)	.12 (GVW)

fined as the product of maximum speed and maximum torque. If these values are defined in terms of vehicle speed in mph and tractive effort, TE, what was called corner horsepower would actually have units of lb · mph. Since these are obviously not horsepower unit, manufacturers have coined various names. We will call it vehicle corner limit, VCL.

To determine the ability of a hydrostatic transmission to match a particular VCL that is an application requirement, some manufacturers use an *applications coefficient*, AC, to relate the capabilities of an HST to the requirements of a machine. A typical plot of an HST pump speed vs AC is shown in Figure 16.34.

The transmission application coefficient is a function of pump speed, pressure, and displacement with a constant applied to convert units to lb · mph.

The transmission application coefficient, AC, for either a variable pump/fixed motor transmission or a variable pump/variable motor transmission is shown in Figure 16. 34. Enter the curve at pump speed and

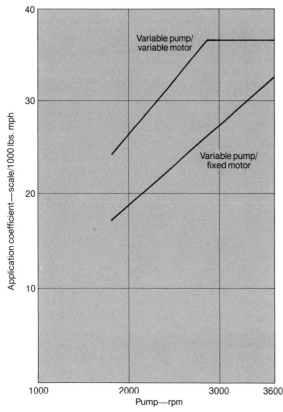

Fig. 16.34. Curves for determining application coefficient values.

read upward to the type of transmsiion being used, then across to the left for the application coefficient. Compare these curves with those shown in Figures 16.16 (*b*) and (*d*).

If the transmission *AC* exceeds vehicle *AC*, the application is viable. If the transmission *AC* is less than vehicle *AC* and a fixed hydraulic motor is being used, consider increasing pump speed and/or using a variable motor. A second alternative would be to reduce vehicle *AC* by lowering required maximum vehicle speed.

Guidelines for using application coefficient

Follow these simple fules of thumb for using an *AC:*
1. The transmission application coefficient must exceed the vehicle application coefficient.
2. In dual path systems, calculate for only one side of the vehicle (one transmission), with tractive — effort-to-slip calculated with 60% of the total weight on the drive wheels on that side.
3. The use of the Application Coefficient method does not guarantee that the transmission will be within rating at the user's design parameters. Pump speed and/or final drive ratio may have to be adjusted for application within rating.

Transmission sizing procedure

To perform the following calculations, refer to list of terms, Table 16.1.

1. Check application coefficient
- Calculate tractive effort to slip/wheels for single path applications (TE = weight on wheels $\times$ C_s). For dual path applications, weight on wheels is 60% of total weight on both wheels (TE = weight on wheels $\times$ .6 $\times$ C_s).
- Machine $MCL = TE \times$ *max. vehicle speed (FLG).*
- Determine the transmission application coefficient, Figure 16.34. Transmission *AC* must exceed vehicle *AC*.

2. Horsepower rating (hp)
- Single path
  = (Input hp $\times$ 1000)/rpm $<$22.5
- Dual path (input hp is split between two pumps; use 80% of total input hp)
  = (Input hp $\times$ .8 $\times$ 1000)/rpm $<$22.5

Note: at this point, it has only been determined that the transmission can meet vehicle requirements within rating. It is *not* known whether this unit will meet the requirements using the final drive ratio, wheel radius and pump speed given on the data sheet.

3. Maximum tractive effort (*TE*

Enter Motor Torque vs PSI curve, Figure 16.35, at maximum pressure (usually relief valve setting) and read motor torque upward at 18-degree yoke angle.

$$TE = (T_m \times FD \times E_{fd} \times \text{Number of Motors})/R_L$$

For single path systems, compare *TE* maximum directly to *TE* to slip. *TE* maximum should be at least 4% higher than *TE* to slip for good application because of tolerance on relief valve setting.

For dual path systems, divide *TE* maximum by number of motors and compare to *TE* to slip with

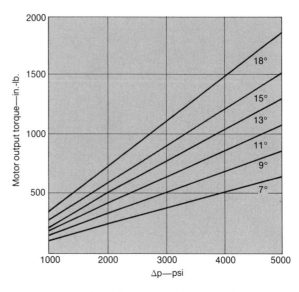

Fig. 16.35. Motor torque vs pressure differential curves.

60% of weight on one wheel. *TE* maximum should be 4% above *TE* to slip. If *TE* maximum is less than *TE* to slip, an adjustment in final drive ratio or wheel radius will be required.

4. Maximum vehicle speed

Enter Flow vs Speed curve, Figure 16.36, at pump input speed (*FLG*). Read flow and motor speed. Divide motor speed by number of motors connected in parallel. Calculate vehicle speed:

$$mph = (N_m \times R_L)/(FD \times 168 \times \text{Number of Motors})$$

5. Tractive effort to slip

Compare calculated values to requirements for maximum tractive effort and speed. Tractive effort to slip one wheel at worst condition should occur at least 4% below maximum tractive effort calculated.

Worst condition for a *single* path system is with weight distributed equally between drive wheels. Worst condition for a *dual* path system will be a condition with assumed 60% of weight on *one* wheel. Maximum *TE* is calculated for total machine, so it must be modified for comparison to *TE*-to-slip by calculating: $TE = TE$ max. $\times$ .6.

If maximum speed is acceptable and maximum tractive effort is at least 4% above tractive effort at wheel slip, the application is acceptable and the application review can proceed. If either tractive effort and/or speed is (are) not acceptable, proceed as follows:

a) Speed too low; tractive effort acceptable

Option 1: Maximum speed was calculated for a constant horsepower condition. Actual vehicle speed will be slightly higher, because volumetric efficiencies increase with decreased pressure and pump speed increases with decreased engine load. Calculate maximum theoretical speed using *NLG* pump speed and 100% volumetric efficiency.

$$mph = (\text{Pump rpm} \times R_L)/\text{Number of Motors} \times FD \times 168)$$

Option 2: Consider increasing pump speed to achieve desired vehicle speed

Option 3: Consider using a variable displacement motor.

Option 4: Consider decreasing final drive ratio, but only if tractive effort can be maintained at an acceptable level.

Option 5: Consider 2-speed final drive.

b) Tractive effort low; speed acceptable

Option 1: Increase final drive ratio and increase pump speed. Use variable displacement motor, or 2-speed final drive to maintain speed.

Option 2: Increase motor displacement by connecting motors in parallel. One or both may be variable displacement to maintain speed.

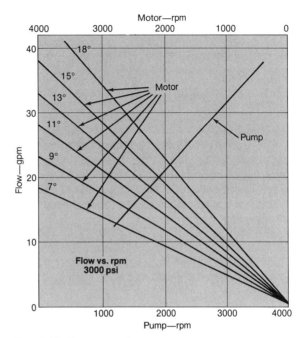

Fig. 16.36. Flow vs speed curves.

6. Final drive ratio

If a single speed final drive is to be used, the ratio is always determined by the maximum tractive effort required to slip the wheels, plus 4% to allow for relief valve tolerances. Using Motor Torque vs Δ PSI curve, Figure 16.35, enter at maximum pressure (relief valve setting) and read motor torque at 18-degree yoke angle.

$$FD = (TE_{SLIP} \times 1.04 \times R_L)/T_m \times e_{fd}$$

7. Variable motor minimum swashplate angle

Using maximum required vehicle speed from data sheet, calculate maximum motor speed:

$$N_m = (\text{mph} \times FD \times 168)/ R_L \text{ql}$$

N_m must be less than 4000 rpm at No Load Governed (*NLG*) pump speed and 100% volumetric efficiencies:

$V_m = (N_p \times V_p)/(N_m)$
= minimum displacement
Swashplate angle
= $\tan^{-1} (V_m \times \tan 18\text{-degrees})/2.5$

Use next *lower* swashplate angle offered (7, 9, 11, 13, 15-degrees) to be sure vehicle speed can be reached. Recheck maximum motor speed at *NLG* engine speed to be sure motor speed does not exceed 4000 rpm.

$N_m = (N_p \times V_p)/V_m$

If motor speed exceeds 4000 rpm, use next *higher* increment of swashplate angle and recheck.

8. Rolling resistance

Calculate vehicle rolling resistance, *RR*, using coefficient of rolling resistance given on data sheet, or from Table 16.3 for the type of vehicle and soil conditions to be encountered.

$$RR = GVW \times CR$$

The rolling resistance must be less than the tractive effort available under any operating condition.

9. Gradeability

Gradeability is usually expressed in percent and is equivalent to the tangent of the angle of the grade from the horizontal times 100, Figure 16.37. A 100% grade is 45-degrees. Calculate the percent grade at maximum tractive effort and tractive effort at maximum speed

where:

$$\Theta = \text{Grade angle,}$$
$$\text{Sin } \Theta = (TE - RR)/GVW$$
$$\% \text{ Grade } = \tan \Theta \times 100$$

EXAMPLE: SINGLE PATH TRANSMISSION — TWO MOTORS CONNECTED IN PARALLEL

The application is a tandem road roller for soil compaction and asphalt finishing. Conditions selected provide a wide range of application possibilities. Given:

Engine hp @ FLG	60 @ 2800 rpm
Gross vehicle weight, GVW	8000 lb
Weight on drive rolls, WD	8000 lb
Final drive ratio	30:1
Final drive efficiency	90%
Radius of drive rolls	20 in.
Coefficient of adhesion	.4
Coefficient of rolling resistance, RR	55 lb/1000 lb GVW 2800
Pump input speed @ FLG	rpm
Pump input speed @ NLG	3000 rpm

Required:

Maximum Tractive Effort (TE)	3200 lb
Maximum speed	8 mph
Maximum grade	15%

Pump, which is direct-driven from engine through a flex drive coupling, is connected hydraulically and in parallel to two motors, one on each of the front and rear rolls. Motors drive through a fixed ratio gearbox. The pump is a multiple pump as shown in Figure 16.38.

Step 1: Application coefficient

$$TE_{slip} = W_w \times U_x$$
$$= 8000 \text{ lb} \times .4 = 3200 \text{ lb}$$

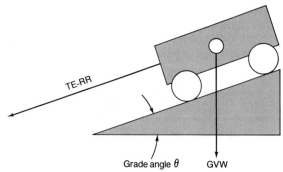

Fig. 16.37. Schematic illustrates interrelationships between tractive effort (TE), rolling resistance (RR), grade angle (GA), and gross vehicle weight (GVW).

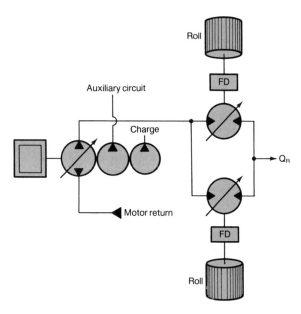

Fig. 16.38. Multiple-section pump supplies fluid to two variable displacement motors connected in parallel.

$$\text{Machine } CL = TE \times \text{mph}$$
$$= 3200 \text{ lb} \times 8 \text{ mph}$$
$$= 25,600 \text{ lb mph}$$

Transmission AC, from Figure 16.33 for the variable pump/variable motor combination at 2800 rpm • FLG is 35,800, so this application is well within rating.

Step 2: Input vs rated horsepower

Pump input horsepower equals engine horsepower less horsepower required for supercharge, plus auxiliary no-load loss. Determine horsepower consumed by charge and auxiliary functions from pump curves. For this example, we will assume they total 3.5 horsepower.

Pump input horsepower/1000 rpm will be,

$$\text{hp} = [(60 - 3.5) \times 1000]/2800 = 20.17$$

Which is less than 22.5, so the application is within the horsepower rating.

152

Step 3: Maximum tractive effort

Data sheet shows that 3200 pounds of tractive effort are required. Determine maximum tractive effort that can be realized with the transmission of Figure 16.34.

Using Motor Torque vs Δ psi curves, Figure 16.35, enter at maximum pressure

$$TE = (1850 \text{ in-lb} \times 30 \times 0.9 \; E_{fd} \times 2)/20$$
$$= R_L = 4995 \text{ lb}$$

Value calculated is well above required 3200 lb.

Step 4: Maximum vehicle speed

A maximum speed of 8 mph is desired. From the Flow vs Speed curve, Figure 16.36, enter at 2800 pump speed and project to pump curve; then across to 18-degree motor curve and read motor speed. Divide result by two because two motors are connected to the pump.

$$N_m = 2450/2 = 1225 \text{ rpm}$$
$$\text{mph} = (1225 \; N_m \times 20 \text{ in})/(30 \; FD \times 168)$$
$$= 4.86 \text{ mph}$$

Since the required 8 mph is not met with fixed displacement motors, alternatives must be explored. Two courses of action are available: 1) change final drive ratio, or 2) use some arrangement with variable displacement motors.

1. New final drive ratio. A change in final drive ratio is the best choice from a cost standpoint, unless the design is committed to the established ratio. Since sizing for wheel slip is required, use tractive effort to determine the new final drive ratio. A slip of *below* the relief valve setting is desired; therefore, the maximum tractive effort for calculating the new final drive ratio will be:

$$TE_{max} = TE_{slip} \times 1.04$$
$$= 3200 \times 1.04 = 3328 \text{ lb}$$
$$\text{New } FD = (3328 \times 30)/4995 = 20{:}1$$

Recalculate vehicle speed using new final drive ratio:
$$\text{mph} = (4.86 \text{ mph} \times 30)/20 = 7.29 \text{ mph}$$

This speed is based on full load governed (FLG) speed and horsepower. Reduced pressure required to overcome rolling resistance will result in higher volumetric efficiency and increased pump speed because of lower torque required. Therefore, check the maximum speed at no load governed (NLG) pump speed and 100% volumetric efficiency. From the data sheet, NLG pump speed is 3000 rpm.

$$N_M = 3000/2 = 1500 \text{ rpm}$$
$$\text{mph} = (1500 \times 20)/20 \times 168) = 8.9 \text{ mph}$$

The result exceeds the required 8 mph, so there is a good chance that it will be acceptable. If either the ratio change or speed is not acceptable, variable displacement hydraulic motors must be considered. Again, there are two options: either using one fixed motor and one variable displacement, or both variable displacement.

2. Specify variable displacement motors. The most economical design, both from cost and simplicity of controls, would include one fixed and one variable displacement motor. Calculate motor speed for 8 mph:

$$N_m = (\text{mph} \times FD \times 168)/R_L$$
$$= (8 \times 30 \times 168)/20 = 2016 \text{ rpm}$$

Calculate the combined motor displacement of the fixed displacement motor at full stroke and the variable displacement motor at minimum stroke, to obtain a motor speed of 2016 rpm. Pump output, at 2800 rpm, from the Flow vs Speed curve, Figure 16.36, is 29 gpm. Therefore, the combined theoretical motor displacement,

$$V_m \text{ total} = (29 \times 231)/2016 = 3.32 \text{ in}^3/\text{rev.}$$

Minimum displacement of the variable displacement motor will be 3.32 - 2.5 or .82. Minimum yoke angle is
$$\text{Tan}^{-1} [(.82 \times \tan 18\text{-degrees})/2.5]$$
$$= 6.08 \text{ degrees}$$

Motor displacement at a swashplate angle of 7 degrees has been established as the minimum displacement that will provide acceptable torque efficiency. Therefore, swashplate stops for swashplate angles of less than 7 degrees are not offered. A 7-degree yoke angle is available, so calculate speed using one fixed motor at 2.5 in³/rev. and one variable motor at 7-degrees (or .94 in³/rev.).

Total motor displacement = 2.5 + .94, or 3.44.

To calculate motor speed:

$$N_m = (29 \; gpm \; Q_p \times 231)/3.44 \; V_m = 1947 \text{ rpm}$$
$$= (1947 \times 20)/(30 \times 168) = 7.7 \text{ mph}$$

If speed is acceptable, also calculate the maximum motor speed in the event the roll with the variable displacement motor slips and total pump output of 29 gpm is consumed by that motor.

$$N_m = (29 \text{ gpm} \times 231) \text{ in}^3/\text{gal}/.94 = 7126 \text{ rpm}$$

Maximum motor speed must not exceed 4000 rpm, so means are required to limit maximum speed.

An alternate approach to using one fixed and one variable displacement motor is to set the variable motor minimum stop at zero degrees. This approach has been used successfully on a number of applications requiring an extended speed range. If such a motor is used, total pump output of 29 gpm will be consumed by the fixed displacement motor. From the Flow vs Speed curve, Figure 16.36, the intersection of 29 gpm and the 18-degree motor curve is found at 2600 rpm motor speed.

$$\text{mph} = (2600 \; N_m \times 20\text{-in.} \; R_L)$$
$$/(30 \; FD \times 168 \; R_L) = 10.3 \text{ mph}$$

If this approach is to considered, the next step is to determine if tractive effort to overcome rolling resistance at maximum speed can be achieved at a reasonable pressure:

$$RR = (8000 \times 55)/1000 = 440 \text{ lb}$$

Then, motor torque required is

$$\begin{aligned} T_m &= (RR \times R_L)/(\times e_{fd}) \\ &= 440 \times 20/(30 \times .9) = 326 \text{ in-lb} \end{aligned}$$

Using the Motor Torque vs Pressure Differential curve, Figure 16.35, enter at 1000 psi to 325 in.-lb. The necessary torque to overcome rolling resistance is achieved at slightly less than 1000 psi.

If a speed of 10.3 mph is too fast, it will be necessary to use two variable displacement motors. Total displacement at 8 mph was calculated to be 3.32 in^3/rev. Therefore, minimum displacement per motor would be 1.66 in^3/rev.

Swashplate angle
$$= \tan^{-1} (1.66 \times \tan 18\text{-degrees})/2.5$$

Use either 11- or 13-degree swashplate stops in the motor, determined by the 8-mph requirement. Half total pump output of 29 gpm for two motors in parallel is 14.5 gpm. From Figure 16.37 and the formula for vehicle speed, motor speed at both stop sizes can be determined:

11 degrees = 2050 rpm or 8.13 mph
13 degrees = 1650 rpm or 6.55 mph

Therefore, the 11-degree stops will be used.

Check maximum motor speed. Because variable displacement motors are used in parallel, total pump output can flow to one motor in the event it slips out. Be sure that maximum motor speed does not exceed 4000 rpm. Assume 100% volumetric efficiency and NLG pump speed of 3000 rpm.

$$N_m = (3000 \times 2.5)/1.5 = 5000 \text{ rpm}$$

Since maximum speed will exceed maximum rated speed, means are required to limit maximum speed. With the exception of a 2-speed final drive, most of the feasible approaches to the application have been explored. Each presents a compromise in either economics or performance, but there are alternatives and data upon which to base a decision.

The preceding illustrations demonstrate that the system designer must consider a multitude of factors in properly specifying a hydrostatic transmission. While the details in sizing procedure may vary from one manufacturer to another, the basic engineering concepts remain the same.

Important Terms

Breakaway torque. The actual torque a hydraulic motor must be capable of delivering when starting from zero initial velocity and accelerating to steady state velocity.

Closed Circuit HST. A transmission in which the flow path in the power circuit is a continuous, uninterrupted path from the pump discharge port to the motor inlet port and directly back to the pump.

Closed Loop HST. A class of hydraulic servo systems incorporating a feedback loop in the control function to make the system self-regulating.

Critical speed. The lowest speed at which maximum constant power can be transmitted by an HST.

Corner horsepower. The product of maximum output speed and maximum output torque in a rotary drive system.

Constant horsepower HST. One which delivers constant power to the load under varying conditions of speed and load magnitude.

Constant torque HST. One which delivers constant torque to the load under conditions of varying speeds.

Open loop HST. One in which no feedback loop is used in the control function to make the system self-regulating.

Open circuit HST. One in which the power flow path is not continuous; fluid drawn from a reservoir by the pump is delivered to the motor inlet port and returned from the motor to the reservoir.

Running torque. Motor capacity under rated operating conditions.

Stall torque efficiency. Ratio of actual torque capacity of the hydraulic motor at zero speed to its theoretical torque capacity, expressed as a %.

Torque-Speed Ratio. Ratio of critical speed to maximum speed of an HST.

Vehicle Corner Limit (VCL). Product of vehicle maximum speed, in mph, and maximum tractive effort in.lb.

Review Exercises

16.1. Define hydrostatic transmission.

16.2. Discuss the advantages of an HST.

16.3. Discuss the implications of Figure 16.1.

16.4. Discuss the function of an HST in matching load and prime mover characteristics as illustrated in Figure 16.4.

16.5. Explain why there is a drop in power at each shift in gear ratio as illustrated in Figure 16.5.

16.6. Discuss the effects on motor performance illustrated in Figure 16.6. What is the significance of *actual* operating point vs *theoretical* operating point?

16.7 Discuss the concept of characteristic variances detailed in Figure 16.7.

16.8. Referring to Figure 16.8: Discuss the significance of the 1st *level approximation*. Why is it considered an approximation only?

16.9. In Figure 16.8: Discuss the relationships between the *function concept* level and the 1st level approximation. Why is it considered to be a refinement of the 1st level?

16.10. Consider the parametric level of Figure 16.8 : Discuss variations in principal parameters corresponding to inlet-outlet locations. Relate to Figure 1.4.

16.11. Why must mechanical losses be added on the inlet side of the pump and subtracted from the outlet side of the motor?

16.12. Why must hydraulic losses be subtracted from the outlet side of the pump and added to the inlet side of the motor?

16.13. Discuss the idea that pumps and motors are functional inversions of each other. How is this illustrated in Figure 16.8? Discuss.

16.14. Where does the pressure indicated on the horizontal axis in Figure 16.8 come from? Relate this to Figure 1.4.

16.15. Discuss the speed matching problem illustrated in Figure 16.9.

16.16. Is is possible (or impossible) to maintain constant output speed in the application of Figure 16.9? Explain your answer.

16.17. Discuss the relationship of the drive illustrated in Figure 16.9 to the concept of Figure 16.8.

16.18. How do the Flow vs Speed plots of Figure 16.9 illustrate the idea of functional inversion between pumps and motors? Discuss the idea of output speed drop as a function of pressure, as illustrated in Figure 16.10. Is is possible for the speed drop curve to change over a period of time in service? Explain.

16.19. If an output speed drop characteristic like that shown in Figure 16.10 is unacceptable for an application, is it possible to correct it in any way? Explain your answer.

16.20. Discuss the potential effect of contamination on the characteristic shown in Figure 16.10. Would excessive operating temperatures affect it? Explain. Discuss possible effect of hydraulic fluid properties on it.

16.21. What is meant by *breakaway torque* relative to a hydraulic motor?

16.22. What load components comprise breakaway torque?

16.23. Discuss the implications of breakaway torque on starting a load-motor system from zero initial velocity.

16.24. What is meant by *stall torque efficiency* as applied to a hydraulic motor?

16.25. Discuss the relationship between breakaway torque and stall torque efficiency for a motor. What effect does this have on selecting a hydraulic motor for an application ? Explain.

16.26. Discuss cogging in conventional hydraulic motors. How can it affect motor performance in an application? Discuss the effect of low speed operation on the efficiency of a conventional motor, particularly volumetric efficiency.

16.27. Given a hydraulic motor with a displacement of $15 \text{ in}^3/\text{rev}$ displacement; assume it turns at a speed of 2000 rpm; volumetric efficiency is 90% at rated pressure. Plot a curve of e_v vs N_o, where $N_o = 400$ rpm, 800 rpm, 1200 rpm and 2000 rpm .

16.28. Repeat exercise 16.27 using SI metric units.

16.29. Discuss the proposition that properly sizing a motor for an application is more difficult that sizing a pump.

16.30. What is meant by an *integrated* HST?

16.31. What other type of HST system is there? How do they differ?

16.32. What four functional types of HST systems are there?

16.33. Discuss horsepower lost over the relief valve as characterized by the curves in Figure 16.16(a). Why does lost hp peak then decrease as the hydraulic motor speeds up? Relate this to the characteristic shown in Figure 6.3.

16.34. In the constant torque HST represented in Figure 16. 16(b) explain why overall efficiency is low at low speeds and increases as output speed increases.

16.35. Figure 16.16(c) represents a constant horsepower HST. Explain the output torque and overall efficiency curves shown in the figure.

16.36. The HST represented in Figure 16.16(d) provides the most flexibility of the four types: ( ) True or ( ) False. Discuss why the characteristics are plotted for two ranges of speed as well as the parametric relationships for each curve over both ranges.

16.37. What limiting condition must be placed on destroking a variable displacement motor 1) in a drive such as illustrated in Figure 16.16(c); 2) in a drive such as in Figure 16.16(d)? Is it practical to destroke the motor to neutral? Explain.

16.38. The application example shown on p. 138 is oversimplified. Discuss what factor(s) would have to be considered to bring it into conformance with an actual application.

16.39. What is meant by *critical speed* in a constant power transmission?

16.40. What is meant by *torque-speed* ratio? Discuss how it relates to HST performance.

16.41. Discuss *corner horsepower* as it relates to a power transmission system. How does it relate to *machine corner limit*?

16.42. How does interposing a multiple step ratio gear box between motor and load affect the corner horsepower characteristic? Sketch a plot similar to that of Figure 16.19(*b*) for a 4-speed gear box. Discuss how an HST would be characterized on such a speed-torque plot.

16.43. Discuss how the circuit schematics for the 4 types of HSTs shown in Figure 16.16 are oversimplified.

16.44. Relating to Figure 16.20, discuss what each element added in steps (*a*) through (*g*) brings to the circuit in improved performance of the HST system. What would be the effect of eliminating each feature from the system?

16.45. Sketch a complete constant power HST circuit diagram incorporating all the elements of Figure 16.20. Use ISO symbols.

16.46. Discuss the similarities and differences between your circuit of exercise 16.45 and the alternative illustrated in Figure 16.21. What are the advantages and disadvantages of each?

16.47. What are the functions of the charge pump in a closed HST circuit? Discuss the cavitation control function in detail.

16.48. What can be the effect on pressure operated automatic controls for variable displacement pumps, if cavitation occurs because of inadequate charge pump capacity? How can this condition be corrected?

16.49. Discuss the proportional flow characteristic for an HST illustrated in Figure 16.25.

16.50. Compare the displacement controls summarized in Figure 16.26.

16.51. Why would servo displacement control be used with a variable displacement HST pump?

16.52. What is the basic difference between an open circuit and a closed circuit HST?

16.53. What consideration limits maximum speed of open circuit HST pumps? Explain.

16.54. What technique can be used to overcome the constraint discussed in exercise 16.53?

16.55. Discuss the differences between charge pump and supercharge pump functions.

16.56. What factors enter into sizing a charge pump?

16.57. What factors enter into sizing a supercharge pump? Discuss.

16.58. Discuss pressurizing the reservoir as a supercharge technique. What safety precautions must be taken?

16.59. Discuss the variable displacement pump controls outlined in Chapter 15, when used in HST applications.

16.60. Discuss constant torque and torque summing controls illustrated in Figure 16.31.

16.61. Discuss applications of contamination control techniques to HST systems. How can they be applied to closed circuit HSTs? Compare to open circuit HSTs.

16.62. Discuss *dynamic braking* in an HST. Discuss the brake valve illustrated in Figure 16.33.

16.63. What is meant by *machine corner limit (MCL)*? How is it used in sizing an HST for an application? How does *MCL* compare with *corner horsepower*?

16.64. What is the significance of application coefficient as illustrated in Figure 16.33?

16.65. Do all HST manufacturers use a similar method for projecting component limitations relative to application requirements? If an HST were applied beyond the limitation defined by the *application coefficient*, what would be the effects on the components?

16.66. What is meant by *single path* and *dual path* in HST systems?

16.67. What is meant by *tractive effort to slip*? How does it affect HST sizing? How does it compare to *maximum tractive effort*?

16.68. If sizing calculations for an HST result in acceptable *tractive effort* but at too low a speed, what can be done to correct the design? Discuss.

16.69. If output speed is acceptable but tractive effort is too low, what can be done to correct the design? Discuss.

16.70. Why must minimum motor swashplate angle be considered? Discuss how it can be calculated.

16.71. What is meant by *rolling resistance*? Why is it important as an HST design parameter?

16.72. What is *gradeability*? How is it used in HST design?

16.73. Rework the example outlined in the text and illustrated in Figure 16.38 using SI metric units.

Earlier, we distinguished between circuit design and analysis. **Design** is largely an intuitive process. It requires broad experience in addition to comprehensive knowledge of the basic "tools of the trade." This is perhaps the reason why newcomers to the fluid power technology are seldom accomplished designers. Previous chapters have attempted to bridge the "experience gap" in the *design* of fluid power systems.

Analysis, on the other hand, is primarily a matter of methodology. Once the method is mastered, it can be applied universally to all relevant situations, thus minimizing the need for intuitive judgment.

A full treatment of the mathematical analysis of a fluid power system is beyond the scope of this book. This chapter on graphic analysis has been included simply to introduce the student to the antithesis of design. The hydraulic motor has been selected to illustrate this technique.

THE IDEAL HYDRAULIC MOTOR

An ideal hydraulic motor is adequately and completely described by these two equations:

$$Q = V_d N / 231 \qquad (17.1)$$

and

$$T = (\Delta p V_m / 2\pi \text{ lb-in} \qquad (17.2a)$$
$$= \Delta_p V_m)/24\pi \text{ lb-ft}, \qquad (17.2b)$$

where

Q — flow rate, gpm
V_a — displacement, in^3
N — shaft speed, rpm
T — output torque, lb-ft or lb-in
Δp — differential pressure, psi

By an ideal device or system we mean one in which there are no losses. The best way to study a non-ideal system is to begin with the ideal, then proceed to explain why the real system departs from this.

Four variables affect the performance of an hydraulic motor: two *input* variables, namely pressure and flow rate; and two *output* variables, torque and speed. The displacement will be considered constant, if in fact it is not fixed. Two of the variables are independent; the other two are dependent. This follows directly from Equations (17.1) and (17.2).

If pressure and flow rate are known, then speed and torque are fixed. One might say that while *two* equations describe a motor, there are *four* unknows. Two variables must be known before the other two can be calculated.

The best way to describe a motor graphically is to plot its input and output characteristics. The input characteristics are represented by the curves of torque versus speed, with pressure as a parameter.

Input characteristics

In an *ideal* motor, flow rate depends only on speed and the one motor constant, namely displacement. Thus, if speed remains constant, flow rate does NOT depend on pressure. Although you can plot as many constant speed curves as you wish, typically, four different speeds will suffice, Figure 17.1

If we specify input pressure and output speed, then flow is fixed. From Equations (17.2) we can calculate output torque. Note that we could have drawn the input curves using output torque as a parameter, but speed is more convenient.

Output characteristics

To examine output characteristics, plot torque versus speed using input pressure as a parameter. Here again, we could use flow rate as a parameter, but pressure is more convenient.

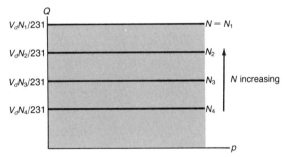

Fig. 17.1. Flow rate depends only on motor displacement and rotating speed.

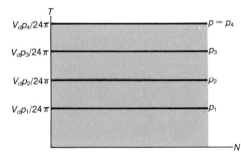

Fig. 17.2. When input pressure is held constant, torque does not depend on speed.

Equations (17.2) show that if input pressure is held constant, torque does NOT depend on speed. The output curves for four pressure values are shown in Figure 17.2.

THE REAL MOTOR

Most manufacturers supply the important data pertinent to the performance of their hydraulic motors, such as
- displacement
- rated pressure
- rated speed
- volumetric efficiency, and
- mechanical efficiency.

If the actual input-output characteristics are not available, the designer can use the above information to estimate the characteristics of the real component.

Input characteristics

First, let us consider why the input-pressure and flow characteristics of a real motor differ from those of the ideal. All positive-displacement motors are constructed of moving parts which are in contact with the fluid. For moving parts to move, they must have suitable clearances. Stated realistically, a well-designed motor is the result of the best compromise between minimum friction and minimum leakage.

It can be reasoned that in any motor, flow attributed to leakage losses (slip) follows a path which begins at the input port and ultimately finds its way either to the output port or to a case drain line. If the motor is used in a circuit where one of the ports is always connected to tank, then in most practical instances the output port and drain line are at the same pressure. Input flow can follow either of two possible internal paths. One is taken by the major portion of oil flow, which displaces the output shaft of the motor, and results in useful work. The other is the leakage path, which allows fluid to return to tank without displacing the output shaft. The fluid that follows this path does no useful work, Figure 17.3. An equation can be written to represent the main flow and the leakage flow:

$$Q_{in} = Q_l = q \qquad (17.3)$$

Now let us see how slip loss will alter the ideal input curves. By definition, the volumetric efficiency, e_v, of a motor is:

e_v = theoretical flow/measured flow) 100%,

or

$$e_v = Q_T/Q_{in}. \qquad (17.4)$$

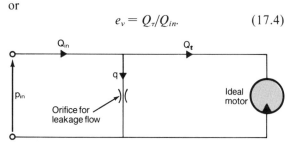

Fig. 17.3. Leakage flow does no useful work.

It is important to remember that a manufacturer's published volumetric efficiency is valid only if the fluid motor is operated at rated speed and rated pressure. These rated values give us a point on the input curves where we can calculate the departure from the ideal fluid motor.

Here is the procedure. Find the rated pressure on the abscissa and project upward to the curve for the rated speed. The flow rate at this point is the *theoretical* flow rate required to operate the ideal motor of the model depicted in Figure 17.3. It follows directly from Equation (17.4) that

$$Q_{in} = Q_t/e_v \qquad (17.5)$$

If we calculate the input flow rate using the theoretical flow rate (at rated speed) and the published volumetric efficiency, we can use the result to determine our operating point of the actual motor, Figure 17.4.

The distance between this new point and the theoretical flow rate represents leakage. From Equation (17.3),

$$q = Q_{in} - Q_t \qquad (17.6)$$

Substituting Equation (17.5) into Equation (17.6), we obtain

$$q = Q_t(1/e_v - 1)$$

or

$$q = Q\left(\frac{1 - e_v}{e_v}\right) \qquad (17.7)$$

This expression can be used to evaluate the dis-

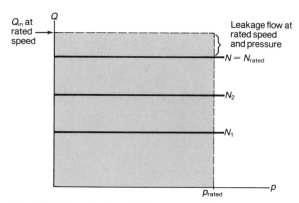

Fig. 17.4. Knowing input flow rate and published volumetric efficiency, the designer can determine an operating point of an actual motor.

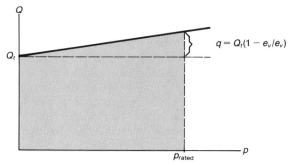

Fig. 17.5. If the actual input flow curve is assumed to be a straight line, the new curve will be as shown above.

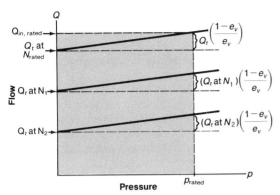

Fig. 17.6. Change in motor speed does not affect leakage flow. Curves are parallel because leakage flow was assumed to be the same at common pressure for all speeds.

tance between the actual and theoretical operating points. It should be emphasized that when the published value of e_v is used, the leakage calculated from Equation (17.7) will be valid only if Q_t is the theoretical flow at rated speed and the motor operates at rated pressure.

A useful approximation consists in remembering that when input pressure is zero (*i.e.,* when there is no mechanical load on the output shaft), slip flow is zero. The actual input flow curve must approach the theoretical value as pressure approaches zero. If we assume that the "curve" is a straight line, the new curve will be as in Figure 17.5.

Changing motor speed does not appreciably change leakage flow, which is relatively independent of speed. The result is a family of curves which intersect the Q-axis at the theoretical flow rate, Figure 17.6. The curves are all parallel because leakage flow, as we assumed, is the same at a common pressure for all speeds.

Consider the assumptions we have made so far:
• leakage losses depend only on pressure, not on speed
• the actual flow rate approaches the theoretical as pressure approaches zero
• leakage flow is directly proportional to input pressure.

These assumptions are not valid in all cases. However, with their help we have managed to describe the hydraulic motor reasonably well over its *entire operating range.* In the absence of empirical data, such a description provides a good approximation to the actual operating characteristics of the motor.

Output characteristics

Let us now consider the output characteristics of the real motor. The ideal motor develops constant torque when the pressure differential across the motor is constant. Torque is *independent of speed,* because in the ideal motor we assumed that there is no friction. In actuality, of course, there is friction. We already know that not all of the theoretically developed torque given by Equations (17.2), can be

realized at the output shaft. Some must be lost in overcoming the friction between moving parts. However, we can gain some insights into the mechanical torque losses from the manufacturer's published figures for mechanical efficiency, for a motor:

$$e_m = actual\ torque/theoretical\ torque$$

or

$$e_m = T_{act}/T_t = T_{act}/(V_m\Delta p/24\pi) \quad (17.8)$$

Manufacturers publish values for mechanical efficiency based on measured data at a specific set of operating conditions, usually rated pressure and speed. Let us consider the speed-torque curves for the ideal hydraulic motor to see how these curves must be modified so they will apply to a real motor.

The available torque at rated conditions can be found from Equation (17.8):

$$T_{act} = p_{rated}V_d e_m/24\pi \quad (17.9)$$

This equation provides one operating point on the speed-torque curves. For lack of experimental evidence to the contrary, we shall use straight-line approximations for the curves between rated speed and zero speed. If we assume that the viscous losses depend only on speed, then the entire family of speed-torque curves for the various pressures will be parallel, Figure 17.7.

A serious objection can be raised to the curves shown in Figure 17.7. We know that more torque is needed to start a body rotating than it does to keep it going once the breakaway process has started.* Reason: to start a rotating body, static friction (or "stiction," as it is sometimes called) must be overcome; once rotation has begun, the friction component changes to a lower, dynamic one. At zero speed the realizable torque is considerably less than the theoretical torque because of stiction. However, the designer is not justified in assuming that it is negligible. If the fluid motor manufacturer does not supply the breakaway torque, there is no alternative but to measure it.

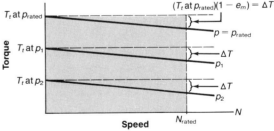

Fig. 17.7. Family of speed torque curves. If it is assumed that viscous losses depend only on speed, curves will be parallel.

A simple method for determining stiction torque is to connect the motor to a variable, low-pressure source with the output shaft free, then slowly increase pressure until the shaft just breaks away. If this pressure is substituted in Equation (17.2), the

---

See Chapter 4.

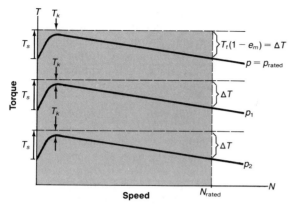

Fig. 17.8. Family of speed torque curves reflect operation at sustained low speeds.

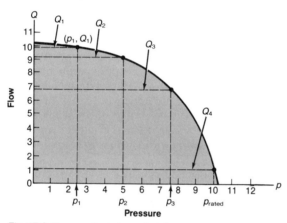

Fig. 17.9. Pump output characteristics.

resulting torque will be approximately the loss due to stiction. If Δp_s is the differential pressure required to just start the unloaded motor, then

$$T_s = (V_d \Delta p_s)24\pi \qquad (17.10)$$

Stall torque efficiency is the ratio of the actual torque available at the motor shaft at zero output speed to the output torque available under rated operating conditions,

$$e_s = T_s / T_t \times 100\%,$$

or

$$T_s = T_s e_s \qquad (17.11)$$

During the same test we might also find out what pressure is required to sustain some speed which is well below rated speed. If the speed is low, viscous friction is negligible; therefore, pressure measured during this test will be that required to overcome Coulomb friction losses.*

If Δp_k is the pressure required to sustain the low speed, then

$$T_k = (V_d \Delta p_k)/24\pi \qquad (17.12)$$

With these new data the speed-torque curves can be

Coulomb friction is friction due to rubbing of surfaces. Unlike viscous friction, it is not related to velocity.

further refined, as shown in Figure 17.8. Any greater accuracy would require experimental tests. The curves developed here describe the speed-torque relationship at the motor shaft when input pressure is held constant.

Output characteristics with variable input

Generally, output flow from a pump is a function of output pressure. Let us assume that the hydraulic motor is connected to a source whose characteristics are as shown in Figure 17.9.

Figures 17.10 and 17.11 show the input and output characteristics of the motor with a set of normalized values for flow rate, pressure, speed, and torque. For the sake of this discussion, let us assume a value of 10 units for rated pressure and 10 units for rated speed.

To determine what the output of the motor will be when it is connected to the source illustrated in Figure 17.9, we proceed as follows:

Step 1. Assume that the source is delivering fluid at a pressure, p_1, of 2.5. Now, find the corresponding value of Q (Q_1) on the curve of the source *output characteristics*. If we regard (p_1, Q_1) as an actual operating point, then output flow is fixed at the value

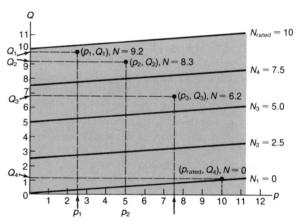

Fig. 17.10. Input characteristics of hydraulic motor with normalized values for flow rate, pressure, speed, and torque.

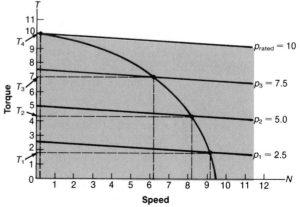

Fig. 17.11. Output characteristics of hydraulic motor with normalized values for flow rate, pressure, speed, and torque.

Q_I, which is approximately 9.8.

Step 2. When the motor is connected to the source, output flow and pressure of the source must be the same as the input flow and pressure of the motor. So let us locate the point (p_I, Q_I) in Figure 17.10.

Step 3. Now, to interpret the location of (p_I, Q_I) in Figure 17.10. Note, first, that the point (p_I, Q_I) does not fall exactly on one of the curves for constant speed. Input flow rate is not high enough to produce a speed of 10, but is higher than the flow rate which will produce a speed of 7.5. The speed of the motor must, therefore, be somewhere between 7.5 and 10. We can assume that the speed will be closer to 10 than to 7.5, because the point (p_I, Q_I) is closer to the curve $N = 10$. By interpolating, we can determine what the speed is.

Step 4. The increment in speed that the motor actually has in excess of the lower speed here appears to be about 0.7 of the distance between the adjacent speed curves, $7.5 < N < 10$. Therefore, the increment in speed is $0.7 \times 2.5 = 1.75$. The actual speed now will be 1.75 greater than the value at the lower of the two curves. Thus $N = 7.5 + 1.75 = 9.2$.

Step 5. To summarize: If the source output pressure is at a level of $p_I = 2.5$, flow out of the source (which is also the flow into the motor) is at a level of $Q_I = 9.8$. This requires that the motor operate at a speed of about $N = 9.2$.

Step 6. Now that we have determined the operating speed of the machine, we can use this value to find the torque from the curve of the motor output characteristics, Figure 17.11. Project a line upward from $N = 9.2$ to the curve $p_I = 2.5$. The corresponding value for T (T_I) will be the output torque of the motor, which is about 1.8.

Step 7. Now, select a new pressure, p_2, and repeat the process. This has been done for three more pressures, p_2, p_3, and p_{rated}, in Figures 17.9, 17.10 and 17.11. A curve drawn through the four points established in this manner is shown in Figure 17.11 and represents the output characteristics of the transmission made up of the source (pump) described in Figure 17.9 and the motor described in Figures 17.10 and 17.11.

Even though we used a hydraulic motor as our example, the technique for graphic analysis described here can be applied to fluid power circuits in general. The application of the method to specific circuit problems is left to the ingenuity of the student.

NODAL DIAGRAMMING

The technique of nodal diagramming was devised by the author to provide a visual display of "steady-state" operating conditions in a multi-branched circuit. In earlier chapters, we described the cycle-profile plotting technique as a method for characterizing a load and the motor requirements to handle it. Nodal diagramming is an extension of cycle-profile plotting in that such a profile is neces-

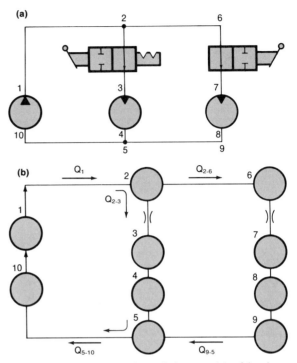

Fig. 17.12. Nodal diagramming technique consists of drawing a line diagram with a circle at each junction point. Two-branch circuit is shown drawn with conventional ISO graphic symbols (a) and nodal diagram, (b).

sary for each branch before a nodal diagram can be made.

The nodal technique consists of drawing a line diagram with a circle at each junction point, or "node." This is illustrated for a two-branch circuit in Figure 17.12. Figure 17.12(a) shows the typical circuit, using conventional ISO graphic symbols; Figure 17.12(b) illustrates the nodal diagram for the circuit.

The usefulness of the diagram lies in its ability to display varying circuit operating conditions, such as pressure drop around the loops, flow rates into and out of junctions, etc. Two fundamental laws governing fluid power systems must be applied.

1. Pressure-drop law. The sum of the pressure drops around any circuit loop must equal the sum of the pressure drops around any other loop with the same terminal nodes.

2. Flow law. The sum of the flows entering a node must equal the sum of the flows leaving it.

Application example — 1

These laws can be illustrated using the circuit of Figure 17.12 as an example. First, we illustrate the pressure-drop law:
1. Fluid will always flow from a point of higher pressure (potential) to one of lower pressure.*

---

*See *Introduction to Fluid Mechanics* by Russell W. Henke (Addision-Wesley Publishing Co.), pp. 48-52, 60-61.

2. The pressure at point 2 of Figure 17.12(a) is the same for branch 2-6-9-10 as for branch 2-5-10. This is true because point 2 is the entrance point for both parallel loops in the circuit.

3. Similarly, the pressure at point 5 must be the same for the inner loop, 1-2-5-10, as for the outer loop, 1-6-9-10, since point 5 is common to both loops.

4. According to the laws of fluid mechanics, the product of flow rate and pressure drop across loop 2-5 must equal the product across loop 2-6-9-5. This is true because both loops terminate at the same node, therefore, at points of equal pressure (or potential). Thus, transferring fluid around either loop results in dissipation of the same amount of energy.

Figure 17.12 can also be used to illustrate the flow law:

1. Fluid flow will divide at a node in such a way that the energy dissipated in the branches leaving the

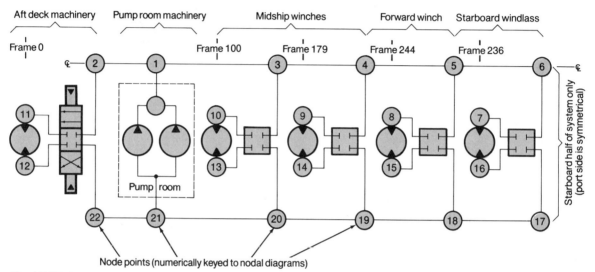

Fig. 17.13. Application illustrates usefulness of nodal diagramming technique in analyzing multibranch circuit.

Machinery location (starboard side)	Case I	Case II	Case III	Case IV	Case V
Aft frame 0	1200 / 610	535 / 280	535 / 280	535 / 280	0 / 0
Midships frame 100	535 / 280	1200 / 610	535 / 280	535 / 280	0 / 0
Midships frame 179	535 / 280	535 / 280	1200 / 610	535 / 280	0 / 0
Forward frame 244	535 / 280	535 / 280	535 / 280	1200 / 610	0 / 0
Windlass frame 236	0 / 0	0 / 0	0 / 0	0 / 0	1000 / 512

rpm / gpm

1200 rpm at 600 gpm = 9,000 lb line pull = maximum speed
535 rpm at 280 gpm = 20,000 lb line pull = maximum torque

Machinery location	Case VI	Case VII	Case VIII	Case IX	Case X
Forward starboard frame 244	535 / 280	535 / 280		535 / 280	
Midships starboard frame 100	1200 / 610		535 / 280		
Aft starboard frame 0	535 / 280		535 / 280	1200 / 610	535 / 280
Aft port frame 0	585 / 280	535 / 280	535 / 280		1150 / 585
Forward port frame 244		535 / 280	1200 / 610	535 / 280	1150 / 585
Midships starboard frame 179		1200 / 610		535 / 280	

Fig. 17.14. Summary of performance envelop of system illustrated in Figure 17.13.

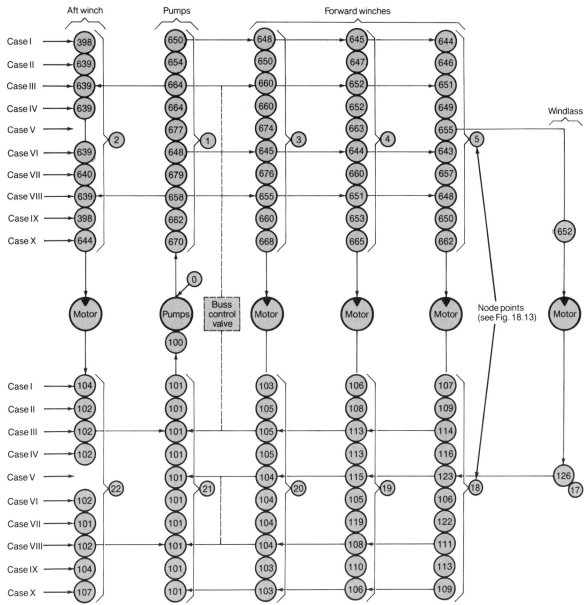

Fig. 17.15. Nodal diagram shows pressure drop pattern for entire circuit according to performance envelope as shown in Figure 17.14.

same node will be equal.

2. Thus, if pump discharge flow rate, Q_1, enters node 2, the flow rates leaving the node will be Q_{2-3} and Q_{2-6}.

3. Flow rates Q_{2-3} and Q_{2-6} will be inversely proportional to the resistance of the flow path in their respective loops.* This resistance is made up of all the lines, control valves, and fittings, plus the pressure drop across the motor, Δp_{3-4} or Δp_{7-8}.

4. Since fluid cannot be destroyed, $Q_1 = Q_{2-3} + Q_{2-6}$. That is, we must account for all of the fluid flowing in

*See Introduction to Fluid Mechanics, pp. 163-165, 168-175. See Introduction to Fluid Mechanics, pp. 65-68, 80-82, 86-98, 168-175.

the circuit as either a flow entering the node or leaving it. The algebraic sum of the flows must be zero. Similarily, in the return line, $Q_{9-5} + Q_{2-3} = Q_{5-10}$.

The nodal diagramming technique is most useful when one wants to display the operating conditions of a circuit under varying loads. The highest load reaction, the lowest load reaction, the highest flow rate, the lowest flow rate, and reactions and flow rates at critical operating points define the "performance envelope" for the fluid power system. It is important to know what the branch flow rates are at such points. It is also important to know what the branch residual pressure drop across the motors will be under varying conditions. Conversely, it is necessary to know what the loop pressure drops are to determine what relief valve setting is required to insure a high enough pressure differential, Δp across the motor to handle the load.

Application example — 2

An actual application will help illustrate the usefulness of the nodal diagramming technique in analyzing a multibranched circuit. Figure 17.13 is a simplified circuit diagram drawn with ISO graphic symbols.

The arithmetic analysis required to arrive at the numbers shown in the sample nodal diagrams is not included here. It consists merely of calculating all the flow-rate vs pressure-drop factors around each loop, being careful to include every element of flow resistance in the branch. Also, refer to Figure 15.1.

The table of Figure 17.14 summarizes the performance envelop, as specified by the designer. The numbers indicate the required speeds at different operating points, and flow rates need to achieve them. Required torques are also specified; torque

figures were used to size the hydraulic motors.

The nodal diagram, Figure 17.15 shows the pressure-drop pattern for the entire circuit according to the performance envelope defined in Figure 17.14. What is shown is the residual pressure at each node under each condition. The pressure drops can be determined by subtracting any downstream pressure from any upstream pressure on the diagram.

Figure 17.16 illustrates some of the flow nodal diagrams. There are ten for this example, because ten conditions were specified in the operating envelope. Only two typical ones are shown here.

These nodal diagrams provide a working tool to anyone involved in checking system performance against design criteria. Since the nodal diagram represents operating conditions at critical points in the cycle, the designer can use it to *size* the circuit components. Once the circuit is installed, field personnel can use the diagram to *check* actual performance against theoretical requirements. This check will indicate the presence of any malfunction and where it might be occurring.

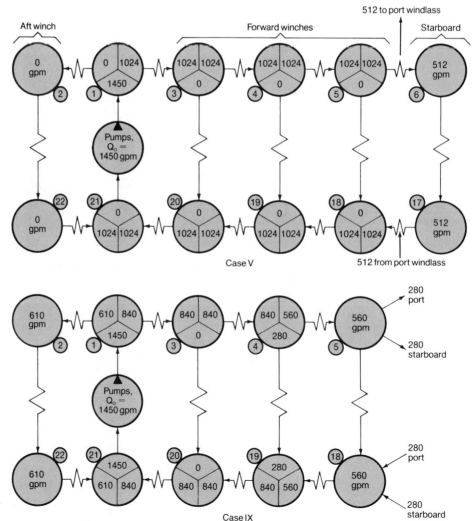

Fig. 17.16. Flow nodal diagram.

164

Important Terms

Actual characteristic is one in which allowance is made for energy losses which occur in real systems.

Graphic analysis is the technique of using graphical plots of a dependent variable as a function of an independent variable to determine the performance characteristics of a component or system within a specified performance envelope.

Ideal characteristic of a component or system is a characteristic in which no account is taken for energy losses: it assumes that all energy input is recovered as useful output.

Input characteristic is the statement, usually mathematical, of the state of an input variable, such as flow rate or pressure.

Node is a point in the system at which the input and output characteristics are to be evaluated. Most nodes are at the junction of two or more branches of a circuit.

Nodal diagramming is a graphical technique for displaying the state of a system variable at each node, usually at one or more points defined by the performance envelope.

Output characteristic is the statement, usually mathematical, of the state of an output variable, such as force, torque, velocity, or speed, as a function of an input variable or variables.

Performance envelope is a set of specified values of component or system characteristics—pressure, flow, temperature, etc.—which define the maximum and minimum operating conditions for the component or system.

Exercises

17.1. Discuss the differences between design and analysis.

17.2. What is meant by the term ideal component or system?

17.3. Sketch a block representation of an ideal hydraulic motor showing input and output variables.

17.4. Sketch a block representation of an ideal cylinder showing input and output variables.

17.5. Discuss why it is important to use pressure differential, Δp, in calculating hydraulic motor torque, rather than input pressure.

17.6. Sometimes pump discharge pressure is used to calculate motor torque. What, if any, inaccuracies result from this practice? Are such inaccuracies significant in analyzing hydraulic motor capabilities?

17.7 Given a hydraulic motor displacement of 2 in^3/rev. Pump discharge pressure is 1500 psi. Calculate the ideal output torque from the motor. What is wrong with stating the question this way? (Hint: what causes pump pressure in the first place?)

17.8. For the motor of example 17.7, sketch the plot of ideal flow rate, Q_t vs. pressure, p; for speeds $N = $ 500 rpm; 1000 rpm; 1500 rpm and 2000 rpm.

17.9. For the motor of example 17.7 sketch the plot of ideal torque-speed curve for pressure levels, $p_i = 750$ psi, 1500 psi, 2250 psi and 3000 psi. What is the relationship between this plot and the load torque-load speed cycle profile plots as developed in Chapters 4 and 5?

17.10. Referring to example 17.9: in fact, where do the pressures stated derive from? Why might motor pressure differential more correctly be considered an output, and load torque an input?

17.11. What is meant by the term internal leakage (slip)? Draw a sketch to show how it might be graphically represented in a hydraulic motor.

17.12. What is the effect of slip on motor performance?

17.13. In example 17.7, given hydraulic motor volumetric efficiency, $e_v = 92\%$ at 3000 psi pressure differential and rated speed of 2000 rpm. For the motor speeds of example 17.8, calculate the input flow rates required and plot the Q vs. Δp curves.

17.14. Referring to example 17.13: calculate the volumetric efficiencies at each speed. Why do they differ from the volumetric efficiency at rated speed? What would the effect be on overall motor efficiency?

Fig. 17.15. Calculate the heat generated under operating conditions stated in example 17.13.

17.16. Discuss the implications of the curves plotted in Figure 17.5 and 17.6 on hydraulic motor performance and circuit design requirements.

17.17. Referring to example 17.9: given hydraulic motor mechanical efficiency, $e_m = 94\%$ @ rated pressure of 3000 psi and speed of 2000 rpm. Assuming a straight line characteristic, what would be the actual output torques for the pressure levels given in the example?

17.18. Referring to example 17.14 and 17.17, calculate the overall efficiencies for the 4 specified operating points.

17.19. Referring to Figure 17.8 and example 17.17, given a stall torque efficiency of 60%, calculate the actual torque the motor can deliver to the load under specified pressures.

17.20. Discuss the implications of stall torque characteristics of hydraulic motors and breakaway (load) requirements as discussed in Chapter 3, on motor selection for circuit applications. What if the breakaway torque requirement is greater than the stall torque capability of the motor?

17.21. Previous discussions have shown that linear actuator (cylinder) variables can be related by the following equations: $F_L = pA_p$ and $Q_{in} = A_p v_p$, where $F_L = $ *load reaction lbs*, $p = $ pressure level at force of the piston, psi $A_{p;tr}$ — *area of the piston over which the load reaction is distributed, in²;* Q_n = input flow rate in³/time, v_p = load velocity, in or ft/time. Using these relationships, draw ideal Q vs. p curves for several load velocities, similar to those of Figure 17.1 for a motor.

17.22. Referring to example 17.21, draw ideal force vs. load velocity curves for several pressure levels, similar to Figure 17.2 for a motor.

17.23. Discuss the relationships between the ideal cylinder and hydraulic motor plots.

17.24. Assume internal leakage exists in the cylinder of example 17.21, represented by q. Draw a diagram similar to Figure 17.3 representing flow rate slip relationships for the cylinder.

17.25. Sketch an actual Q vs p plot, similar to Figure 17.4, for the cylinder at several load velocities.

17.26. Given a cylinder with a 4-in bore and a measured load velocity v_p = 30.65 fpm. Calculate the ideal input flow rate required, Q_{in}.

17.27. In example 17.26, slip is measured and found to be 1 gpm at a load pressure of 3000 psi. Calculate the volumetric efficiency of the cylinder. Why, in your opinion, do cylinder manufacturers not provide volumetric efficiency data for cylinders?

17.28. Given the conditions of example 17.27, what is the ideal force capability of the cylinder?

17.29. Given a mechanical efficiency of 80% for the cylinder of example 17.28, what would be the actual output force? Why, in your opinion, do cylinder manufacturers not provide data on mechanical efficiency of cylinders?

17.30. Referring to the cylinder of example 17.26: draw input characteristics similar to Figure 17.6, for several load velocities.

17.31. Referring to example 17.29: draw output $F_L mntr$ vs. v_p characteristics, similar to Figure 17.7, for several load pressures.

17.32. Discuss what effect backpressure on the head end of the cylinder would have on output force capability as calculated in examples 17.28 and 17.29. A more accurate expression for the $F_L = pA$ relationship is $F_L = (p_i - p_b)A_p + p_b$ were p_i = inlet pressure; p_b = back pressure; A_p = bore area; A_R = rod area. Discuss and derive this expression.

17.33. What two physical laws form the basis for the nodal diagramming technique?

17.34. Discuss the circuit and nodal diagram of Figure 17.12 from the perspective of these two laws.

17.35. Using the example illustrated in Figures 17.13 and 17.14, draw the flow nodal diagrams for Cases II and VII.

CHAPTER 18

HEAT GENERATION AND CONTROL

In previous discussions of fluid power circuits,* we introduced the subject of energy losses and considered qualitatively the conversion of such losses to heat. In this chapter we shall consider heat generation and how it contributes to higher system operating temperatures. We shall also discuss techniques for minimizing heat generation.

HEAT GENERATION IN PUMPS AND MOTORS

Rotating fluid power components, such as pumps and motors, operate at less than 100 percent efficiency. This means that more input energy is put into the system than is recovered as output, Figure 17.10. In other words,

$$HP_{in} = HP_{out} + q_{loss}, \qquad (18.1)$$

where the loss through heat generation

$$q_{loss} = wC_p \Delta T$$

where:
  w —flow rate in terms of mass weight
  C_p —specific heat of the fluid
  ΔT —temperature differential, F

Remembering that the expression for pump efficiency,

$$e_p = HP_{out}/HP_{in},$$

and that

$$1 \text{ hp} = 42.44 \text{ Btu/min},$$

we can rewrite Equation (18.1) as:

$$HP_{out}/e_p = (HP_{out} + wC_p \Delta T)/42.44.$$

Substituting,

$$HP = Q\Delta_p/1714,$$

and solving for ΔT, we get

$$\Delta T = (Q\Delta p/wC_p)\left(\frac{1-e_p}{e_p}\right)(42.22/1714).$$

*See Introduction to Fluid Mechanics by Russell W. Henke (Addison-Wesley Publishing Co.); and Chapters 1, 4, 5 and 17 of this volume.

but since $w = \gamma Q\, 62.4 S_g Q$, the temperature differential, in degrees F, is

$$\Delta T = 2.97 \cdot 10^{-3}(\Delta p/S_g C_p) \\ [(1-e_p)/e_p] \qquad (18.2)$$

Thus, you can estimate the temperature rise that will occur in a pump or motor operating at a given efficiency if you know two elements: (a) the pressure drop across the component and (b) the specific gravity and specific heat of the fluid.

Note that Equation (18.2) presumes that all heat generated is used to increase the fluid temperature. Though this is not quite the case in an actual circuit, Equation (18.2) is still useful in that it gives the *maximum* temperature rise that *could* occur. Its practical value is enhanced by the fact that rates of heat dissipation by convection and radiation are extremely difficult to determine in actual systems.

TEMPERATURE RISE DUE TO THROTTLING

All fluid power control valves use throttling to achieve control. This throttling is evidenced as a pressure drop across the valve with resultant heat generation. Consider, for example, the heat generated and the resulting temperature rise, when hydraulic fluid returns to tank through a relief valve. Let us assume that there is no heat loss at the valve.

Again, starting with the horsepower equation,

$$HP = Q\Delta p/1714,$$

and

$$1 \text{ hp} = 42.44 \text{ Btu/min},$$

the heat equivalent to a given horsepower is

$$42.44\, Q\Delta p/1714 = 2.48 \times 10^{-2} Q\Delta p \text{ Btu/HP}$$

But from Equations (18.1) we see that the heat equivalent to a given horsepower also equals $wC_p \Delta T$. Equating these two expressions for heat:

$$wC_p \Delta T = 2.48 \times 10^{-2} Q\Delta p.$$

But since $w = 8.35 S_q Q$, we can substitute this value in the above equation and solve for ΔT:

$$\Delta T = (2.48 \times 10^{-2} \Delta p)/(8.35 S_g C_p).$$

Thus the temperature differential is, in F:

$$\Delta T = (2.97 \times 10^{-3} \Delta p)/S_g C_p. \qquad (18.3)$$

Now consider the case where the relief valve is bypassing and recirculating fluid back to the inlet port of a pump, Figure 18.1. Note that the fluid is not returned to reservoir, where it would have a chance to mix with and be cooled by cooler fluid already in the reservoir.

Let us first define the bypass ratio R_B as

$$R_B = Q_R/Q_i,$$

where Q_R is bypass or relief-valve flow and Q_i is system flow. Total heat in the system flow is $w C_p \Delta T$. Then,

$$w_s C_p T_s = w_o C_p T_o + w_R C_p T_R,$$

where the subscripts refer to suction or inlet (s), reservoir (o), and relief-valve or bypass flow (R).

Inlet flow equals the sum of the flows from reservoir and bypass. Thus

$$w_s = w_o + w_R.$$

Substituting in Equation (18.3) and dividing by the specific heat of the fluid, C_p, we get:

$$(w_o + w_R) T_s = w_o T_o + w_R T_R.$$

Since by definition,

$$R_B = w_R/w_i, \text{ then}$$
$$w_R = R_B w_i.$$

Also, since

$$w_i = w_s - w_R$$
$$\text{and } w_s = w_o + w_R,$$

therefore,

$$w_i = w_o + w_R - w_R = w_o.$$

Thus,

$$w_R = R_B w_o.$$

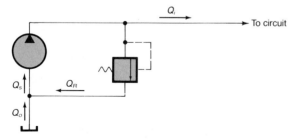

Fig. 18.1. Relief valve is bypassing reservoir and recirculating fluid back to pump inlet port, preventing return fluid from being cooled in reservoir.

Now we can rewrite

$$(w_o + w_R) T_s = w_o T_o + w_R T_R,$$

as

$$w_o T_S + R_B w_o T_s = w_o T_o + R_B w_Q T_R.$$

By rearranging terms, we get

$$T_s - T_o = R_B (T_R - T_s).$$

Since, $T_R - T_s$ is the same as

$$(T_R - T_s) + (T_i - T_s)$$

then Equation (18.4) gives an approximation of the temperature rise between the fluid which leaves the reservoir (Q_o in Figure 18.1) and the fluid in the inlet to the pump when the relief valve is open, (Q_s in Figure 18.1).

To estimate the temperature at the pump outlet, we add to Equation (18.4) the expression for temperature rise across the pump, namely

$$T_i - T_o = (T_i - T_s) + (T_s - T_o).$$

By suitable substitution and simplification, we get

$$T_i - T_o = (2.97 \times 10^{-3} \Delta p)/(S_g C_p)$$
$$\left[(R_B + 1 - e_p)/e_p \right] \qquad (18.5)$$

HEAT GENERATION AND HEAT BALANCE

In a hydraulic system, heat is produced by the dissipation of energy which does no useful work. To keep track of how much energy enters and leaves the system, the designer or analyst develops a heat balance, which could be considered analogous to an accountant's balance sheet. In this section we give the equations needed to create a "heat balance."

First,

$$q_e = q_A + q_d, \qquad (18.6)$$

where:

q_e — heat loss generated internally in the system, Btu/hr,

q_A — heat absorbed by oil, reservoir, and components, Btu/hr,

q_d — heat dissipated or transferred to atmosphere, Btu/hr.

Heat balance is a transient phenomenon, except where long-term, steady-state operation is involved. Hence, we should refine Equation (18.6):

$$g_e \, dt = (\Sigma G_p W_c) \Delta T \, dt + (\Sigma K A) \Delta T \, dt, \qquad (18.7)$$

where:

W_c —combined weight of oil and system components, lb

K —heat transfer coefficient

A —surface area of system, ft^2,

ΔT—temperature differential between system and surrounding air.

Since heat generated is equal to work input less work output, we can write,

$$q_e = (K_1 Q \Delta p / e_p) - K_2 (dG/dt) \quad (18.8)$$

where:

$K_1 = 1.481$ Btu/hr-psi-gal

$K_2 = 1.285 \times 10^{-3}$ Btu/ft-lb,

dG/dt is the rate of work done (ft-lb/hr) ($G =$ energy). Equation (18.8) can also be written as

$$q_e = K_1 Q_p (1 - e_p).$$

Note that if G is cyclic, dG/dt must be the average rate over one complete cycle.

Where system temperature is at equilibrium, the heat generated equals the heat dissipated:

$$q_e = (G_c + G_r) A (T_M - T_s), \quad (18.9)$$

where

G_c —convection heat transfer coefficient, Btu/ft^2—hr-F,

G_r —radiation heat transfer coefficient, Btu/ft^2— hr-F.

T_M —average maximum system temperature, R (Rankine) = F = 460,

T_s —temperature of surroundings, degrees R.

The convection heat transfer coefficient is found from equation:

$$G_c = \left[(\bar{T}_m - T_s)^{0.25} /_D \right] \times 0.22, \quad (18.10)$$

where:

$\bar{D}$ —average diameter of tubing, reservoir, and components is the system (ft)

$\simeq 4 \times$ system volume area

The radiation heat transfer coefficient is found from equation:

$$G_r = F_s F_r, \quad (18.11)$$

where:

F_s — gray-body shape factor,

F_r — temperature factor

$= [0.171 (0.01 \, \bar{T}_M)^4 - (0.01 T_s)^4] / \bar{T}.$

The gray-body shape factor F_s is a function of a geometrical shape factor and an emissivity factor E. For a system installed in a large room or outdoors,

$$F_s \simeq E.$$

For a system installed in an area which is not large in comparison to the system,

$$F_s \simeq 1 / [(1/G) + (A / E_s A_s) - (A / A_s)],$$

where:

A_s — surface area of surroundings,

E_s — emissivity of surroundings.

We can now rewrite Equation (18.9):

$$q_e / A = (0.22 / D^{-0.25})(T_M - T_s)^{1.25} + 0.171 F_s [(0.01 \bar{T}_M)^4 - (0.01 T_s)^4]. \quad (18.12)$$

Earlier, we stated that heat balance is usually a transient phenomenon. Equations (18.11) and (18.12) were developed with this thought in mind. However, it should be noted that when time t is long, a steady-state condition is achieved such that

$$\Delta T_{\max} = q_e / A, \quad (18.13)$$

where $\Delta T_{\max}$ is the maximum steady-state temperature difference.

Application example

To illustrate heat balance, let us consider a hydraulic system in which a cylinder exerts cyclically a constant force of 40.15 lb through a stroke a 1.6 ft. The force is exerted for 3 sec, and the piston is retracted during the next 2 sec; a negligible amount of work is done; system capacity is 7 gallons. The outside area of the system is 22.4 ft^2; flow rate is 4 gpm at 90 percent efficiency. Pump discharge pressure is 625 psi, and we assume that the pump has a negative inlet pressure of -5 psi. The system is in a large room, $E = 0.5$; ambient temperature is 70 F.

Step 1. The rate of work done is

$$dG/dt = (40.15 \times 1.6)/5 \times 3600,$$
$$= 46{,}250 \text{ ft-lb/hr}.$$

Step 2. Recall that the average diameter of the tubing, reservoir, and components in a system is roughly $(4 \times$ system volume$)$/area. Thus,

$$D = (4 \times 7 \times 0.1337)/22.4 = 0.167 \text{ ft}.$$

Step 3. Now, using Equation (18.8), we can find the amount of heat generated in the system:

$$q_e = (K_1 Q \Delta p / e_p) - K_2 dG/dt,$$
$$= (1.481 \times 4 \times 630)/0.90$$
$$- 1.285 \times 10^{-3} \times 46{,}250,$$
$$= 4101 \text{ Btu/hr}.$$

Then,

$$q_e / A = 4101/22.4 = 183.5 \text{ Btu/hr-ft}^2$$

Step 4. By substituting the values we have for q_e / A, D, and F_s in Equation (18.12), we get

169

$$183.5 = (0.22/0.167^{0.25}) (\overline{T}_M - T_s)^{1.25}$$
$$+ 0.171 \times 0.5 [(0.01\overline{T}_M)^4$$
$$- (0.01 T_s)^4],$$
$$= 0.344 (\overline{T}_M - T_s)$$
$$+ 0.0855 [(0.01\overline{T}_M)^4 - (0.01 T_s)^4].$$

Since the value of T_s was given as 70 F, we could solve the above equation algebraically to find T_M, the average maximum system temperature. Ordinarily, however, the solution is best accomplished graphically*. It will be found that T_M is about 175 to 180 F.

HEAT TRANSFER AND DISSIPATION

Here are additional equations and information for calculating heat generation:

1. *Radiation heat transfer can be calculated from:*

$$q = FA(T_2^4 - T_1^4)G,$$

where:

q —rate of heat transferred, Btu/hr/ft^2/F
F —form factor, dimensionless
A area of radiation surface, ft^2
T^2, T_1 —temperatures
G —Stephen Holtzman constant

2. *Newton's Law for convective heat transfer is:*

$$q = hA(T_2 - T_1),$$

where h is the film coefficient of heat transfer, Btu/hr(ft^2)(F). Typical values of h:
- for nominally 2-in-dia. horizontal steel cyl.: $h = 1.1$
- for 1 ft. high vertical plate/free convection in air: $h = 0.8$

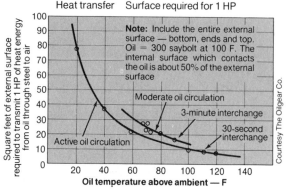

Heat transfer   Surface required for 1 HP

Note: Include the entire external surface — bottom, ends and top. Oil = 300 saybolt at 100 F. The internal surface which contacts the oil is about 50% of the external surface

Moderate oil circulation
3-minute interchange
30-second interchange
Active oil circulation

Fig. 18.2. Area required to dissipate 1 HP of heat energy for various temperatures above ambient.

Refer to heat transfer charts in handbooks on heat transfer, such as Industrial Heat Transfer by Francis W. Hutchinson (Industrial Press, Inc.).

- for air flow @ 2m/sec past 0.2 msq plate: $h = 2.1$
- for air flow @ 35m/sec past 0.75 msq plate: $h = 13.2$.

Empirical equations for free convective heat transfer from reservoir walls/bottom clear of floor:

a — for bottom $h_p = 0.2 (\Delta T)^{0.25}$
b — for top $h_t = 0.38 (\Delta T)^{0.25}$
c — for sides $h_s = 0.30 (\Delta T)^{0.25}$
  where height exceeds 1 ft.
  $h_s = 0.28 (\Delta T)^{0.25}$
  where height is less than 1 ft.

3. *Heat conductivity of typical materials*

material	conductivity: Btu/hr(ft^2) (F)
aluminum	10,500
brass	720
copper	2070
iron	450
lead	240
oil	1.02
steel, mild	1620
steel, alloy	180
water	3.78

Courtesy the Oilgear Co.

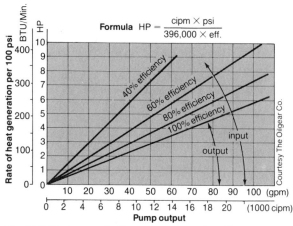

Formula $HP = \dfrac{cipm \times psi}{396,000 \times eff.}$

Fig. 18.3. Heat generated by various sizes of auxiliary pumps.

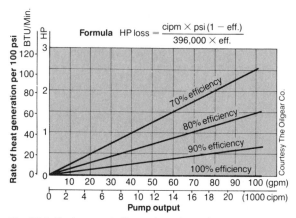

Formula $HP\ loss = \dfrac{cipm \times psi (1 - eff.)}{396,000 \times eff.}$

Fig. 18.4. Heat generated by various sizes of power pumps.

4. *Empirically determined heat transfer character-*
istic of a typical hydraulic installation

The curves shown in Figure 18.2 are based on tests
run on different types of pump-reservoir designs with
pump delivery discharged over a relief valve to the
reservoir.

While test results have been normalized to relate
square feet of external surface required to transmit 1
hp equivalent heat energy from oil-to-steel-to-air,
judgment should be used in applying the curves to

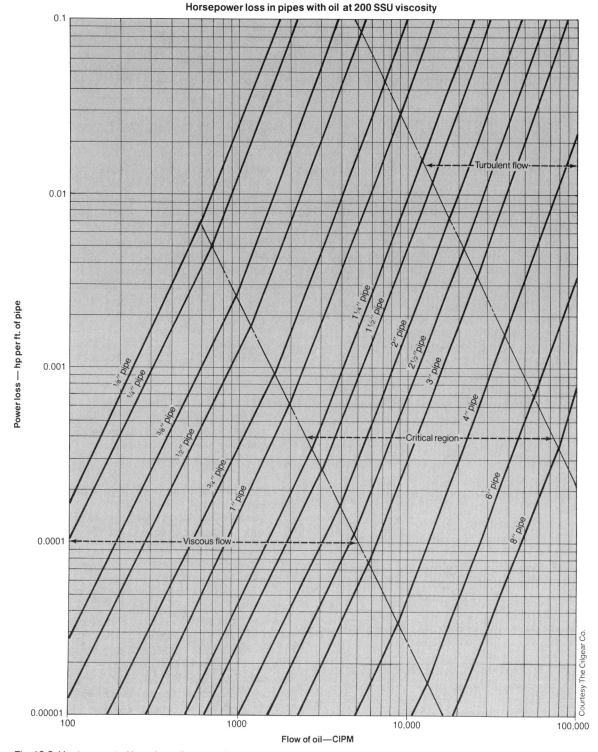

Fig. 18.5. Heat generated in various diameter pipes.

specific hydraulic installations.

5. The curves shown in Figure 18.3, relate rate of heat generation by auxiliary pumps in hydraulic systems to flow and pump efficiency.

6. Figure 18.4 provides heat generation for power pumps at varying flow rates and efficiencies.

7. The curves of Figure 18.5 show power loss in hydraulic system piping for oil with a viscosity of 200 SSU. For oils of other viscosities a correction factor is given in Table 18.1.

Table 18.1

Viscosity, SSU	Head loss in percent of head loss at 200 SSU
100	83
150	92
200	100
300	112
400	120
600	135
800	148
1000	158
1500	170
2000	187
3000	210
4000	222

Correction factors for oil viscosities other than 200 SSU.

Courtesy The Oilgear Company

8. Example:

The steering system of a ship is to be powered by a variable displacement pump; no heat exchanger is to be used. How large must the oil reservoir be to handle the heat by natural heat dissipation?

Power requirements indicate that the designer should specify a pump which delivers 35 hp at 1100 psi and 56 gpm. While steering the ship, the pressure differential varies continuously between 0 and 1300 psi, estimated to equal a continuous pressure of 200 psi at 1 gpm. At such low power, the pump overall efficiency will be about 70%. Figure 18.4, indicates that the heat generated is 0.02 HP/100 psi, or 0.04 HP at 200 psi. To make it easier to use the curve at such low values, divide both scales by 10.

The auxiliary pump delivers 9 gpm at 150 psi at an efficiency of 60%. Figure 18.3 shows that the heat generated is 0.89 HP/100 psi or 1.3 HP.

The pipes and valves are large enough to handle the 56 gpm; the average flow of 1 gpm is so small that these losses are negligible. Thus total heat generated is 1.3 + 0.4 = 1.7 HP.

The radiating surfaces include the sides, bottom, and top of the pump and reservoir. Since the cylinder system is non-differential, oil will flow from one cylinder through the pump into the other cylinder, generating no heat, and not using hot oil from the reservoir. Thus piping and cylinders will remain relatively cool and cannot be considered as components that will dissipate heat. Because the electric drive motor is a separate unit which dissipates its own heat, it, too, is disregarded.

Since the oil interchange rate is about once in 3 minutes, we use the "Moderate Oil Circulation" curve of Figure 18.2. We will assume that room temperature will be 70 F and an oil temperature of 130 F is to be maintained. Thus the temperature rise above ambient is:

$$130 - 70 = 60 \text{ F}.$$

From Figure 18.2, we find that 31 ft² will be needed to dissipate each HP of heat energy at 60 F above ambient. Since we must dissipate 1.34 HP, the required surface area of pump and reservoir must be $1.34 \times 31 = 41$ ft².

Experience with steering installations on more than 100 ships has shown that the temperature estimated in this example was within 4 F of the temperature actually obtained.

CAUSES OF HEAT GENERATION

The following factors generate heat in a hydraulic systems:

1. *Flow restriction or throttling*
2. *Excessive flow velocities*. For example, with a ½-in OD smooth pipe, a flow rate of 10 gpm generates heat at the rate of about 25 Btu/ft-hr. Doubling the flow to 20 gpm increases heat generation 8 times to about 200 Btu/ft-hr. Note, however, that if you specified a 1-in OD pipe, the flow rate of 20 gpm generates heat at the rate of only about 10 to 15 Btu/ft-hr. With a 1-in pipe, the flow rate would have to be about 65 gpm!
3. *Slip in pumps*
4. *Internal leakage in valves*
5. *Gas-filled accumulators*. Pulsating accumulators may develop high temperatures on the gas side, well above the temperature of the oil.
6. *Entrained air*. Expansion and compression of entrained air* can cause localized heating. Tests have shown that these processes can raise temperatures as much as 25 percent.
7. *Non-regenerative release of potential energy*. When a load is lifted hydraulically, potential energy is stored in the load. Release of the load usually involves non-regenerative throttling, which generates heat.
8. *Mechanical losses in rotating or reciprocating components*
9. *Auxiliary pumps*. Since auxiliary pumps, such as supercharge and lubrication pumps, do no useful mechanical work, the entire energy input to such a pump contributes to heat generation in the system. For example, an auxiliary pump with an output of 30 gpm at 80 percent efficiency produces heat at the rate of about 80 Btu/min at 100 psi. By the same

---

Unlike dissolved air (air in solution), entrained air is held mechanically by the fluid.

172

token, a power pump with an output of 30 gpm at 80 percent efficiency produces only about 20 Btu/min at 100 psi.

METHODS OF REDUCING HEAT GENERATION

Here are ways to minimize heat generation in a hydraulic system:

1. *use the most direct flow path*. In other words, use the shortest lines possible.
2. *Use the minimum number of fittings*, bends, and changes in cross sectional areas.
3. *Do not allow the pressure drop* across an open-center, 4-way valve to exceed 50 psi.
4. *Size valves so the flow area* through the valve equals at least 75 percent of the flow area in a comparable length of connecting tubing.
5. *Size the lines to maintain laminar flow*, if at all possible.
6. *Size the pump* so it will supply only the oil needed by the system. Pass a minimum of oil over the relief valve.
7. *Avoid throttling*, whenever possible.
8. *Use the reservoir to dissipate as much heat as possible*. Where practical, specify a reservoir with a capacity two to three times that of the pump. Maintain fluid level in the reservoir at a reasonable height during the working cycle. Use baffles to ensure maximum oil circulation within the reservoir — *i.e.*, the longest possible path between the return line and the intake line. Use materials of high heat conduction capacities, if necessary.

Heat generation levels

1. If the heat generation level is 5000 Btu/hr or less, the problem of heat is minimal. The system will likely be able to dissipate heat all by itself.
2. If the heat generation level is between 5000 and 10,000 Btu/hr, some care must be exercised in system design and installation.
3. If the level of heat generation exceeds 10,000 Btu/hr, expect trouble during periods of high ambient temperatures.
4. If the heat generation level is above 15,000 Btu/hr, you might as well plan on a heat exchanger.

Effects of type of system on heat generation

As mentioned, the two main types of hydraulic systems are constant flow and demand flow. In a constant flow system, the control valve, when in neutral position, allows free flow back to reservoir. In a demand flow system, when the valve is in neutral position, it blocks free flow back to tank.

As discussed in Chapter 7, a *constant flow* system uses a fixed-displacement pump and produces variable working pressures, depending on load. One disadvantage of this system, from the point of view of heat generation, is that maximum efficiency and therefore minimum heat losses occur at only one set of flow and load conditions. Losses under conditions other than optimum flow and load levels depend on the operating point. In addition, a constant flow system generates significant amounts of heat during standby, when full pump output continuously recirculates.

A *demand flow* system, equipped with a fixed-displacement pump and a bypass relief valve, is inferior to constant flow systems because pump output returns to tank over the relief valve when the system is at standby. Indeed, at any but the optimum operating point, part of pump output flows over the relief valve to generate heat.

When a demand flow system is specified with a pressure-compensated, variable-displacement pump, the pump delivers only enough fluid to maintain system pressure, as required by the load. At standby, the pump delivers only enough fluid to make up for leakage, while at maximum work rate it provides full flow. Since service pressure is approximately constant, power loss is incurred (and heat genrated) because of the throttling action of the control valve.

Based on this discussion, here are three more techniques for reducing heat generation:

1. Unload the pump during standby with an unloading valve.
2. Use multiple pumps adjustable to various operating requirements.
3. Use an accumulator to store potential energy received from gravitational or inertial loads.

Some rules of thumb

Several rules of thumb which are widely accepted in industry may be useful in estimating heat generation and dissipation for an average hydraulic system:

1. In an average hydraulic system, about 20 percent of input horsepower turns to heat.
2. Under normal operating conditions, average heat dissipation is about 1.5 to 2 Btu/ft^2-hr-F.

On the basis of these two rules, one would expect a 100-hp-system to generate about 50,000 Btu/hr. To maintain an equilibrium temperature differential of 75 F would require dissipation of between $1.5 \times 75 = 112.5$ Btu/ft^2-hr and $2 \times 75 = 150$ Btu/ft^2-hr. Thus the area of the system would have to be between $A_1 = 50,000/112.5 = 444.44$ ft^2 and $A_2 = 50,000/150 = 330$ ft^2.
3. Oil-to-air heat exchangers are least effective when most needed *i.e.*, under conditions of high ambient temperature.
4. Many heat-generating power losses in pumps and motors continue under no-load conditions. These components can overheat during standby unless proper provision is made for adequate dissipation of the heat.

Important Terms

British Thermal Unit, BTU. — Unit of heat in customary units system equal to the amount of heat necessary to raise the temperature of one pound of water one degree Fahrenheit.

Bypass ratio — Ratio of the flow rate exiting a system across a control device to total system flow rate.

Calorie — Amount of heat necessary to raise the temperature of 1 gram of water from 14.5 to 15.5 C at atmospheric pressure.

Conduction — Transfer of heat between parts of a continuous structure due to temperature difference.

Convection — The transfer of heat by the circulation or movement of the heated parts of a fluid.

Convective heat transfer coefficient, G_c — The heat transfer capacity by conduction of a system or element per unit temperature difference per unit of area per unit of time.

Emissivity factor, E — an empirically determined relationship for heat transfer by radiation.

Gray body shape factor, F_s — an empirically determined relationship between the geometric shape of a radiating body and an emissivity factor.

Specific gravity — The dimensionless ratio between the specific weight or density of any substance to that of water under standard conditions.

Specific heat, C_p — For a hydraulic fluid, the heat energy required to change a unit weight (or mass) of fluid through a unit temperature differential.

Radiation — Heat energy transmitted by electromagnetic waves.

Radiation heat transfer coefficient, G_R — The heat transfer capacity by radiation of a system or element per unit temperature difference per unit of surface area per unit of time.

Temperature — The measure of the heat energy of a body relative to some standard valve.

Exercises

18.1. What two basic conditions are necessary to cause heat generation in a hydraulic system?

18.2. State Pascal's Law[1] and discuss how it relates to heat generation in a fluid power hydraulic system.

18.3. It is impossible to generate a pressure drop without corresponding flow rate, True ( ) Fales ( ). Discuss your answer.

18.4. Discuss Bernoulli's Equation[2] and how it relates to heat generation in fluid power hydraulic systems.

18.5. Discuss the relationship between energy loss and heat generation in a fluid power system.

18.6. What effect does pump/motor case drain have on system heat generation and control?

18.7. Explain why auxiliary pump input power contributes to system energy loss and resultant heat generation.

18.8. Discuss the effect of excessive flow velocities in lines and piping on heat generation in a hydraulic system. On what physical relationship[3] is this phenomenon based?

18.9. Discuss why gas type accumulators contribute to heat generation.

18.10. How does entrained air in hydraulic fluids affect heat generation?

18.11. Does dissolved air have any effect on heat generation? Explain.

18.12. Discuss the relationship between effects of gas filled accumulators and entrained air on heat generation.

18.13. What is the difference between pump/motor slip and case drain? What effect does slip have on heat generation?

18.14. Given a gear pump: Displacement, $V_p = 5.8$ ins3mnxxrevvolumetric efficienncy, $e_v = 88\%$; discharge pressure, $p_i = 2500$; inlet pressure, $p_{s:tr} = -2\ psi$; $N_i = 2000$ rpm. Calculate heat generation due to slip in the pump.

18.15. In the gear pump of example 18.14, assume a mechanical efficiency of 88%; $N_i = 2000$ rpm. Calculate the energy loss due to mechanical losses. Do these mechanical losses contribute to heat generation in the system? Explain.

18.16. Given an axial piston motor with a displacement of 3.4 in^3/rev; output speed, $N_o = 2400$ rpm; volumetric efficiency, $e_v = 92\%$; mechanical efficiency, $e_m = 94\%$; inlet pressure, $p_m = 3000$ psi; back inlet pressure, $p_m = 300$ psi. Assume the motor is used in an open circuit with internal drain. Calculate the heat generation due to slip in the motor.

18.17. In example 18.16, what would be the effect of externally draining the motor?

18.18. In example 18.16, calculate the mechanical energy loss in the motor.

18.19. If the motor of example 18.16 was used in a closed circuit, would there be any effects on slip and mechanical losses? Explain. Calculate the losses for a closed circuit and compare them to those for the open circuit.

18.20. Discuss the effect of relief valve cracking load[4] on heat generation.

18.21. Given: a relief valve for a rated flow of $Q = 30$ gpm at $\Delta p = 1500$ psi. Cracking pr-ssure is 1100 psi. Assuming a straight line Q vs Δp curve in the cracking range, calculate the heat generated due to by-passing when load pressure is 1300 psi.

18.22. Given: a reducing valve with a control (quiescent) flow of 3 gpm at inlet pressure of 3000 psi. Calculate the heat generated by this control flow.

18.23. Given: a hydraulic cylinder with 6-in-bore. Load pressure is 2500 psi. Mechanical efficiency, e_m = 80%. Calculate heat generated by the cylinder as it extends through a 48-in. stroke.

18.24. Assume the cylinder of example 18.23 lifts a load vertically. Calculate the potential energy stored in the load at the end of the 48-in. stroke. Calculate the heat generated as this load is lowered by throttling return flow across a control valve.

18.25. Given: steel hydraulic tubing 2-in. in diameter, 20-ft long. Convective heat transfer coefficient, G_t = 1.1 Btu-hr/ft²-F. If the steel tube is replaced by 2 wire braid rubber hose of like capacity for which G_h = 0.26 Btu/hr-ft²-F, what would be the likely effect on fluid temperature — given the same rate of heat generation? Discuss your answer.

18.26. Discuss the effect on fluid temperature of dirt build-up on exterior surfaces of hydraulic system components.

18.27. Given a two-pass air-to-oil heat exchanger with a pressure drop, Δp = 150 psi at rated flow, Q = 50 gpm. Discuss how this situation contributes to heat generation and resultant change in fluid temperature.

18.28. A system has a constant pump delivery of 50 gpm with a relief valve setting of 3000 psi. A restrictive type pressure-compensated flow control valve is set to deliver 10 gpm of controlled flow to the actuator:
(a) Where does excess pump delivery go?
(b) Calculate the heat generated by excess flow.

18.29. Assuming a meter-in circuit in example 18.28, what alternatives are available to reduce heat generation due to the flow control valve?

18.30. Hydraulic lines in a circuit are sized to produce a flow velocity of 20 fps. What would be the effect on heat generation due to line losses and how much would these losses be if fluid flow velocity was increased to 40 fps?

18.31. A pressure-compensated pump is deadheading at 3000 psi. Its maximum displacement, V_p =2 in³/rev and volumetric efficiency, e_v =92%. Me-

chanical efficiency, e_m = 94%. Input speed is 1750 rpm.
(a) Calculate the estimated heat generated during stand-by under dead head conditions.
(b) Compare this with by-passing full pump flow over a relief valve set at the same pressure.
(c) Compare with by-passing full pump flow over an unloading valve with a Δp = 75 psi pressure drop.

18.32. Assuming that average heat dissipation is 1.5 to 2 Btu/ft²-hr-F, recalculate using SI metric units.

18.33. What is the heat generation rate at which a heat exchanger will be required?

18.34. Discuss the general differences between constant flow and demand flow systems from a heat generation point of view.

18.35. A typical reservoir, elevated above the floor to ensure maximum heat transfer by conduction and convection, is 24 in. high × 36 in. wide × 60 in. long. The reservoir is made of ¼ in thick mild steel. The fluid temperature is to be maintained at 125 F with an ambient temperature of 80 F. Calculate the maximum heat dissipation capability of the reservoir. How would this relate to heat generation rate in the system? If system heat generation rate exceeded the reservoir's dissipation capability, what alternatives are available to the circuit designer? Discuss.

18.36. A hydraulic motor is used for dynamic braking of a vehicle. Motor displacement is 4 in³/rev; Δp_m is 3000 psi; motor speed is 2400 rpm at start of braking mode. Assuming a straight line speed reduction characteristic, calculate the estimated heat generated during the braking period. Is it likely that a heat exchanger will be needed to handle this heat load?

18.37. Based on the rule of thumb that temperature of the oil will use about 7.6 F/1000 psi Δp, what would be the anticipated temperature rise of the fluid in example 18.37?

1 — Introduction to Fluid Mechanics, *Russell W. Henke, Addison Wesley Publg. Co., Reading, MA, pp. 8, 10, 22.*
2 — *Ibid. pp. 48-50, 54, 56, 58, 66, 69.*
3 — *Ibid. pp. 48-50, 159-176.*
4 — *Ref. Chapter 8.*

CHAPTER 19

NOISE and
NOISE CONTROL

Noise is an inherent characteristic of hydraulic systems. In the past, noise was "buried" in overall machine noise levels, particularly those of mobile equipment. With the passage of the Walsh-Healey Act and promulgation of OSHA regulations, noise levels have gradually receded, exposing hydraulic systems to criticism.

BASICS OF NOISE

Sound and noise

Sound is what the human ear hears when the ear drum vibrates because of air pressure waves. Sound is created by anything that disturbs the air sufficiently to send out these waves or walls of pressures: the more powerful the disturbance, the louder the sound.

Sound waves have two important measurable characteristics: *amplitude* (or strength) and *frequency* (or the number of times per second a pressure wave repeats). Amplitude is a measure of loudness; frequency of pitch — how low or high a sound is,

Figure 19.1. Amplitude is measured in decibels, *db*; frequency in cycles per second, formerly cps, now Hertz or Hz.

Noise is *undesirable* sound. Nearly all industrial sounds are classified as noise. For most, 75 db of low-frequency industrial noise is not objectionable. However, 85 db, with frequencies above 3000 Hz, are offensive to most.

The Federal government has legislated the noise amplitude and time to which employees may be exposed, Figure 19.2. A standard also has been set for instruments used in measuring decibel levels. This standard is a conventional sound pressure level meter with a built-in *A* scale filter. It shows sound wave pressures in decibels with a sensitivity comparable to the human ear, Figure 19.3.

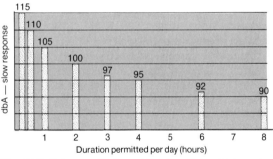

Fig. 19.2. Noise amplitude and time length to which workers may be exposed as permitted by OSHA.

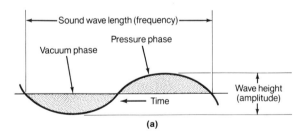

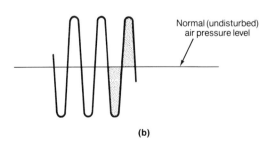

Fig. 19.1. Traces of (a) low decibel (loudness) low frequency (pitch) sound waves as seen on oscilloscope; and (b) high decibel, high frequency sound wave pattern.

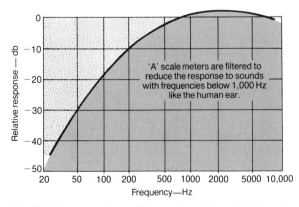

Fig. 19.3. Response of sound level meter as filtered with A scale filter.

When measuring industrial sound levels for compliance with OSHA requirements, this type meter is used. Readings are recorded in *dbA*. While sound pressure is the phenomenon which causes ear damage, sound frequency, even frequency mix and sound wave form, contribute to making sound irritating. Higher frequency sounds, even at the same sound pressure as a lower frequency sound, will be much more uncomfortable.

Types and sources of noise in hydraulic systems

Two types of noise are associated with hydraulic systems:
- fluidborn which is transmitted through the fluid;
- structureborn which is transmitted through the mechanical or structural parts of the system.

Sources of noise in hydraulic systems may be classed as:
- fluid-induced noise generated by high rate pressure gradients, such as cavitation and pump pressure ripple and pressure transients
- mechanically-induced noise generated by impacting mechanical parts, such as gear teeth, dynamic unbalance which sets up vibrations, vanes sticking in slots, and vibrating tubing.

Whatever the noise source, Figure 19.4, hydraulic system components can transmit and even amplify it as illustrated by flat sides of a reservoir functioning as a sounding board. Hard coupling of mechanical elements also intensifies sound transmission.

Hydraulic noise from sudden pressure changes

The most common source of noise in a hydraulic pump is caused by rapid pressure changes in the fluid. The greater and faster the pressure differ-

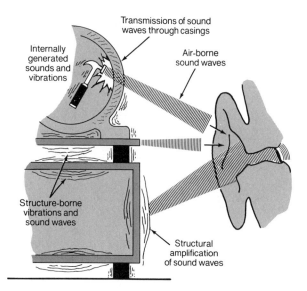

Fig. 19.4. Generation, transmission, and amplification of system noise.

entials, the more prominent the pump noise level.

In all pumps, fluid pressure increases in the chamber which moves fluid from the inlet to the outlet port. This transition area is called the cross-over zone. In an improperly designed pump, pressure builds too rapidly, generating more noise. Ideally, the pressure rise will be gradual over the entire cross-over zone, producing very little noise, Figure 19.5.

Compression and decompression pressure changes at the pump outlet port also create pressure ripple. As each volume of oil passes through the outlet port, it sends a minor shock wave through the system followed by a pressure decay. This establishes a repeating cycle of pressure waves.

When the ripple frequency resonates with mechanical parts in the machine, then the amplitude — and any resulting noise — increases.

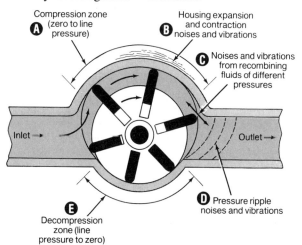

Fig. 19.5. Pressure changes generate noise in hydraulic pumps.

These violent compressions and decompressions cause many simultaneous reactions, affecting all masses and motions involved. The pump housing itself is deflected momentarily then returns to normal: expansion and contraction of the metal cause noise and create a pressure wave in the metal.

These pulsations are transmitted through the air directly to the ear, creating vibrations on the same frequency as the primary pump noise and vibration frequency (revolutions per minute times the number of vanes, pistons or gear teeth).

Pressure peaks and decays slow and speed the pump shaft slightly, also on the primary pump frequency. This shaft torque effect is the main cause of vibrations in any hydraulic fluid power system, transmitting these strong rotational vibrations through the pump housing to the entire system. If, in addition, a pump shaft is out of balance or misaligned, vibrations and noises are multiplied.

If any of the system components happen to be on the same frequency, a resonance is set up causing the entire hydraulic power unit to vibrate more than is normal.

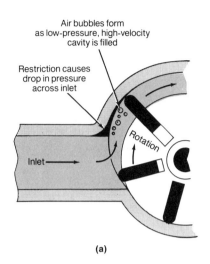

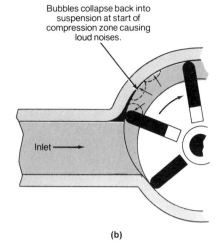

Air bubbles form as low-pressure, high-velocity cavity is filled

Restriction causes drop in pressure across inlet

Inlet →

Rotation

(a)

Bubbles collapse back into suspension at start of compression zone causing loud noises.

Inlet →

(b)

Fig. 19.6. Cause and effect of pump cavitation.

How aeration and cavitation cause noise

Mineral-base hydraulic oil generally contains about 9% dissolved air, which remains in solution as long as the absolute pressure is above a given level. When the fluid passes a restriction, velocity increases and static pressure drops below this level. The air comes out of solution, bubbles form and become suspended in the fluid. This phenomenon happens most commonly at the pump inlet from the oil reservoir, Figure 19.6. The pressure increase in the pump compression zone compresses these bubbles suddenly back into solution generating loud noises, pressure fluctuations, and vibrations throughout the system. Figure 19.7 summarizes typical *dbA* levels for hydraulic pumps.

The probability that cavitation will occur in-

creases when the fluid is aerated by additional air leaking into the system, usually in the inlet line. Cavitation is not rare. However, when it happens, sound level may jump 10 to 15 db with a characteristic shrill. Figure 19.8 illustrates the results of pump cavitation.

High fluid velocity, velocity changes, and turbulence can also cause cavitation in hydraulic motors and valves.

Air in oil

The amount of air a hydraulic fluid can hold in solution is proportional to the pressure the air exerts on the oil surface. A petroleum base fluid can absorb about 9% air, by volume, at atmospheric pressure and room temperature. This dissolved air does not change the viscosity or compressibility of the oil.

Subjecting a fluid saturated with air at atmospheric pressure to a vacuum of, say, 5 in. Hg, when it can only hold 7½% of air, would supersaturate the oil which would begin to release air, Figure 19.9. The rates at which air moves in or out of solution depend on such factors as pressure, temperature, fluid turbulence, and chemical composition. In addition to dissolved air, entrained air can also contribute to cavitation, see Chapter 25.

Pump Type	Decibels**
Screw type *	72-78
Vane (industrial)	75-82
Axial piston	76-85
Gear (powdered metal)	78-88
Vane (mobile)	84-92
Gear (machined stock)	96-104

*1700 gpm, 3500 rpm. (All others 10 gpm at 1200 rpm.)
**Lower range figure is at 500 psi; higher is at 1000 psi.

Fig. 19.7. Typical decibel levels of hydraulic pumps.

Fig. 19.8. Cavitation-damaged pump port.

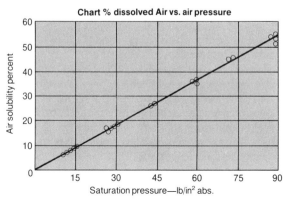

Fig. 19.9. Curve shows percentage of dissolved air as a function of pressure.

179

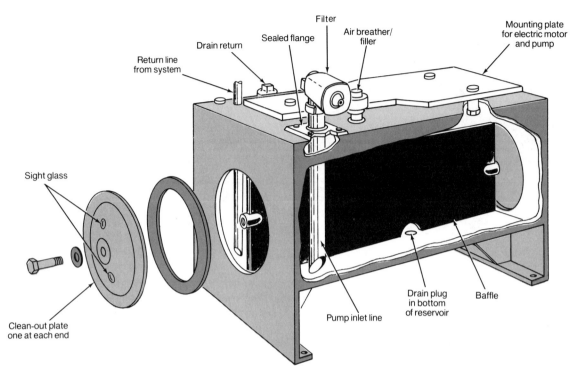

Fig. 19.10. Typical elements of well designed reservoir.

Viscosity, contamination and noise

Fluid viscosity by itself has no direct effect on pump noise. However, if the manufacturer's lubricity requirements are not maintained, rapid wear is likely to take place, which may increase the noise level. The manufacturer's contamination recommendations should be followed for the same reasons.

Outgassing or pump cavitation can be controlled by designing the pump inlet line to minimize the pressure drop from reservoir to pump. Here are good rules to follow:
● keep suction line velocities below 5 fps or 1.5 mps
● keep pump inlet lines short
● use a minimum number of bends and joints
● place the reservoir as high above the pump as practical thus providing a flooded inlet, if possible
● use low pressure-drop, indicating-type inlet filters or strainers; provide for easy servicing and replacement, and
● use a low viscosity oil, but above the minimum recommended by the pump manufacturer at the operating temperature of the system.

Figure 19.10 illustrates a well designed reservoir.

Sometimes air pressurized reservoirs are used to avoid inlet vacuums, Figure 19.11. Unfortunately, reservoir pressurization raises the saturation pressure of the fluid so that high inlet line pressure drops still cause outgassing. Keep in mind that the drop from the reservoir pressure, not the vacuum itself, produces outgassing

Air leaks cause noise

There are other sources of air bubbles in hydraulic

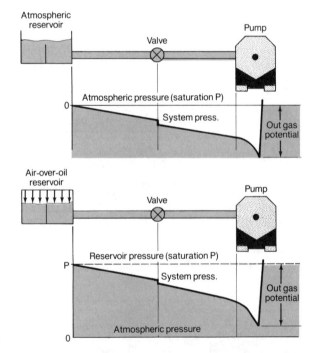

Fig. 19.11. Pressurized reservoir increases outgas potential.

fluids, Figure 19.12. A common one is air drawn into the pump inlet line through improper connections, pump shaft seals, valve stem seals, or any other part of the circuit which is under vacuum. This can occur even when joints are *oil*-tight: the fact that a joint does not leak oil externally when the pump is not

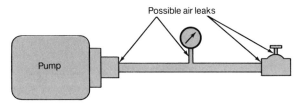

Fig. 19.12. Typical sources of air ingestion into pump inlet lines.

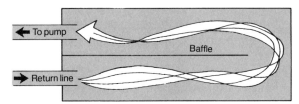

Fig. 19.13. Baffles in reservoir extend fluid travel time and increase bubble release time.

operating does not preclude air from being ingested.

In mobile hydraulics, pressurized reservoirs are used to insure that pressures in inlet lines are above atmospheric pressure, thus completely eliminating air ingestion. Remember, however, that pressurized reservoirs raise the fluid saturation pressure so that high inlet line pressure drop can still cause out-gassing.

Another source of air ingestion is around cylinder rod seals. If an instantaneous flow demand momentarily exceeds pump output, as when a load is dropped quickly, high vacuum conditions are created, causing air noise and shorter component life.

Reservoir must dissipate air

The best place to prevent air bubbles from becoming entrained in the hydraulic fluid is in the reservoir, Figure 19.13. When fluid returns to reservoir, it often contains bubbles which will dissipate, *if given enough time*. For this reason, reservoirs should be made large enough and have enough baffles to provide this time interval, Figure 19.13. A reservoir capacity equivalent to two minutes of maximum system flow is generally considered adequate. Lower capacity reservoirs can be used, but baffling then becomes critical to maximize the dwell time of the oil in the reservoir for bubble dissipation. Tank return lines should end as far from the pump inlet as possible and the discharge directed to produce the longest flow path to the pump inlet.

When adequate reservoir size or baffling cannot be provided, sloping screens can be used to help separate air from oil, Figure 19.14. Experiments have shown that a 60 mesh screen installed at a 30-degree angle from the horizontal will effectively remove to 90% of air bubbles. Also see Chapter 25.

Return lines below oil level

Returning oil *must* enter the reservoir below the

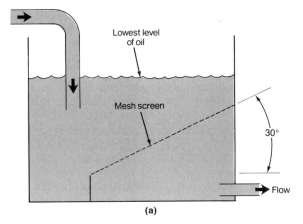

(a)

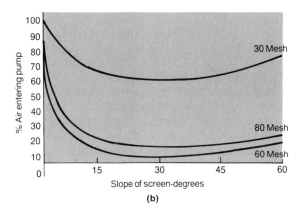

(b)

Fig. 19.14. Diagram shows (a) one angle of inlet screeen and (b) percentage of air entering with various screen meshes.

fluid surface, or jet action will entrain air, Figure 19.15(*a*), again adding to separation difficulties. The best practice ends return lines a few inches below the lowest anticipated oil level in the reservoir, Figure 19.15(*b*). Also, use a diffuser to break up the returning fluid into a number of small, velocity jets, Figure 19.16.

A diffuser can reduce surface turbulence and whirlpooling. A diffuser should have a maximum open area of 40%; exit velocity of the fluid should be less than 2 fps.

Minimum area for diffusers, then, is:

$$A(\text{in}^2) = .4\,\text{gpm}$$

The designer must always plan for the worst condition, namely that the oil will be at its lowest level when the hydraulic cylinders are fully extended. In mobile systems, consider vehicle tilting as it affects oil level in the reservoir.

Similarly, the pump inlet line should *never* be near the reservoir fluid surface, but close to the bottom. Even where the inlet line is several inches below the oil surface, flow into the line can induce a vortex that will entrain air, Figure 19.15(*b*). Note, too, that even when the engineer provides well-designed return and inlet lines, high noise levels are likely if the reservoir is not filled to the proper level.

181

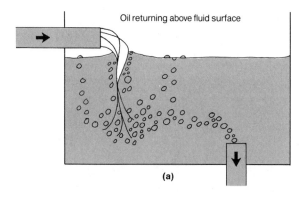

Oil returning above fluid surface

(a)

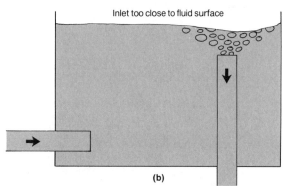

Inlet too close to fluid surface

(b)

Fig. 19.15. Improperly located return (a) and inlet (b) lines will cause air entrainment and aeration.

Fig. 19.16. Typical diffuser.

In mobile equipment, air can be entrained by oil sloshing or pouring over baffles as the vehicle tilts when it travels over rough terrain, Figure 19.17. This can be minimized by adding baffles with holes *below* the oil level to avoid trapping oil between the baffles. A well designed reservoir should be taller than it is long or wide.

Observation ports are recommended in prototype reservoirs during machine development. These ports

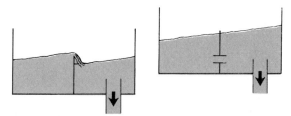

Fig. 19.17. Vertical baffles in reservoir should have fluid equalizing holes.

let the designer observe oil level, air entrainment, and other potential problems that may arise.

Pump noise frequencies

When designing noise controls, think of noise as composed of many single-frequency components, as, for instance, pump unbalance, the drive motor, or the couplings joining them. Shaft speed, in rpm, divided by 60 yields Hertz. Misalignments in this power train produce noise components at twice and four times this frequency.

The largest noise energy component is at the pumping frequency, which is the shaft frequency multiplied by the number of pumping elements *i.e.*, vanes, pistons, or gear teeth. Significant noise amplitudes also occur at many harmonics (multiples) up to 15 to 20 times this frequency. Generally, the amplitudes of these components tend to decrease as frequency increases. However, many pumps are too small to efficiently radiate the energy at the pumping frequency and the first few harmonics. Therefore, the direct sound of small pumps may peak at, say, the 6th harmonic while that of larger pumps at the 3rd, Figure 19.18.

However, vibration and fluid pulse noise energy of such pumps is still highest at the pumping frequency. When this energy excites a surface that is larger than the pump, such as the side of the reservoir, the sound component at the pumping frequency may dominate.

Our ears are not sensitive to frequencies below about 500 Hz. This fact is recognized in setting legal and contractual noise limits by expressing them in terms of *A* weighted levels. This *A* weighting may discount sound at pumping frequency by 10 db. Because of this, and the fact that pump sound peaks in the middle frequency range, most efforts must be directed to control sound frequencies from 500 to 2000 Hz.

Pump noise standards

One of the most effective ways to control noise is to use an inherently quiet pump. How does one judge whether one pump is quieter than another? By inspecting the standardized noise ratings. Present noise ratings are measures of sound radiated directly from a pump. We assume that pump vibrations and fluid pulsations are also proportional to the sound

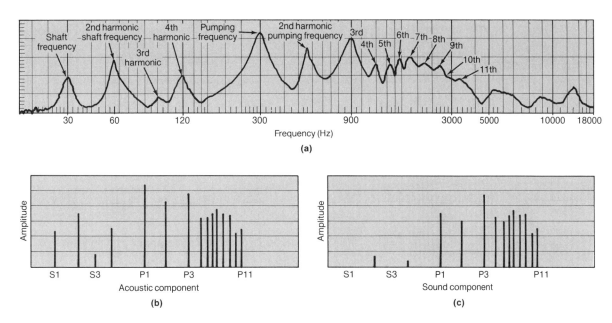

Equations for shaft and pumping frequencies

Shaft frequency and harmonics
 f = hs/60
where: f — frequency, Hz
       h — harmonic number, i.e., 1, 2, 3,
       s — speed, rpm

Pumping frequencies and harmonics
 f = hsn/60
where: f — frequency, Hz
       h — harmonic number, i.e., 1, 2, 3,
       s — speed, rpm
       n — number of pump chamber pressure cycles per revolution

Fig. 19.18. (a) Structureborne or fluidborne spectrum identifies shaft and pumping frequency and harmonics; (b) inherent acoustic energy; (c) effect of poor radiation efficiency at low frequency.

levels in the frequency range of concern. Although not strictly true, it is close enough for practical purposes, Figure 19.19.

The rating frequently used is in terms of *A*-weighted sound pressure levels three feet from the pump.* Actually, this is a computed figure from a mathematical model which assumes that all sound power radiating from a pump is radiated from a *single point*. Again, this is not exactly true, but it is close enough to give practical values.

When a pump is installed in a simple tank type power supply, the sound level three feet from the tank will about equal the sound level rating for the pump. This provides the system designer with a rough rule of thumb, useful in the preliminary planning for new machine developments. Where pump rating substantially exceeds target levels for a new machine, extra sound controls should be included in the original design of the machine.

This rating is in accordance with the National Fluid Power Association Standard, NFPA T3.9.70.12. The International Standards Organization (ISO) is now developing a standard which may rate pumps in terms of sound power. NFPA (Milwaukee, WI) sound pressure ratings can be derived from the anticipated ISO sound power rating by subtracting 7 dbA.

Factors which determine noise

Proper selection of pump operating parameters will also help control noise. Pump *speed* affects noise, while operating *pressure* and pump *displacement* have about equal, but lesser effects. Since these three factors determine horsepower, they provide a basis for noise trade off. To achieve the lowest noise levels, use the lowest practical speed, *i.e.*, 1000 or 1200 rpm, and select the most advantageous combi-

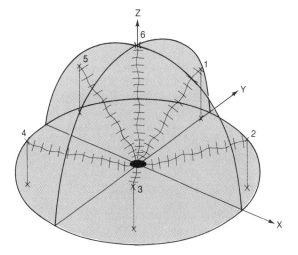

Fig. 19.19. Suggested microphone locations for measuring pump sound power.

183

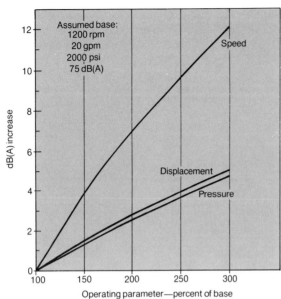

Fig. 19.20. Effects of changes in displacement, pressure and speed on noise.

nation of size and pressure to provide the needed horsepower, Figure 19.20.

Noise generation and radiation

Pumps are one of the major contributing sources of noise in hydraulic systems. However, the noise we hear is not just the sound coming *directly from* the pump. It also includes the vibration and fluid pulsations *produced by* the pump. Pumps are compact components, and because of their relatively small size, they are poor radiators of noise, particularly at the lower frequencies.

Being substantially larger, reservoirs, electric motors, and fluid conductors are better noise radiators so that pump-induced vibrations or pulsations can cause these components to radiate audible noise which actually exceeds that coming from the pump alone. To readily control noise, therefore, we must analyze carefully both forms of pump noise: structureborne and fluidborne.

In addition to pumps and valves, the oil reservoir also transmits sound. If made of relatively lightweight sheet steel, the reservoir also amplifies sound. The reservoir receives every vibration and resonance generated by the pump, valves, couplings, electric motor and fan via structureborne transmission. The reservoir then tends to amplify these wide-band frequencies until it appears that it is actually generating the sounds. In some cases, when the surfaces of the reservoir resonate with one or more of the driving frequencies, the amplification can become intolerable.

Oil reservoirs transmit and amplify most noise. Figure 19.21 shows the principal sources of noise in a hydraulic system and assigns an index number from 1 through 6 as an indicator of relative contribution to overall noise level.

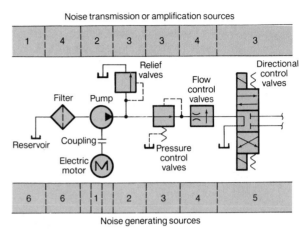

Fig. 19.21. Potential sources of noise in hydraulic systems.

Electric motor noise

Mechanical vibration and noise in electric motors are generated by the magnetomotive torsional forces between rotor bars and stator slots and by misalignment between end caps and motor frame. These, plus sloppy, ill-fitting bearings and dynamic unbalance, set up structural resonances which can be carried throughout the entire power unit. Any electric motor with few force-pole pairs is subject to higher vibration and noise levels. Motors which have stator slots filled with an inert plastic generate lower sound levels.

Noise from the cooling fan for an electric motor is a major noise generator, particularly if it is a TEFC (totally enclosed, fan cooled) motor with metal fan blades and a lightweight sheet metal shroud. Turbulence from a high-speed fan generate loud windage and air stream noises. In addition, the metal blades transmit shaft, bearing, and motor noises. The blades amplify these sounds in addition to the windage sounds. Sometimes a 'siren' effect can be set up if the blades are very close to the motor or shroud, Figure 19.22.

A lightweight metal shroud, held in place with only a few screws, amplifies both structureborne and airborne vibrations and noises.

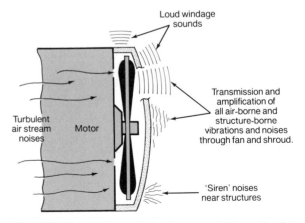

Fig. 19.22. Potential sources of noise generated by cooling fan blades.

Other noise generators

The mechanical coupling between the electric motor and hydraulic pump generates windage noises. Certain couplings cause pronounced mechanical noises which, however, are not nearly as severe as vibrations and noises resulting from improper pump-to-motor coupling alignment. Vibrations strong enough to set up destructive resonances can be generated if misalignment exceeds 0.003 inches TIR (total indicator reading).

All rotating components will have much higher decibel readings if they are mounted without consideration for their centers of gravity. Translation and rotational forces resulting from asymmetrical mountings can combine in such cases to generate both structureborne and airborne noises.

Valve noise

Valves are another source of noise energy in hydraulic systems, though this source is generally not too objectionable. When the valves are inside an operator's cab, they can be quite annoying. Designers should remember, however, that as pumps become quieter, valve noises become more audible.

There are several types of valve noise, the most common being a hissing caused by cavitation. It occurs when fluid flowing at high velocities in the valve throat result in very low fluid pressures which tend to bring air out of solution, creating noise. Increasing backpressure is often effective for reducing this type of valve noise.

Another type of noise is a single tone which can be described as a whistle or squeal, sometimes caused by wear imperfections. Replacing the valve seat, poppet or spring with new ones cures the problem. In other cases, the noise is due to an interaction with the rest of the system and a new, different design valve may be needed. Direct-acting or single-stage pressure control valves are relatively susceptible to this squeal problem. When trouble arises, the best solution is to replace them with pilot-operated or compound valves which are relatively immune to this type of trouble.

Another type of valve noise occurs only when oil flow through the valve is very low as pump pulsations sometimes can cause poppet valves to rattle against their seats. This occurs at pumping frequency and is best described as a very loud buzzing which can be cured with a smaller valve so the poppet opens wider at the low flows. In some circuits, it may be necessary to switch from a poppet to a spool valve. This must be done with care, however, because the dynamic response of the two types of valves tends to differ.

Fast acting directional control valves seldom generate the noises already discussed because they are always either fully closed or fully open. In these positions, they do not produce appreciable pressure drops. They can, however, produce severe shock noise in some systems. This noise problem is best avoided by specifying valves designed to minimize shock. Two

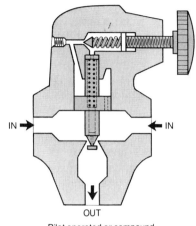

IN ➡   ⬅ IN

⬇
OUT

Pilot operated or compound
pressure relief valve

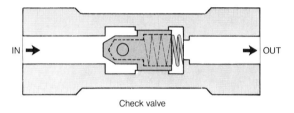

IN ➡   ➡ OUT

Check valve

Fig. 19.23. Pressure and flow control valves can be sources of noise in hydraulic systems.

such valves are illustrated in Figure 19.23.

The additive nature of sound

Sound levels have a peculiar way of adding. For example, if the combined overall noise level of two adjacent systems is, say, 94 *dbA*, and one system is emitting 87 *dbA*, then the other will emit 93 *dbA*. To get the overall decibel level under 90 *dbA* so as to comply with OSHA regulations, it is best to attack the louder system. If you get it down to 87, the *combined* level will then be 90 *dbA*. If you combine the two *equal* intensity sounds in this example, the overall level will jump three db, to 90, Figure 19.24.

Removal of seven *db* from the quieter system would lower the overall reading to only 93.2 *dbA*. More dramatically, if the quieter machine were entirely shut down, the noisy system would still emit 93 *dbA*. So it is vital to attack the *loudest* system first, and the loudest noise sources in that system. Reductions in other than the strongest noises have little impact on the total noise level, Figure 19.23. Figures 19.25 and 19.26 show the additive nature of sounds.

NOISE REDUCTION TECHNIQUES

Reduce prime mover speed

The pumps and electric motors of most hydraulic systems in use today run at 1800 rpm. Often, the electric motor can be replaced with one rated at 1200 rpm. This exchange can be made if any one of the

following conditions is acceptable:
- work cycle can be maintained with a ⅓ reduction in fluid flow
- work cycle is not important, and can accept a ⅓ reduction in flow
- system concept is changed to maintain the current work cycle without increasing flow rate or pressure
- system components are selected to operate at lower flow rates and increased pressures without a significant increase in noise level
- pump displacement is increased by 50% without a significant increase in noise level.

Often, overall system noise levels can be decreased by 6 to 10 db because:

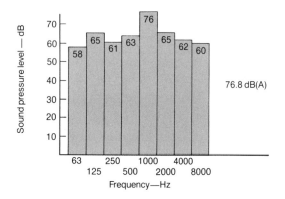

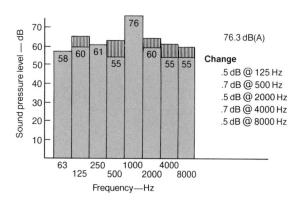

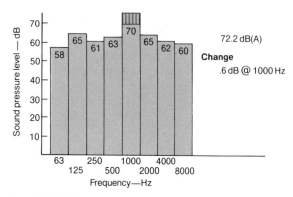

Fig. 19.24. Reducing strongest source of noise is key to quieting hydraulic systems.

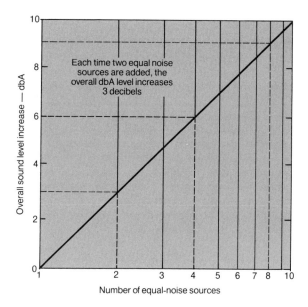

Fig. 19.25. Effects of combining equal sounds.

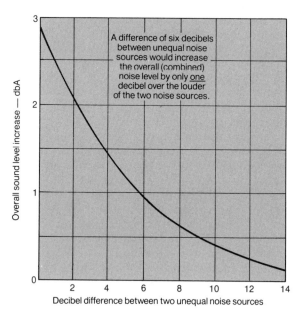

Fig. 19.26. Effects of combining unequal sounds.

- oil velocity and temperature will be reduced, which means less noisy turbulence and lower fluid-borne transmission of noise
- system speed vibration frequency is lower, making it less objectionable to the ear
- an oil-cooled or a TEFC motor with filled stator gaps, plastic fan, and cast iron shroud will provide maximum noise reduction.

Sometimes, switching to a larger-displacement pump in conjunction with the slower speed motor might drop a few more db overall, depending on the resulting oil velocities. Fluid velocities in pressure lines should be kept below 15 fps, and in input lines below five fps.

Internal combustion engines used with mobile

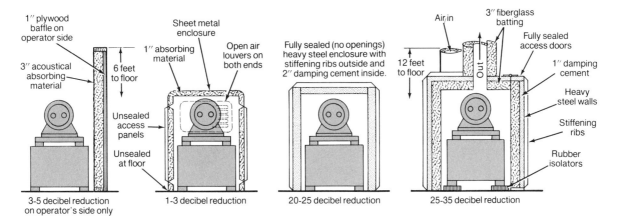

Fig. 19.27. Four methods of enclosing hydraulic power systems.

equipment present a more difficult problem. The designer will find himself at cross purposes: most mobile equipment pumps run at higher speed as a practical means to reduce the size of the pump, which is the opposite of what is needed to reduce noise levels. Depending on the economics of the situation, the only solution may be to house the system in a sound-reducing enclosure, sometimes called a "cocoon." A well insulated cocoon may reduce the noise level by 3-5 dbA overall, but also may present a cooling problem. To be really effective, an enclosure should be totally air-tight. So when the pump is sealed inside, there is no flow of ambient air to dissipate heat through the housing.

On the other hand, thick, sound-absorbing and dampening materials can be added inside a ventilated enclosure covering an entire pump-motor-tank system, and cut only one db from the overall system. In this case, sound travels through the air inlet and exhaust louvers, through access panel cracks, and under wall edges. This approach is a waste of money.

Avoid openings in enclosures

A properly constructed enclosure should be fully sealed, especially at access doors. By extending inlet and exhaust ducts about six feet above ear level, this enclosure can cut 25 to 30 db from overall system noises. However, this is an expensive operation and should be used only in special cases, Figure 19.27.

Before going to an expensive cocoon, be sure to implement every other low-cost noise reduction method. Cocoons are more likely to be needed when several noisy machines are in close proximity in a plant and the additive factor becomes a problem. If the noiselevel of six closely huddled machines had to be lowered to OSHA's 90 dbA level, assuming that four machines were acceptable but two were loud — cocoons can be used to reduce the noise.

First, be sure that all old-style metal drive couplings are replaced and properly aligned, and all fan covers are tightened. These basic measures are easy to take, and can cut three to six db from each system.

Small openings in an enclosure, such as those

around shafts or lines, reduce the effectiveness of the enclosure. Use compliant, non-porous materials to seal such small openings. A number of firms specialize in stock rubber-like moldings which are ideal for this purpose. In the case of shafts, where contact generally cannot be tolerated, minimize clearances or use noise locks, Figure 19.28.

Enclosures often have surfaces that are better sound radiators than the noise sources they are quieting. For this reason, they should be isolated mechanically from hydraulic lines or other machine elements which can transmit noise vibrations to them. Often, rubber-like materials used to seal openings can also be used to isolate the enclosure mechanically as well, Figure 19.29.

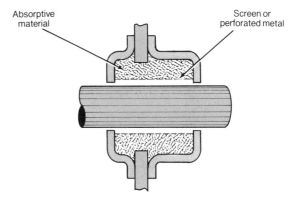

Fig. 19.28. Use of shaft noise lock.

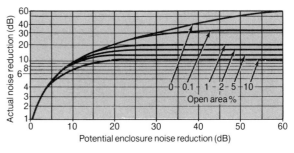

Fig. 19.29. Effect of enclosure openings on noise reduction.

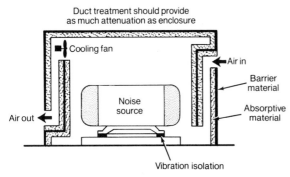

Fig. 19.30. Electric motor and hydraulic pump inside typical commercially built enclosure with air duct silencers.

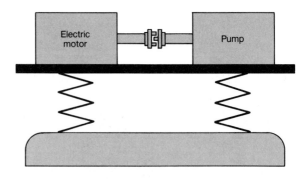

Fig. 19.31. Electric motor and hydraulic pump mounted on subplate isolated from rigid foundation.

Control temperature in enclosure

Most hydraulic equipment can be cooled by the fluid normally flowing through it and does not require special heat dissipating provisions when enclosed. One exception is a pump operating at high pressure but at near-zero flow (deadhead) for long periods of time. Often, enough cooling can be achieved in such cases by providing a bypass which permits a small amount of fluid to circulate.

Because electric motors require air cooling, they are not usually enclosed with the pump. In special cases, *i.e.*, when high horsepower motors are used, electric motors will have to be enclosed and provisions made for air circulation. Although a machine builder can provide air duct silencers, it may be to his advantage to purchase them as stock items from noise control supply firms, Figure 19.30.

CONTROLLING VIBRATION NOISE

Isolating pump-motor mounting plate

Vibration noise control consists primarily of isolating pump vibrations. Common practice is to place pumps and their drive motors on a common base and mount this sub-assembly with resilient means on the machine. Remember that isolation theory is based on the assumption that isolators are mounted on a stiff structure, Figure 19.31. The theory may not hold where the electric motor/pump assembly is mounted resiliently on, say, a flexible tank top.

It is also common practice to use resilient mounts so the assembly will have a natural frequency of ½ to ¼ the pump shaft rotational frequency. While this design provides maximum isolation, in some cases, such a mounting will be too flexible to be acceptable.

As pointed out, the designer is primarily interested in good attenuation of frequencies in the range of 500 to 2000 Hz. He must avoid resonance with the shaft rotation frequency and the lower pumping frequencies. These conditions can usually be met with a fairly stiff mounting with a natural frequency of from 2½ to 3½ times shaft rotating frequency. This rule of thumb assumes that the pump has 6 to 10 pumping elements, Figure 19.32.

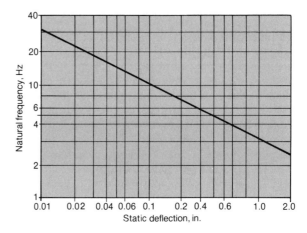

Fig. 19.32. Natural frequency vs static deflection.

Isolate pump

Additional noise control can sometimes be achieved by resiliently mounting only the pump in the pump-motor sub-assembly. If we use a soft mounting system for this purpose, the torque reaction which must be carried through the mounts will shift the pump centerline whenever the pump is loaded. This results in shaft misalignment and a shifting of the hydraulic lines attached to the pump. Using a natural frequency 2½ to 3½ times shaft frequency will minimize these difficulties. Where independent pump isolation is used in addition to a resilient pump-motor sub-assembly mounting, the latter system should have a natural frequency ½ the shaft frequency or less, Figure 19.33.

To implement these suggestions,
● select a mounting plate for the pump-motor which is made of one-inch or thicker steel plate, or better yet, cast iron
● switch from standard bolts to heavy-duty neoprene or rubber isolation mounts between the plate and the reservoir or bed
● use a quiet pump/motor coupling (rubber-faced, lug type) and align to 0.033-in TIR or less
● replace inlet, discharge, and drain line piping with flexible hose
● add isolation mounts under the reservoir to min-

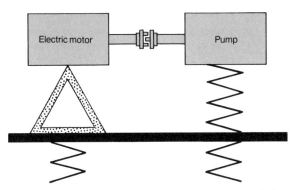

Fig. 19.33. Hydraulic pump mounted resiliently on subplate which is mounted resiliently on machine.

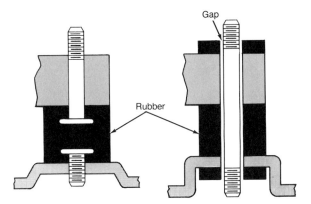

Fig. 19.34. Two types of isolation mounts.

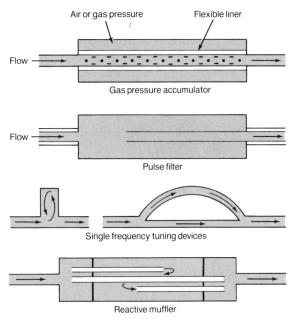

Fig. 19.35. Four types of acoustic filters.

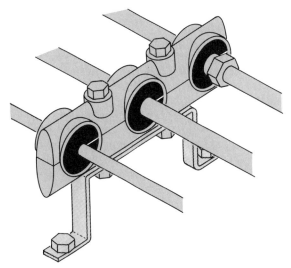

Fig. 19.36. Typical, commercially available fluid line supports.

imize transmission of structureborne vibrations and noises to attached structures. These mounts are particularly important if the reservoir is installed adjacent to the pump/motor assembly, Figure 19.33.

The mass of the heavy steel plate and the dampening characteristics of the vibration isolators are vital factors, Figure 19.34. So are the flexible hoses.

Couplings

Drive couplings must fulfill two noise-control objectives. One is to isolate vibration between the pump and its drive. The other is to compensate for the effect of pump misalignment. Couplings with rubber-like materials in the drive train are favored for these purposes. There are, however, all metal types which also provide adequate isolation.

Pump misalignment can create noise by producing high loads which must be carried by pump and motor bearings. Where good alignment practices are followed, most commercial flexible couplings will accommodate the misalignments that occur without such loading. Where good alignment cannot be provided, or where the pump alone is mounted resiliently and torque reaction causes misalignment,use two couplings separated by a short shaft.

Acoustic filters can be added to reduce noise levels from one to four *dbA*. There are three basic types to choose from: gas accumulator, desurger, and flow-

through. While desurgers and flow-throughs are simpler and less expensive, accumulators tend to do a superior job in special situations. Some filters will dampen pressure surges at certain frequencies only, so be sure to match the filter to the job, Figure 19.35.

Isolate lines

Hydraulic lines frequently provide the primary path for propagating noise energy from its source to components which, in turn, react to this energy and radiate sound. One way to prevent noise energy in the form of line vibrations from reaching machine elements is to isolate the line from the rest of the machine, Figure 19.36. This is done with commercially available, resilient line supports. By the same token, never use bulkhead fittings. Instead, where

189

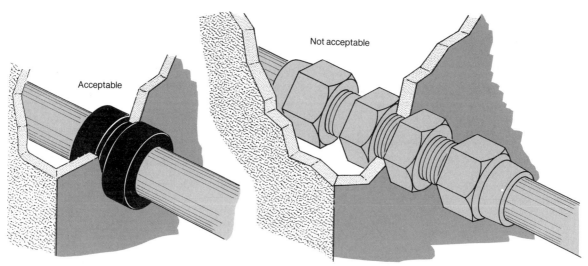

Fig. 19.37. Proper and improper methods for installing bulkhead fittings.

lines must pass through sheet metal be sure to install a resilient grommet or molding to avoid metal-to-metal contact and to provide an acoustic seal when the sheet metal is part of an enclosure, Figure 19.37.

Isolate with hose

Line isolation can also be accomplished with flexible hoses. Hoses must be used when the noise source is mounted resiliently; otherwise, stiff lines attached to the noise generator will interfere with the isolating action of the mounts.

However, be careful: flexible lines can create problems if they are not used correctly. Since hose responds to fluid pulsations, it can become a strong sound radiator if long lengths are used. It also acts like a Bourdon tube when bent, so that pressure generates forces which tend to straighten the hoses. Pressure pulsations, therefore, are converted into cyclic forces which can cause lines and other machine elements to vibrate.

Similarly, pressure changes hose length. Refer to Chapter 25. If such changes are restrained, forces proportional to pressure are generated. This mechanism, then, converts pressure pulsations into vi-

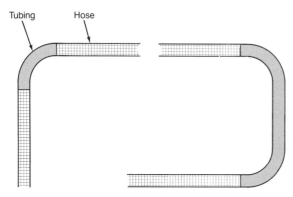

Fig. 19.38. For good isolation in short lines, use either of these hose/tubing combinations.

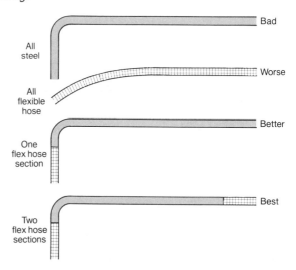

Fig. 19.39. How to (and how not to) isolate long lines.

bration forces. Unless hose is used and installed properly, it can increase rather than decrease noise, Figure 19.38.

The best isolation is achieved when two short flexible hoses, either parallel or at right angles to each other, are joined by rigid lines or fittings. In a straight run line, one flexible hose at the noise generator may be enough—but in some cases, one at each end is better. As discussed earlier, the line itself can be the sound radiator. So to achieve maximum effectiveness when one hose section is used, it should be attached to the noise generator to keep vibrations from reaching the rest of the line or other machine members, Figure 19.39.

PULSATION NOISE CONTROL

Pump pulsation causes noise

As mentioned, pumps do not deliver perfectly constant flow. Instead, flow changes slightly as each pumping element discharges, causing system pres-

190

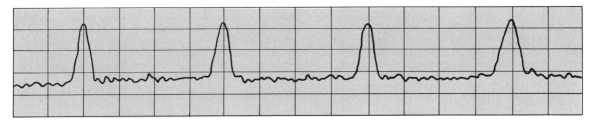

Fig. 19.40. Scope traces of pressure pulses caused by pumping elements.

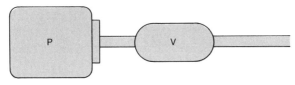

Fig. 19.41. Large volume "capacitor", such as an accumulator, may be effective — but not practical — to absorb pump pulsations.

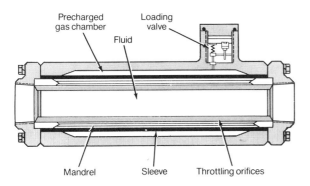

Fig. 19.42. Cross section of typical pulsation desurger.

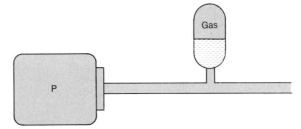

Fig. 19.43. Side branch accumulators can help absorb pulsations in hydraulic system.

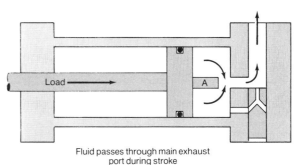

Fluid passes through main exhaust port during stroke

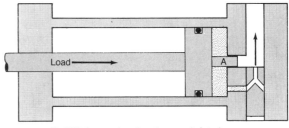

Rod 'A' closes exhaust port near end of stroke causing back pressure cushion while fluid exits through regulated orifice.

Fig. 19.44. Cushioned cylinder helps reduce slam at end of stroke.

sure to pulse. The range of these pressure pulsations is generally only a few percent of mean pressure. If a fraction of one percent of the energy of these pulsations is converted to sound, it may be intolerable. Fortunately, this degree of conversion does not occur often, Figure 19.40.

One way to reduce fluid pulsations is to provide a large oil volume at the discharge port of a pump and let the compressibility of the fluid absorb the flow variations. Because flexible hose expands easily, it also helps smooth pump flow. Attenuations from these sources tend to be small. However, where high pressure circuits consist of a short run of heavy wall line, the use of a flexible hose or an added oil volume can reduce pulsations significantly, Figure 19.41.

Accumulators and desurgers

Gas charged accumulators can be used where larger reductions must be made. Flow-through type accumulators are effective at almost all frequencies. However, they tend to be bulky and expensive, Figure 19.42.

Gas-charged accumulators used as an auxiliary supply source of pressure fluid, can also be used to reduce pulsations. However, they tend to be less effective than flow-through types. Accumulators are usually low frequency devices which reduce the low frequency components of the pulsations with little effect on the critical mid-frequency components. For maximum effectiveness, make the connection to the discharge line with the shortest, largest diameter line possible.

Bladder-type accumulators tend to be more effective than piston types. One cubic inch of gas at system pressure will produce the attenuations needed in most cases; a larger accumulator may not provide more attenuation, Figure 19.43.

Remember, too, that gas-charged accumulators

Table 19.1 — Where to reduce hydraulic system noise

Typical noise and source	Probable cause of noise	What to check	How to cure it	Potential reduction (dbA)
High system noise level, most noticeable at fan end of electric motor.	System turbulence, vibration, windage and amplification.	Higher dbA reading at fan and motor than at pump. (Compare other systems, too.)	Replace 1800 rpm TEFC electric motor with 1200 rpm (lower hp) TEFC motor with cast iron cover and plastic fan or with open drip-proof motor.	6-10
High system noise level, equally noticeable at fan and pump.	System turbulence vibration, windage and amplification.	Unusually high pump/motor noises compared to other systems.	Replace motor as above. Also replace pump with one of larger capacity.	7-12
Loud mechanical-type noises at reservoir and fan.	Excessive vibration transmission throughout system.	Compare dbA reading at reservoir and fan with other (quieter) systems.	Install 1″ or heavier pump/motor bed plate; heavy isolators under plate and reservoir; new quiet coupling (aligned to .003″ T.I.R.); and hoses at pump suction, discharge and drain.	6-9
Noise and vibrations at pipes and fittings.	Characteristic of metal pipes.	Compare dbA reading with all-hose systems.	Change to flexible hosing with correct psi ratings throughout system.	3-12
Loud ripple and pressure surge noises in lines.	Sharp changes in line pressure.	Compare with system containing desurger.	Insert desurger, gas accumulator or pulse filter.	1-4
Noticeable increase in *overall* noise. (Spongy or jumping operation of hydraulic cylinders.)	Turbulence caused by *aeration* (reservoir too small to allow air to come out of suspension).	Look in oil reservoir. See if oil is "milky" or "frothy", but reservoir is full.	Replace reservoir with one of larger capacity, proper baffling and heavier walls.	2-6
Noticeable increase in *overall* noise. (System performance is satisfactory.)	Fluid-borne transmission of noises caused by thin, hot oil.	Check oil temperature in reservoir. 150° to 180° is too hot.	Change to larger capacity tank with heavier walls or add a cooling unit.	2-6
Continued louder noises in pump, motor or valves *after* oil reservoir has been modified.	Components probably have worn parts. (Long operation at high noise levels.)	Remove and inspect *noisy* components for excessive wear tolerances.	Replace worn parts, or if housing also is badly worn—replace entire component.	1-10

Table 19-2—Additional noise reduction techniques

Technique	Description	Potential reduction (dbA)
Hydraulic system enclosures and baffles	Sealed 'pump tent' around pump only.	3-4
	Add sound absorbing material inside existing sheet metal enclosure.	1-3
	Add six-foot absorbent baffle between power unit and operator's station.	3-5
	Fully sealed, dampened system enclosure.	20-25
	Rigid, dampened, vented enclosure lined with absorbent material and unit mounted on heavy isolators.	25-30
Central hydraulic system (remote)	Pumps, motors and large central reservoir located in nearby isolated room. Accumulators and machine controls located at individual machines in plant.	70-100
Increasing distance	Move noisy machines farther apart to reduce noise level at each operator station.	3 dbA reduction each time distance doubles.
Operator enclosure	Shield adjacent operators from noise of a loud machine operation by installing 3-sided enclosure around noisy operation.	15-25 dbA reduction at adjacent operator's stations.
Ceiling treatment	Sound absorbing materials applied to or suspended from ceilings.	5-8 dbA ambient reduction.
Wall treatment	Sound dampening and/or absorbing materials applied to walls or baffles.	4-10 dbA ambient reduction.

require servicing. Sometimes bladders must be replaced and gas charges periodically renewed. While such servicing is usually infrequent, it still must be scheduled and implemented.

Valve and cylinder noise

Sometimes components other than pumps and motors contribute to overall system noise. If so, it may be necessary to repair or replace the troublesome component.

The amount of db reduction which can be achieved depends on the cause of the noise. If only one component needs replacing, the overall reduction may be only one db. If three or more noisy components are replaced, the reduction could be as much as 8-10 db.

Always make sure every maintenance function has been completed before replacing a noisy component. If a particular component operated quietly when the system was new, it was probably correctly specified for the system, but became noisy through use. It could be worn or sticking, or perhaps aeration could be the problem. Check the component before replacing it.

If components are noisy even when new, the noise is inherent in their design. Replace direct-acting relief valves with pilot-operated or differential-area types. Avoid needle valves or check valves that crack at low pressures. Use cushioned cylinders or load-decelerating orifices built into their cap or head ends, Figure 19.44. Hydraulic intensifiers and piston-type accumulators also are available with built-in cushions to help reduce noise.

Table 19.1 summarizes sources of noise in fluid power systems and possible cures. Table 19.2 lists additional techniques for critical situations.

Much of the material in this Chapter is based on information supplied by the Parker Hannifin Corporation.

Important Terms

Airborne noise is noise transmitted through air.
Amplitude is a measure of the loudness or strength of a sound wave which is equal to peak to peak wave height.
Aeration is a process which introduces air into a hydraulic fluid.
Cavitation is the phenomenon wherein bubbles of air or gas form in a liquid.
Decibel is the unit of sound amplitude measurement.
Fluidborne is that noise transmitted through a fluid.

Frequency is the number of cycles of a sound wave in a medium/per unit of time. Frequency is a measure of pitch of a sound.
Harmonic is the frequency which is an integral multiple of the primary frequency of cyclic (wave) motion.
Structureborne noise is that noise transmitted mechanically through a structural part of a system.

Review Exercises

19.1. Discuss why noise is of concern to hydraulic system designers.
19.2. What, if anything, is the difference between sound and noise?
19.3. What variable is used to measure the loudness or strength of sound? What units are used for this variable?
19.4. On what variable does pitch of sound depend? In what units is this expressed?
19.5. Referring to Figure 19.1: Compare the two sounds illustrated graphically.
19.6. What are the lower limits of loudness and pitch to noise for the average person?
19.7. What are the U.S. Government regulations for maximum noise exposure?
19.8. What two kinds of noise are associated with hydraulic systems?
19.9. Which of the two kinds of noise is the most difficult to control?
19.10. What variable is primarily responsible for ear damage?
19.11. What is the prevailing source of noise in a hydraulic pump?
19.12. Referring to Figure 19.5: Discuss the sources of pump noise illustrated.
19.13. How does air in hydraulic fluid contribute to noise? Discuss the effect of cavitation. Does cavitation occur only in pumps? Explain.
19.14. How does quantity of dissolved air vary with pressure? Temperature?
19.15. Discuss the typical pump noise levels shown in Figure 19.7.
19.16. What effect does viscosity have on noise? Explain.
19.17. What can be done in hydraulic system design to help minimize air in the fluid? Discuss in detail.
19.18. Discuss Figure 19.20 and the relative contribution to noise generation of circuit components illustrated.
19.19. Why do electric prime movers contribute to noise generation?
19.20. Discuss cooling fan noise.
19.21. Discuss the NFPA T3.9.70.12 pump noise standard.
19.22. What principal factors determine pump noise?
19.23. Discuss pump noise frequency and the concept of harmonics.

19.24. What are some considerations of valve generated noise and how can it be reduced? How do valves compare to pumps/motors as noise generators?

19.25. Discuss a general strategy for reducing hydraulic system noise.

19.26. Discuss sound level additive effects. Sketch a curve illustrating the point.

19.27. Discuss the trade off in reducing pump speed to reduce noise.

19.28. Discuss housing the pump in a sound-proof enclosure (cocoon) as a noise reduction technique. What are the trade offs?

19.29. Why is it advantageous to provide pump-prime mover isolation from the reservoir and balance of the system? Discuss what must be done to accomplish isolation.

19.30. Discuss how prime mover-pump couplings can contribute to isolation.

19.31. What part can acoustic filters and accumulators play in reducing noise?

19.32. How can hoses be used effectively to reduce noise transmission? What considerations must be made in applying hose for this purpose? Discuss the effect on heat dissipation if an entire system were connected with hoses. What's the best compromise?

19.33. What techniques can be used to isolate noise transmission by rigid lines?

19.34. Discuss the noise control techniques summarized in Tables 19.1 and 19.2.

CHAPTER 20

CONTAMINATION CONTROL

For many years, users of hydraulically actuated machinery did not understand the impact of contamination in hydraulic fluids on the performance and life expectancy of hydraulic components and machines.*

Although oil is refined and blended under *relatively* clean conditions, after it is delivered, the oil is usually stored in drums or in a bulk tank. At this point, the fluid is no longer clean because the filling lines contribute metal and rubber particles, and the drums usually add flakes of metal and scale. Storage tanks can be a serious problem, because water condenses in them causing rust. Contaminants from the atmosphere find their way into the drums unless they are equipped with satisfactory air breather filters.

DIRT INPUT
TYPES AND SOURCES OF CONTAMINATION

If new oil is stored under reasonably clean conditions, the most common contaminants in make-up fluid will be metal, silica and fibers. Samples of oil received from reputable suppliers have shown average counts of 30,000 to 50,000 particles above 5 micrometre per 100 ml. with a relatively low silt level.

If new oil is received in 55 gallon drums and these are outdoors, they should be stored horizontally and at an angle to prevent rain water from collecting on the head lip. The bungs or caps should be aligned horizontally so that any water which may collect at the lower lip of the head will not be drawn into the drum by the partial vacuum formed during thermal cycling of the drum.

With a portable transfer cart or other filtration arrangement, the user can remove much of the contaminant in new oil before it enters the hydraulic system and is ground into finer particles.

Built-in contamination

While manufacturers of fluid power components go to great length to provide internally clean products, new machinery usually contains some "built-in" contaminants. Care in assembly and system flushing reduces their numbers but never eliminates them. Typical built-in contaminants include burrs, chips, flash, dirt, dust, fiber, sand, moisture, various pipe sealants, weld splatter, paints, and flushing solutions.

The amount of contaminant removed during flushing depends not only on the effectiveness of the filter used, but also on the velocity of the flushing fluid. Unless high velocities are attained, many contaminants will not be dislodged until the system is in actual operation when component failures are almost certain to occur.

Regardless of flushing thoroughness, an off-load running-in period should be regarded as essential.

Some "built-in" contaminants such as weld scales often remain undisturbed until high pressure oil is forced between them and the parent metal, loosening these contaminants and putting them into the fluid stream.

Some basic precautions

The level of cleanliness a user expects may well depend on the contractual agreement with the machine builder. If the user expects a well flushed and cleaned hydraulic system, he must negotiate with the machine builder and expect to pay for these extra services.

It might be advantageous for the flushing procedure to start at the mill during the manufacture of pipe and tubing, or sheet and/or plate used for making reservoirs. Tubing should be pickled to remove mill scale and corrosion inhibitors, and sealed before shipping. Interior surfaces of reservoirs should be pickled, never sand blasted, and treated with a protective coating compatible with the fluid to be used in the system.

If not coated, reservoir interior surfaces should be sprayed with hydraulic system oil, or an inhibitor compatible with the fluid to be used, and the reservoir sealed until installed. Never use shop air to "blow out" dirt from any hydraulic components. The compressed air is usually contaminated and only compounds the contamination problem. Use only lint-free rags to wipe components. Seal ports and threads and keep them sealed up to assembly time.

Basic research in contamination was conducted under the direction of Dr. Ernest Fitch, Director of the Basic Fluid Power Research Center, Oklahoma State University, Stillwater, Oklahoma.

Guideline for flushing a system

Here are 10 suggestions for successful system flushing:

1. Never flush a system with actual components, such as pumps, motors, cylinders, valves and other precision components in place. Instead, install spool pieces, jumpers, or dummy pieces in place of the real components.

2. Remove the filter elements in the main lines to be flushed.

3. Use a flushing velocity of 2 to 2½ times anticipated system flow rates.

4. If practical, it is advantageous to use warm (about 185 F) flushing fluid.

5. Design the flushing procedure like the whole system:
- always flush only in one direction of flow
- flush each circuit branch off the main branch one at a time, starting with the one closest to the flushing pump, and proceeding downstream. It may be necessary to install block valves in the system to achieve this pattern.
- in blind runs, provide vertical dirt traps by including short standpipes *below* the level of the branch piping.

6. Never use system pumps as flushing pumps. Generally, a hydrodynamic pump, such as a centrifugal pump, will provide adequate head, greater flow rates, will operate more economically, and will better tolerate contaminants circulating during flushing.

7. Always use a clean-up filter in the flushing system. Be sure its capacity matches the flow rates used. Micrometre rating should be as fine as practical, but no greater than proposed system filter rating.

8. If possible, use an *auxiliary* flushing fluid reservoir to avoid trapping contaminants in the system's reservoir.

9. Establish a fluid sampling schedule to check contamination levels to determine when to stop.

10. After flushing, take every precaution to avoid introducing contaminants while reinstalling working components.

Environmental contamination

Contaminants from the immediate surroundings can enter a fluid power system. On large installations, *i.e.,* steelworks, environmental conditions are predictable, though they vary considerably. For example, a coke oven operates in an environment vastly different from that of a cold mill. Sometimes the best solution is to isolate the hydraulic equipment in a clean room where maintenance can be carried out under controlled conditions. Unfortunately, it is not uncommon to see hydraulic power sources exposed to the worst possible environments, while alongside, electronic controls are protected in pressurized and temperature-controlled cabinets.

In most machine shops, relatively large contaminant particles ranging from 10 to 15 micro- metres, do not require a stringent level of filtration. On the other hand, foundries and stone quarries demand a very high standard of filtration because of the high concentration of airborne abrasive particles.

The mobile equipment field presents special problems because the OEM usually designs and sells a standard machine to operate in a wide range of environmental conditions.

Entry points for environmental contamination

The designer must carefully analyze how contaminants can enter a hydraulic system.

1. Air breathers. These units are usually specified in nominal ratings. The amount of air passing through the breather depends on the drop of fluid level in the reservoir as fluid is withdrawn to extend the cylinders in the system.

2. Power unit access plates. In some plants, it cannot be assumed that access plates will always be replaced. In power unit design, good sealing is vital. In dirty environments items such as strainers should not be positioned inside the reservoir if access requires removing and replacing plates. Removal of many items will allow contaminant ingress during maintenance. Good design should minimize these problems.

3. Cylinder seals. It is unreasonable to expect rod wiper seals to be 100% effective in removing very fine contaminants. If seals were that effective, they would wipe the oil film from the piston rod; it is well established that dry rods wear out seals. When cylinders remain extended in a heavily contaminated atmosphere, considerable quantities of fine particles can get into the system unless the rod is protected with boots or bellows.

Dr. E. C. Fitch has shown that cylinder piston rod seals normally ingress about six particles larger than 10 micrometres for each square inch of swept rod area.

Worn seals or wipers can increase the ingression rate considerably. For example, in dirty ambient conditions, a 2-inch diameter rod in a 4-inch bore cylinder, cycling at a speed of 36 feet per minute, could ingress more than 16,000 particles larger than 10 micrometres every minute; this quantity could increase by a factor of 100 for every 100 hours of running time. Although these figures would occur under severe conditions, they are nevertheless realistic.

Contamination is created internally by the moving parts of hydraulic system components. The internally-generated contaminants are products of wear, corrosion, cavitation and fluid breakdown *i.e.,* decomposition, oxidation, etc. Experience shows that in a system which has been carefully flushed and filtered oil added to the sealed reservoir (incorporating an effective breather), contamination will be mainly system-generated.

Effects of types and sizes of particles

Contaminants come in a multitude of shapes and

sizes. The finer the particles the more difficult it is to count them and to determine the materials of which they are made. The majority are abrasive and when interacting with surface protrusions, they gouge and cut fragments from that surface. This wear accounts for about 90% of failures caused by contamination.

Contamination related failures fall into three categories:

1. Catastrophic failures occur when a large particle lodges in a main component such as a pump or valve. For instance, if a particle were to cause a vane to jam in a rotor slot, the pump or motor may seize. In a spool valve, a large particle trapped at the right place could prevent a spool from shifting. Another example of catastrophic failure might occur when the pilot orifice of a valve becomes blocked by a large particle. Fine particles can also cause catastrophic failures; a valve, for example, can fail because of silting.

2. Intermittent failures might be caused by contaminants settling on the seat of a poppet valve preventing it from reseating properly. If the seat is too hard to allow the particle to become embedded into it, the particle may be washed away when the valve opens again. This creates a pattern of annoying and potentially dangerous intermittent failures.

3. Degradation failures follow wear, corrosion and cavitation erosion all of which cause progressively increased internal leakage in system components. However, these failures are often difficult to detect at first. The ultimate result, particularly with pumps, is likely to be catastrophic. The contaminants most likely to cause wear are clearance size particles which barely pass between moving parts, Figure 20.1. Figure 20.2 defines and com-

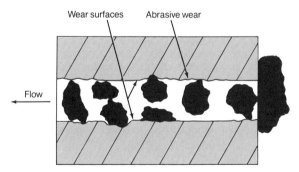

Fig. 20.1. Particles, same size or slightly smaller than the clearance between moving surfaces, will interact with both surfaces to cause wear. Very large particles (right) do not normally get into critical clearance areas and thus cause little or no wear. Very small particles (less than one micrometre) usually flow through without abrading either surface.

pares a micrometre with several common elements.

Manufacturing clearances within hydraulic components can be divided into two principal zones: (1) around 5 micrometres for high pressure units and (2) from 15 to 40 micrometres for low-pressure types. The actual clearance may vary considerably, depending on the type of component and operating conditions it experiences. Good component design is

How small is a micrometer?

$$1 \text{ micrometer} = \frac{\text{meter}}{1,000,000} = \frac{\text{inch}}{25,400}$$

$$= 0.000039 \text{ inches}$$

$$\frac{\text{inch}}{10,000} = 0.0001'' = 2.54 \text{ microns}$$

Resolving power of the unaided human eye is about 40 micrometers or 0.0016″

Diameter of average human hair = 74 micrometers

Diameter of red corpuscle of human blood = 7.5 micrometers

Micron is a shortened form for micrometer . . .
its symbol is μ or μm

Fig. 20.2. Micrometre defined and compared.

Table 20.1 — Typical clearance in various components

	μm	in.
Gear pump		
(Pressure loaded)		
Gear to side plate	1/2-5	0.00002-0.0002
Gear tip to case	1/2-5	0.00002-0.0002
Vane pump		
Tip of vane	1/2-1*	0.00002-0.00004
Sides of vane	5-13	0.0002-0.0005
Piston pump		
Piston to bore (R)**	5-40	0.0002-0.0015
Valve plate to cylinder	1/2-5	0.00002-0.0002
Servo valve		
Orifice	130-450	0.005-0.018
Flapper wall	18-63	0.0007-0.0025
Spool sleeve (R)**	1-4	0.00005-0.00015
Control valve		
Orifice	130-10,000	0.005-0.40
Spool sleeve (R)**	1-23	0.00005-0.00090
Disc type	1/2-1*	0.00002-0.00004*
Poppet type	13-40	0.0005-0.0015
Actuators	50-250	0.002-0.010
Hydrostatic bearings	0-25	0.00005-0.001
Antifriction bearings	*1/2-	0.00002-
Slide bearings	*1/2-	0.00002-

*Estimate for thin lubricant film.
**Radial clearance.

essential to minimize the effect of small clearances. See Table 20.1.

CONTAMINATION SENSITIVE AREAS IN COMPONENTS

Let us examine the factors which affect critical clearances and at the types of failures which may occur in various groups of components.

Pumps and motors

All hydraulic pumps and motors have component parts which move relative to one another, separated by a small fluid filled clearance. Generally, these components are loaded toward one another by forces related to pressure, and this pressure always tends to force fluid through these clearances.

197

Because the life of most components depends on a very small quantity of material being removed from a few surfaces, it follows that if the fluid within the clearances is heavily contaminated, rapid degradation and eventual seizure will occur. In systems operating at low pressures, pump design can tolerate relatively large clearances and the effect of contamination is likely to be minimal. Also, at lower operating pressures, less force is available to drive particles into critical clearances. Higher pressures therefore, are of major significance in determining the effect of contamination on a pump or motor.

Another factor affecting clearances is the thickness of the fluid film which is related to fluid viscosity. An optimum viscosity oil should be specified to provide adequate film thickness to support loads hydrodynamically. However, oil viscosity should be *low* enough to fill the pump or motor adequately to avoid cavitation. It has generally been found that filtration requirements become less critical when higher viscosity fluids are used, and for this reason, a fluid with maximum viscosity compatible with the pump's inlet conditions should be chosen. Similarly, proper temperature control is highly beneficial for long-life operation.

Possible problem areas

Here are areas where pumps and motors are particularly susceptible to clearance problems:
Vane pumps and motors — vane tip to cam ring; rotor to side plate; vane to vane slot, Figure 20.3.

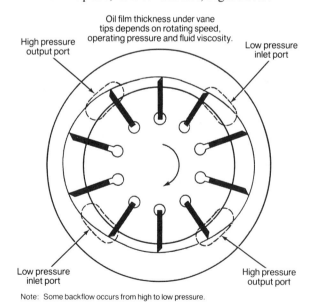

Note: Some backflow occurs from high to low pressure.

Fig. 20.3. Critical clearance areas in pressure balanced vane pump.

Gear pump and motors — tooth to housing; gear to side plate; Figure 20.4.
Axial piston pump and motor — shoe to swashplate, cylinder block to valve plate, piston to cylinder block, Figure 20.5.

Frequently, the clearances are effectively self-

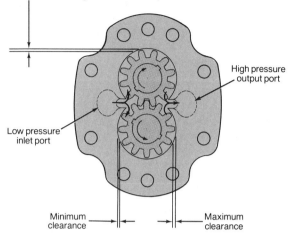

Fig. 20.4. Critical clearance areas in gear pump.

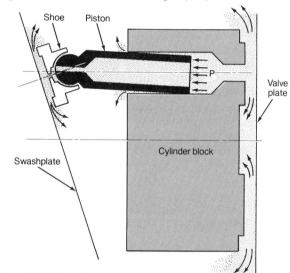

Fig. 20.5. Critical clearance areas in axial piston pump. Although piston clearances are nominally fixed, actual clearances may vary with eccentricity due to load and fluid viscosity.

adjusting under operating conditions, *i.e.*, with increasing pressure, clearances become smaller. Under adverse operating conditions, and particularly in the presence of shock loading, smaller clearances increase a pump's vulnerability to smaller contaminant particles. Even where clearances are nominally fixed, components under high loads may assume eccentric positions which make them vulnerable to small particles. It is extremely difficult to be precise about either the magnitude of these clearances (particularly under dynamic loading) or the effect of different size particles in the clearances.

A pump should be replaced when it stops delivering the required output at a given shaft speed, discharge pressure and fluid temperature. As a rule of thumb, 30% loss of flow indicates the need to service the pump. Often, degradation goes undetected until catastrophic failure releases vast quantities of contamination into the system. If, after such a failure, the system is not cleaned thoroughly, expect the life of the replacement pump and other components to be shortened.

It is the system designer's responsibility to specify the minimum acceptable flow rate from a pump while still maintaining satisfactory machine performance. Pump output should be monitored with suitable instrumentation so routine checks can be performed to minimize the risk of catastrophic failures. Where pumps and motors are provided with case drains, leakage can be measured as a guide to the component's condition. A significant change in case drain flow is an indication that the component is damaged or worn.

Directional valves

Radial clearances specified between the bore and spool in most directional control valves range from 5 to 13 micrometres. As a practical matter, the production of perfectly round and straight bores is exceptionally difficult if not impossible. For this reason, it is unlikely that any spool can be positioned in the exact center in the clearance band. In a nominal, ⅛-inch valve, for instance, a good spool fit is likely to have clearances of less than 2.5 micrometres.

In an electrically operated valve, the forces acting on the solenoid are shown in Figure 20.6. These include flow, spring, friction, and inertia forces.

Flow, spring and *inertia* forces are inherent factors, but *friction* forces to a large extent, depend on filtration. If the system is heavily contaminated, higher forces will be needed to move the spool.

A worse situation results from silting. Here, contaminants are driven into clearances under pressure, eventually leading to oil film breakdown and spool hang-up, Figure 20.7.

This situation occurs when valves, which are constantly pressurized, are operated *infrequently*. Such valves should preferably have fine local filtration in the adjacent pressure line. However, the designer should then remember to consider possible pressure surges which may arise when a component is operated. The use of high efficiency filters as a special protection for single or groups of components may require a high dirt capacity filter if low micrometre levels of filtration are generally used.

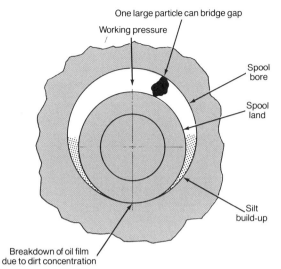

Fig. 20.7. Valve spool critical clearance areas — end view.

To get an idea of the forces needed to break spool stiction, compared with the force available from the solenoid, consider a nominal ⅛ in. valve operating at 3000 psi. If this valve were to remain in an offset position for a long period of time, the area between spool and bore will silt up. Empirical data has shown that a force of 30 lb would be needed to dislodge the spool. Because spring and solenoid can exert only 10 lb of force, silting could cause system failure.

Pressure controls

Highly abrasive particles suspended in high velocity streams of fluid erode internal valve surfaces. This occurs commonly in pressure controls, particularly relief valves which are subjected to maximum system pressure drop and fluid velocities up to 90 ft/sec. Pilot control stages generally see low volumes at high velocities; heavy contamination affects both the stability and repeatability of the valves.

Flow controls

The contamination tolerance level of flow control valves depends on orifice configuration. Figure 20.8 illustrates two orifices of different shapes but equal

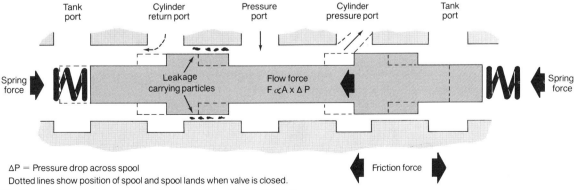

ΔP = Pressure drop across spool
Dotted lines show position of spool and spool lands when valve is closed.

Fig. 20.6. Critical clearance areas of valve spool — longitudinal view.

areas. The groove type orifice (*a*) can tolerate a high contamination level, except when used at a low flow setting; the flat cut orifice (*b*) is much more susceptible to silting at all settings.

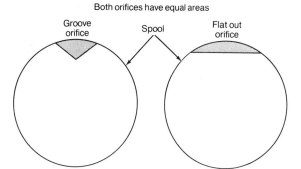

Fig. 20.8. *Flow control valve throttle sections. Profile (b) is more prone to silting.*

Performance of the pressure reducing element in all types of pressure-compensated flow controls can be affected by contamination, regardless of valve setting. Damage to the metering orifice can also occur and become particularly apparent at lower flow settings.

Generally, all spool-type control valves are affected by system contamination, especially at high pressure. Effects are likely to be magnified if precise axial spool positioning is essential as, for example, in pressure reducing valves where limited forces are available to shift the spool. On the other hand, poppet valves, though affected by large particles, tend to be more tolerant of silting because of the self-cleaning action of the seat. However, erosion is still likely to occur.

Other types of contaminants are summarized in Table 20.2. *Air*, as a contaminant, is discussed in Chapters 19 and 25, in relation to noise and reservoirs, respectively.

The effects of *water*, as a contaminant in oil, is also discussed in Chapter 25. Heat can be a contaminant, though not often so considered.

Fibers function as contaminants because their intertangling and intertwining can block control orifices. Some fibers are abrasive and can accelerate component wear.

Specifying cleanliness levels

Generally, 25 micrometres is a typical level of filtration, specified without regard to working pres-

Table 20.2—Contaminants in hydraulic systems

Contaminant	Character	Source and Remarks
Acidic by-products	Corrosive	Breakdown of oil. May also arise from water-contamination of phosphate-ester fluids.
Sludge	Blocking	Breakdown of oil.
Water	Emulsion	Already in fluid or introduced by system fault or breakdown of oxidation-inhibitors.
Air	Soluble / Insoluble	Effect can be controlled by anti-foam additives. Excess air due to improper bleeding, poor system design or air leaks.
Other oils	Miscible but may react	Use of wrong fluid for topping up, ets.
Grease	May or may not be micsible	From lubrication points.
Scale	Insoluble	From pipes not properly cleaned before assembly.
Metallic particles	Insoluble with catalytic action	May be caused by water contamination, controlladle with anti-rust additives.
Paint Flakes	Insoluble, blocking	Paint on inside of tank old or not compatible with fluid.
Abrasive particles	Abrasive and blocking	Airborne particles (remove with air filter).
Elastomeric particles	Blocking	Seal breakdown. Check fluid, compatibility of seal design.
Sealing compound particles	Blocking	Sealing compounds should not be used on pipe joints.
Sand	Abrasive and blocking	Sand should not be used as a filler for manipulating pipe bends.
Adhesive particles	Blocking	Adhesives or jointing compounds should not be used on gaskets.
Lint or fabric threads	Blocking	Only lint-free cloths or rags should be used for cleaning or plugging dismantled components.

sure, local environment, or duty cycle. It is, however, well known that under similar environmental and operating conditions, the effectiveness of a 25-micrometre filter will vary depending on its location in the system. Also, filtration performance may actually improve under *steady* flow conditions as contaminants build up on the filter element.

Under *varying* or *intermittent* flow conditions, the results can be different because contaminants may be dislodged from the filter element pores, to allow more fine particles to pass.

Use obviously influences the contamination level obtained with a specific filter. Thus, it is generally unwise for the manufacturer to offer or the user to accept without qualification, a blanket recommendation of, say, 25-micrometre filtration.

An acceptable contamination level is required and it is the end user's responsibility to maintain it. The system designer, after considering the environment, system pressure, and duty cycle, should specify an element and locate the filter(s) to provide the desired level of filtration and cleanliness.

Such a systematic approach is still difficult to implement because it is not yet possible to define specific sizes; nor correlate particle size and distribution with desired results. Some filter manufacturers cannot always guarantee exactly what types and sizes of contaminants the filters they manufacture will intercept.

Ideally, filters should not only be used to prevent catastrophic failures, but also retard wear and provide longer component and fluid life.

Based on research done by a number of investigators, a general guideline chart has been developed to suggest acceptable contamination levels for various hydraulic systems, Figure 20.9. After a designer has analyzed the dirt sensitivity levels of components used in a system, and knowing the intended operating pressure, he can find acceptable recommended contamination ranges in the graph in Figure 20.10.

What causes abrasive wear?

Because abrasive wear leads to degradation fail-

ures, it would be helpful to define what size particles in typical hydraulic systems cause abrasive wear.

Particles which are removed from the parent metal surfaces and circulated through a system in turn generate more particles. This process is known as the *contamination/wear regeneration cycle*.

Many observers have recorded that silt levels build very rapidly with time in most hydraulic systems. The contamination/wear regeneration cycle shows how a relatively small concentration of built-in or ingested contamination similar in size to the moving clearances can cause the system to gradually abrade itself to failure. The wear rate continues to increase until a maximum is reached which is equivalent to having abrasive particles damaging all moving surfaces.

Further increases in silt concentration above this level cause no additional abrasive wear. Conversely, reduction in silt levels below this level can substantially reduce abrasive wear. Since such degradation failures are commonly caused by abrasive wear which is usually attributed to contamination in the fluid, it will be useful to examine the contamination found in some typical mobile hydraulic systems.

Contaminants in typical hydraulic system

Hydraulic system contaminants can be traced to four basic sources: built-in, ingested, internally generated, and maintenance generated. Despite precautions taken while assembling a hydraulic system, substantial amounts of contaminants are often inadvertently introduced during assembly, in addition to built-in contaminants already present. As these contaminants circulate in the fluid system, they, in turn, create more abrasive wear.

To verify the problem of assembly and maintenance, a test was conducted using- 10 size male steel fittings screwed into a aluminum housing. It was found that from 6,000 to 60,000 particles larger than 5 micrometres were introduced into the oil with each assembly.

To obtain information on the range of particle count data typical of mobile vehicles, a series of tests

Target Contamination class to CETOP RP70H		Suggested maximum Particle level		Sensitivity	Type of system	Suggested filtration rating
5µm	15µm	5µm	15µm			$\beta\chi > 75$
13	9	4,000	250	Super critical	Silt sensitive control system with very high reliability. Laboratory or aerospace.	1-2
15	11	16,000	1,000	Critical	High performance servo and high pressure long life systems, i.e. aircraft, machine tools, etc.	3-5
16	13	32,000	4,000	Very important	High quality reliable systems. General machine requirements.	10-12
18	14	130,000	8,000	Important	General machinery and mobile systems. Medium pressure, medium capacity.	12-15
19	15	250,000	16,000	Average	Low pressure heavy industrial systems, or applications where long life is not critical.	15-25
21	17	1,000,000	64,000	Main protection	Low pressure systems with large clearances.	25-40

Fig. 20.9. Suggested, acceptable contamination levels for various hydraulic systems.

were conducted on a fleet of vehicles in Maine. The data for each vehicle tested are tabulated, Table 20.3, and are based on a sample size of 100 ml, analyzed according to SAE-ARP-598.

The samples were taken from the hydraulic reservoir of each vehicle after a minimum of 10 minutes circulation of the hydraulic fluid. The samples were

Table 20.3—Contamination survey of fleet of mobile vehicles

Type	Hours	Exceeding 5 μm	% Metallic
Road packer	—	1,600,000	10
Crawler	2,218	5,000,000	45
Crawler	1,303	150,000	5
	1,867	8,200,000	45
	3,844	150,000	15
Crawler	1,530	11,300,000	35
Crawler	1,918	1,200,000	35
	3,851	1,300,000	40
Crawler	3,879	13,000	5
Crawler	920	6,000	5
Loader	5,896	19,000	5
Grader	3,478	300,000	10
Truck	20,000	91,200,000	65
Scraper	2,824	3,200,000	30
	—	150,000,000	—
Backhoe	6,575	9,400,000	5
Excavator	1,807	2,600,000	25
Truck	1,283	20,000,000	55
Excavator	2,396	8,300,000	50

drawn from the reservoir through a pre-cleaned and pre-rinsed volumetric pipette for transfer to pre-blanked sampling bottles.

Some of the fluids data reported in Table 20.3 are so highly contaminated as to make analysis very difficult. Each system contained filters of conventional capabilities; the filters were changed as recommended.

In general, most typical hydraulic systems using conventional filters show results as listed in Table 20.4 when analyzed in accordance with SAE-ARP-598. Test results of a typical hydraulic system from a gravimetric standpoint as measured per SAE-ARP-785 are 3-20 mg/100 ml.

To convert these figures to more convenient terms, it can be seen that each 10 gallons of hydraulic fluid in the total system contains 300 million to 1.35 billion particles larger than 5 micrometres and 1.1 to 7.5 grams of contaminants.

It can be concluded that a count of a typical system in the 1- to 5-micrometre range would be 2 to 7 million particles/100 ml., which would total 750 million to 2.6 billion particles for each 10 gallons of oil. This yields an estimated total count of from 1 to 4 billion particles larger than 1 micrometre for a typical hydraulic system using conventional filters.

Practical control of silt particles

Table 20-5 appears to indicate that conventional filters are at best at least 17 times too coarse for effective control of silt particles in the 1- to 5-micrometre range. Since mean pore size is an ef-

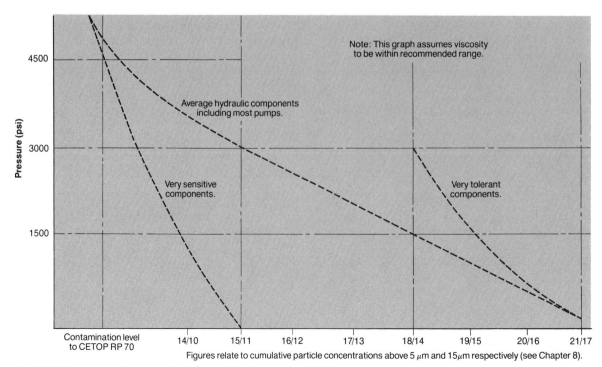

Fig. 20.10. Suggested cleanliness levels for satisfactory component life.

Table 20.4 — Particle count contamination level per SAE-ARP-598 of typical vehicle hydraulic system using traditional filters

Particle size, μM	Number per 100 ml.	Number per 10 gal.
1 - 5	2,000,000 — 7,000,000	.75 — 2.6 x 10^9
5 - 25	750,000 — 3,500,000	.28 — 1.3 x 10^9
25 - 50	30,000 — 100,000	1.1 — 3.7 x 10^7
50 - 100	5,000 — 20,000	1.9 — 7.5 x 10^6
100 +	500 — 2,000	.19 — .75 x 10^6
Total above 5 μM	785,000 — 3,600,000	0.3 — 1.35 x 10^9
Total above 1 μM	2,785-000 — 10,600,000	1 — 4 x 10^9

Table 20.5—Comparison of various filter materials

Medium	Type	RATING (MICRONS)		
		Nominal	Mean	Absolute
Traditional				
100-Mesh Screen	Cleanable	135	140	220
200-Mesh Screen	Cleanable	70	74	105
Sintered Dutch Twill Weave Woven-Wire Mesh Epoxy Impregnated	Cleanable	10	17	25
Paper	Disposable	10	18	30
Wear Protective M-39 Media	Disposable	0.45	0.9	3

fective measure of the removal rating below which a filter becomes ineffective, it appears that a mean pore size of 1 micrometre or smaller is required to effectively remove the wear generating silt ranging from 1 to 5 micrometres.

However, Table 20-5 also shows that the mean rating of traditional filters varies from 17 to 140 micrometres. Thus, the filter needed should be 17 to 140 times *finer* than that typically used in mobile vehicle fluid systems.

One important consideration is whether or not filtration removes additives from the oil. Since true additives are normally in solution, it is unlikely that they can be removed by filtration. If the oil is contaminated with water for extended periods of time, it is possible for certain additives to be precipitated. The best solution is to use oils with good stability in the presence of water. Field tests with many types of vehicles have shown that once a system has been thoroughly cleaned, fine filters will perform satisfactorily.

In Table 20-6 are summarized the results of contamination level tests run with 25- and 3-micrometre filtration. After the 3-micrometre tests, a new 25-micrometre-nominal filter was installed in place of the 3-micrometre filter. A fluid sample was taken after 100 hours: the particle count had risen from less than 2500 to over 800,000/ml.

Table 20-6 indicates that with a 25-micrometre nominal filter, the estimated percent of metallic contaminant was 20 to 30 percent. With the 3-micrometre filter, metallic contaminant made up one percent or less after 40 hours. The results of

Table 20.6—Vehicle test with and without 3 μm filter

Hour meter reading	Filter rating	Total no. of particles exceeding 5 μm/100 mi.	% of metallic particles
182	25 μm nominal	2,053,000	20 - 30
182.3	3 μm abs.	20,700	1 - 5
221	3 μm abs.	14,500	1
255	3 μm abs.	12,300	0.5
343	3 μm abs.	6,500	0
498.7	3 μm abs.	6,000	0
513	3 μm abs.	2,400	0
616.8	25 μm nominal	800,000	25 - 30

contamination level vs. time are shown in Figure 20.11.

A systematic approach to filtration

The objective of filtration is to achieve stable levels of contamination acceptable and appropriate to various parts of the system.

For stabilized contamination, "dirt in" must equal "dirt out", as collected by the system filters. "Dirt in" is made up of built-in contaminants, those already present in the oil and those drawn in from the atmosphere, all of which contribute to the generation of particles through the process of wear.

Figure 20.12 illustrates the relationship between the *design* contamination level and *actual* level *before* start-up. This diagramming method follows from the logarithmic distribution of particle sizes which occurs in actual practice. The relative slopes of the initial and acceptable contamination curves point to the type of filtration needed.

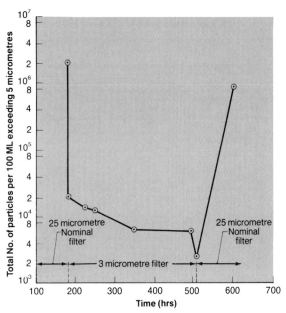

Fig. 20.11. Contamination level vs. vehicle operating time.

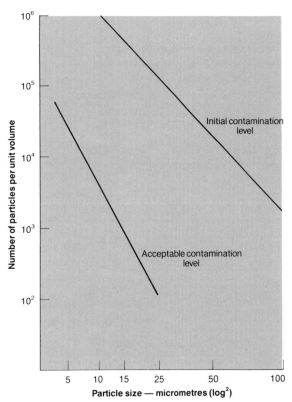

Fig. 20.12. Typical relationship between desired design contamination level and actual before start-up.

Methods for determining and controlling contamination are discussed in detail later in this chapter. Here is a summary of the practical and performance requirements of a filtration system:
1. Reduce initial contamination to the level desired within an acceptable period of time, without causing premature wear or damage to the hydraulic components
2. Achieve and maintain the desired level, and provide a suitable safety factor for a concentrated ingress of contaminants which might occur, as for example, when a system is "topped-off"
3. Offer the quality of maintenance the end user can provide
4. Be readily accessible for maintenance
5. Include means for showing filter condition
6. Provide means for changing elements without interfering with system operation
7. Have enough dirt holding capacity to provide acceptable time intervals between element changes
8. Provide sampling points to monitor initial and subsequent levels of contamination
9. Must not affect adversely the operation of components, *i.e.,* high backpressure on seal drains.

The Glossary of Fluid Power Terms* published by the National Fluid Power Association defines an absolute rating as being the diameter of the largest hard spherical particle which will pass through a filter under specified test conditions. This is an indication of the largest opening in the filter element and measures only one physical characteristic of a filter medium, *i.e.,* the magnitude of the larger holes.

Bubble test is used by filter manufacturers to determine a filter's area of greatest porosity. The test is performed by pressurizing the inside of the filter element while it is submerged in a liquid, such as alcohol. The operator rotates the filter element at each pressure level and records the pressure at which the first stream of bubbles rises from the filter element. The test can be continued to measure the pressures of the second, third, fourth, etc. largest hole.

By slowly increasing pressure, the test reaches the "open bubble point" when air bubbles appear over the entire surface of the filter element.

Mean filtration rating measures the *average* size of pores of the filter media. This rating, which is an indication of particle sizes *above* which the filter starts being effective, can be measured with *open bubble point* method.

Multipass filter test provides a method for describing the performance characteristics of a filter and involves the continuous injection of controlled

---

American National Standard, Glossary of Terms for Fluid Power, ANSI/B93.2-1971 and Supplementary Glossary of Terms ANSI/B93.2A-1978. National Fluid Power Association, Milwaukee, Wisc.

contaminants into a test system, Figure 20.13. Because the contaminants can be removed only by the test filter, they continue to circulate throughout the system unless intercepted. The separation capability of the test filter is established by analyzing upstream and downstream fluid samples. A filter's dirt holding capacity is measured by the number of grams of test contaminants which can be added to the system before a specified terminal pressure drop occurs across the filter.

The mathematical relationship which describes the test is developed from the expression:

| Number of particles downstream of size $>x\mu m$ | = | Number of particles originally of size $>x\mu m$ | + | Number of particles injected of size $>x\mu m$ | − | Number of particles removed of size $>x\mu m$ |

Beta ratio

The separation characteristics of a filter are given by the *Beta ratio*,

$$\beta x = \frac{\text{Number of upstream particles larger than } x\mu m}{\text{Number of downstream particles larger than } x\mu m}$$

Thus, a Beta ratio of 1 indicates that no contaminant particles are being removed. A figure smaller than 1 is impossible, unless the filter is *adding* contaminants to the system.

For a filter with a Beta ratio greater than 1, the downstream concentration of particles above a given size will stabilize to provide an almost constant contamination level. Figure 20.13 illustrates the standard circuit for testing filter elements.

Practical classification of filter performance

Whatever format the filter manufacturer uses to provide filter performance information, the degree of filtration will fall into one of three categories depending on the level of silt control required. While typical data corresponding to these categories are given in Figure 20.14, the manufacturer should state the proper product classification. At present there is no universally recognized standard classification, but work being carried out by various organizations should lead to an internationally acceptable definition.

Two adverse factors affect the actual performance of filters in service: pulsating flow and the sometimes uncertain performance of internal seals and bypass valves.

Pulsating flow may drive fine particles through the filter medium, particles which would otherwise be trapped among the fibers and between already intercepted larger particles. The effect may be compared with a sieve holding a mixture of stones, some larger, others smaller than the openings in the mesh. When the sieve is stationary, many of the small stones are retained by the larger ones, but fall through when the sieve is shaken. Pulsating flow has a similar effect: it increases the proportion of silt particles in the system *downstream* of the filter. This

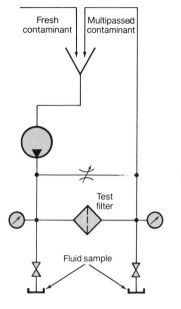

Fig. 20.13. Multipass filter performance test.

Category	Nominal rating *μm	Absolute rating	Beta ratio
Silt control	½ to 1	3 to 5	$\beta_{3-5} > 75$
Partial silt control	3 to 5	10 to 15	$\beta_{10-15} > 75$
No silt control (Chip removal)	10 to 15	25 to 40	$\beta_{25-40} > 75$

*Nominal ratings given for reference only. Their use is not recommended and this table should not be used for nominal/absolute conversion.

Fig. 20.14. Definition of practical classification categories.

phenonemon is reflected in the performance curve of the filter, Figure 20.15.

For filters *not* designed for permanent bypassing, the system designer will expect the bypass valve to operate only when the filter element approaches the point of malfunction. Therefore, the effects of premature opening of the filter bypass valve or a faulty internal seal must be considered.

Since bypassing, for whatever reason, does not discriminate between fine and coarse particles, the effect is to weight the contamination profile heavily at the coarse end. Figure 20.16 shows the effect of increasing percentages of bypass flows. Note that even at 0.1% bypass, the maximum particle size has almost doubled; at 1% it has more than tripled and at 10% it has increased by a factor of five.

The practical significance of fluid bypassing within a filter, and the need to provide for it, depend on the location of the filter in the system. For example, for pump inlet filters, a bypass valve is *mandatory* to protect the pump from cavitation as the filter element becomes clogged. The purpose of pressure filters is to protect a system in case of catastrophic failure of the pump. Should such a failure occur when the filter is bypassing, the system has *NO* protection.

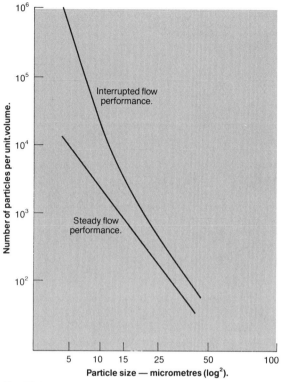

Fig. 20.15. Filter performance deteriorates under conditions of intermittent of pulsating flows. The effect is more marked with finer particles.

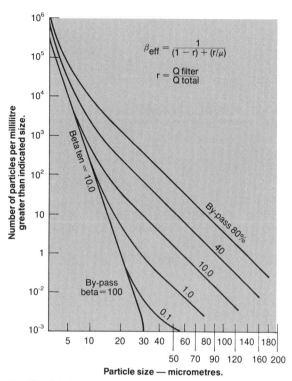

$$\beta_{eff} = \frac{1}{(1-r) + (r/\mu)}$$

$$r = \frac{Q \text{ filter}}{Q \text{ total}}$$

Fig. 20.16. Influence of bypass leakage on filter performance.

Silt remover

Size μm	Cumulative count	
	Steady flow	Pulsating flow
5	16,000 (14)	64,000(16)
15	1,000 (10)	2,000 (11)

N.B. Range number as per
CETOP RP70H shown in brackets

Partial silt remover

Size μm	Cumulative count	
	Steady flow	Pulsating flow
5	32,000 (15)	25,000 (18)
15	2,000 (11)	4,000 (12)

N.B. range number as per
CETOP RP70H shown in brackets

Chip remover

Size μm	Cumulative count	
	Steady flow	Pulsating flow
5	250,000 (18)	16,000 (24)
15	16,000 (14)	64,000 (16)

N.B. range number as per
CETOP RP70H shown in brackets

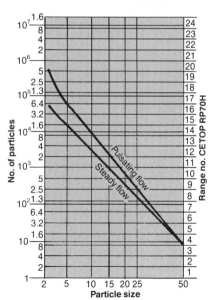

Fig. 20.17(a). Assuming mean pore rating of 3 micrometres, curves show deterioration of filter performance with respect to particles below this size under pulsating flow.

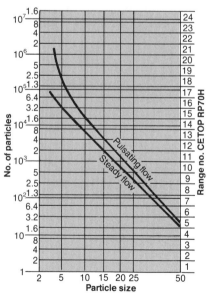

Fig. 20.17(b). Assuming mean pore rating of 7 micrometres, curves show deterioration of filter performance with respect to particles below this size under pulsating flow.

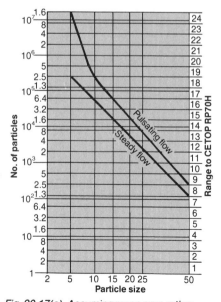

Fig. 20.17(c). Assuming mean pore rating of 15 micrometres, curves show deterioration of filter performance with respect to particles below this size under pulsating flow: there is little or no control of 5-micrometre particles.

In some designs, non-bypass pressure filters must be used. The designer must then specify an element which will withstand total system pressure. These filters are also more expensive. Since gradual clogging of the element will cause system performance to drop off, a reliable indicator is essential to provide an early warning.

Where filter bypass is permissible, the system designer must weigh carefully the effects of premature opening caused by cold starts vs surge flows. Eliminating surges, even those occuring at low pressures, reduces the tendency for the bypass to open under normal operation.

At present, little information is available on the effect that pulsating flow has on filter performance. Hopefully, Beta ratios will eventually provide some measure of what filters encounter in actual practice. Steady flow is related more closely to laboratory test conditions, and predicts more accurately anticipated filter performance. Using the limited knowledge now available, likely performance levels for each category are shown in Figure 20.17.

Curves in Figures 20.17(a), (b), and (c) show cumulative numbers of 5- and 15-micrometre size particles. These figures were selected based on the standard set by the CETOP RP70H*. For easier understanding, the range numbers are also quoted. In addition to fixed figures at the two plotted values, the curves are extended to show anticipated trends for typical filters.

FILTER SIZING

Manufacturers commonly provide users with flow ratings at specific clean pressure drops, Figure 20.18. While this information provides a guideline regarding flow capacity, the system designer may have to plan on *additional* dirt capacity to ensure that the hydraulic system has adequate size elements. Filters which are sized based only on flow rate usually have a short element life. While larger capacity filters cost more at the outset, the cost differential is usually recovered quickly in reduced operating costs, *i.e.*, fewer element changes, reduced labor costs and downtime, and more productivity.

Correct filter sizing requires relating the dirt entering the filter to the effective element area and the maximum allowable pressure drop. However, the relationship of area to pressure drop is not simple and filter inlet dirt levels are seldom known.

Comparative tests

Comparative life of "dirt capacity" laboratory tests compare the dirt holding capacities of hydraulic filters. An artificial contaminant is added at a *constant rate* to a continuously recirculating oil system and the resultant increase in differential pressure is plotted against the weight of contaminant added, Figure 20.19. The resulting curve has a characteristic form which is constant for a given filter media.

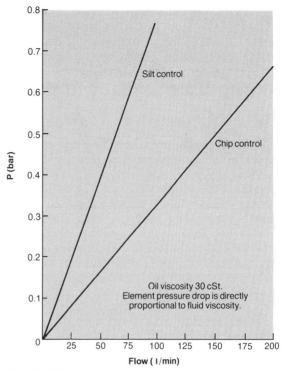

Fig. 20.18. Typical pressure drops for clean silt control and chip control elements of similar size.

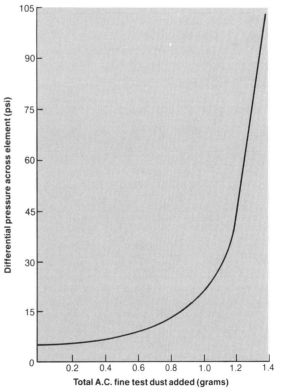

Fig. 20.19. Typical dirt holding capacity curve for hydraulic filter element.

CETOP code for the level of contaminant in hydraulic fluids.

When contaminants are first added, pressure drop increases slowly at first, then very rapidly. The curve in Figure 20.19 illustrates why little additional element life is gained if a filter is allowed to operate at a high differential pressure after the "knee" of the curve has been passed. The curve also shows the irrelevancy of being concerned with pressure drop only when the filter element is clean. The more significant factor, by far, is the differential pressure across the filter *after* a specified amount of dirt has been added.

Except with non-bypass filters, the maximum pressure drop across the element is usually determined by the setting of the bypass valve. The system designer must also insure that system performance is maintained when the pressure drop reaches its maximum value. Remember that if filters are oversized, the bypass valve may pass a substantial amount of flow *without indicating*.

It is commonly held that packing more media area in the filter envelope will insure longer filter service life without sacrificing filter efficiency. This is not so because envelopes have optimum areas and it is detrimental to exceed this area-to-envelope relationship.

Figure 20.20 compares the dirt holding capacity of two filters of *identical* envelope size. Filter *A* has a lower "clean pressure drop" than filter *B* because filter *A* has more surface area. However, the optimum area has been exceeded and, for this reason, filter *A* would have a *shorter life* than *B* for a given pressure differential.

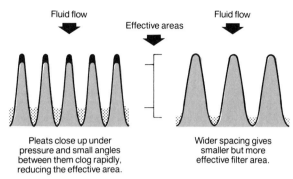

Fig. 20.21(a). Increasing filter area within a given package may actually reduce filter's dirt holding capacity.

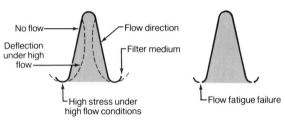

Fig. 20.21(b). Changes in flow and pressure drop cause sides of element corrugations to flex and roots to stretch.

Close pleating reduces a filter's effective area, Figure 20.21. The filter element pleats close up under pressure and the small angles between the pleats tend to clog rapidly. Fatigue failures can also occur when the element is pressurized. Because data on the results of dirt capacity tests are not readily available, the designer must rely on the manufacturer's flow rating at a specific *clean* pressure drop and use this to assess dirt holding capacity.

Since the designer's objective is to achieve a "dirt-in-equals-dirt-out" condition, the desired dirt holding capacity of the filtration system must depend, to a large extent, on controlling dirt input. Dirt input is a product of built-in and ingressed contamination, which in turn produces system-generated contamination. Let us examine each source of contamination and the factors controlling its input.

Based on data in Figure 20.22, we can grade the cleanliness level of a system using a point system graduated from 1 to 7. For example, a grade 1 clean system would be a clean workshop with effective control over all contamination ingress. A grade 7 might be a foundry with little or no control over contamination ingress where a system is operating several exposed cylinders. Figure 20.23 helps make a numerical assessment between these values, based on the environment and the degree of control over contamination.

The designer can now relate this point system to the effective element area and the maximum allowable pressure drop. The relationship between area and pressure drop is not simple, but by using broad ap-

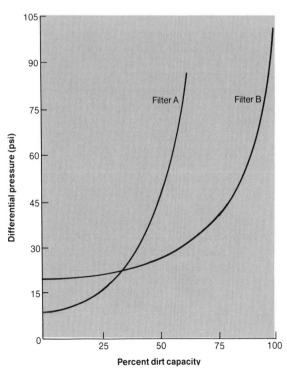

Fig. 20.20. Comparison of dirt holding capacities and differential pressures for two filters.

Contamination source	Controller
Inbuilt in components, pipes, manifolds, etc.	Good flushing procedures, system not operated on load until acceptable contamination level obtained.
plus Present in initial charge of fluid	Integrity of supplier. Fluid stored under correct conditions (exclusion of dirt, condensation, etc.). Fluid filtered during filling.
plus Ingressed through air breather	An effective air breather with rating compatible with degree of fluid filtration.
plus Ingressed during fluid replenishment	Suitable filling points which ensure some filtration of fluid before entering reservoir.
plus Ingressed during maintenance	This task undertaken by responsible personnel. Design should minimize the effects.
plus Ingressed through cylinder rod seals	Effective wiper seals or, if airborne contamination, rods protected by suitable gaiters.
plus Further generated contamination produced as a result of the above and the severity of the duty cycle.	Correct fluid selection and properties (viscosity and additives) maintained. Good system design minimizing effects of contamination present on system components.

Fig. 20.22. Guidelines for controlling contamination in hydraulic systems.

Environmental conditions			Degree of control
Good	Average	Bad	
3	6	7	Little or no control over contamination ingression (many exposed cylinders).
2	4	5	Some control over contamination ingression (few cylinders).
1	2	3	Good control over contamination ingression (gaitered cylinders).

Fig. 20.23. Classification of system cleanliness levels into 7 grades.

proximations of these values, and assuming that the manufacturer's flow rating at a specific clean pressure drop is a good guide to dirt holding capacity, the following selection guides can be used: Figure 20.24 for pressure line filters, Figure 20.25 for return line filters, and Figure 10.26 for off-line filters.

LOCATING THE FILTER

Proper oil supply to the pump is essential for satisfactory hydraulic system operation. Often, not enough attention is paid to the total pump inlet configuration, an oversight which is likely to result in cavitation, a major cause of pump failure.

Pump inlet filtration

The most common method of supplying oil to the pump is to let atmospheric pressure force fluid into a pump inlet chamber. For sake of convenience, though not necessarily good design practice, the pump is usually placed *above* the fluid level, Figure 20.27.

For oil to flow *upward*, the pump must create a vacuum (negative pressure) thus creating the pressure differential required to force oil from the reservoir into the pump inlet port. Manufacturers usually

To use this graph:
1. Decide on maximum acceptable pressure drop. This will depend on system requirements or bypass pressure. Draw horizontal line through this value.
2. Assess cleanliness grade in system, from Fig. 20.23. Draw vertical line through intersection of pressure drop and cleanliness grade line.
3. Read off multiplication factor where vertical line crosses horizontal axis. Multiply this factor by the actual flow rate at chosen pressure line location. Now select a filter element to handle this revised flow rate at a pressure drop of 15 psi (according to manufacturer's clean rating).

Actual flow × multiplication factor = recommended filter capacity.

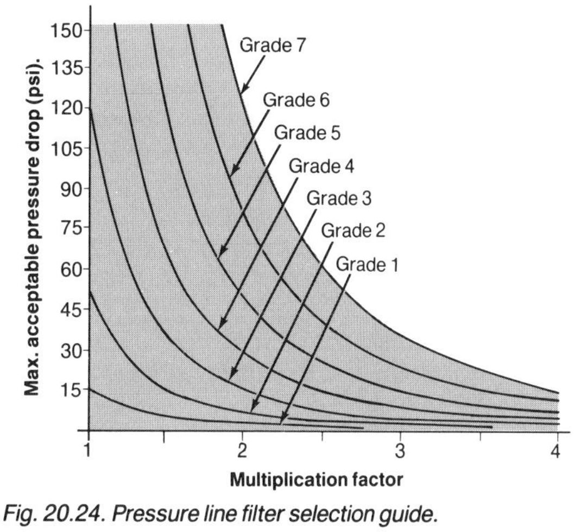

Fig. 20.24. Pressure line filter selection guide.

209

quote a maximum allowable negative pressure at the pump inlet of about 5″Hg. Thus, with normal pressure drops accounted for, only a very small pressure drop can be tolerated across the filter. For this reason the size and cost of inlet filters often exceed those of return line filters.

To use this graph:
1. Decide on maximum acceptable pressure drop. This will depend on system requirements or bypass pressure. Draw horizontal line through this value.
2. Assess cleanliness grade in system, from Fig. 20.23. Draw vertical line through interesection of pressure drop and cleanliness grade lines.
3. Read off multiplication factor where vertical line crosses horizontal axis. Multiply this factor by the actual flow rate at chosen return line location. Now select a filter element to handle this revised flow rate at a pressure drop of 4.5 psi (according to manufacturer's clean rating).

Actual flow × multiplication factor = recommended filter capacity.

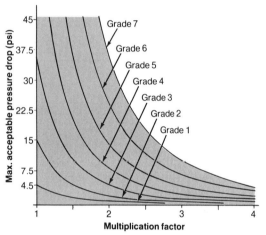

Fig. 20.25. Return line filter selection guide.

To use this graph:
1. Decide on maximum acceptable pressure drop. This will depend on system requirements or bypass pressure. Draw horizontal line through this value.
2. Assess cleanliness grade in system, from Fig. 20.23. Draw vertical line through intersection of pressure drop and cleanliness grade lines.
3. Read off multiplication factor where veritcal line crosses horizontal axis. Multiply this factor by the actual offline pump flow rate. Now select a filter element to handle this revised flow rate at a pressure drop of 4.5 psi (according to manufacturer's clean rating).

Note: To achieve reasonable life a minimum multiplication factor of 2 is recommended.

Actual flow × multiplication factor = recommended filter capacity.

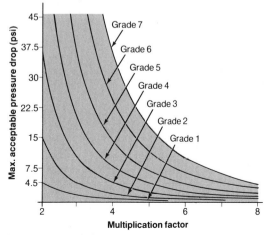

Fig. 20.26. Off-line filter selection guide.

Fire resistant fluids have higher specific gravities than mineral oils. Higher specific gravities increase pressure drop to the pump, at the same time requiring a higher pressure to accelerate the fluid into the pump. Because water glycols and water-in-oil emulsions have a high vapor pressure, vacuum at the pump should be held, to *half* that for mineral oils, even when temperature is limited to 120 F. With or without inlet line filters, it is usually essential to provide a positive head at the pump inlet when using these fluids, Figure 20.28. Refer to Chapter 25.

Regardless of fluid type, a positive head will improve inlet conditions because it increases the fluid pressure available to provide required flow.

For both negative and positive head inlet arrangements, the designer must make sure that any filter and associated pipework meet two important requirements:
- pass the full pump volume within the permitted inlet vacuum for that pump, and
- provide bypass flow which is still within that limit when the filter element is blocked.

All calculations should take into account the effect of higher viscosity fluid, *i.e.,* cold temperature starts; otherwise, cavitation will occur.

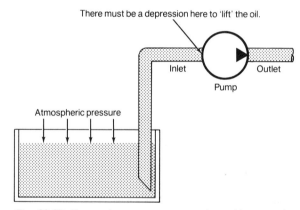

Fig. 20.27. Reservoir-pump arrangement provides negative head (vacuum).

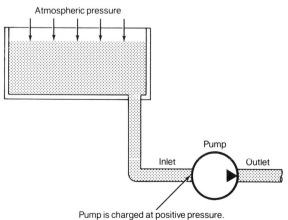

Fig. 20.28. Reservoir-pump arrangement provides positive head.

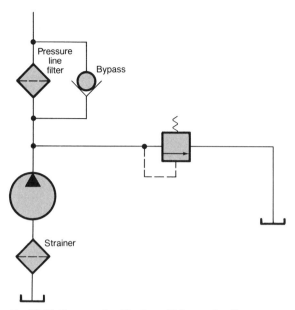

Fig. 20.29. Pressure line filtration with bypassing filter.

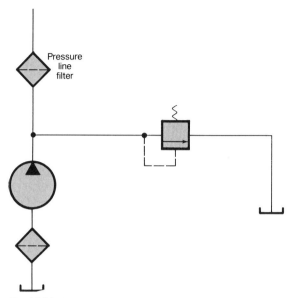

Fig. 20.30. Pressure line filtration with non-bypassing filter.

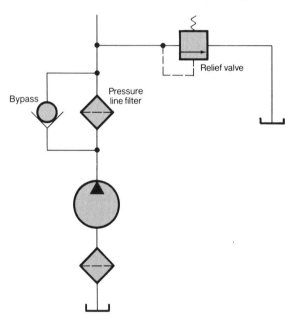

Fig. 20.31. Locating pressure filter upstream of relief valve insures constant flow through filter.

The usual rating for inlet filters is 74 or 149 micrometres. However, units are available with elements down to 10 micrometres. These may require larger housings and probably oversized inlet configuration.

The 74- and 149-micrometre elements will remove most particles above their ratings, but are relatively ineffective in intercepting smaller ones. Magnets will retain some of the fine ferrous particles. The magnets must be so placed within the filter that under no circumstance can accumulated contaminants "break away" and pass a conglomerate into the pump.

One advantage often claimed for inlet filtration is ease of servicing. However, incorrect re-assembly of access covers can result in *air* ingress which often goes undetected and can be harmful to the system.

Inlet filters are generally used in systems where maintenance procedures do not prevent large particles from entering the reservoir. If there is no bypassing, inlet filters will protect the pump from this type of contamination.

If the filling requirements of a pump are critical and supercharging is necessary (often used with large variable-displacement piston pumps), it is common practice to place a filter between the supercharge and main pumps. For such applications, the same guidelines given for sizing pressure or return line filters can be used. However, vacuums can occur when a variable pump is stroked rapidly from zero to full displacement, and the likely effect on filter performance must be carefully considered.

PRESSURE LINE FILTRATIONS

The designer has several options regarding the location of a pressure line filter relative to the pump and relief valve. In Figure 20.29, the bypass type

pressure filter is *downstream* of the relief valve. For *non-bypass* type filters, the arrangement shown in Figure 20.30 is *mandatory*. Actual flow through the filter during an operating cycle depends on system demand; during off-load periods there is virtually no flow if a closed center directional valve is used. If off-loading is achieved through open-center directional valves, the filter will pass *full* pump output for this period.

To maintain constant flow across a pressure filter, it is common practice to install it *between* the pump and relief valve, Figure 20.31. Those who favor this arrangement point out that the relief valve is then protected from pump-generated contaminants. In this design, a filter bypass valve is *mandatory*, and the designer must be sure that filter malfunction will not cause excessive pressure rises at the pump outlet.

Where variable-displacement pumps are used, the designer must carefully analyze the flow actually passing through the filter. For example, with a pressure compensated pump operating near deadhead, pump output is low. Refer to Chapter 15. With a pressure line filter, contaminant removal is limited due to low flow rates.

As illustrated in Figure 20.17, filter efficiency depends on the type of flow through it. At present, there are no standard tests for assessing the effects of flow surges, pressure transients, and mechanical vibration on filters. Practice has shown there is a reduction in efficiency; its extent depends not only on the quality of the filter medium, but also on how well the medium is supported, and characteristics of bypass valve operation. In the future it will be essential that the system designer know the performance of integral bypass valves under system operating conditions.

In addition to these transients, a pressure line filter is also subjected to pump pulsations.

Because pressure filters must withstand full system pressure, there is a tendency to make pressure filter envelopes small, thus limiting their dirt-holding capacities. Manufacturers usually quote a rated flow at around 15 psi differential for bypass filters, and a slightly higher pressure for non-bypass types, but which incorporates high pressure differential elements.

Pressure filters are used in some applications to protect the system in case of catastrophic failure of the pump, or to provide special protection to a single unit or group of components, as for example, a servovalve. Note, however, that a pressure filter does not protect a servovalve from dirt ingress through cylinder rod seals. In such cases, the designer should specify a non-collapsible, non-bypass filter. If bypass types are used, an indicator should be provided to warn of a partially blocked element.

For maintenance, changing pressure filter elements requires shutting down the hydraulic system, unless external bypass valving is provided.

RETURN LINE FILTRATION

In the commonly used return line filtration arrangement, Figure 20.32, all *return* flows pass through the filter. Drain lines from pumps, motors, and certain valves are not normally subjected to pressure surges from the system return lines, and should return to tank separately.

Where high flow surges occur, it may be undesirable to pass them through the filter. To prevent element collapse because of high-viscosity oil, such as cold start, or when the element is loaded with dirt, internal or external bypasses should be provided.

When bypassing occurs under minimum flow and surge conditions, the circulating fluid should not

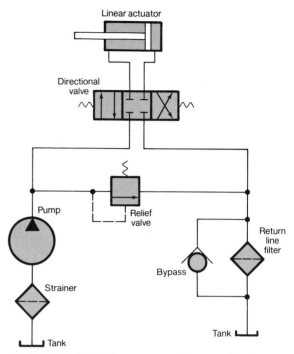

Fig. 20.32. Basic circuit arrangement for return line filtration.

become contaminated by dirt already retained in the filter. In most return lines, surges reduce filter efficiency and, in the absence of precise data, the filter should be selected based on the pulsating flow conditions of Figure 20.17.

Full flow return filtration should have enough capacity to handle *maximum* return flow without opening the bypass valve.

In some systems, *partial* return line filtration is acceptable with the bypass (internal or external) valve always passing a percentage of the flow. With this arrangement effective filtration depends on the continuous rate of flow across the filter. Satisfactory fluid cleanliness can sometimes be achieved with as little as 10% passing across the element.

OFF-LINE FILTRATION

As was stated, the effectiveness of pressure and return line filtration is reduced by shock, surges, pulsation, vibration, etc., depending on media types and how well they are supported.

Steady flow, relatively free of pressure fluctuations, provides optimum filter performance. The simplest way to achieve this is to remove the filter from the main system and place it in an independently powered circulating system where filter performance is more predictable, Figure 20.33.

Assuming that reasonable engineering standards are used in the design and construction of the system, the most relevant factors a designer must consider in selecting the flow rate through off-line filtration are *environment* and *reservoir size*. Based on present field experience, the guidelines given in Figure 20.34

can be applied and the flow rate derived can be used to size the filter by the procedure outlined previously.

With off-line filtration, the designer is not governed by the flow and pressure characteristics of the main system. The best filter, flow, and size can be selected to achieve the desired frequency of maintenance.

Should the desired contamination level not be reached, flow rate or filter type can be altered readily without affecting the design of the main system. Furthermore, the off-line installation can be run before starting the main system to clean the oil in the reservoir and reduce the contamination level the pump will be subjected to at start-up.

A simple valve can be added to filter the initial charge of fluid and any subsequent make- up fluid. Ideally, off-line filtration should run continuously to provide clean fluid for every start-up.

Unlike line filters, an off-line installation continues to clean the fluid when variable delivery pumps are running at *minimum* displacement.

Being independent of the main hydraulic system, off-line filters can be placed where they are most

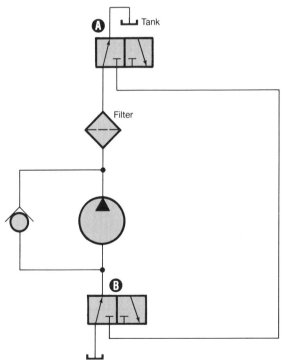

Fig. 20.33. Layout of off-line filtration circuit. Valves A and B can be shifted so filter will provide filtered fill or discharge.

Engironment	Flow rate (l/min) as percentage of tank capacity (litres).
Good	5%
Average	10%
Bad	20%

Fig..20.34. Suggested flow rates for off-line filtration.

convenient to service. Element changes do not affect the main system, the change can be performed at any time without stopping or introducing air into the main system.

Whether or not off-line filtration can be the *only* filtration depends on many factors related to the character, quantity, and origin of the contaminants. Since it provides *partial* filtration, the designer must decide whether it is necessary to protect individual or groups of components from stray particles likely to cause a catastrophic failure.

SUMMARY OF FILTER LOCATION
The most important factor system designers must remember is that, like all branches of engineering, system filtration engineering involves risk. A single 5- to 10-micrometre size particle, for example, at the wrong place and at the wrong time, could cause a system to malfunction.

The machine tool designer may have the benefit of a prototype to evaluate filtration system performance and make changes prior to the first production run. The designer of heavy steelworks equipment must be right the first time and may have to use all the filter selection procedures available to minimize the risk of expensive stoppages. This risk will remain until a) more realistic data on filter performance is available and b) maintenance practices are greatly improved.

The preceding discussion can perhaps best be summarized diagramatically, Figure 20.35. It shows that built-in contamination can best be controlled with good installation practices, and by designing to limit the amount of ingress contamination. Such practices keep system-generated contamination at an acceptable level.

The level of contamination entering the pump is a critical factor. Inlet filters should be used only to prevent large particles from entering the pump and causing catastrophic failure.

Downstream of the pump, the ability of a pressure filter to trap particles is influenced, by flow and pressure transients which tend to drive particles through the filter media. It has been established that bypass valves can malfunction and it is essential that the filter be designed to prevent contaminants from migrating should failure occur.

Ingress of contaminants — most commonly through cylinder rod seals — although in the smaller particle size range, can nevertheless add up to significant quantities. The performance of any return line filter will depend on the magnitude of flow and pressure changes.

Off-line filtration provides optimum filter performance, thus controlling contamination levels more effectively. The ability to remove contamination depends not only on the filter's micrometre rating, but also on the flow rate across it. Filters must have enough dirt holding capacity to ensure an element life acceptable to the end user.

Design procedure summarized

This guideline should help the system designer select the proper filtration for a system.

1. Identify the system's critical component or components. Although the most critical component in many systems is the pump, infrequently operated spool valves which are subjected to continuous pressure, must be protected from high silt concentrations. Low setting flow controls, regardless of pressure, must be protected against silt. Flow and

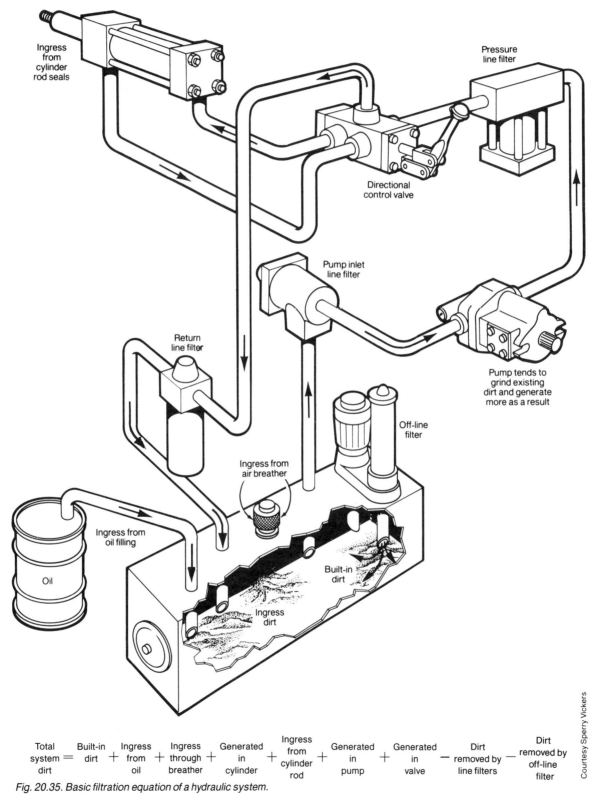

| Total system dirt | = | Built-in dirt | + | Ingress from oil | + | Ingress through breather | + | Generated in cylinder | + | Ingress from cylinder rod | + | Generated in pump | + | Generated in valve | − | Dirt removed by line filters | − | Dirt removed by off-line filter |

Fig. 20.35. Basic filtration equation of a hydraulic system.

214

pressure control valves provide greater operating repeatability when silt content is under control. Using the cleanliness level chart, Figure 20.10, define the dirt sensitivity of the system components, *i.e.*.

    a. *very sensitive*: proportional controls

    b. *average*: most pumps

    c. *very tolerant*: those operating at low pressures

    Knowing system pressure, the desired contamination level (band width) can be determined.

2. Determine, from Figure 20.17, which filter category is required for both steady and pulsating flow conditions. This will be just one of the factors to consider when locating the filter or filters in terms of quantity, type and size.

3. Assess carefully all potential contamination ingress points. Figure 20.22 will help determine what to look for. By protecting the system more effectively from ingress contamination, initial costs may be higher, but long term operating costs will be lower. Remember, *total costs* are the most important. Each method for controlling contamination, Figure 20.20, must be examined carefully; the system may then be graded using Figure 20.23.

4. Select filter location or locations, again remembering that the best economic solution must be based on *both* initial and operating costs.

5. Determine flow rate at each filter. Remember that variable displacement pumps, such as the pressure compensated types, may operate for considerable periods of time while stroked to low displacement, but under full working pressure. For this reason, the pump still must be protected. Flows in excess of maximum pump output may pass through the filter, *i.e.*, exhaust flow from the cap end of a cylinder. Uncontrolled fluid decompression can result in very high flows for short periods of time.

6. Evaluate maximum acceptable pressure drop at each filter. This assessment should take into account all operating conditions such as cold starts, maximum flow rate, fluid viscosity, etc.

7. Analyze the type of flow at the chosen location; in the pressure or return lines it is likely to be pulsating, Figure 20.17; off-line location can be considered steady. The actual filter rating can now be selected.

8. Size the filter. For a

- pressure filter, use Figure 20.24
- return line filter, use Figure 20.25
- off-line filter, use Figure 20.26.

9. Select suitable filter condition indicator to meet user's stated requirements. Obtain these requirements; *never* assume them.

10. Ensure filters are readily accessible for maintenance.

11. Provide, especially on continuously operating machines, properly designed facilities for changing the element without stopping the machine. This precaution is not necessary for off-line filtration.

12. Make sure that in-line filters will not adversely affect the operation of other components in the system.

13. Ensure that the filter medium is compatible with the system fluid.

14. Consider long-term operation. In large systems, in particular, provide means for flushing sections where fluid is likely to be trapped.

15. Provide sampling points.

16. Prepare, for the user, recommended contamination control practices.

PRACTICAL EXAMPLES

Here are three design problems — and solutions — to show how the various graphs and charts are

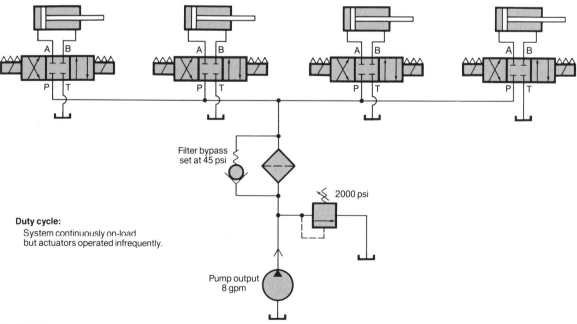

Duty cycle:
System continuously on-load but actuators operated infrequently.

Filter bypass set at 45 psi

2000 psi

Pump output 8 gpm

Fig. 20.36. Typical circuit for pressure line filtration.

used after filter location has been established for pressure, return, and off-line filtration.

Example 1. Pressure line filtration

Figure 20.36: maximum system pressure, 2000 psi; fixed displacement pump output, 8 gpm. Dirt sensitivity of components: small sliding spool valves subjected to system pressure and therefore *possible silting*.

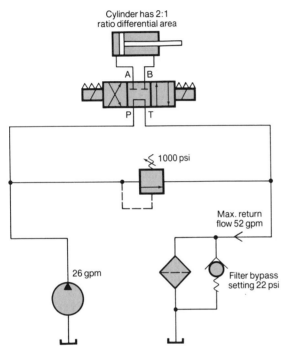

Cylinder has 2:1 ratio differential area

1000 psi

Max. return flow 52 gpm

26 gpm

Filter bypass setting 22 psi

Duty cycle:
Pump driven continuously but cylinders operated, for example, every two minutes.

Fig. 20.37. Typical circuit for return line filtration.

From cleanliness level graph, Figure 20.10, follow the line for average components at 2000 psi. The recommended profile is 17/13.

From Figure 20.17, select a filter which will achieve a 17/13 level at 5 and 15 micrometres, remembering the possibility of silting. Choose partial silt remover.

The environment is considered good but with little or no control over contamination ingress, since the system is equipped with cylinders. Recommended environment rating is Grade 3, Figure 20.23.

Pressure across element is limited by bypass to 45 psi. From pressure line filter selection guide, Figure 20.34, intersection of Grade 3 and 45 psi gives multiplication factor of 1.4.

Summary. System requires partial silt removal filter which will pass 13.7 gpm at a clean pressure drop of 15 psi at the predicted system fluid viscosity.

Example 2. Return line filtration

Figure 20.37: maximum system pressure, 1000 psi; fixed displacement pump output, 26 gpm. Dirt sensitivity of components: pump, valve and cylinder would be classed as having *average* dirt tolerance.

From cleanliness level graph, Figure 20.10, follow the line for average components at 1000 psi. Recommended contamination profile is 19/15.

From Figure 20.17, choose a filter to achieve this level. In this instance a chip remover could be used but, since a relief valve discharges through the filter and decompression surges are likely, a partial silt remover is recommended.

Maximum flow through the filter will be 52 gpm with a 2:1 area ratio cylinder.

The environment is considered good with some control over dirt ingress. Suggest Grade 2 be used,

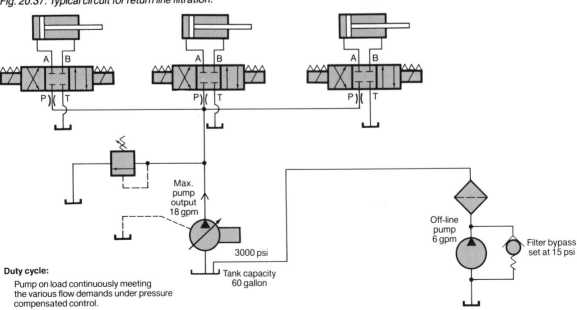

A B A B A B

P)(T P)(T P)(T

Max. pump output 18 gpm

3000 psi

Tank capacity 60 gallon

Off-line pump 6 gpm

Filter bypass set at 15 psi

Duty cycle:
Pump on load continuously meeting the various flow demands under pressure compensated control.

Fig. 20.38. Typical circuit for off-line filtration.

Figure 20.23.

Pressure across element is limited by filter bypass to 22 psi. From return line filter selection guide, Figure 20.25, the intersection of Grade 2 and 22 psi would give a multiplication factor of less than 1. In such cases, use the minimum factor of 1. In this problem, we are providing enough capacity to accept all the flow from the cap end of the cylinder. During an off-load period, only 26 gpm will flow through the filter.

Summary. This application needs a filter which can be classified as a partial silt remover and will pass 52 gpm at a clean pressure drop of 4.5 psi at predicted system fluid viscosity.

Example 3. Off-line filtration

Figure 20.38: maximum system pressure, 3000 psi; variable displacement, pressure compensated pump; maximum output, 18 gpm; reservoir capacity, 60 gallons. Dirt sensitivity of components: pump is critical component.

From cleanliness level graph, Figure 20.10, follow the line for *average* components at 3000 psi. Recommended contamination profile is 15/11.

From Figure 20.17, choose a filter to achieve this level. Under the steady flow conditions which apply in this case, the 15/11 level is likely to be achieved by either a silt or partial silt remover. The question then becomes one of *risk*. In practice it is only a simple matter to change from one category to another *on site*, minimizing the risk.

From Figure 20.34, assuming *average conditions*, off-line pump flow rate is 6 gpm.

The environment is considered *bad* but, by using recommended design practices, a good control over ingress is achieved. Assume Grade 3.

Pressure drop across filter element is limited by filter bypass to 15 psi. From off-line filter selection guide, Figure 20.26, intersection of Grade 3 and 15 psi gives a multiplication factor of 2.7.

Summary. For this application, the off-line system would consist of a 6-gpm pump and a partial silt remover filter, which could be changed easily to a silt remover if the desired cleanliness level was not attained. The element should pass 14 gpm at a clean pressure drop of 4.5 psi and at the predicted system fluid viscosity.

Reporting particle contamination data

For graphic representation many of the existing classification standards use a log-linear relationship, Figure 20.39, the number of particles plotted being on a cumulative basis. This type graph tends to accentuate the larger size particles, which, in actuality, represent a small percentage of the total, and tends to crowd together particles below 15 micrometres. To examine the relationship of the smaller particles in greater detail, the graph can be replotted on an enlarged scale using a log/log^2 plot, Figure 20.40.

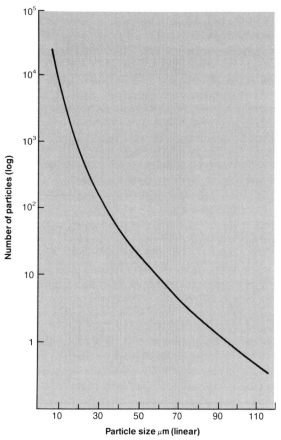

Fig. 20.39. Typical particle count plotted on a log/linear graph.

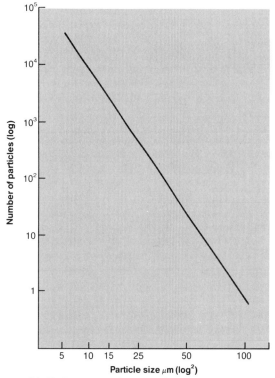

Fig. 20.40. The curve of Figure 20.39 re-plotted on log/log^2 axes to give a straight line relationship.

Producing contamination classes from such data would be easier if straight lines with common slopes were assumed. In practice, this is not likely to happen. For example, the slope depends not only on the filter element but also on its location in the system.

What is needed then is a more logical and simpler numbering system which takes into account the limits of measurement accuracy and portrays more accurately the different slopes. It must also be a simple, effective and consistent means of communication between suppliers and users of hydraulic equipment, whereby the level of solid contaminant in the fluid can be described clearly and consistently.

The CETOP RP70 system goes a long way to meet these requirements. Here is a summary of its relevant sections.

The profile is intended for use in fluid specifications, but the standard is not intended to recommend or specify the acceptable levels in any specific system. It neither specifies nor recommends a method of measurement, nor does it identify types of contaminants.

Most existing methods for defining solid contaminant quantities are based on the assumption that all contaminants have a similar particle size distribution. While this may be true of natural contaminants, such as airborne dust, it is not necessarily true for contaminants which have been circulated in a hydraulic system, subjected to crushing in pumps and separation in filters.

To allow for such changes in particle size distribution, the profile is defined by two numbers which indicate the number of solid particles above 5 micrometres and 15 micrometres, respectively, per 100-ml-sample of fluid.

To keep the number of ranges to a reasonable minimum and still ensure that each step is meaningful, a step ratio of two has been used. Figure 20.41 shows how each quantity has been allocated to a range number.

Here is the procedure to follow:

Selecting a 100-ml sample, first count all the particles *above* 5 micrometres and allocate a range number from the right hand column. Next, sum all particles above 15 micrometres and again allocate a range number.

For example, Figure 20.42 shows the results of a typical millipore particle count.

In this case the number of particles above 5 micrometres is 200,668 and would thus have a range number of 18; similarly, the number of particles above 15 micrometres is 5,468 with a range number of 13. By connecting the two numbers with a solid line, we get an 18/13 profile, Figure 20.43.

Particle size range	No. of particles per 100 ml of oil
5 — 15 micrometres	195,200
15 — 25 micrometres	3,880
25 — 50 micrometres	1,280
50 — 100 micrometres	232
Above 100 micrometres	76

Fig. 20.42. Results of typical particle count.

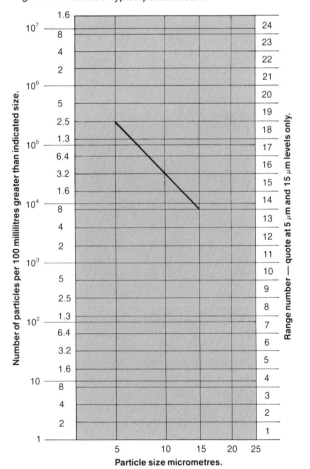

Fig. 20.43. Contaminant code is constructed by allocating a range number to total number of particles above 5 micrometres, allocating a second range number to number of particles above 15 micrometres, then combining these range numbers with a diagonal line, thus: 18/13.

No. of particles per 100 millilitres More than & up to		Range Number	No. of particles per 100 millilitres More than & up to		Range Number
8M	16M	24	2k	4k	12
4M	8M	23	1k	2k	11
2M	4M	22	500	1k	10
1M	2M	21	250	500	9
500k	1M	20	130	250	8
250k	500k	19	64	130	7
130k	250k	18	32	64	6
64k	130k	17	16	32	5
32k	64k	16	8	16	4
16k	32k	15	4	8	3
8k	16k	14	2	4	2
4k	8k	13	1	2	1

M = million; k = thousand

Fig. 20.41. Allocation of range of numbers in CETOP or RP70 system to particle counts.

There are two ways to use this system: one is by adhering rigidly to the rules just stated; the other by comparing the results of actual measurements plotted on a graphic background.

The table in Figure 20.44 gives 34 examples of contaminant profiles which can be created easily from Figure 20.41.

The CETOP code is based on the fact that hard abrasive particles, measuring about 5 micrometres, have an apparent aspect (length-to-width) ratio approaching unity, and that sizes above 15 micrometres do not generally exceed an aspect ratio of 3.

Thus, additional information is needed to describe the fibrous content, the abrasiveness of the contaminants or any special contaminants. In some cases it may be essential to specify the method of measurement, *i.e.*, microscope or type of automatic counter.

Summary

The advantages claimed for the CETOP RP70 system can be summarized:

● the prime number of the class, *i.e.*, the quantity of particles above 15 micrometres is produced relatively accurately by all current systems of counting, both manual and automatic

● it classifies the contaminant levels in the two most important zones describing the relationship of coarse and fine particle quantities

● it allows for and indicates differing slopes between the 5- and 15-micrometre counts

● a classification can be made directly from the counts without the need to compare with a graph, although the latter will sometimes be beneficial

● it does not seriously conflict with any existing system

● the ratios chosen allow the most common contaminant ranges to be described with two figures, yet the ranges are adequately spaced to have useful significance.

Code	Number of particles per 100 millilitres			
	Over 5μm		Over 15μm	
	More than	& up to	More than	& up to
20/17	500k	1M	64k	130k
20/16	500k	1M	32k	64k
20/15	500k	1M	16k	32k
20/14	500k	1M	8k	16k
19/16	250k	500k	32k	64k
19/15	250k	500k	16k	32k
19/14	250k	500k	8k	16k
19/13	250k	500k	4k	8k
18/15	130k	250k	16k	32k
18/14	130k	250k	8k	16k
18/13	130k	250k	4k	8k
18/12	130k	250k	2k	4k
17/14	64k	130k	8k	16k
17/13	64k	130k	4k	8k
17/12	64k	130k	2k	4k
17/11	64k	130k	1k	2k
16/13	32k	64k	4k	8k
16/12	32k	64k	2k	4k
16/11	32k	64k	1k	2k
16/10	32k	64k	500	1k
15/12	16k	32k	2k	4k
15/11	16k	32k	1k	2k
15/10	16k	32k	500	1k
15/9	16k	32k	250	500
14/11	8k	16k	1k	2k
14/10	8k	16k	500	1k
14/9	8k	16k	250	500
14/8	8k	16k	130	250
13/10	4k	8k	500	1k
13/9	4k	8k	250	500
13/8	4k	8k	130	250
12/9	2k	4k	250	500
12/8	2k	4k	130	250
11/8	1k	2k	130	250

Above tables cover most **usual** series of codes between ranges 8 and 20. Other codes, not shown above, can be constructed from Fig. 20.43.

Fig. 20.44. Tabular presentation of contamination levels and corresponding codes.

Checklist for filter selection criteria:
1. Pressure levels — These are obtained from the Cycle Profile plot. Refer to Chapters 3, 4, and 5.
2. Flow rates — These are also obtained from the Cycle Profile.
3. Pressure or flow pulsations — Remember that they can affect filter performance adversely and should be evaluated.
4. System contaminant sensitivity — (Ref. Omega Rating). Determine component sensitivity to contaminants of varying particle size.
5. System contaminant ingress — Contaminant level is a function of the amount of contaminant into the system.
6. System reliability — Designer must determine at what point component failure is acceptable and match components and filters accordingly.
7. Filter structural integrity — A number of ISO standards cover various factors in this area:
   a. *Fabrication integrity test,* ISO 2942/ANSI B93.22-1972/NFPA T3.10/8.4-1972. Filter is examined for defects using a bubble test approach.
   b. *Collapse/burst test,* ISO 2941/ANSI B92.25-1972/NFPA T3.10.8.5-1972. Evaluates filter element's ability to withstand pressure differentials.
   c. *Material compatibility test,* ISO 2943/ANSI B93.23-1972/NFPA T3.108.6. Evaluates aging of filter materials caused by high temperatures.

d. *End load test*, ISO 3723/ANSI B93.21-1972/NFPA T3.10.8.2-1972. Evaluates axial compression strength of filter elements.

e. *Flow fatigue*, ISO 3724/ANSI B93.24-1972/NFPA T3.10.8.7-1972. Evaluates filters resistance to fatigue caused by cyclic flow.

8. Filter contaminant capacity — Establishes how much contaminant a filter element can remove. Refer to discussion in this chapter for detail.

9. Filter pressure drops — Flow rate vs. pressure differential specification for a filter.

10. Degree of filtration — ISO DIS 4572/ANSI B93.31-1973/NFPA T3.10.8.8-1973. Related to Beta Ratio. Refer to discussion in this chapter.

11. Cost — Correlates closely with location in a system and includes such factors as pressure, flow rate, allowable pressure drop, performance requirements, etc. as discussed in this chapter.

12. Acceptability — Determine whether customer will accept filter selected.

13. Availability — Make sure that a filter encompassing all specified performance characteristics is readily available.

14. Serviceability — Make sure that the filter can be readily serviced in the field.

15. Compatibility — The filter must be compatible with existing products in the customer's operating environment. The customer may have to be re-educated to accept new, better practices.

16. Special features — Are special features, such as pressure differential indicators, electrical switches, by-pass capability (inlet filters), bidirectional flow capability, magnetic separators, etc. required for the system?

Much of the material in this Chapter is based on information supplied by Hydreco, A Unit of General Signal, Pall Corporation, and Sperry Vickers.

Important Terms

Additive is a substance added to a hydraulic fluid to overcome deficiencies and enhance performance of the fluid.

Absolute rating is the diameter of the largest hard spherical particle which will pass through a filter under specified conditions.

Beta Rating is the ratio of particles larger than a specified micrometre size upstream from the filter element to the number larger than the same size particles downstream.

Contaminant is any material foreign to a hydraulic fluid which has a deleterious effect on its performance in a system.

Filter is a component designed to remove and retain solid contaminant from a hydraulic fluid.

Ingress rate is the rate at which particulate contamination enters a hydraulic system.

Mean filter rating is the average size of pores in a filter element.

Micrometre (Micron) is the unit of size for particulate material. 1 micrometre = meter/1,000,000 = inch/25,400 = 0.000039". 0.0001" = 2.54 micrometres.

Nominal rating is the rating of a filter element which will retain 95% by weight of particles of the specified size.

Review Exercises

20.1. What is contamination control? Why is it so important to hydraulic system design and performance?

20.2. Discuss contamination in "new" fluids. How can this be controlled or minimized in a system? Explain.

20.3. What is meant by built-in contamination? What can be done to minimize it?

20.4. Discuss flushing procedure for a large scale hydraulic system.

20.5. What is environmental contamination? Discuss its effects on hydraulic systems.

20.6. What are the entry points for environmental contamination in a hydraulic system?

20.7. What is an estimated ingestion rate for particulate contamination at the piston rod-wiper interface? Can anything be done to eliminate such ingestion?

20.8. Discuss generated contamination and its implications for performance of a hydraulic system.

20.9. What three classes of failure are associated with system contamination? What differentiates one from the other?

20.10. Referring to example 20.9, to which class does fine filtration belong?

20.11. What unit is used in describing size of particulate contamination? What is the size of this unit, dimensionally?

20.12. How do typical clearance in hydraulic components compare to particulate contaminants size encountered in fluids? Discuss.

20.13. Describe the major contamination sensitive areas in gear pumps and motors.

20.14. Discuss the major contamination sensitive areas in vane pumps and motors.

20.15. What are the major contamination sensitive areas in piston pumps and motors?

20.16. Discuss the effect on system performance on degradation of volumetric efficiencies of pumps and motors due to contamination.

20.17. What are specific areas of contamination sensitivity in directional control valves?

20.18. How can contamination affect spool valve shifting forces? What effect does this have on valve performance?

20.19. Are pressure and flow controls affected by contamination? Discuss.

20.20. What other kinds of contaminants are there other than particulate? Discuss their effects on system performance.

20.21. Of the contaminants discussed in this chapter, which is/are most deleterious to component performance? System performance?

20.22. Discuss the problem of setting contamination level specifications for a hydraulic system. Refer to Figure 20.9.

20.23. Discuss Figure 20.10 as it relates to cleanliness level. What is CETOP RP70?

20.24. Discuss 3 μm (or silt) filtration vs. more conventional filtration at 10-25 μm. What is the relationship between the two approaches?

20.25. Discuss the relationship between particle size and abrasive wear. What are the implications of the data shown in Tables 20.3 and 20.4?

20.26. What relationship does contaminant have to oil breakdown?

20.27. Discuss the implications of Table 20.5 data.

20.28. What three questions relate to use of fine, or silt filtration?

20.29. What condition must be met to achieve a stable contamination level in a system?

20.30. Discuss the implications of Figure 20.12. What is required of the filter system?

20.31. What is meant by nominal size or rating of a filter element?

20.32. What is meant by absolute rating and how does it relate to nominal?

20.33. What is mean filter rating and how does it compare to nominal and absolute ratings?

20.34. What is the bubble test and how is it used?

20.35. Describe the multipass filter test. What is its purpose?

20.36. What is Beta ratio? What is its purpose?

20.37. Why are nominal filter ratings no longer recommended for specifying filter elements?

20.38. What classifications are used for particle filter performance?

20.39. What is the effect of pulsating flow on filter performance? How might this affect performance of return line filters?

20.40. Discuss by-pass filtration. Refer to Figure 20.16.

20.41. Relate the curves of Figure 20.17 to performance levels for the three categories of filters.

20.42. How is a filter sized? Refer to Figure 20.18. How does this relate to dirt capacity? Refer to Figure 20.19. Discuss.

20.43. Does excess filter element area increase longer service life? Discuss.

20.44. Discuss the implications of Figure 20.20.

20.45. Discuss the 7 grades of cleanliness described and how Figure 20.23 can be used to assess these numerically.

20.46. Discuss the application of the curves in Figures 20.24, 20.25, and 20.26 to their respective types of filters.

20.47. What basic filter locations are available to the circuit designer?

20.48. Discuss design and application considerations for inlet line filtration.

20.49. What are the implications of locating the pump as in Figure 20.27 as compared to Figure 20.28? Refer to Chapter 25.

20.50. Where should pressure line filtration be located? Discuss alternatives.

20.51. How do variable displacement pumps, *i.e.,* pressure compensated, affect filter location and sizing considerations?

20.52. What effects can line surges and pulsations have on filter performance?

20.53. What special considerations must be given to pressure-line filters because of high pressures?

20.54. Under what conditions, if any, might it be advisable to by-pass fluid around a return line filter? Discuss.

20.55. Why is it generally advisable to use pulsating flow criteria for selecting return line filters?

20.56. For what maximum flow rate should a return line filter be sized?

20.57. Discuss off-line filtration. When should it be considered? Is it as effective as on-line filtration?

20.58. Discuss the implications of Figure 20.35.

20.59. Discuss design procedure for sizing, selecting and locating filters in a system.

20.60. Example: Assume you must select a pressure line filter, Figure 20.36. Maximum system pressure is 2500 psi; 17/13 level filters by-pass setting 35 psi; pump delivery 12 gpm; assume Grade 3. Select a filter for this application.

20.61. In example 20.60, assume level 16/12 and Grade 4 was used. What would be the effect on filter selection?

20.62. Referring to Figure 20.37: Maximum system pressure 1500 psi; assume very tolerant components; pump delivery, 20 gpm; differential cylinder area ratio 3:1; filter by-pass setting, 25 psi; assume Grade 2 conditions. Select a return line filter for this application.

20.63. Assume: Maximum system pressure 2000 psi. Pressure compensated pump, maximum delivery, 25 gpm; reservoir capacity, 75 gallons; critical component is pump; filter by-pass setting, 20 psi. Select an off-line filter for this application.

20.64. Why is a log/log^2 plot used to represent particle contaminant data?

20.65. What do the two numbers in a CETOP RP70 designation signify?

20.66. What is Omega rating? For what purpose is it used in selecting components for hydraulic systems?

20.67. What effect does pump pressure cycle, as might be obtained from a Cycle Profile, have on selection based on Omega rating?

20.68. Filter ratings and component Omega ratings are determined empirically. True or False? Discuss.

CHAPTER 21

ELECTRICAL/ ELECTRONIC CONTROLS

Electrical controls are the dominant method for controlling fluid power systems. The solenoid-operated directional control valve is the basic building block for electrical control circuits.

Just as the designer had to learn ISO graphic symbols to communicate about fluid power circuits, he must also learn standard electrical symbology. This chapter deals primarily with electrical *control* circuits, not power circuits.

Switches and other electrical controls

Switches are the basic devices for generating control signals. Figures 21.1 through 21.10 illustrate and briefly describe the symbols of most commonly used types of electric switches, contacts, relays, and motors.

RATINGS AND SPECIFICATIONS

Electrical power circuits

Electrical power is primarily used to drive fluid power systems. Alterating current (AC) power circuits are rated at 110-120 V (volts), 220-240 V, 440 V, 880 V, and 2300 V. They may be either single- or three-phase systems. Small motors, up to 1 hp, may be started "across the line," *i.e.,* with a simple push-button control.

In these fractional horsepower motors, the inrush current during start-up is not large enough to cause significant problems. However, motors larger than 1 hp must have a *motor starter* built into their control circuit.

Motor starters protect against excessive inrush current during start-up. They may also provide "overload" protection when the electric motor is running to prevent overheating of the motor windings and damage from excessive loads on the motor shaft. Motor starters must be matched to the electric motor on the basis of voltage rating, phase, and horsepower rating. For the higher-horsepower motors, the starter costs almost as much as the motor. Thus, the motor starter is a significant cost factor in the design of the system and cannot be overlooked.

Electrical control circuits

Direct-current (DC) electrical control circuits are rated at 6, 12, 24, or 36 volts; the first three are the most popular.

Alternating-current ratings for control circuits are 6, 12, 24, and 110 volts. Control circuits can operate at any voltage level suitable for the system. However, operating control systems at high voltages is inefficient and introduces unnecessary hazards for personnel.

Switches are rated on the basis of system voltage and the maximum current they can handle safely. A typical rating for a push-button switch designed for 1½-hp duty is 20 amperes (A) and 120 V, or 10 A and 250 V. Some switch ratings include data on DC as well as AC current and voltage. Others specify further that the rating given applies to a non-inductive load. Inductive loads can cause high current surges in the circuit which the switch may not be able to handle.

When relays are used, it is necessary to specify coil *and* contact ratings. For example, a designer might use a relay with a 6-V DC operating coil and contacts capable of handling a 10-A, 240-V load. Or he may want a relay to operate on the same voltage as the contact circuit; in this case the designer could specify 110 V for the coil, and 20 A and 110 V for the contacts. Specifications for a relay can become as complex as those for a directional control valve. The designer *must* include the voltage ratings, the contact pattern, and any special control functions, such as time delay, latching, or stepping.

Application example 1

One of the simplest control applications in fluid power involves the actuation of a double-acting cylinder through a cycle: start, extend through a given stroke, reverse, and stop after full retraction. Figure 21.11(*a*) illustrates the hydraulic circuit for this application using ISO graphic symbols. The sequence diagram, (refer also to Chapter 22), determines the order of events, Figure 21.11(*b*); the electrical control circuit, Figure 21.11(*c*) shows how the

Fig. 21.1. Basic electrical pushbutton switches

PUSH BUTTON SWITCHES
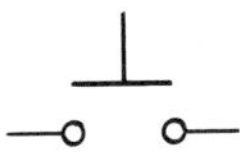 **NO-SPST** Normally open - single pole, single throw
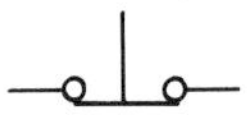 **NC-SPST** Normally closed - single pole, single throw
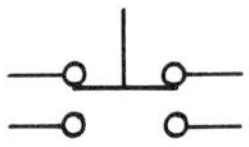 **NO/NC-DPST** Double contacts normally open/ normally closed - double pole, single throw
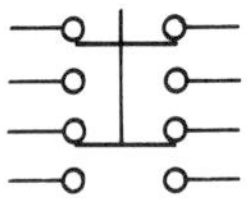 **NO/NC-DPDT** Two pairs normally open and two pairs normally closed - double pole, double throw

Fig. 21.2. Basic electrical limit switches

LIMIT SWITCHES
 **NO** Normally open
 **NO** Normally open, held closed
 **NC** Normally closed
 **NC** Normally closed, held open
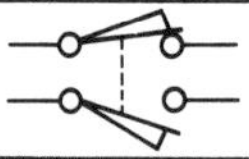 **NC/NO** Double pole, normally closed/ normally open

Fig. 21.3. Basic pressure switches

PRESSURE SWITCHES
 **NO** Normally open
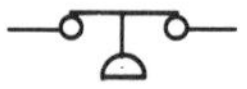 **NC** Normally closed

Fig. 21.4. Basic temperature switches

TEMPERATURE SWITCHES
 **NO** Normally open
 **NC** Normally closed

Fig. 21.5. Float switches

FLOAT SWITCHES
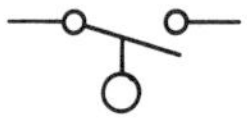 **NO** Normally open
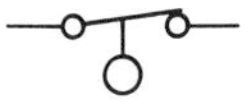 **NC** Normally closed

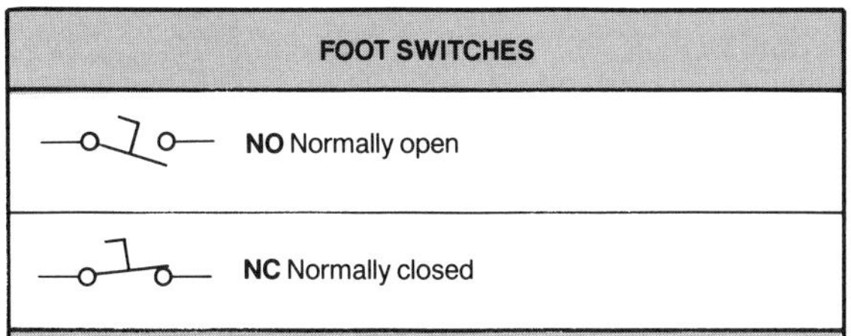

FOOT SWITCHES	
⎯o⟍⟋o⎯	**NO** Normally open
⎯o⟍o⎯	**NC** Normally closed

Fig. 21.6. Foot actuated switches

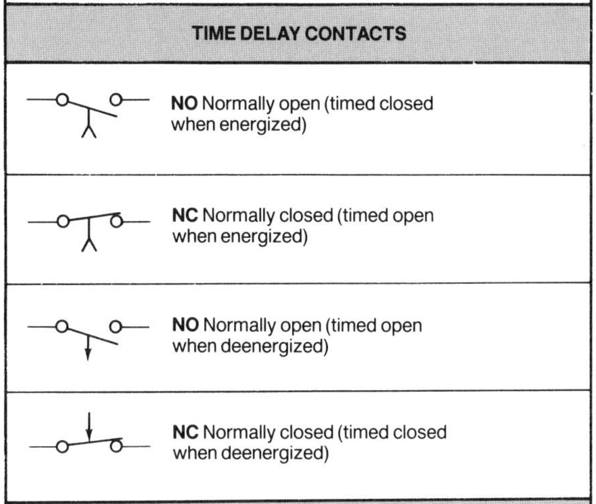

TIME DELAY CONTACTS	
⎯o⟍o⎯	**NO** Normally open (timed closed when energized)
⎯o⟍o⎯	**NC** Normally closed (timed open when energized)
⎯o⟍o⎯	**NO** Normally open (timed open when deenergized)
⎯o⟍o⎯	**NC** Normally closed (timed closed when deenergized)

Fig. 21.7. Time delay contacts

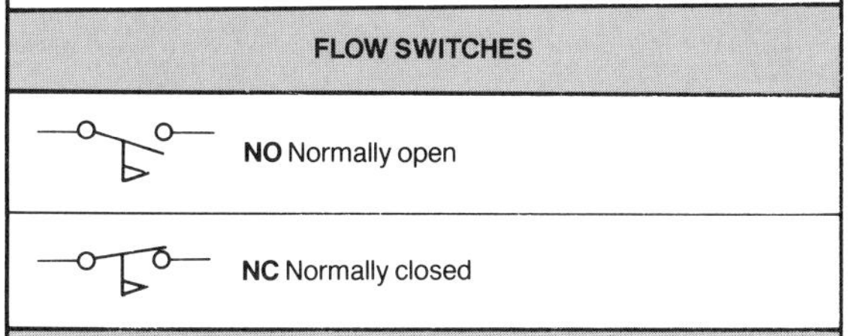

FLOW SWITCHES	
⎯o⟍o⎯	**NO** Normally open
⎯o⟍o⎯	**NC** Normally closed

Fig. 21.8. Flow switches

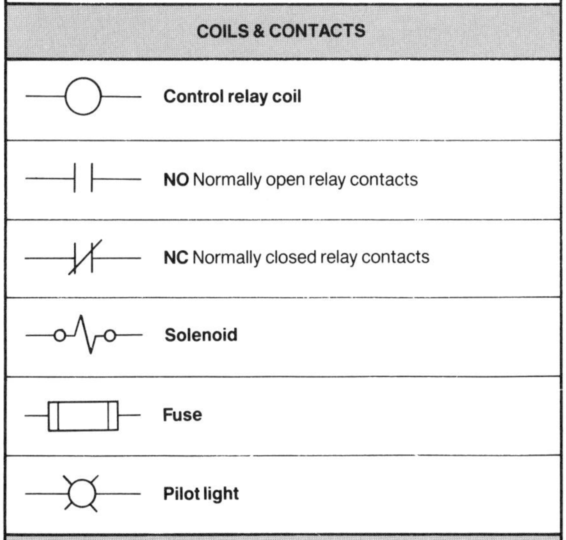

COILS & CONTACTS	
⎯◯⎯	**Control relay coil**
⎯┤├⎯	**NO** Normally open relay contacts
⎯┤/├⎯	**NC** Normally closed relay contacts
⎯o√o⎯	**Solenoid**
⎯▭⎯	**Fuse**
⎯✕⎯	**Pilot light**

Fig. 21.9. Coils and contact symbols

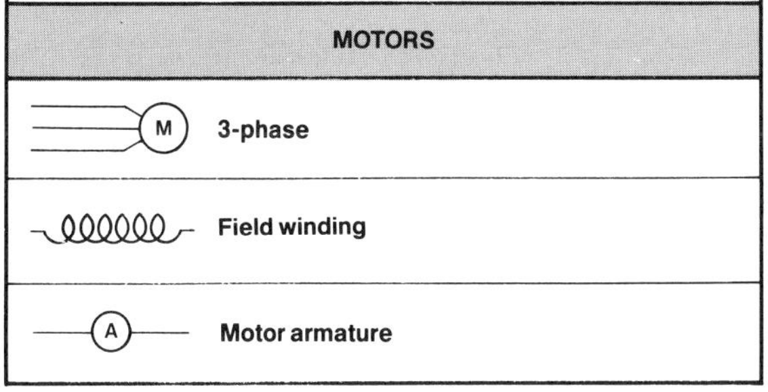

MOTORS	
⎯(M)	**3-phase**
⎯0000000⎯	**Field winding**
⎯(A)⎯	**Motor armature**

Fig. 21.10. Electric motor symbols

225

control functions are accomplished.

A normally open SPST push button initiates the cycle. When the operator depresses the *cycle start* push button, it energizes control relay, CR-1. The coil closes one pair of contacts CR-2 holding the relay *in* — that is, it maintains a circuit to keep the coil energized *after* the push button is *released* because the push button and the *holding contacts* are in parallel. Control relay CR-1 also closes a second pair of contacts, CR-3 which energize solenoid SOL-1 in the directional control valve. The hydraulic valve shifts, porting pressure fluid to the cap end of the cylinder which extends.

When the piston rod reaches the end of its stroke, it opens a NC limit switch, 1-LS connected in series with the contacts CR-2 in the holding circuit. When 1-LS opens, it breaks the holding circuit and deenergizes the relay coil. This opens the contacts, CR-3 which deenergizes the solenoid. When the solenoid is deenergized, the valve spring shifts the valve spool to port oil to the head end of the cylinder which retracts.

The circuit should include a reversing switch which is a NC push button connected in series with the start button, the holding contacts, and the limit switch. Opening this reversing switch breaks the holding circuit for the relay coil. This causes the solenoid circuit contacts to open — the same action that was initiated by limit switch, 1-LS. See 1 LS, Figure 21.11(b).

Application example 2

Another common fluid power control application involves two cylinders which must extend and retract

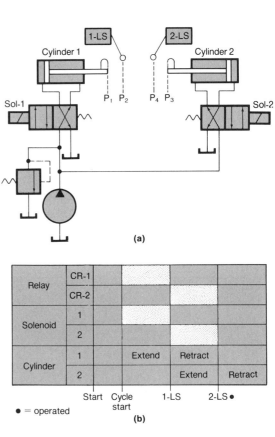

(a)

			Start	Cycle start	1-LS	2-LS ●
Relay	CR-1					
	CR-2					
Solenoid	1					
	2					
Cylinder	1			Extend	Retract	
	2				Extend	Retract

● = operated

(b)

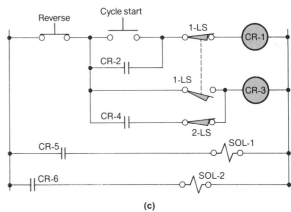

(c)

Fig. 21.12. System for operating two cylinders sequentially with limit switches (a) hydraulic circuit; (b) sequence diagram; (c) electrical circuit.

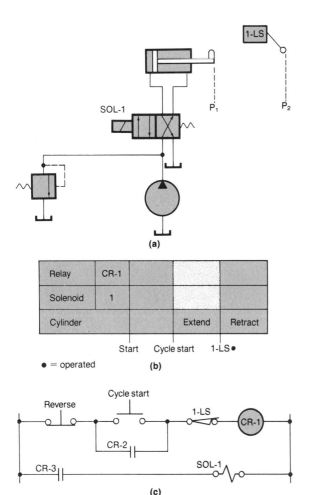

(a)

		Start	Cycle start	1-LS ●
Relay	CR-1			
Solenoid	1			
Cylinder			Extend	Retract

● = operated

(b)

(c)

Fig. 21.11. System for operating a double-acting cylinder: (a) hydraulic circuit using ISO symbols; (b) sequence diagram; (c) electrical control circuit.

226

alternately. Figure 21.12(*a*) shows the fluid power diagram; the sequence diagram, including electrical control designations, is shown in Figure 21.12(*b*); the electrical diagram is in Figure 21.12(*c*).

The cycle is started by depressing a push button, as was the case in Example 1. Limit switch, 1-*LS*, is now of the DPST type.

Camming 1-*LS* opens the holding circuit for the first relay *CR*-1 and simultaneously closes the holding circuit for the second relay, *CR*-3. Limit switch 1-*LS* energizes relay *CR*-3.

The circuit diagram in Figure 21.12(*c*) shows that the electrical control circuit is essentially that of Example 1, with extra paths added to control cylinder 2. The two branches of the circuit are interlocked through limit switch *LS*-1.

Application example 3

The hydraulic circuit, Figure 21.13(*a*) must provide the following work sequence: Cylinder 1 extends, contacts the workpiece, dwells until a preset pressure is reached, reverses, and retracts. When Cylinder 1 reverses, Cylinder 2 begins to extend, contacts the workpiece, dwells until a preset pressure is reached, then reverses and retracts. The sequence diagram for the operation is shown in Figure 21.13(*b*); the electrical ladder diagram is shown in Figure 21.13(*c*).

Application example 4

A further modification of the basic cylinder circuit uses the retracting cylinder to trigger the extending cylinder at some preset point along the retraction stroke. The fluid power circuit is shown in Figure 21.14(*a*), the electrical ladder diagram in Figure 21.14(*c*).

The sequence of events, as shown in the sequence diagram, Figure 21.14*(b)* is as follows: Cylinder 1 extends. When it reaches its end of stroke position, the cylinder rod trips limit switch 2-*LS* to reverse the stroke direction of Cylinder 1, which begins to retract. At some point along its return stroke, Cylinder 1 actuates limit switch 5-*LS* which initiates the extension stroke of Cylinder 2. Cylinder 1 continues to retract, trips limit switch 1-*LS* and stops at the end of its stroke. Cylinder 2 extends until it reaches the end of its stroke, when it actuates limit switch 3-*LS* and reverses its direction. When Cylinder 2 is fully retracted, it actuates limit switch 4-*LS* which stops the cycle.

Application example 5

A cylinder must reciprocate a preset number of cycles. The fluid power circuit is shown in Figure 21.15(*a*); the sequence diagram in Figure 21.15(*b*); the electrical ladder diagram in Figure 21.15(*c*).

Fig. 21.13. System for operating two cylinders sequentially with limit switches and pressure switches: (a) hydraulic circuit; (b) sequence diagram; (c) electrical circuit.

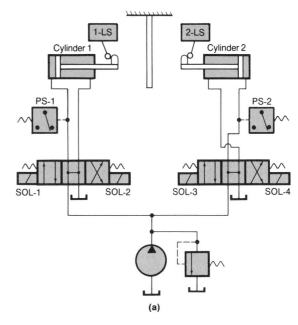

(a)

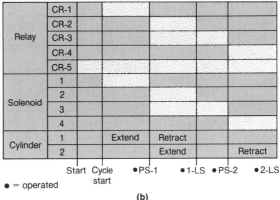

(b)

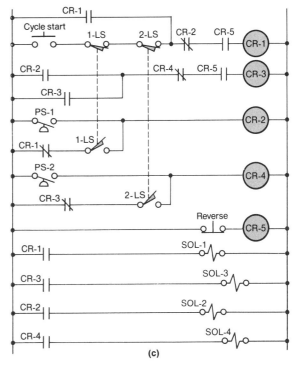

(c)

227

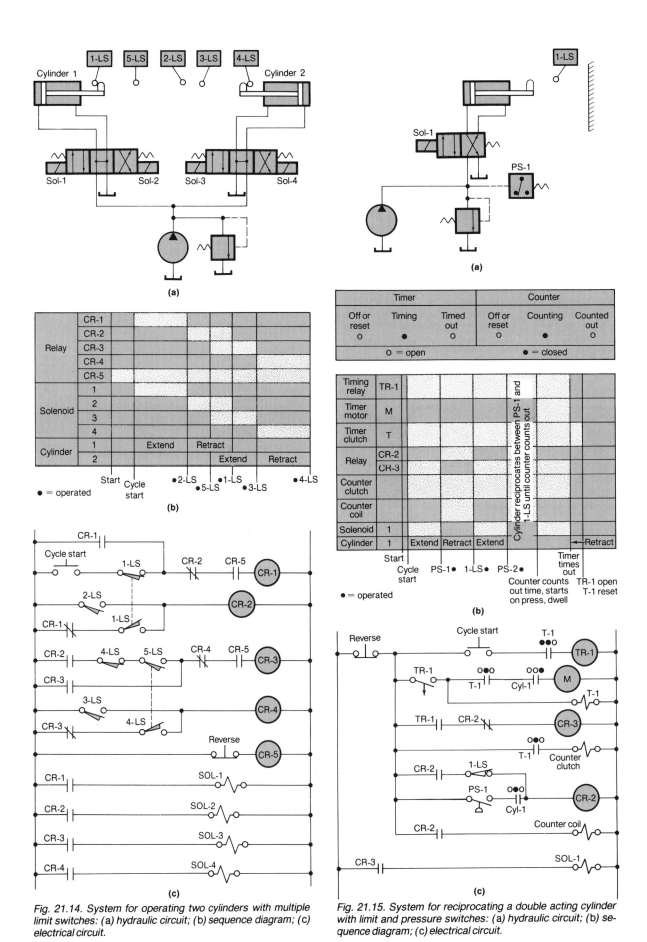

Fig. 21.14. System for operating two cylinders with multiple limit switches: (a) hydraulic circuit; (b) sequence diagram; (c) electrical circuit.

Fig. 21.15. System for reciprocating a double acting cylinder with limit and pressure switches: (a) hydraulic circuit; (b) sequence diagram; (c) electrical circuit.

The cycle is as follows: the cylinder extends and contacts the workpiece. When a preset pressure as controlled by pressure switch, PS-1, is reached, the cylinder reverses and retracts. At some point during the retract stroke, the cylinder actuates limit switch 1-LS, causing the cylinder to reverse and extend again until it contacts the workpiece, again actuating pressure switch PS-1. The cycle is repeated a preset number of times, as controlled by a counter.

The counter is an electrical control which, for each pulse it receives, subtracts one digit from a number preset into it. When the balance in the counter reaches zero, the counter performs a control function — for example, it may open a switch or send an electrical pulse. These type counters are commonly used to control numbers of cycles or events. The operator merely dials into the counter the number of events desired before starting the system.

This system is also equipped with a timer. Electrical timers are mechanisms driven by synchronous motors. These motors run at constant speed, usually based on 60-Hz, AC current in the United States and Canada — (the current would be 50-cycle in Europe). Suitable gear trains provide the desired time delay. At the end of a timed period, the timer initiates some control action such as opening or closing a switch. Pneumatic and electronic timers are also available.

In this example, the timer shuts down the entire circuit after a preset length of time by controlling the solenoid operator on the directional control valve.

Application example 6

An interesting control application is shown in Figure 21.16(a) in which a cylinder reciprocates, each successive stroke being longer than the preceding one. This stepped control is achieved with a number of limit switches appropriately spaced along the cylinder stroke. The electrical ladder diagram is shown in Figure 21.16(c). When a cycle is started, the cylinder extends until it contacts the *second* limit switch, 2-LS. The cylinder reverses and retracts until it contacts 1-LS. Limit switch 1-LS reverses the cylinder which extends again until it contacts 3-LS, and so on.

The sequence diagram, Figure 21.16(b) displays the switching sequence for this circuit. Two additional control functions are not apparent from the operating sequence. First, it is possible to reverse the cylinder and return it to its start position at any point in the cycle. Second, any time the retract function has been depressed, the cyle start button must be operated to initiate a new cycle.

The need for these additional control functions brings up an important point. Designers of control circuits must have the necessary skill and experience to perceive the need for these little "extras." Such extras are frequently required to convert a *theoretical* circuit derived from a sequence diagram into a *practical* system. The diagram alone cannot encompass and display all the requirements such as the need for interlocks between parts of a circuit, emergency shutdowns, etc. The sequence diagram may indicate where these functions ought to be included, but it is up to the designer to recognize the need for them.

MICRO ELECTRONICS

The electronics technology was stimulated not only by aerospace and defense systems and associated research and development efforts, but also through spectacular developments in the communications industry, television, consumer-oriented activities.

The result was a series of advances in electronics: from vacuum tube technology, to discrete element solid-state devices, to integrated circuitry based on solid-state devices, to macro-integrated circuits, and finally to micro-integrated circuits. To progress from the solid-state equivalent of the electromechanical relay to the microprocessor took but one decade.

To put these developments into proper perspective, we must distinguish between:

1. The control or data processing function of micro-electronic technology and
2. The power transmission and control function of fluid power.

Industrial controls, to which fluid power is closely related, have barely begun to adopt new electronic developments. The use of state-of-the-art electronics by aerospace-defense, the computer industry, the communications industry, and process control is far ahead of current practices in basic manufacturing, hard goods, and metal working industries. Most control installations use old, standby, electromechanical relays.

Keep in mind that electrohydraulic systems are only *one part* of a fluid power control system; other controls include: manual, mechanical, cam-operated, levers, push buttons, treadles, and air-to-oil as well as oil-to-air pilots.

Programmable controllers

According to NEMA Standard I-28-1976, a programmable controller is a "digitally operated electronic apparatus which uses a (programmable) memory for the internal storage of instructions for implementing specific functions such as logic, sequencing, timing, counting, and arithmetic to control, through digital or analog input/output modules, various types of machines or processes."

A designer who is also experienced in the fluid power technology should expand the definition of *programmable controllers,* (PCs), to include fluid-mechanical and electro-mechanical sequencing devices such as drum-switch programmers, fluidic sequences, etc.

Some definitions

Figure 21.17 illustrates a block diagram of a

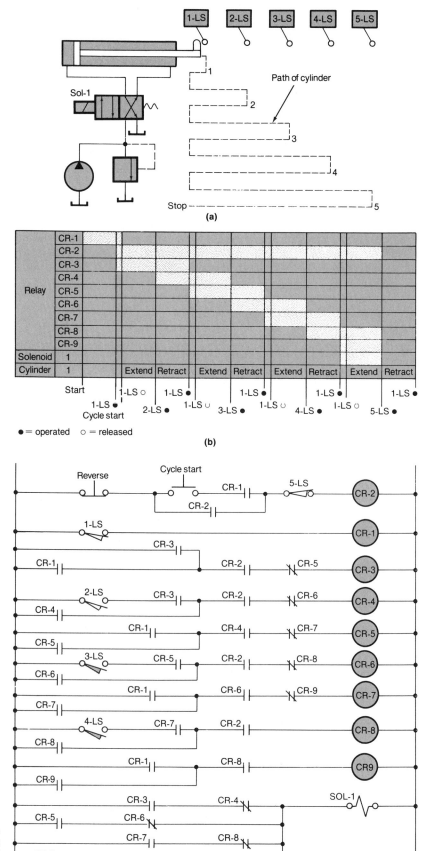

● = operated   ○ = released

Fig. 21.16. System for reciprocating a double acting cylinder in successively longer strokes: (a) hydraulic circuit; (b) sequence diagram; (c) electrical circuit.

230

microprocessor-based programmable controller. Note that many of these functions are also used in microcomputers.

Programming device may be a built-in section of the PC or a separate, self-contained accessory.

CPU (Central Processing Unit) is an integrated circuit (IC) on a chip which includes the necessary circuitry, logic functions, etc., to provide the functions required of the PC.

Power supply is the electrical power source for the PC. It is a regulated power supply which provides electricity to the PC at required voltage and current levels.

Memory is another integrated circuit which may be on the same chip as the CPU or on an individual chip depending on PC requirements. Some micro-electronic systems are totally contained in the circuitry on a single chip. Others are "board level" systems in which individual functional chips are mounted on a board or card and interconnected by conducting paths deposited on the board or card.

The *memory* is the part of the programmable controller where instructions (the program) are stored. Data from inputs or to outputs may also be stored in appropriate *addresses* in the memory. One of the functions which the CPU processes and controls is the routing, storing, and retrieval of data in the memory.

Input/output (I/O) modules are the integrated circuits designed to handle input or output data (in the form of an electrical voltage) from external input or output devices.

Input devices for fluid power systems typically may include push-buttons, limit switches, selector switches, relays, punch cards readers, sensors, transducers, or any device which can supply an electrical voltage signal to the PC input module. Input devices are hard- wired to the terminal strip on the PC.

Output devices typically might be relay coils, valve solenoids, motor starter coils, etc. Output devices are also hard wired to the PC. The CPU program instructions from memory and feedback signals on the status of the I/O devices to control the operating sequence of the output devices.

Programmable controllers of the type described above range from very simple systems, Figure 21.18 to highly sophisticated distributed systems which are hardly distinguishable from computer control installations.

The principal difference between *relay logic* and *programmable* controllers is *programmability and cost*. To change a relay logic system, components may have to be added or removed and the system hard rewired. To make a corresponding change in a PC requires only reprogramming, or at worst, adding additional modules, if increased capacity is required.

Implementing PC controls for fluid power applications must meet some limitations and satisfy certain

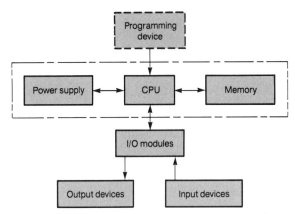

Fig. 21.17. Block diagram of a microprocessor-based programmable controller.

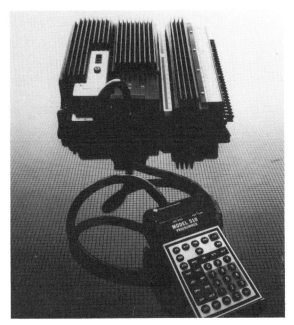

Fig. 21.18. Illustration of simple programmable controller.

requirements. Typically, the designer must properly match the characteristics of I/O devices, timing requirements, program faults, defective memory, irrational commands, faulty logic, etc. all of which make programmable controllers more difficult to use than might be construed by an *inexperienced* designer. Such detailed discussion is beyond the scope of this book. However, the concerned reader should study the abundant available literature which describes the PC technology.

Microprocessors and microcomputers

Why should the fluid power technology prepare to interface with control computers? Because that is the direction industrial controls are following. Fluid power is not a lead technology. When the growth of a given industry is spurred by market demands or technological innovations within that industry, there

231

are changes in production techniques, machinery, and processes. Fluid power must accommodate these changes.

Most areas of industrial activity inevitably adopt computer control. The microprocessor has made this possible because of the capability incorporated into low-cost control components.

At the time of this writing, the adaptation of electronic and micro-electronic control is proceeding much more rapidly than had been anticipated in the late 1970s. The industry will need to train *hybrid* engineers/technicians who understand micro electronics and fluid power and have the knowledge and skill to combine them.

Some component problems may have to be resolved before the hybrid technology can overcome existing constraints.

Signal level — Because solenoid valves currently used in fluid power systems operate at power levels substantially above the normal signal level generated by microprocessors, signal amplification is necessary. The amplification stage could be:

● part of the microcomputer package

● a separate, third level between the microcomputer and the fluid power valve, or

● part of the fluid power valve package, for example, by adding it to the solenoid operator. Because the majority of solenoid valves are digital devices, they would be most compatible with microcomputer output signals.

Electrohydraulic servovalves are analog devices and therefore harder to interface than solenoid

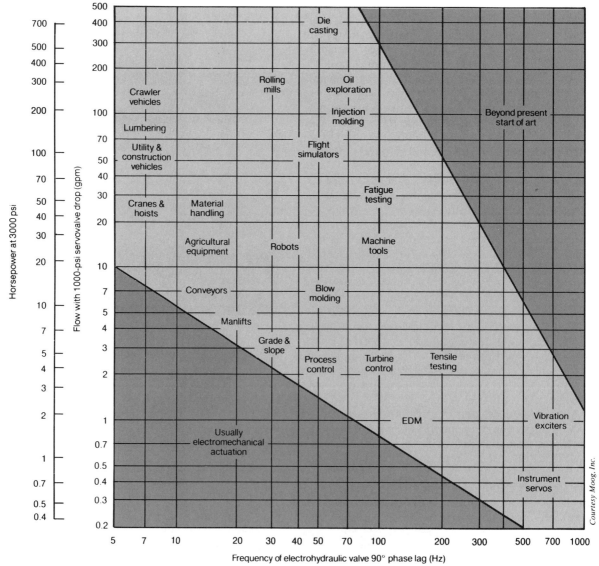

Fig. 21.19. Central region of graph represents major application area for today's electrohydraulic systems. Shaded area below 100-Hz bandpass, indicates where typical microprocessors could be used as closed-loop controllers. However, such controls would add little to systems operating at these speeds. Above 100-Hz bandpass, microprocessors are too slow to perform well as closed-loop controllers and have no time for other system activities.

valves. Refer to Chapter 12. Signal amplification may be less than required for solenoids because the torque-motor interface operates at lower power levels than most solenoids. But with the limits of current technology, a digital-to-analog (D/A) conversion would be necessary. Perhaps converting the torque motor to a frequency modulated, (FM) or pulse width modulated, (PWM) device might provide a solution.

Sensors/transducers — At present, most sensors/transducers used in fluid power systems are analog devices. Digital transducers are particularly compatible with microprocessor inputs; a swing toward micro controls would increase demand for digital transducers. However, the differences between analog or digital transducer outputs presently lie in the area of signal conditioning rather than basic transducer design. The solution may be within the electronics related to the sensor system.

FM- and PWM-controlled valves — Because microprocessor output is digital, some method must be used to make the conversion from digital-to-frequency or digital-to-pulse-width. The choices resemble those of amplifying the signal to a solenoid valve. Signal amplification would also be necessary because a solenoid interface would be required.

Hydraulic systems can pack a lot of power in a small package. However, they often require greater positioning accuracy and response. Electronic control of hydraulic systems is helping overcome these problems, making possible the development of a new breed of equipment which will be able to do more work at less cost.

In some instances, microprocessor-based controls are replacing conventional fluid-logic devices. The electronic packages make it possible to alter system parameters with simple programming changes rather than by altering orifice or piston sizes, or by rerouting connections.

Beyond these retrofit applications, the use of microprocessor controls promises to usher in a new breed of intelligent fluid-power systems. The computational power and programmability of these controls make radically new automated machines possible. Figure 21.19 is a graphic representation of the spectrum of applications for electrohydraulic servovalves.

Types of systems

Applications of microprocessor-controlled hydraulic systems typically fall into six categories.

1. Closing a loop. This is the most tempting application of microprocessors in electrohydraulic systems: the microprocessor replaces the analog or digital summing point and conditions the error information driving the hydraulic controller.

However, to serve effectively as a closed-loop controller, a microprocessor must handle information at a rate compatible with the servo bandpass. A typical microprocessor controller, operating at a clock fre-

quency of 2 MHz on 16 bits of data, might have an update time of 500 ms. Thus, if the bandpass is considered the frequency for a 90-degree phase shift, the microprocessor controller would have a bandpass of 1 kHz.

As a rule of thumb, the signal processor should be 5 to 10 times more responsive than the power-control elements in the loop. Thus, practical servos which could use microprocessors to close the loop would have a bandpass of less than 100 Hz. In this region, the use of microprocessors would provide little economic advantage.

There are techniques for increasing the speed at which signal information is processed. However, they are highly specialized and increase hardware development costs.

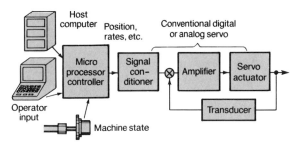

Fig. 21.20. Pre-loop processing is most common use of microprocessor-based controls in hydraulic systems. Typical control consists of components shown in block diagram. One advantage of such controls is that same, or similar, hardware can be used for a variety of applications.

2. Pre-loop processing. Using a microprocessor as a pre-loop processor or command generator for a conventional analog servo is probably the most common application today. In such a system, a microcomputer can be used for interface functions, such as keyboard reading, or to process available information, such as calculating feed rates or end points. This information is then transmitted to a high-performance servo for implementation, Figure 21.20.

The same, or essentially the same hardware can be used in a variety of pre-loop processing applications. Minor sizing changes may be needed, but most fine-tuning can be done in the processor section, that is, by software rather than hardware changes.

The key to this variety of possible applications is the similarity of system components. Most electrohydraulic positioning servos are similar in concept, although different in size and shape. Thus, if characteristic gains can be made similar, the microcomputer can be applied to a variety of systems. This versatility can reduce the high costs of custom control systems.

A more common advantage of pre-loop processing is that two vastly different processes, having complex interrelationships, can be tied together. This requires, of course, that the interrelationships be described and predicted with measurable variables.

3. Peripheral processing. In this type of system, a

microprocessor handles related information ahead of and after a conventional closed loop. Because the microprocessor usually is idle while the servo is performing, the processor can handle other duties in the system. Further, because the microprocessor works with output information generated by servo operation, it can use this information to improve the next cycle.

In general, peripheral processing is better suited for intermittent processes (cyclic or single events) than continuous operations. Also, the combined use of a conventional servo and a dedicated microprocessor often requires both hardware and software development.

4. Adaptive control. This may be the "most logical" application for microprocessor-controlled hydraulics. An adaptive control system can adjust itself to provide optimal, consistent control in response to identifiable system changes.

Typically, adaptive controls are used where constant output is required, in spite of long-term changes in the physical process, flunctuations in available power, loading changes, and gain changes with amplitude. Because of the variety of possible changes, several different conditions may be controlled, based on past or predicted performance. These conditions could include limits, gains, non-linearity boundaries, and control modes.

5. Smart redundancy. Redundancy to enhance reliability is becoming increasingly common in electrohydraulic systems. Such systems typically are used when a failure would be extremely costly or would jeopardize personnel safety.

Depending on the type of failure and the action which must be taken, these systems can become very complex. A primary cause of complexity is that the state or cause of the failure is unknown; therefore, the worst case must be assumed.

A computer-controlled redundant system with the ability to interpret failures and selectively shut down channels can increase the useful on-time of the system. Minor failures do not cause a complete shutdown, and failures are considered on the basis of system need, not on a conservative scale.

6. Time-optimal control. Many force-limited systems require minimum response time for any change in position. In such systems, full force, or torque, is applied until the actuator travels halfway through its stroke. Then, the polarity of the applied force is reversed to stop the actuator at the specified end point.

The role a microprocessor could play here is twofold: it could:
● provide an accurate switch point, and
● correct the switch point from cycle to cycle, providing almost heuristic control.

Building an electronic control system

A microcomputer-based control system has some or all of the components shown in the block diagram, Figure 21.21. In addition to the microcomputer, typical components include digital and analog sensors, signal conditioners, A/D and D/A converters, digital and analog actuators, and a power supply.

In most cases, the selection of a suitable microcomputer is only a small part of the hardware design procedure. The integrated circuits which make up the microcomputer are widely used, and their proper configuration is usually well documented.

However, this is not the case for some of the other components. For example, only a limited number of electrohydraulic actuators are available. Furthermore, these components often display characteristics such as contaminant sensitivity which may prevent the system from operating as specified. In short, *ALL* system components must be carefully considered when evaluating the feasibility of a microcomputer-based system.

Design considerations

Despite the capabilities of microprocessor-based controls, they may not see widespread usage until several technical problems are resolved.

Transducers. Probably the most critical phase of the design of microprocessor-based control systems is the electrohydraulic interface. Ideally, transducers providing input to controllers should be rugged, accurate, and inexpensive. Unfortunately, while most of today's transducers are highly accurate, they also are delicate and expensive.

Fig. 21.21. Block diagram shows major components which make up a microcomputer based control system.

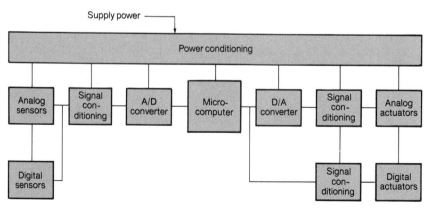

This problem is being relieved somewhat by the automotive industry's development of microcomputer-based vehicle controls. However, inexpensive transducers suitable for use on general industrial and off-highway equipment are not yet available. Also, many of the transducers being developed for automotive use operate in ranges too low for industrial hydraulic systems. However, some of the sensing techniques may be transferable.

Electric power. Many of the available microcomputers require several different supply voltages. For instance, a typical microcomputer requires $+12$, $+5$, and -5 V DC to operate. Also, standard analog conversion circuits often require $+15$ and -15 V DC. Therefore, as many as five different voltages may have to be derived from the available power source.

Inverters often can produce the required voltages; however, they can be expensive and frequently are bulky and unreliable. In addition, microcomputers with large memories often require large amounts of power, and the low efficiency of inverters can increase power dissipation.

Multiple power requirements were characteristic of early microcomputers. New ones usually require only $+5$ V DC, a voltage level which is easy to generate with a simple voltage regulator. However, care must be taken, when setting the voltage regulator, to filter out the effects of low voltage and voltage spikes.

Temperature variations. Electronic components typically provide reliable output over only very limited temperature ranges. Common temperature ranges are 0 to 70 C for commercial units -25 to 85 C for those for industrial service and -55 to 125 C for military devices.

To be useful for general hydraulic system applications, a microprocessor should be able to operate in commonly encountered industrial temperatures. To date, only a few rated for this range have been introduced; most operate in the commercial temperature range. Some microprocessors which can operate in the military range are available, but at a premium price.

Shock and Vibration. Most electronic components cannot withstand shock and vibration loads. For this reason, care must be taken to shock-mount the control section to isolate the electronics from such loads. Also, components such as mechanical relays, edge-type connectors, and large printed-circuit cards should be avoided in such environments.

Sensor fundamentals

Signal-generating instruments may be considered the interface devices between the physical variable, in its own environment, and the so called "outside" world. For example, when a gage is exposed to fluid pressure, it transduces this physical effect into a pointer indication.

Instruments. An instrument senses the state of a variable and displays an output signal which describes that state. Instrument outputs can be mechanical, electrical, thermal, and fluid.

Typical *mechanical-instrument outputs* include the motion of a pointer along a dial scale, digital readout, position of a vane, or rotation of a propeller or turbine wheel.

Electrical outputs include a DC voltage proportional to the state of the variable, AC frequencies and phase shifts are pulses. Most electrical indicators use electrical and mechanical phenomena to provide an output.

Thermal instrument outputs are generally the length of a column of fluid which is related to temperature, or an electrical signal generated because of thermoelectric effects. Radiation phenomena are also used, as with infrared devices. Here, the output is usually an electrical voltage

Photoelectric instruments also use radiation effects, such as light intensity, to produce a proportional electrical signal. Lasers are also used in sensing applications.

Fluid-effect instruments generally use a mechanical output. Some produce an electrical output proportional to the motion of some mechanical member.

Transducers. These components transfer energy from one system to another. Current practice suggests a more restricted definition; transducers sense and generate signals uniquely describing the condition or state of a system variable. Often, the terms transducer and instrument, are used interchangeably. However, in this text, an instrument is considered to be a device used for *data acquisition*, a transducer for *control situations*.

Operating principles. Figure 21.22 shows the function of a variable-sensing device, either an instrument or a transducer. The instrument is designed to accept the input variable, Figure 21.22(*a*), and operates on the input signal to produce a unique output signal. Some losses are incurred in the processing of the signal. All data-acquisition and/or control functions consume energy to perform the function itself. This fact is frequently overlooked.

Instrument characteristics. A "characteristic curve," Figure 21.22(*b*), relates the state of the measured variable to the output signal over the range of the instrument. The state of the measured variable is usually plotted along the abscissa as the independent variable. The output, or dependent variable, which depends on the variations in the measured variable, is plotted along the ordinate.

One of the major problems encountered in instrumentation is establishing the efficiency of a particular instrument. In addition to energy loss, each instrument is unique because of the physical variations in its parts. Thus, ten apparently identical instruments are, in fact, not identical. Each instrument can be regarded as having its own "personality." It reacts uniquely to a given input.

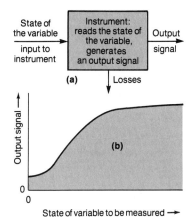

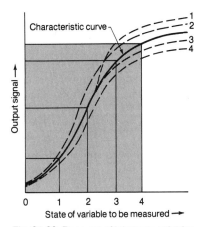

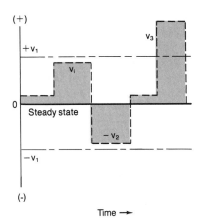

Fig. 21.22. Function of variable sensing device (a) accepting variable input, (b) characteristic curve relating to state of measured variable to output signal.

Fig. 21.23. Because of inherent variables, each instrument reacts slightly differently to identical inputs.

Fig. 21.24. Deadband characteristics of instruments are important in control applications.

For example, assume four ostensibly identical instruments. If they were truly identical, one characteristic curve would describe the performance of all four. However, because of such factors as energy losses in the instruments, differences in manufacture, and varying degrees of wear, each instrument reacts slightly differently to identical inputs, Figure 21.23.

At point 1 for example, instruments 2 and 4 are on the characteristic curve, whereas instrument 1 falls below, and instrument 3 above, the curve. Similarly, at points 2, 3, and 4, the readings form a range of values. Which instrument is reading correctly? It depends on the interpretation of the term "correct."

If all readings must fall on the characteristic curve, no one instrument is acceptable over the full range of the independent variable. Instruments 2 and 4 are acceptable at point 3, none at point 4. Thus, the requirements for acceptability may have to be reduced or modified, especially if these are the best devices available for the measurement to be made.

Accuracy. Assume the deviation of the reading of instrument 1, at point 4, to be 2 percent *above* the characteristic curve, and instrument 4 to be 1½ percent *below* the curve. If limits of accuracy (or perhaps more appropriately "estimated uncertainty") of ±2 percent at point 4 were selected as acceptable performance, all four instruments would meet the requirements.

If the process required a maximum of ±1 percent deviation from the characteristic curve, only instruments 2 and 3 could meet the requirements at point 4. Thus, instruments 1 and 4 would be disqualified for this application.

A tolerance on the ability of an instrument to indicate accurately the state of a physical variable is required. For instance, in Figure 21.23, if the accuracy of ±1 percent at point 4 is required over the entire range of the variable, permissible error at point 1 is only 0.02. Thus, the instrument must be able to generate signals of much smaller amplitude at the low end of the scale than at the high end, if it is to maintain a constant accuracy.

Since *accuracy* is such an elusive quality, it should be specified for each application of an instrument.

Backlash. Each instrument has some lost motion inherent in its design and construction. In mechanical systems, this is known as backlash. In electrical and thermal components, these are termed hysteresis losses.

Deadband. The minimum excursion of an instrument which produces no sensible output is called the deadband. This characteristic, Figure 21.24, is important in control applications.

Disregarding the magnitude of the signals, assume a steady-state condition of the variable, V_i, at point 4 of the characteristic curve of Figure 21.23. Because in practice few inputs are constant, an input signal might vary as shown by the dotted line in Figure 21.24. During part of the time interval during which the instrument is observed, the independent variable exceeds the steady-state value; at other times, it is less than the steady-state value. If the instrument does not respond to variations in V, unless they exceed $+V_i$ or $-V_i$, the instrument's deadband is $2V_i$ wide. Thus, the instrument will not respond to signal V_i or $-V_2$, because both are within the deadband. However, the instrument will indicate the magnitude of signal V_3.

The greater the sensitivity of the instrument, the narrower the deadband.

Since no instrument provides an absolute indication of the state of a physical variable, a reading is *correct* only in relation to recognized standards. These standards are defined — frequently on an international basis — by law, and become the measuring sticks against which all instrumentation is calibrated. In the U.S., these standards are maintained by the National Bureau of Standards.

Sets of carefully controlled primary standards are maintained in select locations throughout the nation. These are the working standards against which secondary standards — greater in number than the primary — are calibrated. The commercial instrumentation and gaging equipment of the nation is calibrated to these secondary standards — within defined limits of accuracy and to specific tolerances.

Getting the signal

Regardless of the parameter to be measured, instrumentation can be classified on the basis of the physical phenomenon used to generate the signal: mechanical, electrical, thermal, nuclear, and chemical. Of these, mechanical, electrical, and thermal are the most widely used in fluid power systems.

Mechanical instruments can be further subdivided into those using rigid members — such as linkages, gears, cranks, shafts, and springs — and those using fluid interactions.

Electrical instruments can be divided into those using voltage or current directly and those using magnetic effects.

Few instruments use only one phenomenon; most use a combination, such as fluid-mechanical or electro-mechanical. Refer to Table I for a summary of *Fluid Power Variables*.

Sensor-microprocessor-computer interfacing

In the microcomputer system, Figure 21.21, blocks labeled *analog sensors* and *digital sensors* are connected to a signal conditioning block which is linked in series to an *A/D converter* and then to the *microprocessor*. This is precisely the sequence of events which must take place to get a signal to the microprocessor so it can process the signal.

To the right of the microprocessor, the signal first goes to a *D/A converter*, than a *signal conditioner* to prepare the signal for the actuator. All these steps are necessary for a number of reasons:

1. Microcomputers operate exclusively as **digital** devices, using ON-OFF signals received in the form of present (or absent) voltages

2. Many transducers and servos are **analog** devices: their output signals are proportional to the state of the variable generating a ramp output

3. Many transducers and servos operate at different voltages than do microcomputers

4. Some sensors produce outputs which are a function of factors such as frequency, phase lags or leads, etc. All these outputs must be conditioned to yield a digital signal which the A/D converter can handle and forward to the microcomputer

5. The inverse is also true with microcomputer outputs which are *always* **digital**. Often, they must be converted to equivalent *analog* **outputs** and then conditioned so the analog actuator can use them, and

6. Even if digital servos or actuators are used, the

Table 21.1—Fluid-Power Variables

Physical variable	Definition of variable	Dimension of variable	Units of variable
Displacement	Change of position of a body, linear or rotational.	linear—length rotational—angle	ft, in., m deg, rad
Velocity	Change of position with respect to time.	linear—length/time rotational—angle/time	in./sec, ft/sec deg/sec, rad/sec
Acceleration	Change of velocity with respect to time.	length/time^2 angle/time^2	in./sec/sec, ft/sec/sec, deg/sec/sec, rad/sec/sec
Force	External reaction on a body which tends to produce a change of position.	force	lb, Newton*
Time	A basic descriptor of an interval during which a system may be subjected to a change in state.	time	sec, min
Pressure	Distributed reaction of a force acting through a fluid.	force/area	lb/sq in., lb/sq ft, bar/Pascal*
Flow rate	Volume of fluid passing a reference point per unit time.	volume/time	cu in./sec cu cm/sec
Mass flow rate	Mass of fluid passing a reference point in unit time.	mass/time	slug/sec, lb-sec/ft, kilogram/sec. or min.
Torque	Moment of a force acting at a distance from an axis of rotation.	force x length	lb-in., Newton-meter
Temperature	Measure of the internal heat energy of a substance.	Btu, calorie	deg F, R, C, K
Viscosity	Measure of the resistance of a fluid to shearing.	force x time/length^2	lb-sec/ft^2

*SI Metric terms, def. Appendix A.

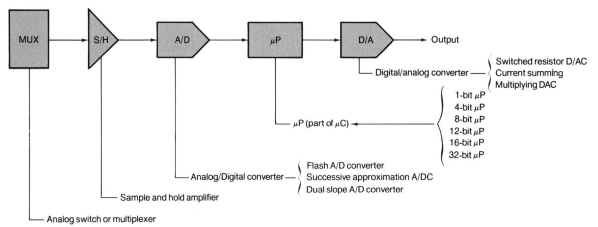

Fig. 21.25. Typical electronic instrumentation components in a system.

signals must be conditioned to match the balance of the system.

The diagram in Figure 21.25 illustrates the typical components in a system, with two additional components not yet discussed:

● sample-and-hold amplifier which presents a constant analog signal level to the A/D converter, and

● analog switch or multiplexer which permits several analog input devices to supply signals to a single A/D converter servicing a microcomputer.

Computer language

It is well established that those involved with computers tend to communicate in *acronyms*. Fluid power technologists will have to learn computer language to be able to communicate with others.

Important terms

Analog. Devices in which output is proportional to input and is a ramp function.

Digital. Devices in which an output signal is ON or OFF

Float switch. Switch actuated by motion of a float which senses liquid level

Flow switch. Switch actuated by flowing fluid

Foot-operated switch. A switch which an operator actuates with his foot

Interlocking. Process used to (1) isolate one cycle event from another during a control sequence; (2) prevent the occurrence of a subsequent event before the completion of a prerequisite one; or (3) ensure that all requisite simultaneous events are actuated and occurring

Limit switch. Switch operated mechanically by an output motion from the system

Microelectronics. Electronic circuitry integrated onto a chip

Normally closed, NC. A switch condition indicating that a circuit is made or ON, when the switch is deenergized or not actuated. Binary designator is 1. (*opposite*, in sense, to NC term as used in fluid power).

Normally open, NO. A switch condition indicating that circuit is *not* made or OFF, when the switch is deenergized. Binary designator is 0. (Opposite, in sense to NO term used in fluid power).

Pressure switch. Switch actuated by pressurized fluid in system.

Programmable controller (PC). Device which delivers control signals to operate system functions in accordance with a set of instructions stored within the device.

Push-button switch. Switch actuated by depressing a mechanical input device manually

Relay. Electrically-operated switch

Sensor. Device which monitors the state of a system variable and produces a signal proportional to it

Sequence diagram. A graphic representation of events which occur in a control system and their relationships to each other

Stepping switch. Electrically-operated device with multiple sets of contacts. Pairs of contacts are made and broken sequentially as electrical pulses are fed into the operating coil of the switch

Switch. Electromechanical device designed to make or break electrical circuits by opening or closing pairs of electrical contacts

Thermal switch. Switch actuated by a change in temperature

Time delay. Function used to create a finite time lag between the instant of actuation of a control device and the output from the device.

Review Exercises

21.1. Referring to Chapter 4: Design an electrical control circuit using the principles outlined in this chapter for the example discussed and illustrated in Fig. 4.2.

21.2. Referring to Chapter 5: Design an electrical control circuit for the example shown in Fig. 5.1.

21.3. Referring to Chapter 5: Design an electrical control circuit for the example of Figures 5.3, 5.4 and 5.6.

21.4. Referring to Figure 21.15(a): Discuss how the approach to designing this control system might change, if a drum type programmable controller was used. Would it change the sequence diagram shown in Figure 21.20 in any way?

21.5. In the above problem, would a timer and/or counter still be required? Discuss.

21.6. In exercises 21.4 and 21.5, what would be the differences, if a microprocessor based programmable controller was used?

21.7. If we wanted to change the cycle in example 21.4, which approach would be simpler: relay logic or PC? Which would be less expensive? Discuss.

21.8. Given example 21.5, Figure 21.16(a): Discuss the relative complexity of the sequence diagram and control hardware for the relay logic and PC approach.

21.9. What name is generally applied to the diagram of Figure 21.16(c)?

21.10. Discuss the differences between a microprocessor and a microcomputer.

21.11. Define a programmable controller. What kinds of programmable controllers are there?

21.12. How does a programmable controller differ from a microprocessor?

21.13. Is a microcomputer considered to be a programmable controller? Discuss.

21.14. Discuss the selective power levels of microprocessors/computers and fluid power systems. What are the implications of these differences? Discuss.

21.15. What is a programming device? How is it used in a microprocessor?

21.16. What is a CPU? What is its function?

21.17. What is meant by memory? What is its function in a microprocessor?

21.18. What is an address? How does this relate to memory?

21.19. The term input/output modules is applied to microprocessor/computers. What does it mean?

21.20. What is the function of an input device? Discuss some common types.

21.21. What is the function of an output device? Discuss some typical output devices.

21.22. How does signal conditioning relate to input/output devices? What is its relationship to the microcomputer?

21.23. Discuss interfacing problems between micro-computers and fluid power devices. What is the principal problem to be overcome?

21.24. Referring to Chapter 12: What are the implications for microcontrol of proportional valves?

21.25. What problems in the area of interfacing sensors/transducers to microcomputer- controlled fluid power systems must be overcome? What is the primary problem at the present time?

21.26. Discuss FM or PWM valves on a potential solution to the problem of matching microcomputer control to fluid power systems. How do these techniques relate to proportional valves?

21.27. Into what categories can microprocessor-controlled hydraulic systems be divided? Discuss.

21.28. In a closed-loop hydraulic system, what would be the function of the microprocessor/computer?

21.29. What is the recommended ratio of response capability for microcomputers to that of the fluid power system? How would this affect application of microcomputers to closing the loop?

21.30. What is meant by pre-loop processing? What are the advantages of this technique for fluid power applications? Refer to Figure 21.20.

21.31. To what kinds of machine cycles is peripheral processing best suited? How does pre-loop processing work in a fluid power application?

21.32. What is adaptive control? Is adaptive control commonly used? Under what conditions?

21.33. Redundancy is used for what purpose in fluid power systems? What condition requires redundancy in a system?

21.34. What is time optimal control? How might μC be used to implement time optimal control?

21.35. Discuss Figure 21.21 as representative of a microcomputer based system.

21.26. What is the purpose of a transducer? How, if at all, does a transducer differ from a sensor? Discuss.

21.37. Discuss the basic operation of a sensor/transducer.

21.38. What is meant by "instrument characteristic?" Debate this to the concept of pump or motor characteristics discussed in previous chapter.

21.39. Discuss the analogy between Figures 21.27 and 16.7.

21.40. What is meant by the accuracy of a sensor/transducer? How is full scale accuracy related to accuracy at a single operating point?

21.41. What is *backlash*? Does it affect instrument performance? If so, how?

21.42. Discuss instrument *deadband*. How does this relate to the use of the term for hydraulic valves in Chapters 7 and 12?

21.43. How does *sensitivity* relate to deadband? How does it relate to accuracy?

21.44. The term *repeatability* is sometimes applied

to instruments. Discuss the relationship between repeatability, accuracy, sensitivity, and deadband. What effects, if any, are the characteristics of a sensor/transducer likely to have on fluid power system performance?

21.45. Discuss the fluid power variables summarized in Table 21.1. How does each relate to fluid power systems? How would each be used in designing or troubleshooting fluid power systems?

21.46. What is meant by analog-to-digital conversion? Why is it necessary? What acronym is used in computer jargon to represent it?

21.47. What are the three types of A/D converters currently used with microcomputer systems?

21.48. *Research Question:* Search the computer literature and find what each of the three types of ADCs looks like; diagram each; and discuss performance.

21.49. What is meant by *digital-to-analog* conversion? Why is it necessary? What acronym is used to represent it?

21.50. What types of DAC's are currently used with μC systems?

21.51. *Research Question:* Search the computer literature and find what each of these DACs are, diagram them and discuss how they work.

21.52. What is a multiplexer? What is its function in a μC system?

21.53. What is the purpose of a sample-and-hold amplifier in a μC system?

21.54. Discuss programming of a μC for a fluid power application? Why it is necessary?

CHAPTER 22

CIRCUIT DIAGRAMMING

Up to now, we have developed a circuit design philosophy based on an analysis of the load cycle the fluid power circuit must perform. We have used examples of past solutions to various circuit design problems to illustrate certain points. This chapter considers the **total** approach to a practical circuit design problem using an actual example: a hydraulic excavator, Figure 22.1.

First, analyze the machine cycle. This analysis is equivalent to a time-and-motion study of an operating cycle of the machine. If an actual study is not available, the designer must create an estimated cycle.

A flow diagram, Figure 22.2, provides a valuable starting point. Two possible work cycles are analyzed. Cycle 1 applies when the excavator is loading a dump truck; Cycle 2 when the operator spreads the excavated material on the ground.

The events listed in the left-hand column of Figure 22.2 describe the action at each stage of the cycles. When the system designer has completed the diagram, he has a visual reference for a step-by-step progression through the **work cycle**. With this tool, the designer should have no difficulty producing a **cycle sequence diagram**.

Cycle sequence plot

The next step is to *draw* the cycle sequence diagram, Figure 22.3. The diagrams of machine operations across the top of Figure 22.3 are not mandatory, but they simplify the communication problem when conveying the meaning of the plot to those not familiar with machine operation.

Each hydraulic actuator on the machine has been assigned a code letter from *A* through *J*, although in Figure 22.3 *I* and *J* are not used because tractive effort is not discussed. These code letters are listed in the left hand column of the sequence diagram in their order of actuation in the work cycle. The length of each horizontal bar (shaded area) in the diagram tells how long each particular actuator is ON. Where bars overlap the designer knows that several actuators are operating simultaneously. This, incidentally, is an example of how an important point can be brought out graphically through a sequence diagram — in this case, simultaneous operation of cylinders. It is very difficult to forecast all such instances of overlapping through an intuitive analysis of a circuit.

We can now start the load plot, which is the first step in drawing the cycle profile.*

Fig. 22.1. Typical hydraulic excavator.

Courtesy Caterpillar Tractor Co.

Refer to Chapters 3, 4 and 5.

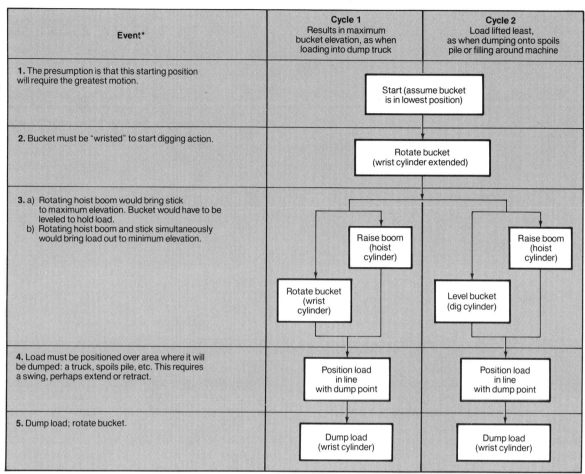

Event*	Cycle 1 Results in maximum bucket elevation, as when loading into dump truck	Cycle 2 Load lifted least, as when dumping onto spoils pile or filling around machine
1. The presumption is that this starting position will require the greatest motion.	Start (assume bucket is in lowest position)	
2. Bucket must be "wristed" to start digging action.	Rotate bucket (wrist cylinder extended)	
3. a) Rotating hoist boom would bring stick to maximum elevation. Bucket would have to be leveled to hold load. b) Rotating hoist boom and stick simultaneously would bring load out to minimum elevation.	Raise boom (hoist cylinder) Rotate bucket (wrist cylinder)	Raise boom (hoist cylinder) Level bucket (dig cylinder)
4. Load must be positioned over area where it will be dumped: a truck, spoils pile, etc. This requires a swing, perhaps extend or retract.	Position load in line with dump point	Position load in line with dump point
5. Dump load; rotate bucket.	Dump load (wrist cylinder)	Dump load (wrist cylinder)

*It is understood that adjustments may be necessary which would necessitate simultaneous operation of actuators. The flow diagram shows primary action only.

Fig. 22.2. Flow diagram of work cycle for hydraulic excavator.

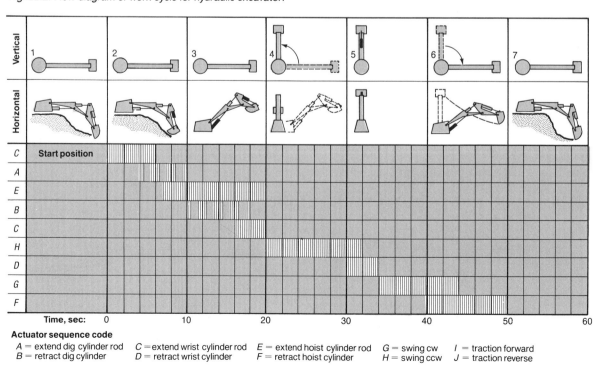

Actuator sequence code

A = extend dig cylinder rod	*C* = extend wrist cylinder rod	*E* = extend hoist cylinder rod	*G* = swing cw	*I* = traction forward
B = retract dig cylinder	*D* = retract wrist cylinder	*F* = retract hoist cylinder	*H* = swing ccw	*J* = traction reverse

Fig. 22.3. Cycle sequence diagram relates motion to time and sequence in which they occur during machine cycle.

242

LOAD PLOTS

Each actuator in the circuit must have its own, separate load plot. To better understand the function of a cylinder and its effect on loading, let us consider the load conditions which occur during one cylinder's extension stroke, Figure 22.4.

Breakaway

The first question we must answer is: "Which load should we consider?" It is common practice to design for the calculated or estimated *maximum* load. If the engineer is fortunate enough to have an operating machine at his disposal, he might instrument the tractor and observe the pressure transients that occur at the instant the operator shifts the directional control valve; the cylinder first begins to move, then extends. A pressure peak, also called pressure spike, is generated over an extremely short period of time. This stage is called "breakaway."*

In the time increment $0 < t < dt$, the cylinder must overcome load resistance caused by the static friction of the total system, including external and internal friction. The cylinder must also overcome any *residual* external load applied to the system, such as the weight of the excavator arm and bucket and any material in the bucket. Note that we have not yet considered acceleration forces, because in the time increment dt, the system has not yet started to move. It might be said that, so far, the cylinder has only taken up the "lost motion" or "backlash" in the system.

This brings up an important point which is often ignored. Capacitance in a system, caused by the compressibility of the fluid and slip in components, is generally regarded as a negative quantity — that is, one that detracts from the performance of a fluid power system. The common view is that if capacitance could be eliminated, system efficiency would improve.

However, consider this: if the system is at zero velocity at time $t = dt$, and if it is accelerated to some velocity, v_1, in an infinitesimally small increment of time $+dt$, then as $+dt - dt$ approaches zero, the system must accelerate from zero velocity to some finite velocity in zero time, an achievement which would require infinite acceleration. It is capacitance in the system which allows us to transfer energy into the fluid over a finite time interval to eliminate the need for infinite acceleration. Conceivably, a fluid power system could not be started if the fluid and system were perfectly rigid.

Actual system

In an actual system the relief valve would, of course, open and bypass excess fluid every time a cylinder started up, until the steady-state velocity of the cylinder piston matched the output rate from the pump.

*See Chapter 6, and Figs. 6.6 and 6.7.

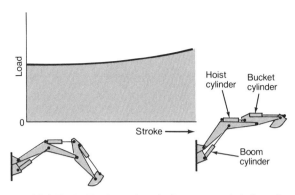

Fig. 22.4. Typical load reaction plot for excavator's hoist cylinder.

In the time interval $dt < t < \Delta t$, the external portions of the system begin to move. Two changes in loading take place.

● an acceleration force is introduced: $F = ma$, in accordance with Newton's Second Law of Motion, and

● friction forces change from static to dynamic. The static coefficient of friction is greater than the dynamic coefficient.

At the end of the time internal Δt, the cylinder piston has reached a steady-state velocity:

$$v_{ss} = Q/A_p.$$

At this point, the acceleration force disappears and the steady-state load is reduced to its components of dynamic friction and external load.

Does this mean that the steady-state load is constant? Certainly not! It is essential that the circuit designer recognize this, particularly when dealing with *multi-branched* circuits supplied by *one* pump. In such systems, auxiliary controls, *i.e.*, pressure reducing valves, flow control valves, or flow dividers may be necessary. The designer will not recognize these needs unless he develops a complete picture of the load cycle.

A simplified load reaction plot for the excavator hoist cylinder is shown in Figure 22.4. This plot is determined only from a layout of the arm and bucket mechanism at different angles during its complete range of motions. Figure 22.5 shows the complete load plot for the same actuator.

A similar plot must be made for each actuator on the machine. Where does the hydraulic system designer get this information? From the excavator designer, who had to go through this analysis to engineer the machine in the first place. If the hydraulic engineer does not have this information, he cannot design the proper hydraulic system.

After the designer has made individual load cycle plots for each actuator, he must compare them with the sequence plot to determine the possibility of simultaneous actuations. When this analysis shows

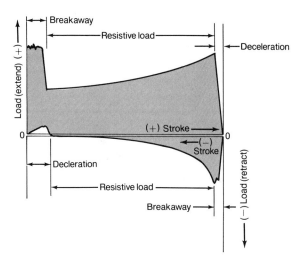

Fig. 22.5. Typical load plot for one actuator.

that two critical operations occur simultaneously, the designer should seriously consider placing these actuators in **separate** circuits rather than installing them as branches of the same circuit. (By definition, a circuit, whether single or multibranched, is supplied by a single source of energy, such as a pump.)

The reason for this separation of critical functions is that in a multiple-actuator circuit, the actuator moving the lightest load requires the lowest pressure and receives all the fluid until its cycle is completed. Besides the inconvenience of temporarily "losing" one or more critical operations, there is the danger of dropping a raised load because of changes in pressure relationships caused by unwanted motion of the system.

PRESSURE PLOTS

The pressure plots will be the same as the load plots except for the introduction of a constant which reflects the piston area over which the load is distributed:

$$p = F_1(1/A_p).$$

Note that the constant, $1/A_p$, will differ for each size cylinder.

Once the designer has completed the load and pressure plots, he has defined the level of energy transfer occurring throughout the machine cycle.

FLOW PLOTS

The next step is to define the **rate of energy transfer** in the machine. This is a function of the velocities of the various cylinder piston rods and/or hydraulic motor shafts, in the system.

To determine the required rod velocities, the designer should consult the sequence diagram, Figure 22.3. The time scale along the X-axis indicates how much time is required to complete each part of the machine cycle. Time* has two basic implications in

the design of a cycle. It determines:
- flow-rate requirements relative to the actuator motion pattern, and
- horsepower requirements of the circuit or branch.

Having established the appropriate time increments, the engineer must turn to the layouts of the machine elements to determine the length of stroke necessary to complete each motion. With this information, he can calculate the required steady-state velocity of the piston, allowing for acceleration and deceleration. At this point the hydraulic system designer must choose velocity patterns.‡

The superimposition of the flow plots for individual actuators bears an important implication. If the sequence diagram reveals simultaneous operation of two or more actuators, their flow plots must be superimposed, as shown in Figure 22.6. Such plot superimposition shows the maximum flow rates which will be required and help the designer select the appropriate size pump or pumps, and alert him whether to consider separating circuit branches.

POWER PLOTS

Having developed the information for the pressure and flow plots, the designer should now prepare the power plots. This is a necessary preliminary step before selecting the prime mover.

The power plot is particularly useful in pointing out power peaks which might otherwise be hidden in "averaged" calculations. Such peak power demands often occur when least expected, and could be high enough to stall an undersized prime mover. Fluid horsepower can be calculated from the formula

$$HP_f = pQ/1714.$$

The input horsepower of the prime mover would then be

$$HP_i = HP_f/e_o,$$

where e_o is the overall efficiency of the pump.

CYCLE PROFILE

A complete cycle profile for a single cylinder is illustrated in Figure 22.7. Remember to plot the cycle for extend *and* retract.

If the circuit designer has dilligently followed the cycle-profile procedure, he will have generated a complete graphic picture of what should happen at any point in the cycle of operation of the machine. The designer should be able to formulate any information that may be necessary to understand the operational capabilities and limitations of the equipment. More important, he should be able to spot any malfunction of the machine more rapidly and with greater certainty than if he were faced with the proposition of guessing what combinations of events

---

*See Chapter 3, p. 15.

‡Refer to Chapter 4, and Fig. 4.1.

were supposed to take place and compare them with what he observed happened.

CIRCUIT DESIGN

Fluid power circuits consist of four basic sections, Figure 22.8. Section I represents **energy in-**

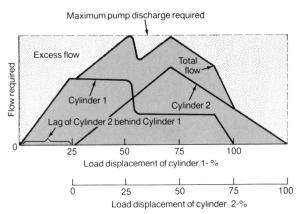

Fig. 22.6. Superimposed flow plots for two cylinders which operate simultaneously.

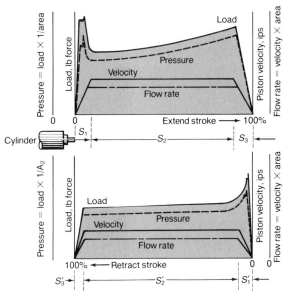

Fig. 22.7. Complete cycle profile for one actuator.

put, where energy is transferred to the load across the mechanical interface, involving a cylinder or a motor. Section II is the **control area**, where fluid switching and energy modulation take place.

Section III is the **energy output** which includes the pumps. Section IV includes **auxiliary components** such as piping, fittings, fluids and all other auxiliary components and equipment necessary to make a circuit work. These elements are analyzed in detail in Chapter 25.

Figure 22.8 suggests a logical method for attacking a circuit design problem. A format, such as shown in Figure 22.9, is helpful. Divide the sketch sheet into three sections with vertical lines. Column 1 is reserved for *energy output* devices, *i.e.*, fluid motors or cylinders; Column 2, for *control devices*; and Column 3 for *energy input* devices, *i.e.*, pumps.

Next, sketch output component symbols in Column 3, in vertical order, Figure 22.9. Then divide the page into rows by drawing horizontal lines which separate each actuator from its neighbors. We now have a matrix, of sorts, with vertical columns representing **circuit functions** (energy output, control, and energy input) and horizontal rows representing **machine functions** as typified by the actuators, which have been defined by their cycle profiles.

The circuit designer is now ready to select the proper control functions to match the machine's requirements. Refer to Chapter 24. For example, the designer can go to the sequence and cycle plots and determine what the functional cycle of the first actuator is. In the excavator, this happens to be the wrist cylinder. Assume that it has been determined that the only control requirement is switching, *i.e.*, direction control. The designer can then place the appro-

priate ISO symbol for a directional control valve in the *controls* column.

The next actuator is the double-acting dig cylinder which requires a 4-way, 3-position directional control valve. A pair of double-acting cylinders provide the hoist function. These, too, require a 4-way directional control valve.

The traction motors must be reversible; hence, they require a 4-way directional control valve. Finally, the swing motors also require a 4-way directional control valve to provide reversing capability.

With two columns tentatively specified, the designer can turn his attention to the pumps. At this time, he must make a fundamental decision: should he specify a single pump with valve control of each branch, or would multiple pumps be more suitable?

Decision considerations

Economics will play a major role in this decision. What is the relative cost of single and multiple

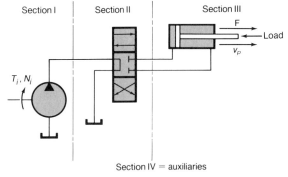

Fig. 22.8. Simple hydraulic circuit divided into four sections: I Energy input; II Control; III Energy output; and IV Auxiliary components.

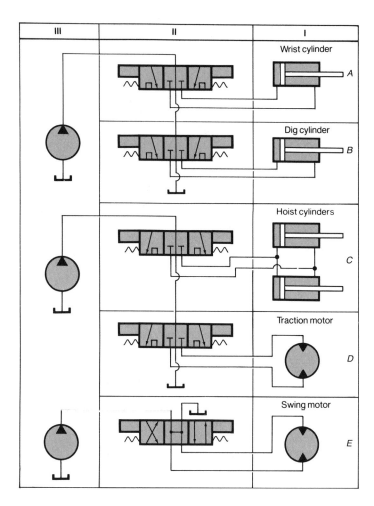

III	II	I

Wrist cylinder — A

Dig cylinder — B

Hoist cylinders — C

Traction motor — D

Swing motor — E

Fig. 22.9. Analysis format shows circuit function in columns 1, 2 and 3; and machine functions in horizontal rows A, B, C, D *and* E.

pumps? How do the costs of gear, vane, and piston pumps compare? Refer to Chapter 23. Does the machine on which the circuit is to be used require an expensive pump, or would a more economical one be satisfactory?

How about breakdown? Will failure of one pump lead to complete machine shutdown? If so, is it worthwhile to use multiple pumps, making it still possible to operate the machine, though at reduced speed.

Circuit isolation is another important consideration. Here, sequence and cycle plots come into play. What machine functions are likely to occur simultaneously? Would it be wise to isolate these functions from each other by putting them in different circuits?

How do customers generally react to the various types of pumps which might be used? For example, do the customers prefer gear pumps? If so, would the selection of a piston pump become an obstacle to the sale of the machine? How about availability of the component? Is the most desirable choice difficult to obtain? Is it obtainable from only limited suppliers?

Isolating circuits?

A study of the sample problem indicates that the

hoist and wrist or dig cylinders will probably operate simultaneously. The hoist operation is a critical one, because load interaction between the cylinders could cause the load to drop. Wrist and dig operations are not as critical, since a malfunction would probably result only in spilling of material or the operator's inability to move the excavator arm. Failure of the dig cylinder might cause the upper arm to drop. Thus, it appears that the hoist cylinders ought to be isolated from the wrist and/or dig cylinders.

Further study of the excavator functions shows that it is unlikely that the traction motors will be used simultaneously with the hoist cylinders. This suggests that they might be placed in the same circuit branch.

Swing operations might occur in combination with any other function. Thus the swing motors should probably be placed in an isolated circuit branch.

A study of the sequence diagram and cycle plots indicates that three separate circuits will satisfactorily meet the functional requirements of the machine. It also appears that multiple pumps will have to be used. The particular choice of pump displacements must be matched to flow requirements as developed in the flow plot of the cycle profile, Figure

22.6. When the designer has made the sizing calculations, he can add the ISO pump symbols and specifications to the circuit layout, Figure 22.9. The basic circuit configuration is now complete.

Design refinements

Next, the designer can review the information collected and make a second round of refining decisions. For example, which cylinders, if any, might require cushioning? Would external shock absorbers be preferred? If cushions or shock absorbers are needed, they can now be added to the specifications.

Would load-holding check valves be desirable in cylinders which might be required to hold an elevated load? Should the check valves be placed at the cylinder port, in case of a hose or pipe-line failure? Would load checks in the directional control valve suffice? Would counterbalance valves provide better performance than load checks? In our example, it appears that checks or counterbalance valves should be used in at least the hoist cylinder and dig cylinder circuits.

What about cross-over relief valves to limit load pressures in the hydraulic motors? Would inertial loads be so great that components ought to be protected against overload? This may not be much of a problem in the traction circuit, but it appears that the swing circuit should be protected. Should the cross-over relief valves be placed at the motor ports to protect against line failure? Should they be integral with the directional control valve?

Should stack valves be used, or individual valves? Can we rely on one main system relief valve or should each circuit branch have its own relief valve to limit pressure?

What kind of valve operators should be specified — manual, pilot, solenoid? The answer to this question will be provided by the policy decisions of the particular engineering department involved, since in our example all of these operators are feasible.

If this excavator hydraulic system is to include state-of-the-art technology, as described in Chapters 12, 15, 16 and 25, the designer must consider these techniques at this point of the design process. What type of pump controls will be required? See Chapter 15 and 16. Should engine speed sensing, whether hydraulic or electronic, be used? Will microprocessor or microcomputer control be advantageous? Refer to Chapters 21. If so, what kinds of sensors may be required? Where should they be located? What must their characteristics be?

Further design refinements may result from system dynamic considerations, as discussed in Chapter 27. In the final circuit design, consideration must be given to heat generation and control, Chapter 18; noise, Chapter 19; and contamination control, Chapter 20.

Note that these refining decisions still lie in the realm of functional considerations. No attention has been given to component selection. Let us assume that the circuit designer has received unanimous approval from the engineering and sales departments on the proposed circuit. He must now implement the circuit diagram of Figure 22.9.

COMPONENT SELECTION

We have reached the stage of selecting components* for the circuit. It is not implied that hardware considerations have not influenced earlier design decisions. The engineer must always keep in mind the implementation of his design. Obviously, he cannot design for a nonexistent component. Here are some broad guidelines for selecting components. These factors apply universally:

1. Application considerations
a. Area of applications:
- industrial,
- mobile,
- aerospace,
- marine, etc.

b. Type of machine to be used
c. Environmental conditions (temperature, cleanliness level, etc.)
d. Prime mover characteristics:
- speed,
- speed variation,
- pulsating vs. smooth input, etc.

e. Mounting requirements and availability
f. Drive methods:
- direct,
- chain vs belt, etc.

g. Power available to drive
h. Economics (cost, maintenance, etc.)

2. Circuit requirements
a. Pressure
b. Flow
c. Shock loading
d. Duty cycle

3. Maintenance requirements
a. Serviceability
b. Field service conditions
c. Levels of mechanical skills available for field service
d. Accessibility on machine
e. Required life between overhauls

4. Types of fluids to be encountered
a. Motor oil
b. Transmission or brake fluid
c. Kerosene
d. Crankcase oil
e. Hydraulic fluids:
- mineral base
- water-glycol
- emulsions
- phosphate esters
- other synthetics
- high water content

Refer to Chapters 23, 24, and 25.

5. Economic considerations
a. Initial cost
b. Quantity to be used
c. Life requirement
d. Replacement cost
e. Availability
f. Customer acceptance

Answers to these questions will provide a sound base for sound selection of components for the system. Refer to Chapter 23, 24 and 25.

Specifications

Specificatons for pumps and motors are essentially defined by the design analysis. Note, however, that the only item the design analysis indicates about control valves is their function. Nothing is specified about their performance characteristics.

Once the designer has determined that a directional control valve is needed at a certain location to perform a specific function, he specifies the valve on the basis of flow-rate vs pressure-drop characteristics. Note that a single valve might have several such characteristics, depending on the flow pattern, Chapter 24. For example, a valve could have one flow-rate vs pressure-drop characteristics when the input pressure line is connected to C_1, a second when C_2 is connected to tank, and a third when the pressure line is connected to the tank port. Whether or not the designer pays attention to more than one of these characteristics depends on the nature of the application. All pressure drops contribute to system heating and energy loss.

Remember, too, that all devices placed between the pumps and motors or cylinders induce a pressure drop as a function of flow rate and will, therefore, contribute to energy losses and resultant heat generation. The circuit designer must determine the magnitude of the losses, for two reasons; he must know:

• at what level energy must be put into the system so there will be enough energy left to perform a work function after transmission losses, and

• whether or not auxiliary cooling should be provided to retain an acceptable temperature level.

ESTIMATING SYSTEM HEATING

We can estimate heat generation in the system with the help of the circuit diagram of Figure 22.9. First, there will be a temperature rise across the pump. This can be estimated from the equation:

$$\Delta t = [2.97(10^{-10}\Delta p)/S_g C_p] [(1-e_p)/e_p]$$

Where
ΔT— temperature differential, F
Δp — pressure differential across the pump, psi
C_p — specific heat of fluid

e_p — overall efficiency of pump
S_g — specific gravity of fluid.

The line looses between the pump and control valve can be approximated from the Darcy-Weisbach equation,

$$h_f = fLv^2/2Dg,$$

and converting the head loss obtained to equivalent heat generation. The problem is to estimate the amount of heat which will be dissipated by radiation.

The temperature rise across a relief or other throttling valve can be estimated from the equation,

$$\Delta T = 2.97(10^{mn}3\Delta p)/S_g C_p.$$

To estimate the temperature rise accurately, the designer should know (a) the length of time throttling occurs and (b) what the natural heat dissipation would be.

A point frequently overlooked by the circuit designer is that all potential energy of a system due to elevated loads generates heat. This applies not only to payloads, but also to a machine's structural members. For example, if the excavator bucket contains 6000 lb of material and if the bucket weighs 2000 lb, 80,000 ft-lb of potential energy would be stored in the system when the bucket and load are raised 10 ft. Should it be necessary to lower the load to the ground, all of this energy must be dissipated. If the load is lowered in 5 sec, then heat is generated at a rate of

$$(80,000/778.3)5 = 20.5 \text{ Btu/sec}$$
$$\text{or } 1230 \text{ Btu/min.}$$

This is one reason why active, high-performance machines heat up quickly.

The pressure drop across each of the directional control valves, Figure 22.9 can be obtained from the manufacturers' characteristic curves for the valves.

Line losses between control valves and actuators can be calculated from the Darcy-Weisbach formula. Finally, losses in the cylinders can be estimated.

A plot of this energy-loss study, simplified to one actuator, is shown in Figure 22.10. For a given input, the plot indicates how much energy will be available at the output end of the system. This information enables the designer to determine how much energy will have to be put into the system to insure adequate energy to do the job at the output end. The summation of all such plots for the circuit would give some indication of the heat-generation problem.

Summary

This chapter encourages the fluid power circuit designer to use a defined procedure for attacking circuit design problems. The application example

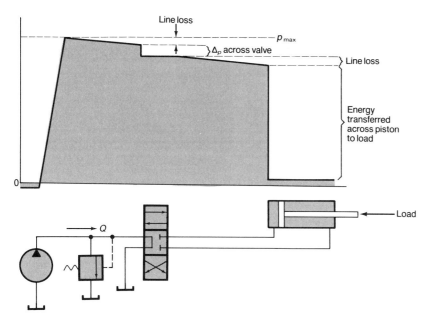

Fig. 22.10. Plot of energy losses in one actuator.

demonstrates that the cycle-profile method works.

Busy engineers may tend to gloss over the initial phases of the cycle-profile technique and attempt to handle them intuitively. Experience has shown, however, that time saved at the outset will be expanded later — possibly many times — in troubleshooting and modifying a circuit in the field and in placating dissatisfied customers.

Important terms

Cycle profile: The graphic representation, as a function of time, of the load variables and corresponding hydraulic variables during a machine cycle.

Flow Diagram: A method for graphically presenting defined steps in a machine cycle.

Flow Plot: Diagramatic representation of actuator or motor flow rates corresponding to load velocity profile.

Load Plot: Diagramatic representation, as a function of time, of load reactions on actuator or motors during a machine cycle.

Machine Cycle: A sequence of events with a defined starting point which repetitively occurs during operation of a machine returning it to its starting point at the end of the sequence.

Pressure Plot: Diagramatic representation of pressures corresponding to load reactions on actuators or motors.

Velocity Plot: Diagramatic representation, as a function of time, of load velocity requirements during a machine cycle.

1 — "Introduction to Fluid Mechanics," Russ Henke, Addison-Wesley Publishing Co., Reading, MA. p. 150, p. 156.

Review Exercises

22.1. Why is it necessary to analyze the cycle of a machine as the first step in designing a fluid power circuit?

22.2. To what can we compare the analysis of the machine cycle?

22.3. Referring to Example 22.2: if this information is not available, what must the circuit designer do? Discuss the dangers inherent in skipping this step in the design process.

22.4. Discuss the value of the flow diagram illustrated in Figure 22.2 to the circuit design process.

22.5. Discuss the relationship of the flow diagram, Figure 22.2, to the cycle plotting techniques illustrated in Figures 4.1, 5.2, and 5.7.

22.6. Referring to Figure 22.2, why are two machine cycles shown in the flow diagram? Are you limited to two cycles, only, in hydraulic circuit designs? Explain.

22.7. Referring to Figure 22.2, event 3: what is the significance of the parallel functions shown in the flow diagram?

22.8. What is the function of the sequence diagram in the design process?

22.9. Relate the sequence diagram, shown in Figure 22.3, to the cycle profiles shown in Figures 4.1, 5.2, and 5.7.

22.10. Why is time used as the X-axis on the sequence diagram?

22.11. Explain how this relates to velocity/flow plots in Figures 4.1, 5.2, and 5.7.

22.12. Where do the time intervals come from for each event called for on the sequence diagram? Who is responsible for providing this information? What should the circuit designer do if the information is missing?

22.13. Referring to Figure 22.3, events C, H *and* D *in order:* discuss the significance of each bar representing ON condition ending before the next event is turned ON. What kind of operation is this? Discuss implications related to placing the wrist actuator and swing motor in the same circuit branch.

22.14. Referring to Figure 22.3, consider events C, A, E, B *and* C as shown on the diagram. What is the relationship of these events to the time base? When events overlap, as indicated, what kind of operation is it? Discuss implications of placing the wrist cylinder, dig cylinder and hoist cylinder in the same or in different circuit branch(es).

22.15. In relation to the sequence diagram as a circuit design tool — discuss the idea of "critical functions." How might designation of a function as "critical" affect its placement in the circuit?

22.16. Discuss the implication of the load cycle plots as shown in Figures 4.1, 5.2, and 5.7; and in Figures 22.4 and 22.5. What are the essential differences? Discuss.

22.17. Discuss the differences in considerations leading to the cycle profile shown in Figures 5.2 and 22.7. Which is a more accurate representation of a load cycle? Discuss.

22.18. Relate the flow cycle profile of Figure 22.6 to the sequence diagram of Figure 22.3. Discuss.

22.19. Discuss the relationship of the typical circuit diagram shown in Figure 22.8 to the discussions in Chapter 1 relating to Figures 1.2 and 1.3.

22.20. Discuss the advantages of drawing fluid power circuit diagrams in the format shown in Figure 22.9. How does this technique relate to cycle profile plotting?

22.21. After the circuit diagram of Figure 22.9 is completed, what is the next step in the implementation of the design?

CHAPTER 23

SELECTION CRITERIA –
ENERGY INPUT
AND OUTPUT DEVICES

After load requirements have been established and the performance of the fluid power circuit analyzed, the remaining task is to select the appropriate system components. Components used in fluid power circuits fall into four basic classes:

a. energy input devices, *i.e.*, pumps
b. control devices, *i.e.*, valves
c. energy output devices, *i.e.*, fluid motors
d. auxiliary devices, *i.e.*, lines, reservoirs, fittings, filters, etc.

The first three classes are directly involved in the energy transfer function of the circuit, Figure 1.2. Auxiliary components are needed to improve the functioning of the circuit; as far as energy transfer is concerned, they only play a passive role.

PUMP SELECTION CRITERIA

The work cycle profile, determined from the analysis of the load, indicates the energy input requirements during the cycle. Whether choosing a design or selecting a prime mover, the designer must always consider pump characteristics. Yet, he should not lose sight of the fact that the cycle profile indicates only the load requirements. Special demands, made by a pilot or control circuit, must also be considered if they are to be supplied by the main pump.

For instance, in a multi-branched system, it is possible that return flow from one circuit branch can be used regeneratively to power another branch or to fulfill pilot requirements. The designer must take such factors into account when sizing the pump for the system.

Once the designer has analyzed the available methods of achieving desired energy input to all parts of a system and decided which method he will use, he must then select a pump that will meet the maximum overall demand at any given time in the cycle. This maximum demand is determined from the flow-rate plot of the cycle profile: maximum flow rate gives the required pump displacement, Figure 3.7. If a multi-branched circuit is involved, the flow-rate plots must be superimposed, *i.e.*, added to each other, to provide the overall maximum flow rate occurring at any given time.

The pressure plots indicate how system or branch circuit pressures vary during the cycle. The designer must give careful consideration to pressure requirements in the various branches. If pressure levels are not the same in all branches (and usually they are not) branch isolation must be introduced into the circuit. To achieve this, the designer might use multiple pumps or isolation valves.

Multiplying fluid pressure and flow rate that occur simultaneously at any point in the cycle gives the required power at *that* point. Since most pumps are currently selected on a basis of maximum pressure rating and displacement, the power demand plot is most frequently used in selecting a prime mover.

The pressure rating of the pump ensures that it will deliver the necessary force to overcome load resistance. Because flow rate is proportional to displacement, pump displacement controls the speed at which a load moves.

Cost

Engineers must also consider cost as a major factor affecting the selection of a pump. From an engineering point of view, the most economical pump is the one that costs least and still does the required job. Thus, it is of paramount importance that the engineer do a thorough job of analyzing application requirements. Unless one intuitively knows what constitutes "doing the required job," one cannot intelligently select the most economical pump.

1. Fixed-displacement pumps are usually the least expensive. In all but the simplest circuits, lower initial cost of the fixed pump must be weighed against the cost of the control components which may be needed to make the system work properly.

2. Variable-displacement pumps cost more than fixed-displacement pumps, but the engineer should remember that less control equipment may be needed to achieve the same result. Reduced control costs may more than offset the higher initial cost of the pump.

For any given displacement, as a rule of thumb, gear pumps are usually the least expensive and piston pumps the most. Vane pumps fall in between.

A strong argument can be made for expressing costs in terms of dollars per horsepower. However, no clear-cut rules have been formulated, and each case must be considered on its own merits. Refer to Chapter 16, analysis of LSHT motor for discussion of technique for evaluating components.

Duty rating

In chapters 3, 4, and 5 we showed how to arrive at the load cycle profile for a given application. However, the analysis shows only what occurs during *one* cycle. It neither tells how often the cycle occurs, nor does it relate the load cycle to the life of the components in the circuit. *Duty rating* is a specification which is intended to spell out the relative severity of an application.

There are two major types of duty cycles: intermittent and continuous:

1. In an **intermittent** duty cycle, active or work periods are interrupted by inactive or dwell periods, each lasting at least as long as the work period, Figure 23.1(*a*);

2. In a **continuous** duty cycle, active or work function is successively repeated with negligible inactive or dwell periods in between, Figure 23.1(*b*).

Within this framework, there are several degrees of duty:

● A *light-duty* application is one in which the load factor is not more than 25 percent of the rated maximum capacity of the components in the circuit, Figure 23.2

● A *medium-duty* application is one in which the load factor is between 25 percent and 75 percent of the maximum rated capacity of the components, and

● A *heavy-duty* application is one in which the load factor is more than 75 percent of the maximum rated capacity of the components.

Maximum rated capacity of components refers to the manufacturers' published ratings of speed, pressure, and flow capacity. The manufacturers must,

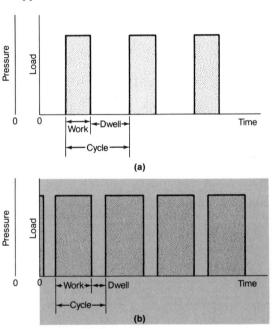

Fig. 23.1. Bar graphs illustrate duty cycles for (a) intermittent and (b) continuous type duty circuits.

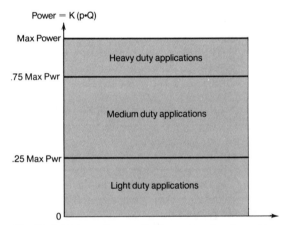

Fig. 23.2. Various duty applications as a function of horsepower.

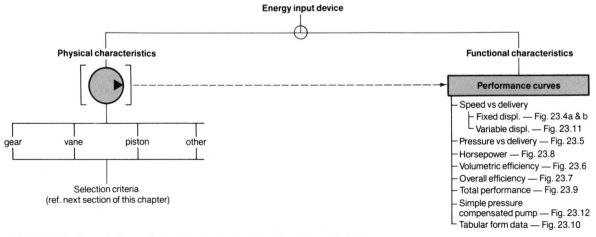

Fig. 23.3. Selection criteria are divided into physical and functional characteristics.

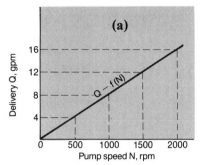 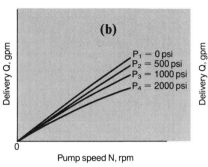 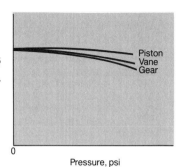

Fig. 23.4. Pump delivery/speed curves at one pressure, left, and at different pressures, right.

Fig. 23.5. Pump delivery/pressure curves for three types of pumps.

after all, be the final authority on their products. To determine the duty cycle of an application, the designer uses the manufacturers' ratings in conjunction with the cycle profile.

Energy input characteristics

Although pump type, design, construction and other factors are important, pump performance characteristics are the key considerations. Selection can be visualized as a parallel path process, Figure 23.3.

Pump curves are graphic representations of certain characteristics or anticipated performances under stated conditions. A typical example, Figure 23.4(a), shows the independent variable represented on the X-axis; the dependent on the Y axis.

The independent variable or speed of rotation can be controlled; the dependent changes are functions of the independent. Pump output, Q, is a function of pump speed, N. The curve $Q = f(N)$, represents the plot of all coordinate points. For example, at 500 rpm, pump output is 4 gpm; at 1000 rpm, 8 gpm; etc. These are determined by actual test although they may be estimated from graphical analysis, Chapter 17. From this fundamental formula we can proceed to specific curves useful in actual design practice.

Pump characteristics

Previously, we discussed the fluid power system as an energy transfer system. Pressure and flow rate characteristics affect pump selection for specific applications. Pressure is a function of load resistance reacting on the system and is an independent variable.

Flow rate varies with speed, Figure 23.4(a). Theoretically, this is a straight line function. However, slip must also be considered. Slip is a difference between calculated output and actual pump output. Refer to Chapters 16 and 17.

Remembering the deviation from the theoretical, characteristic curves are frequently plotted, Figure 23.4(b). As pressure rises, internal leakage increases. Since we can only plot two variables on a pair of axes, pressure is displayed by a family of curves. Each is plotted for speed vs flow rate with pressure

held constant. Flow rate drops off as pressure increases. Typical of fluid power pumps, the relation of pressure to flow affects selection for a given application, refer to Figures 16.8 and 16.9.

The designer must choose a pump which continues to deliver the fluid required, even at higher pressure levels. The curves in Figure 23.5 show relative performances of three major pump types: gear, vane, and piston. As pressure increases, piston pumps exhibit the least slip, followed by vane, then gear pumps. It must be emphasized that the curves in Figure 23.5 represent a broad generalization. These curves cannot be applied to any two pumps without knowing their specific operating characteristics. It is, indeed, possible to find gear pumps with less slip than a comparable vane pump.

The curves in Figure 23.4 and 23.5 differ because the independent variable has been changed. In Figure 23.4, speed was represented on the X-axis. At zero output, as speed increases, output increases. In Figure 23.5 pressure is the independent variable instead of speed. Here, output is greatest when pressure is zero, because of minimum slip. As pressure increases, slip increases and output drops.

Generally, the curves in Figure 23.5 would not be found in manufacturers' literature because there is a more satisfactory way of showing this information. It is included here to explain volumetric efficiency, which relates more adequately to overall pump performances. Volumetric efficiency, e_v, is equal to the sum of actual and theoretical outputs multiplied by 100, and is expressed as a percent, Figure 23.6.

When selecting a pump, remember: the higher the volumetric efficiency, the better the performance that can be expected. The problem is to justify higher cost for higher performance.

Overall efficiency is important because it expresses how much horsepower is actually being delivered to the system: e_o is equal to hydraulic horsepower divided by input horsepower, again multiplied by 100 and expressed as a percentage. It accounts for both slip and mechanical losses. Thus, e_o reflects both volumetric and mechanical efficiencies:

$$e_o = e_m \times e_v.$$

It is desirable to obtain as high an overall effi-

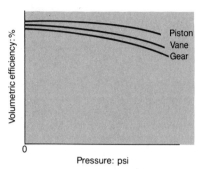

Fig. 23.6. Volumetric efficiency/pressure curves for three types of pumps.

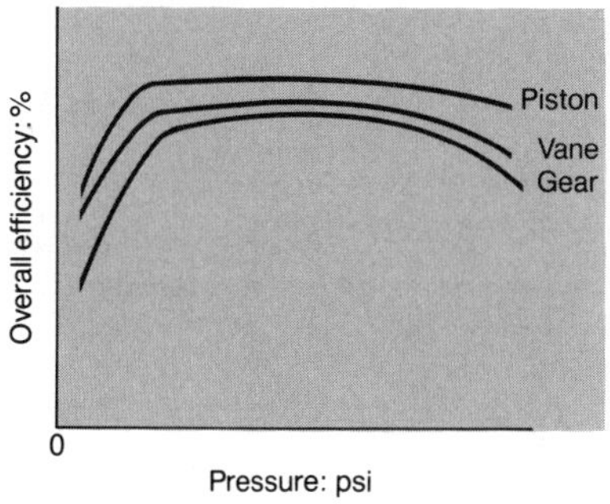

Fig. 23.7. Overall efficiency/pressure curves for three types of pumps.

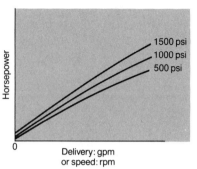

Fig. 23.8. Horsepower/delivery curves for one pump at three different pressures.

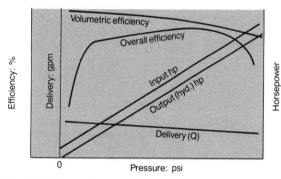

Fig. 23.9. Curves for volumetric and overall efficiencies, and input and output horsepower plotted as functions of pressure and pump output.

ciency as practical.

Figure 23.7 shows overall efficiencies. All pumps exhibit reduced e_o at low pressures. Mechanical losses are relatively higher when compared to output horsepower. The limiting condition is at zero where no horsepower is being delivered; however, it is consumed rotating the pump and e_o is zero. Efficiency rises as pressure increases until it levels off throughout normal operating pressure. As pressure increases e_o drops again. This is due to increasing slip at higher pressures and higher mechanical losses as bearing loads increase, parts deflect etc.

How horsepower curves are plotted is shown in Figure 23.8. Flow rate in gpm and speed in rpm are the independent variables; horsepower is the dependent one. Pressure is again expressed through a family of curves. Each curve represents horsepower at constant pressure as a function of flow rate. If this information were displayed for a pump whose displacement was known, speed would be used instead of flow rate, in rpm and gpm, respectively.

The preceding are basic characteristic or performance curves likely to be encountered in pump selection studies. There are two others: one curve showing input and output horsepower vs pressure for a given flow rate; the other a family of curves for output, Q, vs speed, in rpm. Each curve is plotted with constant line pressure. This point stresses the importance of cavitation in pump performance. One such curve for a piston pump, showed a drop in output flow from 4.2

to 2.8 gpm as inlet line pressure varied from supercharge inlet pressure of 6 psig to a vacuum of 10 in. of Hg.

Some manufacturers combine these pressure curves into one display, Figure 23.9. Using separate scales for ordinates, all data can be represented on one display. This example shows volumetric and overall efficiencies plotted against one Y-axis scale, pump output plotted against another; and horsepower plotted against a third. Comparable information, as it appears in Figure 23.10 in tabular form, is more difficult to interpret than in graphical form.

Variable displacement and pressure compensation

Until now, we discussed fixed- and variable-displacement pumps set at one constant output. The performance for variable-displacement or pressure compensated pumps is a more complex matter. Refer to Chapter 16.

The curves in Figure 23.11 are typical of those required to show pump delivery vs speed for a variable displacement pump. The four curves correspond to stroke positions of 100, 75, 50 and 25 percent of maximum displacement, respectively. Constant pressure is assumed. If it were introduced as another variable, a family of curves would have to be plotted for each stroke position. Only maximum rated characteristics are diagramed for variable pumps. If data are required for a performance other than maximum, the manufacturer would have to supply this information.

The pressure compensated curves in Figure 23.12

Speed		Pressure: psi					
		500	600	700	800	900	1000
500 rpm	gpm	1.1	1.07	1.03	0.98	0.92	0.84
	hp	0.32	0.375	0.42	0.46	0.48	0.49
600 rpm	gpm	1.32	1.29	1.25	1.20	1.14	1.06
	hp	0.38	0.45	0.51	0.56	0.60	0.62
700 rpm	gpm	1.54	1.51	1.47	1.42	1.36	1.28
	hp	0.45	0.53	0.60	0.66	0.71	0.75

Fig. 23.10. Tabulated performance data summarized from information appearing in closing the loop.

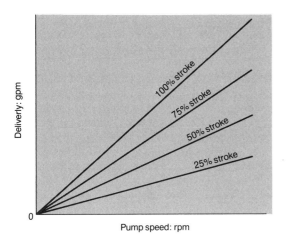

Fig. 23.11. Delivery/speed curves for one variable displacement piston pump at four stroke settings.

show a typical delivery, Q, vs pressure, with a corresponding horsepower curve. Remember that a pressure compensated pump acts like a fixed displacement pump up to cut-off pressure, so the output curve is flat to that point. Horsepower increases to maximum at cut-off because pressure increases. Depending on compensator characteristics, output drops to zero at deadhead pressure, Chapter 16. Horsepower also decreases to this point — only leakage losses must be made up since no energy is being transferred to the system.

Conventional delivery vs speed curves lose some significance with pumps because it would be necessary to know the pressure at which a pump will operate. Thus, curves look the same at any pressure up to cut-off. One would have to know the relationship between pressure and change in displacement between cut-off and deadhead. Efficiency would also have to reflect this characteristic. To the cut-off point, efficiency curves look also like those for a fixed displacement pump.

For pressure compensated vane pumps, efficiencies tend to be lower than for comparable fixed

pumps. This is often offset by improved overall cycle efficiency of the compensated pump. Refer to Chapter 16.

The concept of separating physical parameters from performance characteristics is important to system designers and troubleshooters. It can be visualized as illustrated in Figure 23.13.

Specific pump selection criteria
Within the broad framework previously discussed, here are criteria the designer should follow when selecting a particular type, make, or model of pump:
● **Pump displacement** determines flow rate to the output devices, and hence their respective speeds.
● **Pressure rating** sets the maximum forces the output devices can safely generate. It is related to load cycle profile and duty cycle. Refer to Chapters 3, 4 and 5; ISO, ANSI, NFPA and SAE standards.
● **Prime mover speed** controls flow rate to the circuit and is a function of pump displacement: $Q = V_d N$.
● **Rated pump life** is the manufacturers' rating, usually based on the B-10 rating* (in hours) of the pump bearings plus wear characteristics as determined by tests. It is also related to the duty cycle. Refer to Chapter 19 for discussion of fatigue life ratings.

Physical parameters ∝ Performance characteristics

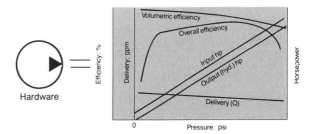

Fig. 23.13. Parameters are divided graphically into physical and performance characteristics.

● **Available mounting** types may determine the pump's compatibility with other equipment already in service. Ease and cost of mounting are important considerations in pump selection. The designer should refer to ISO, ANSI, NFPA and SAE standards.
● **Porting connections** come in a variety of options, such as SAE Straight Thread O-ring, NPT, etc. Refer to ISO, ANSI, NFPA, MIL and SAE standards.
● **Size and weight** may be a limiting factor. In many applications the ability to fit a pump of re-

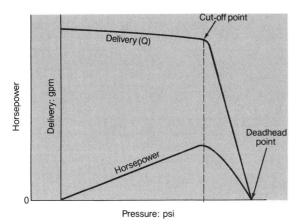

Fig. 23.12. Typical delivery and horsepower curves for pressure compensated pump.

The B-10 rating for bearings is the number of hours that 90 percent of the bearings in a given group will exceed. The NFPA is currently working on a broader based technique for fatigue rating of fluid power components. Refer to NFPA T2.6.1M-1974.

quired horsepower into available space is the deciding selection factor. Weight may play a similar role. See Chapter 16.

● **Efficiency** is a complex matter. When comparing pumps, the designer should consider three efficiencies: (a) *volumetric efficiency, e_v,* which is the ratio of actual to theoretical output; (b) *mechanical efficiency, e_m,* which is the ratio of hydraulic horsepower output to prime mover input; and (c) *overall efficiency, e_v,* which is equal to the product of the other two, $e_o = e_v \times e_m$, Figures 23.6 and 23.7.

● **Initial cost** of the pump affects the selection and becomes a trade-off with other factors. See Chapter 16.

● **Serviceability is** frequently overlooked. The designer should consider ease of servicing, both in the shop and in the field, as well as availability of service and parts.

● **Availability,** especially from stock. If a replacement is not readily available, how long will it take to get it?

● **Compatibility** has many facets. Is the pump acceptable to the customer? Does it conform to current practice? Is it compatible with similar equipment now in use, such as competitive equipment?

● **Product history** should be reviewed. What has been the pattern of performance of the pump as used in similar applications? Do not rely on sales representatives claims, alone; be sure to investigate other sources of information.

ACTUATOR SELECTION CRITERIA

We discuss input and output devices in the same chapter because, in many instances, one device may be the functional opposite of another. This is particularly true of hydraulic motors, which frequently are of almost identical construction as their pump counterparts.

Output devices, or actuators, can be divided into two basic classes: linear and rotary. A typical **linear** hydraulic actuator is the cylinder, which converts the energy transferred to the system fluid by the pump to a mechanical output — namely, the linear thrust of the piston rod. A discussion of the variety of cylinder configurations available is outside the scope of this book.*

Rotary hydraulic actuators are commonly known as hydraulic motors or fluid motors and are available in two basic types: continuous-rotation and limited-rotation.

Cylinders

On the surface, cylinders appear to be relatively simple fluid power components; yet their proper application requires careful consideration and considerable expertise. The selection criteria for cylinders include:

● **Fluid medium.** What will be the working fluid in the system? Will it be a petroleum base, high water content, or types of fire-resistant fluids? Refer to Figure 23.14.

● **Pressure.** What are the maximum continuous and intermittent pressures to which the cylinder will be subjected?

---

*Refer to "Fundamentals of Fluid Power," *W. Wolansky, J. Negoshian & R.W. Henke, Houghton-Mifflin Publishing Co., Chapter 6, pp. 171-211.*

General fluid-seal compatibility

Seal materials	Mineral oil		Fire-resistant fluids					
	Low aniline point	High aniline point	Water-glycol	Phosphate ester	Phosphate ester base	Halogenated	Di-ester	Silicate ester
Leather, W[1]	G	G	P	G	F	P	P	P
Leather, PS[2]	E	E	P	G	F	P	P	F
Leather, PU[3]	E	E	P	P	P	—	—	—
Chloroprene	F	G	E	P	P	P	P	P
Buna N	E	E	E	P	P	P	F	F
Buna S	P	P	E	P	P	P	P	P
Butyl	P	P	E	E	F	P	P	P
Polysulfide	E	E	E	F	F	P	P	F
Silicone	P	G	P	P	F	P	F	F
Fluorinated Polymer (Eslastomeric)	E	E	E	G	E	G	G	G
Fluorinated Polymer (Plastic)	E	E	E	E	E	G	—	—
Polyurethane	E	E	P	P	P	—	—	—
Ethylene Propylene	P	P	E	E	G	P	P	P

E=Excellent, G=Good, F=Fair, P=Poor.
[1]Impregnated with wax   [2]Impregnated with polysulfide   [3]Impregnated with polyurethane

Fig. 23.14. Seal compatibilities with various fluids.

● **Rod end.** The designer can choose from a number of rod end types; however rod end choice must be matched to the application. As before, the designer should refer to appropriate standards.

● **Cylinder action.** Does the application require single or double action, Figure 23.15? Consider also telescopic cylinders where long strokes must be combined with short retracted length. Figure 23.16.

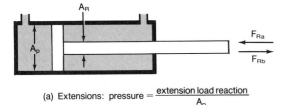

(a) Extensions: pressure = $\dfrac{\text{extension load reaction}}{A_p}$

(b) Retraction: pressure = $\dfrac{\text{retraction load reaction}}{(A_p - A_R)}$

Fig. 23.15. During extension, system pressure equals extension load reaction ÷ A_p. During retraction, system pressure equal retraction load ÷ $(A_p - A_R)$.

● **Type of load.** In choosing a cylinder, it makes a considerable difference whether the load on the rod is in tension or in compression. Another important factor is whether or not there is a friction torque at the rod end caused by load rotation about the clevis pin, Figure 23.17.

● **Stroke.** The distance through which the load must be moved determines stroke which, in turn, will influence cylinder selection. Rod loads must also be considered, Figure 23.18. Manufacturers of cylinders supply data on rod diameter vs. stroke for given loads, Figure 23.19. Figure 23.20 shows the use of stop tubes in cylinders.

● **Duty cycle.** It is important to match the duty cycle to which the cylinder will be subjected and the duty rating. Refer to Figure 23.21.

● **Shock loading.** The possibility of shock loading indicates that a cylinder may be subjected to pressure spikes several times greater than design pressure. Correlate with duty rating of cylinder.

● **Cushioning.** Some cylinders have built-in cush-

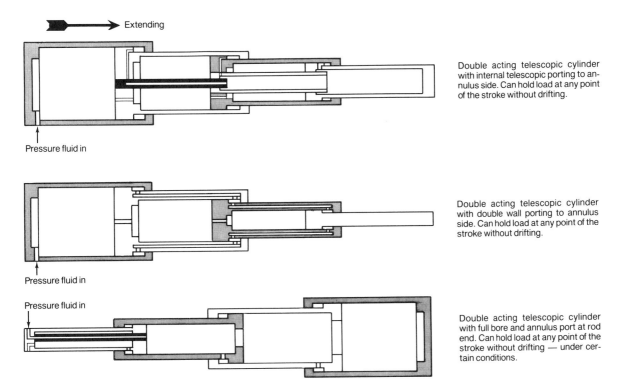

Extending

Double acting telescopic cylinder with internal telescopic porting to annulus side. Can hold load at any point of the stroke without drifting.

Pressure fluid in

Double acting telescopic cylinder with double wall porting to annulus side. Can hold load at any point of the stroke without drifting.

Pressure fluid in

Pressure fluid in

Double acting telescopic cylinder with full bore and annulus port at rod end. Can hold load at any point of the stroke without drifting — under certain conditions.

Fig. 23.16. Multi-stage, double acting telescoping cylinders.

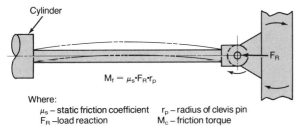

$M_f = \mu_s \cdot F_R \cdot r_p$

Where:
μ_s – static friction coefficient r_p – radius of clevis pin
F_R – load reaction M_c – friction torque

Fig. 23.17. Friction torque can cause cylinder rod to bend where cylinder swings with load motion.

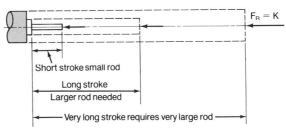

Short stroke small rod
Long stroke
Larger rod needed
Very long stroke requires very large rod

Fig. 23.18. Rod diameters are a function of load and stroke.

ions or shock-absorbing devices to decelerate the piston-and-rod assembly gradually as it approaches the end of its stroke and prevents the piston from impacting on the cylinder head. In some applications this feature is desirable, in others essential. Because they increase costs, cushions should not be specified

The designer should not depend on the rigidity of oversized rods to absorb rod side loads because the greater flexibility of the smaller standard diameter rod transmits less of the undesirable side loading back to the piston rod bushing. The practical and economical answer is to use the *correct* diameter for the particular application.

Standard rod diameters are recommended for all *PULL* stroke applications. To determine the correct rod diameter for *PUSH* stroke applications, follow these guidelines:

Step 1: Determine the value of *L* from Group *A*, below left, or use the Adjusted Value of *L*, calculated in Figure 23.20.

Step 2: From the cylinder bore size and maximum operating pressure, determine the *PUSH* stroke thrust from the Equation: $F = p.A$.

Step 3: In the table, below right, find thrust, *T*, in the vertical, left hand column and locate the *L* dimension or adjusted value of *L* on the same horizontal line to the right. If the exact *L* dimension is not shown, use the next *larger* value to the right. Read vertically up from this value to the rod diameter shown. This is the correct rod diameter for the cylinder in this application.

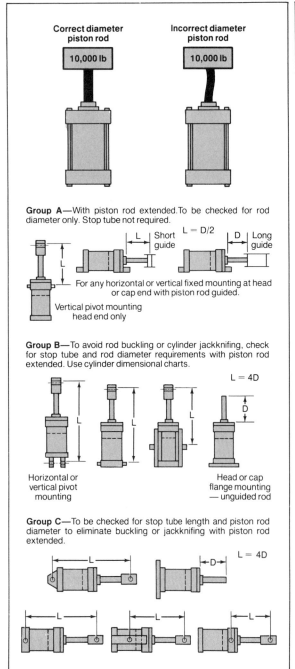

Value of "T" lb.	Piston rod diameter — inches															
	⅝	1	1⅜	1¾	2	2½	3	3½	4	4½	5	5½	7	8	9	10
250	43	94	146														
400	37	83	134	186													
700	30	68	118	168	202	275											
1,000	27	60	105	155	190	257	330										
1,400	24	53	92	142	174	244	308	385									
1,800	23	48	82	127	160	230	296	366	440								
2,400	19	45	75	114	145	213	281	347	415	488							
3,200	16	41	67	103	130	194	261	329	400	461							
4,000	13	38	63	94	119	175	240	310	378	446							
5,000	9	34	60	87	110	163	225	289	360	426	494						
6,000	5	30	56	82	102	152	208	274	342	410	476						
8,000	5	26	50	76	93	137	188	245	310	375	447						
10,000	4	21	45	70	89	125	172	222	279	349	412	482					
12,000	3	17	41	65	84	118	155	210	269	326	388	454					
16,000		9	34	57	75	110	142	188	235	292	350	420					
20,000		8	28	52	68	103	136	172	218	270	326	385					
30,000		6	12	39	55	87	120	156	189	230	285	330					
40,000			11	22	43	74	108	142	177	210	248	294					
50,000			9	15	30	66	96	130	165	200	234	269	408				
60,000				14	18	57	88	119	154	190	225	256	384				
80,000				12	16	36	71	104	137	170	204	240	336				
100,000					14	22	57	90	120	154	189	222	324	400			
120,000					12	21	45	77	108	140	175	207	313	377			
140,000						19	27	64	98	128	160	194	301	365			
160,000						17	26	47	86	118	148	182	279	350	421		
200,000						14	23	31	67	98	131	161	260	330	402		
250,000							19	28	36	72	109	141	236	301	375		
300,000								25	34	42	86	120	212	281	351	420	
350,000								22	31	39	52	100	195	261	328	396	
400,000									19	37	45	77	182	241	309	374	
500,000										32	41	49	152	212	274	341	
600,000											37	45	114	183	247	310	
700,000											32	41	70	162	221	280	
800,000												37	63	118	197	260	
900,000													60	82	168	237	
1,000,000													57	73	115	212	
1,200,000													51	68	84	170	
1,400,000													45	62	79	105	
1,600,000														57	74	91	
1,800,000															70	86	
2,000,000															65	82	

Values of *L* for slenderness ratios (slenderness ratio = length ÷ radius of gyration = 4 x length ÷ piston rod diameter) greater than 50 have a safety factor of 5 to 1. Values of *L* for slenderness ratios less than 50 are based on compressive strength only (S = thrust ÷ rod area) and have safety factors between 2.4-1 and 5-1 which are directly proportional to *L*. Thus, the greater the value of *L* the greater the safety factor.

Fig. 23.19. Hydraulic cylinder applications requiring high column strength and/or long push strokes may need oversized piston rods.

unless needed.

- **Piston velocity.** Manufacturers may rate each cylinder design and construction for maximum piston velocity, Figure 23.22.
- **Cylinder life.** It is usually specified in terms of number of cycles. Manufacturers should be consulted for this information.
- **Available mountings.** Many different types and styles of mountings are available, Figure 23.23. The designer must choose the one best suited for a given

The use of stop tubing is a generally accepted and preferred method for reducing piston and bearing loads on long push stroke cylinders and for preventing jack-knifing or buckling of horizontally-mounted, long, push stroke cylinders. For long seal and bearing life, bearing stress should be less than 200 psi. To reduce bearing loads on the rod, stop tubing is more effective, less costly, and lighter than oversize piston rods. As illustrated, the stop tubing is placed between the piston and the cylinder head to restrict the extended length of the rod so that the lengthened space between the piston and the bushing provides additional strength and side support for the extended rod.

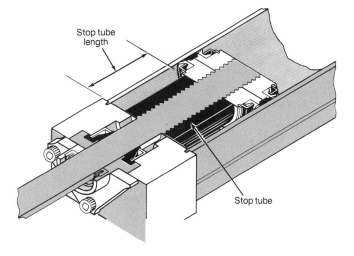

WHEN TO SPECIFY STOP TUBING

Following these simple steps . . .

STEP 1 — Determine if cylinder corresponds to any of those illustrated in Groups A, B, C, at lower left.

STEP 2 — If cylinder is in Group A, stop tube is not required but an oversize-rod may be required. If cylinder is in Groups B, or C, a stop tube is recommended as shown.

STEP 3 — Determine the value of L from instructions in Group B, or C. Be sure to include thickness of cylinder head, cap, and piston assembly plus 2 × cylinder stroke. Find L dimension in table below and read to right to find required inches of stop tube length for cylinder.

STEP 4 — Add stop tube length to original L dimension to obtain adjusted L dimension. For column strength, cylinder may also require an oversize piston rod in addition to the stop tube. For the answer, use the adjusted L dimension.

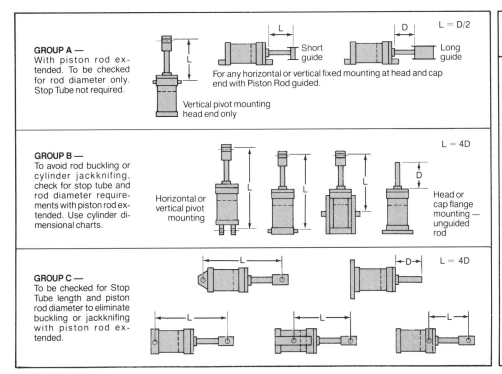

"L" (inches)	Stop Tube Length (inches)
0-40	0
41-50	1
51-60	2
61-70	3
71-80	4
81-90	5
91-100	6
101-110	7
111-120	8
121-130	9
131-140	10
141-150	11
151-160	12
161-170	13
171-180	14
181-190	15
191-200	16
201-210	17
211-220	18
221-230	19
231-240	20
241-250	21
251-260	22
261-270	23
271-280	24
281-290	25
291-300	26
301-310	27

GROUP A — With piston rod extended. To be checked for rod diameter only. Stop Tube not required.

L = D/2
Short guide
Long guide
For any horizontal or vertical fixed mounting at head and cap end with Piston Rod guided.
Vertical pivot mounting head end only

GROUP B — To avoid rod buckling or cylinder jackknifing, check for stop tube and rod diameter requirements with piston rod extended. Use cylinder dimensional charts.

L = 4D
Horizontal or vertical pivot mounting
Head or cap flange mounting — unguided rod

GROUP C — To be checked for Stop Tube length and piston rod diameter to eliminate buckling or jackknifing with piston rod extended.

L = 4D

Courtesy Miller Fluid Power

Fig. 23.20. On long cylinder strokes, stop tubing can prevent excess bearing wear and rod buckling.

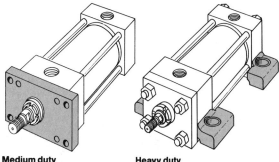

Medium duty
Bores from 1″ to 8″
Nominal pressures to 1000 psi

Heavy duty
Bores from 1½″ to 12″
Nominal pressures to 3000 psi
(Non-shock pressures to 5000 psi)

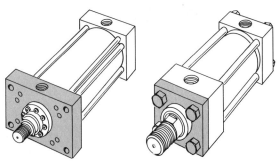

Heavy duty
Bores from 10″ to 20″
Nominal pressures to 3000 psi
(Non-shock pressures to 5000 psi)

Heavy duty - automotive
Bores from 1½″ to 8″
Nominal pressures to 3000 psi
(Non-shock pressures to 5000 psi)

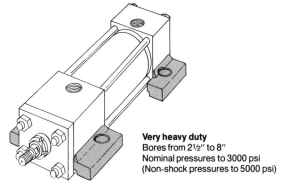

Very heavy duty
Bores from 2½″ to 8″
Nominal pressures to 3000 psi
(Non-shock pressures to 5000 psi)

Fig. 23.21. Range of cylinders classified by duty ratings. Available in standard, medium and heavy duty ratings.

application. Consult appropriate standards.

• **Porting connections.** The type of ports or connections available must be considered. Consult appropriate standards.

• **Size and weight.** The size and weight of a cylinder can be just as critical as those of a pump or motor, and for the same reasons.

• **Efficiency.** Though not all engineers consider this factor, cylinders are subject to mechanical losses, and therefore operate at less than 100 percent efficiency. In a well-designed circuit, the efficiency of the cylinders will have been considered as well as the efficiencies of pumps and motors. Figure 23.24 shows a typical mechanical efficiency curve. Should fluid bypass the piston, the cylinder will have its own

volumetric efficiency characteristic.

• **Special features.** Cylinders are available with a wide variety of special features. Circuit designers should become familiar with the many options available to maximize cylinder use. Mechanical locking of cylinders, for instance, is one important option. Some cylinders come with integral position transducers, Figure 23.25; others with special purpose integral valving, Figure 23. 26.

• **Initial cost.** The initial cost of the cylinder must be related to other factors.

• **Serviceability.** Ease of servicing, in the shop and in the field, may be an important consideration.

• **Availability and compatibility.** These two factors are just as important in the selection of cylinders as in the selection of pumps.

This chapter discusses considerations in the use and application of fluid power components to circuits, not in the design of the components themselves. For this reason, we have purposely omitted many of the criteria which deal with cylinder design, because it is assumed that the circuit designer will approach the selection from a functional viewpoint.*

Limited-rotation actuators

In one sense, a limited-rotation actuator may be thought of as a special form of cylinder whose output motion is rotational rather than linear, Figure 23.27. The advantage of this type of actuator lies in its compactness; hence it is very useful in applications requiring limited rotary motion and relatively high output torques. The selection criteria closely parallel those for cylinders, except for example, such considerations as whether the load is applied in tension or in compression. Limited-rotation actuators are available in models with rotations from 180 degrees to several complete revolutions. Output torques can range from less than 100 to more than one million lb-in.

Limited-rotation actuators come in a number of types: vane, piston, and gear, and piston-and-helix. The rotary-vane type is normally limited to less than 310 degrees of rotation for single vane models and 150 degrees for double vane, Figure 23.28 and is usually the most compact.

Because of limited motion capabilities of the vane type rotary actuators, other designs were developed, *i.e.,* rack-and-pinion, Figure 23.29. This design consists essentially of two cylinders with offset rods with gear racks cut into the rod surfaces. A pinion shaft is positioned so the pinion engages each rod. When the pistons are pressurized, forces are generated to move the racks toward each other. When rack-and-pinion are engaged, the pinion rotates. The number of rotations is a function of pinion diameter and length of

For a more detailed discussion of energy input and output devices, refer to Introduction to Fluid Power *by Russell W. Henke.*

Hydraulic cylinder speeds: ipm

Piston dia.	Rod dia.	1 GPM	3 GPM	5 GPM	8 GPM	12 GPM	15 GPM	20 GPM	25 GPM	30 GPM	40 GPM	50 GPM	75 GPM
1½	None	130	392	654	1034								
	⅝	158	476	792	1265								
	1	235	706	1176	1880								
2	None	73	221	368	588	883	1120						
	1	97	294	490	782	1175	1465						
	1⅜	139	418	697	1115	1673	2090						
2½	None	47	131	235	376	565	675	940	1175				
	1	56	168	280	448	672	840	1120	1400				
	1⅜	67	203	339	542	813	1015	1355	1695				
	1¾	92	277	463	740	1110	1385	1850	2310				
3¼	None	28	83	139	223	334	417	557	696	836	1115		
	1⅜	34	102	170	271	407	510	680	850	1020	1360		
	1¾	39	118	196	313	472	588	784	980	1176	1568		
	2	44	134	224	358	537	672	896	1120	1344	1792		
4	None	18	55	92	147	220	276	368	460	552	736	920	
	1¾	22	68	113	182	273	339	452	565	678	904	1130	
	2	24	73	122	196	294	366	488	610	732	976	1220	
	2½	30	90	150	241	362	450	600	750	900	1200	1500	
5	None	12	35	58	94	141	174	232	290	348	464	580	870
	2	14	42	70	112	168	210	280	350	420	560	700	1050
	2½	16	47	78	125	188	235	315	390	470	630	780	1170
	3	18	55	92	147	220	275	365	460	550	730	920	1380
	3½	22	66	111	178	266	333	444	555	665	888	1110	1665
6	None	8	24	41	65	98	123	162	202	245	320	405	606
	2½	10	30	50	79	118	150	200	250	300	400	495	750
	3	11	33	54	87	130	165	206	270	325	435	545	810
	3½	12	37	62	99	148	185	245	310	370	495	615	830
	4	15	44	73	117	176	220	295	365	440	585	735	1095
7	None	6	18	30	48	72	90	120	150	180	240	300	450
	3	7	22	37	59	88	110	145	185	220	295	365	555
	3½	8	24	40	64	96	120	160	200	240	320	400	600
	4	9	27	45	71	107	135	180	225	270	360	445	675
	4½	10	31	51	82	122	153	205	255	305	410	515	765
	5	12	37	61	98	147	185	245	305	370	490	615	915
8	None	4	14	23	36	55	69	92	115	135	185	230	345
	3½	5½	17	28	45	68	85	115	140	170	230	285	420
	4	6	18	30	49	73	90	122	150	180	240	305	450
	4½	6½	20	33	53	80	100	135	165	200	265	335	495
	5	7½	22	38	60	90	114	150	185	225	300	375	555
	5½	8½	26	43	70	104	129	172	215	255	345	430	645
10	None	3	9	15	23	35	44	60	73	88	115	145	220
	4½	3½	11	18	29	44	55	75	92	111	150	185	275
	5	4	12	20	31	47	60	80	100	120	155	195	300
	5½	4½	13	21	34	50	63	84	105	132	165	210	315
	7	5½	17	29	46	69	87	115	145	174	230	285	435

Hydraulic cylinder speed

Figures shown in chart are cylinder rod travel speeds in inches per minute. Extension speeds represent net piston area for various rod diameters shown.

Air cylinder speed

Because of the compressibility of air, the exact speed of an air cylinder cannot be calculated. Air cylinder sizing depends on the degree of overpowering required to move the load at the desired speed, valving, piping, and other factors which usually are unknown and cannot be measured.

When fast speed is required, bore size and line pressure should be twice that needed to balance load resistance. Lines to valves and cylinders should be as short as possible. When selecting directional valves for air application, valve orifice should equal cylinder port size.

Fig. 23.22. Chart gives hydraulic cylinder speeds for a variety of bores and flows.

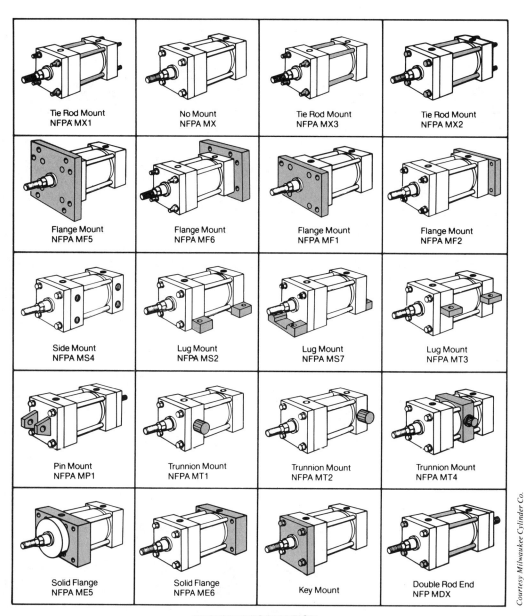

Tie Rod Mount
NFPA MX1 | No Mount
NFPA MX | Tie Rod Mount
NFPA MX3 | Tie Rod Mount
NFPA MX2

Flange Mount
NFPA MF5 | Flange Mount
NFPA MF6 | Flange Mount
NFPA MF1 | Flange Mount
NFPA MF2

Side Mount
NFPA MS4 | Lug Mount
NFPA MS2 | Lug Mount
NFPA MS7 | Lug Mount
NFPA MT3

Pin Mount
NFPA MP1 | Trunnion Mount
NFPA MT1 | Trunnion Mount
NFPA MT2 | Trunnion Mount
NFPA MT4

Solid Flange
NFPA ME5 | Solid Flange
NFPA ME6 | Key Mount | Double Rod End
NFP MDX

Courtesy Milwaukee Cylinder Co.

DESIGN INFORMATION

Tie Rod Mount

When using tie rods extended on the head end, the best application is a tension load. For a thrust load application, the tie rods should be extended on the cap end of the cylinder. Tie rod mounts are suited for many applications, but they are not as rigid as flange mounted cylinders and often require additional support for long stroke applications.

Flange Mount

One of the strongest, most rigid methods of mounting. With this type of mount, there is little allowance for misalignment. When long strokes are required, the free end opposite the mounting should be supported to prevent cylinder sagging and possible binding. When the cylinder is used in a thrust load application, a cap end flange should be used. For tension applications, head end flange mounts should be used.

Side and Lug Mounts

Side or lug mounted cylinders provide a fairly rigid mount. It can tolerate a slight amount of misalignment when the cylinder is fully extended, but as the piston retracts, the tolerance for misalignment decreases. It is important to note that if the cylinder is used properly (without misalignment), the mounting bolts are either in simple shear or tension without compound stresses.

Pin and Trunnion Mount

All pin and trunnion mounted cylinders need a provision on both ends for pivoting. This type of mount is designed to carry shear loads and requires that the trunnion or pivot pins be held rigidly by closely fit bearings for the entire pin length.

Solid Flange Mount

The solid flange mount is the strongest, most rigid method of mounting a cylinder. Industry standards for this type of mounting only cover 3¼" through 8" bore cylinders.

Key Mount

The key mount retainer plate is an option designed to add stability to foot and side mounted cylinders. The retainer plate is extended below the mounting surface of the cylinder. This extension may be fit into a milled keyway, eliminating the need for welded keys or locator pins.

Double Rod End Cylinders

Available in every mounting style except the clevis mount. The designer should note that when a double flange mount is required, tie rod nuts will protrude on one end.

Fig. 23.23. Standard NFPA mounting styles for various designs of tie-rod hydraulic cylinders.

rack stroke. The unit might also be designed to provide several rotations of pinion and output shaft.

Figure 23.30 illustrates one type of actuator which uses a piston with a separate rod running the length of and extending beyond the cylindrical housing. This rod has a high lead helix cut into it which engages a pin in the piston. As the piston is forced along the cylinder, the pin in the groove causes the rod to rotate. Extending beyond the cylinder head, the rod projects as a shaft for coupling to rotary loads.

Another design, uses two parallel cylinders, piston interfaces, and chain and sprockets to convert linear piston motion to rotary motion of an output shaft, Figure 23.31.

These devices are primarily used where a limited, rotary output is required, *i.e.*, operating doors, opening and closing large jib or fixture covers, parts indexing, clamping, etc. These are applications where a push-pull cylinder and crank mechanism may currently be used. Because of space limitations, limited rotation actuators might do a better job.

They can provide the same torque output as a cylinder, while occupying less space.

They also can be mounted co-linearly with the motion axis of the load, instead of to one side, as is

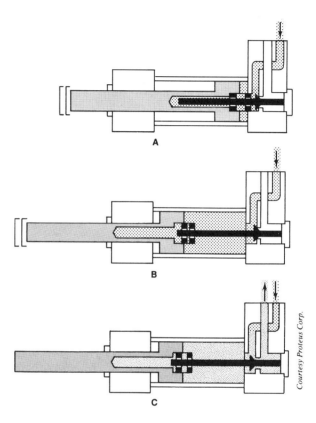

Pressure fluid enters cylinder at **A**, retracting piston and creating holding force on outlet poppet. As piston approaches maximum extending stroke, **B**, determined by length of actuating rod, spring force rises to act against holding force. When spring force exceeds holding force at outlet poppet, **C**, poppet unseats instantly.

Fig. 23.26. Cylinder with integral controls.

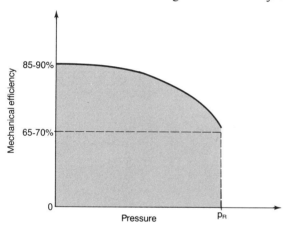

Fig. 23.24. Typical mechanical efficiency curve for a cylinder.

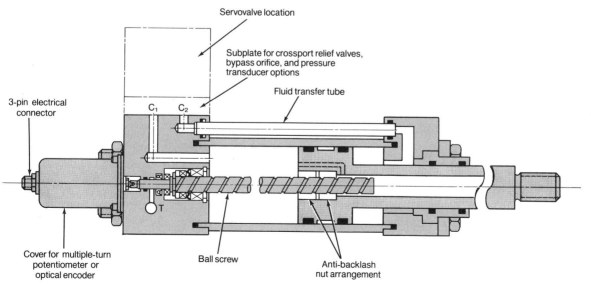

Fig. 23.25. Cylinder with integral position feedback.

263

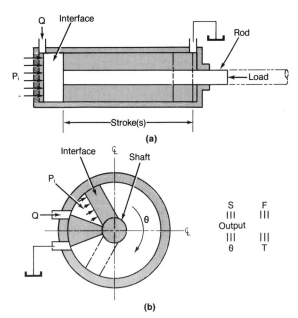

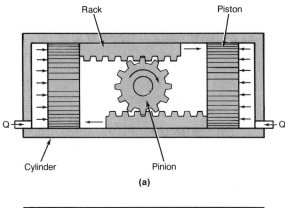

Fig. 23.29. Rack-and-pinion type limited rotation actuators.

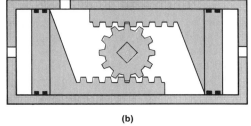

Fig. 23.27. Limited rotation actuator can be viewed as a special form of cylinder.

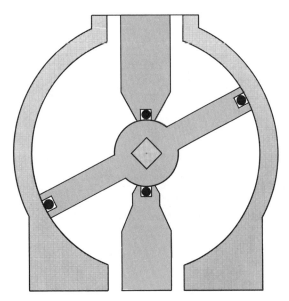

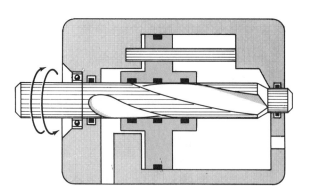

Fig. 23.28. Double vane, limited rotation actuator.

necessary with a cylinder and crank arrangement. Since motion is internal, they are safer than exposed mechanisms.

Limited rotation actuators provide designers with greater flexibility when approaching problems where rotary motion is important. Selection criteria for limited rotation actuators closely parallel those already outlined for linear actuators.

Figure 23.32 illustrates how torque is calculated. Force is equal to the product of pressure and area. Area of vane:

$$A_v = (R - r)w,$$

where:

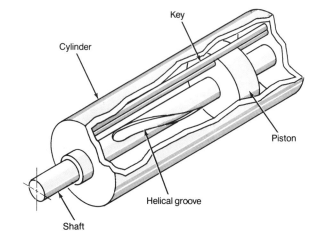

Fig. 23.30. Piston-and-helix limited rotation actuators.

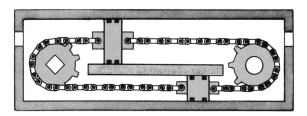

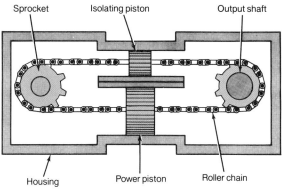

Fig. 23.31. Chain-and-sprocket limited rotation actuators.

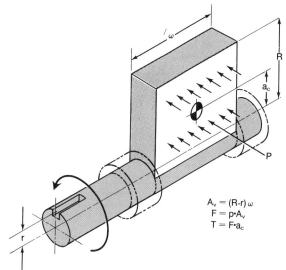

$$A_v = (R-r)\,\omega$$
$$F = p \cdot A_v$$
$$T = F \cdot a_c$$

Fig. 23.32. Analysis of forces acting on vane type limited rotation actuator.

R — outside radius of vane
r — inside radius, also equal to radius of shaft
w — width of vane.

Force on the vane is: $F = p(R - r)w$. The point at which force reacts is the center of vane areas or centroid. Since the vane rotates about the centerline of the shaft, only distance from centerline to centroid need be measured to get the moment arm for calculating torque. The centroid is half way between outer and inner edge of the vane:

$$a_c = (R - r)/2 + r.$$

Radius of shaft r, must be added to get the full distance from centerline of shaft. Torque is:

$$T = F \times a_c.$$

Obviously, torque rating could be doubled by using a double vane design, Figure 23.28. However, this increase in torque output may reduce available angular motion. Because two separators are used, maximum rotation would be about 150 degrees.

Efficiencies almost equal those of well designed cylinders, i.e.: approximately 85-90 percent, depending upon operating pressure, speed of rotation, etc. Limited rotation devices of this type exhibit curves similiar to cylinders because of breakaway, acceleration and deceleration, etc., the difference being a rotational frame of reference rather than a linear one.

FLUID MOTORS

There are three basic types of fluid power motors: gear, vane, and piston. These motors can also be

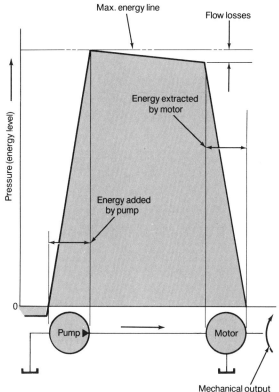

Fig. 23.33. Graphic representation of energy level of oil as it passes through pump.

classified according to their duty cycle as high speed low-to-medium torque and low speed high torque. Figure 23.33 illustrates the fundamental energy relationships in a pump-motor transmission system.

Typical performance curves for gear, vane, and piston motors are illustrated in Figure 23.34. Plotted on the same set of axes are motor output torques as a function of speed for several input pressures; and flow rates as a function of speed (shown over a range of pressures). Note that these curves are the same as those of Figure 16.12.

Pressure and speed

All three types of fluid motors show a torque curve droop as speed increases, pressure remaining constant. The piston motor curves are more level, follow-

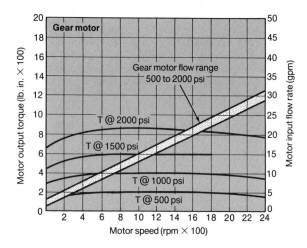

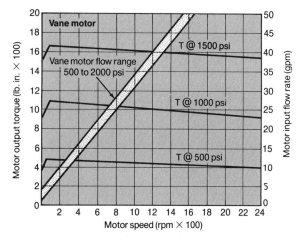

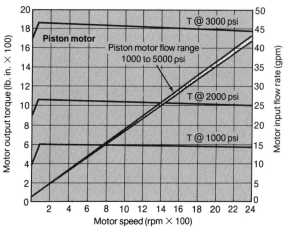

Fig. 23.34. Typical performance for gear, vane, and piston fluid motors.

ed by the vane, then the gear motor. The torque curve droop reflects greater volumetric and mechanical efficiency of the piston designs. In all three, mechanical losses increase as speed increases and as pressure rises.

Since slip increases with pressure, it is reasonable to expect that the motors with the lowest mechanical volumetric efficiencies (indicating highest leakage) will exhibit the greatest changes in torque over the speed and pressure ranges. The gear motor curves bear this out. Vane motor curves are next with piston curves exhibiting the least droop.

The curves in Figure 23.34 illustrate two basic factors:

(1) speed regulation of the drive can be no better than that exhibited by the characteristic motor curve. That is, as load reaction increases, system pressure rises, pump and motor slip increase and motor speed drops, Figure 23.35. Refer also to Figure 16.10. The only way to insure constant speed is with a servo system which adjusts to these deviations.

(2) a fluid motor cannot deliver constant torque over its entire speed range with constant pressure and flow rate input. When discussing hydraulic motors in generalities, we are inclined to say that a motor will delivery a given torque at a certain pressure. However, as a practical matter, this is not true, as shown by the curves in Figure 23.35 as speed parameters must also be taken into account.

Note that the data plotted bears no direct comparison because the three motors have different displacements. This is established by different slopes of flow rate vs. speed curves. This relationship also accounts for the fact that the vane motor shown has greater output torque (pressure for pressure) than the piston motor. It should, because its displacement is greater. Similarly, the gear motor displays a smaller torque than it would if it were of the same displacement as either the vane or piston motors.

This phenomenon points to another important conclusion: when you review and evaluate the plotted information for different types of motors made by various manufacturers, be sure that your comparisons are valid by making sure that the bases for comparisons are *consistent*. You cannot compare motors of varying sizes directly and get a true picture of the potential differences in performance.

Motor-pump characteristics as selection criteria

Flow vs. speed curves confirm the above statements concerning change in slip characteristics as a function of changes in pressure. If you match a pump to a given motor, you must take slip into account. For example, the vane pump curves are labeled "Flow @ 500-2000 psi pressure range." If we were to take the curves shown in Figure 23.34 and expand them, as in Figure 23.36, the result would be a family of curves which would relate input flow rate requirements vs.

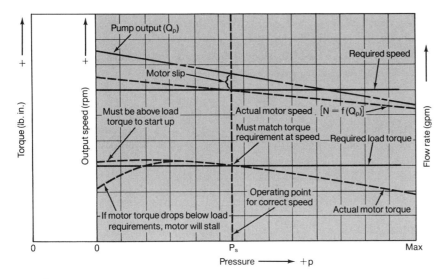

Fig. 23.35. As pressure rises, slips in pump and motor increase and motor speed drops.

speed, at constant pressure.

Assume that an application requires a fluid motor to run at 1600 rpm. If torque needs require an operating pressure of 2000 psi, the designer might select a fixed displacement pump with an output of 57 gpm. However, if the load requires an operating pressure of only 500 psi, a 50-gpm pump would be adequate to produce the required motor speed. However, in applications with a varying load, many problems may arise.

For instance, assume that a varying load requires operating pressures ranging between 500 and 2000 psi. If we select the 57-gpm pump to cover top requirements, we overspeed at 500 psi as the motor would rotate at 1825 rpm. On the other hand, if a pump were selected on the basis of an operating pressure of 500 psi, the motor would slow to 1400 rpm at 2000 psi.

Fluid vs electrical motors

Why then use fluid motors? One reason is that their electrical counterparts have the same problems. These, too, exhibit speed droop characteristics. They also reflect changes in load, not as pressures, but as changes in amperage. Fluid motors can do things electrical motors cannot; or cannot do as well or as economically. Specifically, fluid motors:

● give infinitely variable, stepless speed changes over their entire range. Below about 20 hp, new developments in variable speed AC and DC electric drives make them competitive with hydraulic drives.

● can deliver essentially, full torque over their range. However, at very low speeds, where mechanical losses become a disproportionate part of the total — the torque curve droops significantly.

● deliver full load torque from start-up, if sized properly.

● can absorb severe shock loadings without damage to the motor, i.e., sudden stops, load reversals, load transients, etc.

● can be stalled at full torque, indefinitely, with no

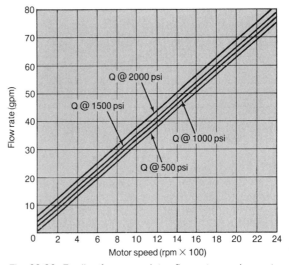

Fig. 23.36. Family of curves relates flow rate requirements vs speed — at constant pressure.

damage to the motor.

● are explosion proof and can be used in hazardous environments.

● respond faster and more efficiently than electrical motors because their rotating parts have a moment of inertia of about $\frac{1}{40}$ of the rotating parts in an electrical motor of the same rating.

● are substantially smaller than their electrical counterparts; in some designs they occupy only $\frac{1}{50}$ the volume, giving fluid motors a substantially higher power density.

The combination of fluid power pumps and motors, in a well designed feedback system, comprises one of the stiffest, highest response systems available today.

Stall torque as a selection criterion

An important difference between pump and motor applications results from the lower start-up torque capability of a hydraulic motor, as shown in the curves of Figure 23.34. Manufacturers specify this characteristic in the form of a stall torque efficiency which is the ratio of torque delivery capability at zero speed to that over its rated speed range. It is a measure of the ability of a motor to start and accelerate a load from zero speed. Because of this characteristic, hydraulic motors must frequently be oversized, see Chapter 16. If the motor is sized on the basis of external load reaction alone, there is a danger that the motor may not be able to start the machine under full load conditions.

Conversely, the maximum speed of a motor with a variable-speed drive is limited by the dynamics of the rotating parts, internal friction, and other factors. A typical horsepower curve for a fluid motor operating at constant pressure would show an increase in horsepower output as a function of speed, up to some limiting value. Beyond this critical value, horsepower would drop off with speed as mechanical losses become the overriding factor, Figure 23.34.

Motor selection criteria

Because most conventional high-speed low-torque hydraulic motors are the functional inverse of pumps of similar design, general selection criteria discussed relative to pumps apply to motors as well. Another way to see this relationship is to view pumps and motors as "mirror images" of each other.

If you consider, for instance, *mechanical* inputs and outputs, mechanical losses must be *added* to the theoretical input to a pump, whereas they must be *subtracted* from the theoretical output of a motor.

On the other hand, if the main consideration is *hydraulic* losses, slip losses in a pump must be *subtracted* from theoretical pump output, but *added* to the required input flow rate to the fluid motor.

Pressure drops around a circuit must be *added* to load pressure to provide discharge pressure at the pumps. However, they must be *subtracted* from pump discharge pressure to provide an effective pressure differential across the motor.

Low speed, high torque motors

Conventional high speed, low torque hydraulic motors display unsatisfactory characteristics in the speed range from 1 or 2 rpm to 250 to 300 rpm. Primary deficiencies include:
- cogging; jerky, uneven rotation, associated with stick slip phenomena, and
- non-uniform torque output as a function of geometric position of the displacement mechanism. This is called torque ripple.

As a result of these deficiencies in high speed, low torque motors, there emerged a new class of hardware in Europe during the 1960s: low speed, high torque motors, abbreviated, LSHT motors. The section on LSHT hydraulic motors covers a selection technique which was proposed to minimize problems

in choosing a rotor of this type. While the technique is applied to LSHT motors here, it is general and could be applied to the selection of any component. The intent is to minimize the impact of conflicting claims and reduce the selection process to a logical, quantitative procedure.

The fact that low-speed high-torque hydraulic motors differ significantly from the more familiar high-speed low-torque motors makes them difficult to select. The task is made harder still by the large number of LSHT motors with overlapping displacements, torques, and speed ranges; widely varying weights, sizes, and costs; and significant differences in reliability.

Here is a new approach to selecting LSHT motors, based on a normalization technique that accounts for inherent differences in characteristics among the different types.

Three basic types

Currently available LSHT motors can be divided into three categories on the basis of the method used to produce high torques and low speeds.

Internal multiplication (arbitrarily designated Type I) motors combine displacement elements with

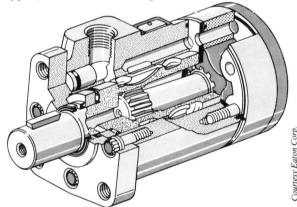

Fig. 23.37. Orbital-cam, internal reduction motor. Most have relatively small displacements.

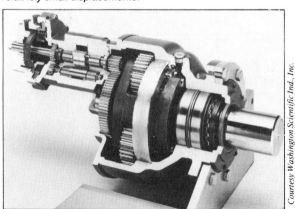

Fig. 23.38. External reduction motors combine gear reducing system with conventional low torque, high speed motor. Displacement range is similar to that of internal multiplication motors.

268

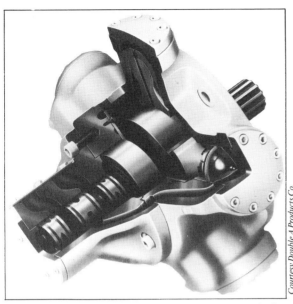

Courtesy Double A Products Co.

Fig. 23.39. Low speed, high torque motors rely on high displacements to produce high torques at low speeds.

motion-transfer mechanisms to provide an inherent mechanical advantage, Figure 23.37. These motors generally have relatively low displacement.

External multiplication (Type II) motors combine conventional low-torque high-speed motors with integral gear reduction, Figure 23.38. Displacement range is approximately the same as that of Type I motors.

High-displacement (Type III) motors typically combine radial pistons with orbital cams or crankshafts, or use sliding vanes, Figure 23.39. Their displacement range is wider and extends higher than that of the other two types.

Some circumferential-cam Type III motors offer two-speed operation. During high-speed operation, half the pistons are retracted so that they do not contact the cam—cutting motor displacement in half. In some designs, all the pistons can be retracted so that the motor free-wheels. Reductions to half displacement or free-wheeling can be made with the motor in motion, but the procedure cannot be reversed without stopping the motor.

Table 23.1—Characteristics of high-torque low-speed motors

Internal multiplication	External multiplication	High displacement
Displacement range, cu in. 0 10 20 30 40 50 60	**Displacement range, cu in.** 74 10 13.6 19.8 25.3 27.3 33.7 9 14.9 18 20.4	**Displacement range, cu in.** 24-21+ 116.9 216.5 373.3 42.4 186.7 433
Envelope size, cu in. 55.24 737 490 508 508 533	**Envelope size, cu in.** 847 894 926 926 926	**Envelope size, cu in.** 2405 8235 11,747 117.6 5639 12,424
Weight, lb 10 13.25 66 66 76	**Weight, lb** 90 90+ 98 98 98	**Weight, lb** 25 285 620 810 1270 1290
List price, $ 86.50 121.50 610 625.50 646.5	**List price, $** 716 770 805 805 805 735	**List price, $** 412 918 11.43 1,879 2,865 3,052 731 1,343
Relative cost, $/cu in. 28.83 6.79 21.21 15.30 11.19	**Relative cost, $/cu in.** 96.76 51.68 40.68 29.49 23.89 81.67	**Relative cost, $/cu in.** 171.7 21.7 9.78 8.68 7.67 7.05 34.81 7.19
Relative wt., lb/cu in. 3.33 0.74 2.29 1.62 1.32	**Relative wt., lb/cu in.** 12.2 6 4.95 3.6 2.9	**Relative wt., lb/cu in.** 10.4 6.7 5.3 3.74 3.4 2.98
Relative size 18.41 4.09 17.59 12.44 9.23	**Relative size** 114.5 60 46.8 33.9 27.9	**Relative size** 49 48.2 38.04 333 56.7 26.5

Characteristics of the three types are summarized in Table 23.1. Characteristics of sample motors are aligned vertically. For example, reading down the chart, the 33.7-cu in. Type II motor has an envelope size of 926 cu in., and weighs 98 lb.

Some designers mistakenly assume that LSHT motors can be selected on the basis of power rating alone. But primary selection criteria are output torque and speed. Pressure, flow, and power are variables which depend on required speed and torque. Pressure is a function of load torque and displacement; flow is a function of displacement and speed; and power is determined by torque requirements and the speeds at which they occur.

Needed data

All the information needed to select high-torque motors may not be readily available in typical product-description literature. In some cases, direct inquiry to the manufacturer, or supplier, may be necessary. In extreme cases, data may have to be obtained by test of a sample unit. At a minimum, data for comparing competing types should cover the following areas:

● **Displacement ranges** of Type I and II motors overlap considerably, so they offer two options for low-displacement applications. However, Type III motors overlap the other two types only in the lower end of their ranges, so high-displacement applications require Type III motors.

● **Envelope size** may be more important than displacement in some situations. For a given displacement, Type I motors generally have the smallest envelope, Type II motors are next, and Type III motors are generally largest.

● **Relative size,** defined as the ratio between envelope size and displacement, is perhaps more useful than absolute envelope size. Typically, relative size decreases with displacement for all three motor types.

● **Weight** of Type I motors is generally less than that of Type II models, which in turn weigh less than Type III motors.

● **Relative weight** is the ratio of motor weight to displacement. Typically, it follows roughly the same pattern as relative size.

● **Cost** data alone may hide the relative merits of competing motor types. For better comparison, relative cost or torque cost index should be used.

● **Relative cost index** is the ratio of motor cost to displacement. Within a given motor type, relative costs generally decrease with displacement, although absolute costs tend to increase with displacement.

Motor torque requirements encompass many factors beside the obvious steady-state load torque. Although friction and viscous torques may sometimes be small enough to be ignored, torque required to accelerate the load—and the motor itself—cannot be ignored unless substantial time is available for the load to creep up to operating speed.

Considering all the effects, total torque required of the motor is

$$T_m - (T_R + \Sigma T_{Gi}) = T_{aL} + T_L + T_p + T_f$$

where T_m = total torque required, T_R = torque required to accelerate motor rotor, T_{Gi} = torque required to accelerate gears, T_{aL} = torque required to accelerate the load, T_L = steady-state load torque, T_p = torque required to overcome mechanical friction.

This basic torque equation can be restated for all three types of high-torque motors in terms of acceleration:

$$T_m = \Sigma J_i \alpha_i + T_{s3}$$

where J_i = mass moment of inertia of ith rotating element, α_i = angular acceleration of ith rotating element, and $T_{s3} = T_L + T_r + T_f$. For Type I motors, the acceleration equation becomes

$$T_{m1} = \alpha_L (J_R + J_D + J_S + J_L) + T_{s3}$$

Type I — Internal Multiplication

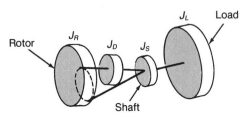

Fig. 23.40. Analysis of effect of inertia on torque.

For **Type II** motors,

$$T_{m2} = J_R \alpha_R + \Sigma J_{GL} \alpha_{Gi} + J_L \alpha_L + T_{S3}$$

Type II — External Multiplication

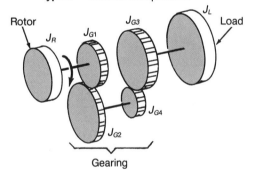

Gearing

and for **Type III** motors,

$$T_{m3} = \alpha_L (J_R + J_L) + T_{S3}$$

Type III — High Displacement

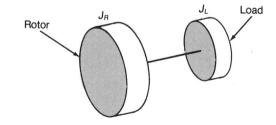

- **Torque cost index** is the ratio of motor cost to rated output torque, and is preferred to relative cost when torque is the primary performance criterion.
- **Torque-Envelope Index** is the ratio of output torque to overall motor size. In the low displacement ranges, where all three types of high-torque motor are commercially available, Type I motors have indexes around 12 lb-in./cu in., Type II motors have indexes around 16 lb-in./cu in., and Type III motors have indexes around 7 lb-in./cu in. weight. Type II motors tend to have the highest indexes, followed by Type I models. The index of Type III motors is half to a third of other two types.

The advantage of the torque indexes is that they include the effects of pressure rating, whereas the *relative* indexes include only displacement. For example, doubling the maximum continuous pressure rating of a motor doubles its torque indexes, but leaves its *relative* indexes unchanged.

Analyzing the data

The first step in determining motor requirements is to analyze the load for required torque and speed. These are determined by the load, *not* the motor. The analysis should include speed and torque profiles for the complete load cycle, with particular attention to peak torque requirements at any speed. Determine how closely the motor will approach peak power at any operating point in the load cycle — then select the motor size to supply those peak demands.

Next, determine the mass polar moment of inertia of both motor and load, since inertia adds to the apparent torque requirement for acceleration. The general expression for inertia of a series of rotating elements such as a motor rotor, gears, and load is

$$J = J_1 + J_2(\omega_2/\omega_1)^2 + \ldots + J_n(\omega_n/\omega_1)^2$$

where:
J — mass polar moment of inertia,
ω — angular velocity, and

subscripts indicate element 1, element 2, and so forth. Equations for calculating internal motor moments of inertia and their effect on required torque are in the box, *How Inertia Affects Torque,* Figure 23.40.

Next, determine required displacement. If a displacement greater than about 60 in³ is needed, Type III motors are the only commercially available choice. Between 30 and 60 in³, both Type I and Type III motors are available; between 20 and 30 in³ all three types are available; and below 20 in³ Types I and II are preferred.

With this information in hand, compare available motors which have appropriate speed and torque capabilities. The comparison should be normalized on the basis of displacement, Tables 23.2 and 23.3. The example motors compared in these tables were chosen from commercially available models and have displacements as closely matched as possible, for purposes of illustration. With widely divergent displacements, scaling effects would distort the comparison.

Torque characteristics are compared in Table 23.3. All of the torque-pressure curves were plotted from published catalog data. The various torque indexes permit an evaluation of the various *costs* of obtaining the required torque.

Torque or speed ripple is most severe in Type III motors. In circumferential-cam Type III motors, the

Table 23.2—Speed Comparison of Example Motors

Quantity	Type I (Internal Multiplication)	Type II (External Multiplication)	Type III (High Displacement)
Element Displacement (cu in.)	5.11	3.39	42.40
Multiplication	8	10	1
Overall Displacement (cu in.)	40.84	33.90	42.40
Speed Ripple (%)	2—3	*	4.8**

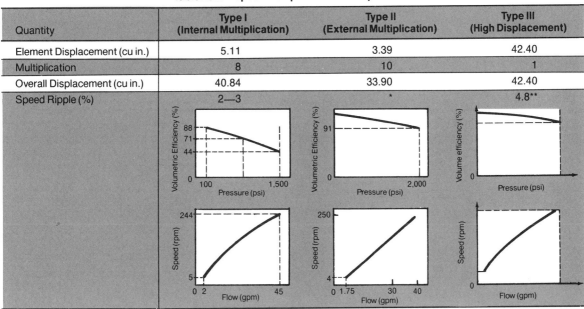

*Not available. **Theoretical value.

271

Table 23.3—Torque Comparison of Example Motors

Quantity	Type I (Internal Multiplication)	Type II (External Multiplication)	Type III (High Displacement)
Overall Displacement (cu in.)	40.8	33.9	42.4
Torque-Pressure graph	Torque (lb-in): 9,749; 9,195; 8,636; 0. Theoretical. $\eta_m = 94\%$ at 5 rpm; $\eta_m = 89\%$ at 244 rpm. Pressure (psi): 1,500 Cont, 3,000 Int	Torque (lb-in): 16,090; 0. Theoretical, Actual. η_m 92%. Pressure (psi): 2,000 Cont, 3,000 Int	Torque (lb-in): 26,993; 16,870; 0. Theoretical. Pressure (psi): 3,000 Cont, 4,000 Int
Torque Index (lb-in/cu in.) @ Rated Pressure	225.2	436.7	397.9
@ 100 psi	15.0	14.6	15.9
Torque-Weight Index (lb-in./lb)	130.9	151.0	59.2
Torque-Envelope Index (lb-in./cu in.)	17.0	16.0	7.0
Torque-Cost Index (lb-in./$)	13.8	20.0	24.2
Speed-Displacement Ratio @Max. Cont. Speed	6.2	7.4	7.1
Stall Torque Efficiency (%)	95	91	86
Torque Ripple (%)	2-3	*	6
Pressure Differential (psi) Peak	3,000	3,000	4,000
Continuous	2,000	2,000	3,000
Acceleration (rad/sec²/100 psi)	2.6	*	6.6
Backlash (mrad)	4.4	*	0
L-10 Life (hr) @ 2,000 psi	2,700	*	*
@300 rpm	*	*	2,000
Noise Level (dB)	*	*	80

*Not available

cam is designed to keep the algebraic sum of individual piston torque components constant to minimize ripple. But even these motors have some ripple, probably the result of unequalized volumetric efficiencies of the pistons.

In eccentric-crank Type III motors, instantaneous shaft speed can vary significantly as a function of piston position. If the motor is coupled to a high-inertia load, the speed ripple is damped out, but pressure peaks are generated at piston frequency. With a low-inertia load, speed ripple can increase bearing wear.

The speed-displacement ratio compares the relationship between torque and speed. Low ratios indicate high torques; high ratios suggest low torque capability.

Stall-torque efficiency indicates the ability of a motor to start under load. In some motors stall-torque efficiency drops with increased pressure because of increased mechanical losses.

Bearing life is an important factor in reliability. Typically Type II motors require the most bearings, Type I motors somewhat fewer, and Type III motors the least.

To illustrate the effect of bearings on reliability, assume that a single bearing failure stops the motor.

Life expectancy of a group of bearings can be expressed as

$$\kappa = 0.9^n B_{10}$$

where:

κ — life expectancy of the group before the first bearing failure, hr,

B_{10} — B-10 life of individual bearings, hr; and

n — number of bearings in the motor.

Assuming that individual motor bearings all have a B-10 life of 10,000 hr, a six-bearing motor has a life expectancy of 5,300 hours, whereas a two-bearing motor has a life expectancy of 8,100 hours. For equal motor life expectancy, bearings in the six-bearing motor need a B-10 life of 15,300.

A qualitative consideration not shown in the tables is the availability of controls for the motors. Type I and III motors must depend on external controls, either pump control or valves in the circuit. Type II motors can be variable-displacement motors, so there is a wide selection of compensators, constant-power and constant-torque controls available. Type II motors have not usually been used in high-performance systems where these controls are found, but their availability provides some useful options.

A final consideration is the ease or difficulty of attaching an auxiliary brake in applications demanding creep-free load-holding. Load-holding valves between motor and control valve are insufficient because of internal leakage in high-torque motors.

Important Terms

Characteristic curve. Graphic representation of interaction between selected variables. Dependent variable, plotted on the vertical axis (ordinate), changes as a function of change in the independent variable, which is plotted on the horizontal axis (abscissa).

Continuous duty. A continuous-duty application has a cycle in which the active or work function is successively repeated with negligible inactive, or dwell periods between.

Heavy duty. A heavy-duty application is one in which the load factor is more than 75 percent of the maximum rated capacity of the components.

Intermittent duty. An intermittent-duty application has a cycle in which there is an inactive, or dwell period, between the active or work periods, of duration at least equal in length to the time required by the work period.

Light duty. A light-duty application is one in which the load factor is a maximum 25 percent of the rated maximum capacity of the components in the circuit.

Mechanical efficiency. For a pump: ratio of theoretical input torque to actual input torque expressed as a %: $em_p = T_r/T_a \times 100$. For a motor: ratio of actual output torque to theoretical output torque expressed as a %: $em_m = T_a/T_t \times 100$.

Medium duty. A medium-duty application is one in which the load factor is between 25 and 75 percent of the maximum rated capacity of the components.

Overall efficiency: for a pump or a motor: overall efficiency is the product of the volumetric and mechanical efficiencies: $e_m = e_m \times e_v$.

Stall torque efficiency: for a motor: ratio of the output torque capability at zero speed to the output torque at rated speed expressed as a %: $e_{st} = T_s/T_r \times 100$.

Volumetric efficiency. For a pump: ratio of actual flow rate delivered at a given speed to theoretical flow rate expressed as a %: $ev_p = Q_a/Q_t \times 100$. For a motor: ratio of theoretical flow rate required to achieve a given output speed to actual flow rate expressed as a %: $ev_m = Q_t/Q_a \times 100$.

Review Exercises

23.1. Discuss the relationship between the cycle profile (as discussed in Chapters 3, 4, and 5) and curves representing pump or motor performance characteristics.

23.2. Why must cost be included in an engineering evaluation of pumps or motors?

23.3. Discuss the implications of an intermittent duty machine cycle on pump or motor selection.

23.4. Discuss the concept of light, medium and heavy duty applications.

23.5. How do the factors discussed in problems 23.3 and 23.4, relate to manufacturers' ratings for pumps and motors?

23.6. Discuss the differences between physical (hardware) characteristics of pumps/motors and their functional characteristics. Are there any relationships between the two?

23.7. How do the relationships of problem 23.6 apply to component selection for a circuit application?

23.8. How do the relationships of problem 23.6 apply to troubleshooting a circuit in an application?

23.9. Referring to Figure 23.4a: What does this performance curve represent? Why do we say this curve represents a theoretical characteristic rather than an actual one? If you saw this kind of a curve in a piece of manufacturers literature, how would you determine whether or not it represented theoretical (calculated) or actual (test) data describing a pump or motor characteristic?

23.10. Referring to Figure 23.4(b): What does this plot represent? Why are there several curves instead of just one? Given any input speed, why is the delivery greater at 0 psi than at any higher pressure?

23.11. Referring to Figure 23.5: What is the difference between this plot and those of Figure 23.4? What do the curves in Figure 23.5 tell us about the particular pump represented by the plots?

23.12. Referring to Figure 23.6: How do the plots relate to those of Figure 23.5? What do these characteristics tell us about the performance of the pumps represented?

23.13. In selecting and applying a pump or motor for a circuit, what considerations must be given to manufacturers specified volumetric efficiency values? At what operating point are volumetric efficiencies usually determined?

23.14. Referring to Figure 23.7: What is the significance of the plots shown in this illustration? Why do we seldom see mechanical efficiencies plotted alone?

23.15. To what factors is the drop in overall efficiency at low pressures related?

23.16. Referring to Figure 23.8: What is the significance of the plots shown? Why is a "family of curves" used to represent this characteristic? How would such characteristic curves be used in designing a hydraulic circuit?

23.17. Referring to Figure 23.9: What does this plot represent? How would it be used in selecting a pump for a circuit application? How could it be used in troubleshooting?

23.18. Referring to Figure 23.11: Discuss this plot and compare it to that shown in Figure 23.4.

23.19. Referring to Figure 23.12: Discuss the implications of this plot. How could it be used in selecting a pump for a circuit design? How could it help in troubleshooting a circuit using this type of pump?

23.20. Using a mathematical expression, show how pump displacement, as a selection factor, relates to delivery. In using this sizing calculation, how does volumetric efficiency affect the result? What value of volumetric efficiency should be used?

23.21. Given a flow rate requirement of 12.4 gpm @ load pressure of 5000 psi, calculate theoretical pump displacement required for an input speed of 1000 rpm. If volumetric efficiency is 92% at 5000 psi, what would be the actual displacement required?

23.22. Repeat problem 23.21, using SI metric units.

23.23. Discuss how pressure rating, as a selection factor, relates to the application cycle profile. When the designer selects a design pressure level for a circuit, what effect does it have on sizing actuators and motors?

23.24. Discuss how the factors considered in problem 23.23, affect required flow rates for actuators or motors to be used in a circuit.

23.25. Discuss the relationship between an application cycle profile and the 4 step design sequences: 1) determine load reactions, 2) select design pressure level, 3) size output device, 4) determine required flow rate.

23.26. Given a cycle profile which shows a maximum load reaction on an actuator of 100,000 lbs. Using a design pressure level of 2500 psi, calculate the bore of a cylinder for this application assuming a mechanical efficiency of 87%.

23.27. The cycle profile of problem 23.26, shows a maximum load velocity of 5 ft/sec, calculate the required input flow rate to the actuator assuming a 98% volumetric efficiency.

23.28. Based on the data calculated in problems 23.26 and 23.27, calculate the mechanical power out and the hydraulic horsepower input, calculate overall efficiency of the cylinder.

23.29. Referring to Figure 23.17: Use the actuator of problem 23.26: given a coefficient of friction of 0.45 and pin diameter of 2 in, calculate the estimated friction torque generated at the rod eye.

23.30. Repeat problem 23.29 using SI metric units.

23.31. How would the condition considered in problem 23.29 affect the diameter of the piston rod?

23.32. What is the function of a hydraulic motor?

23.33. What causes pressure differentials across a hydraulic motor?

23.34. What is meant by the statement that a motor is the mirror image of its equivalent pump? How does this affect pump and motor performance characteristics?

23.35. Why must we *add* mechanical losses to characteristics on the input side of pumps; and *subtract* them on the output side of motors.

23.36. Why must we *subtract* hydraulic losses to characteristic on the output side of pumps; and *add* them to the input side of motors?

23.37. Referring to Figure 23.19: Discuss the drop in motor output torque at low motor speeds. What effect does this have on sizing motors for circuit applications?

23.38. Referring to problem 23.37: Do pumps also show similar characteristics? If so, why is this not considered a problem in pump applications?

23.39. Referring to Figure 23.36: What is the significance of the shaded area labeled motor flow range 500-2000 psi? Does this correspond to any of the pump characteristics previously considered? If so, which one(s)?

23.40. Referring to problem 23.39:. Discuss the implications of the "mirror image" concept for these two sets of characteristics.

23.41. What is meant by stall torque efficiency? What are its implications in sizing a motor for an application?

23.42. Given a motor application: ideal input flow rate calculated at 12.4 gpm; pressure level 5000 psi; volumetric efficiency 92% at 5000 psi; operating mechanical efficiency 95%; and stall torque efficiency 75%.

a) Calculate the load reaction torque on the motor

b) Size the motor necessary to start the load and accelerate it from zero-speed conditions.

c) How does this compare with a motor size necessary to drive load under rated conditions?

23.43. Recalculate problem 23.42 using SI metric units.

23.44. Given the motor sized in problem 23.42: assume published volumetric efficiency data shows $e_v = 92\%$ @ 5000 psi at a rated speed of 2400 rpm. Calculate the volumetric efficiency under the same conditions at 400 rpm. What does this suggest to you about applying volumetric efficiency data under conditions of variable input?

23.45. Discuss the statement, "fluid power pumps and motors are not single operating point devices!" What implications does this have for selecting pumps and motors for hydraulic circuit applications? How does this relate to the cycle profile?

23.46. What is the fundamental difference between a low speed high torque (LSHT) motor and a high speed low torque (HSLT) motor?

23.47. Why was the LSHT hydraulic motor designed?

23.48. What is meant by the term "cogging?"

23.49. What is meant by torque ripple in a hydraulic motor?

23.50. What characterizes a Type I LSHT motor?

23.51. What characterizes a Type II LSHT motor? How does it differ from Type I?

23.52. What is a Type III LSHT motor? How does it differ from Types I and II?

23.53. What kinds of Type III motors are there?

23.54. What is the value of the displacement range scale illustrated in Table 23.1? Does it provide for comparison of the three types of motors? Discuss.

23.55. What is meant by the envelope size? How does the envelope size scale in Table 23.1 affect the selection process?

23.56. Consider the weight range shown in Table 23.1 for the three motors. Does it provide for direct parametric comparison of the motor?

23.57. What is the value of the list price range shown in Table 23.1? Does it provide adequate information on which to base selection? Discuss.

23.58. Discuss relative cost. Are there any advantage of relative cost index over list price in comparing cost of these motors? Discuss.

23.59. How does *relative weight index* compare to *total weight* as a selection factor? Which provides a better picture of the relationship of weight to performance? Discuss.

23.60. What is meant by *relative size*? How does it compare to *total envelope size*? Which is more meaningful as a selection criteria or are they both important? Discuss.

23.61. What motor parameter is used as the basis for the indexes shown in Table 23.1. Discuss why this parameter was selected for this purpose.

23.62. Referring to Table 23.2: What motor parameters are compared?

23.63. Referring to Table 23.2: Discuss the meaning and relationship of "element displacement" and "multiplication" for LSHT motors.

23.64. Discuss "speed ripple". Why does this occur? Is it a factor in actual applications and, if so, why?

23.65. Does Table 23.2 contain sufficient information on which to base a motor selection? Discuss.

23.66. Referring to Table 23.3: What motor parameters are compared?

23.67. How might we "normalize" the different pressure ratings for the three motors?

23.68. Discuss *torque index* as summarized in Table 23.3. Why does it vary from motor to motor when rated pressure is used?

23.69. When torque index is based on 100 psi pressure differential, why is it almost constant? Why is it not actually constant?

23.70. Discuss the significance of *torque-weight index* as a selection criterion. What does a high torque-weight index mean? A low one?

23.71. Discuss *torque-envelope index*. How would this help the circuit designer compare motors of different designs? Discuss the significance of high values vs. low values.

23.72. Repeat the procedure of exercise 23.71 for *torque-cost index*.

23.73. Discuss the probable accuracy of stated stall torque efficiencies shown in Table 23.3, manufacturers information.

23.74. Referring to Figure 23.40: Discuss the torque-inertia relationships shown. Which would be the best configuration in your opinion? Discuss implication for selection of a LSHT motor.

CHAPTER 24

SELECTING CONTROL VALVES

Though only the pump and the motor are directly concerned with transfer of energy into and out of a fluid power system, the successful performance of the circuit frequently hinges on control valves. Ideally, valves should not affect total energy transfer in a system. In practice, however, they do, since all valves contribute to system losses, Figure 24.1.

We saw in earlier chapters that the two fundamental control functions in a fluid power circuit are
• routing or directing the flow of energy to the proper location in the circuit at the appropriate time, and
• modifying the energy level of the fluid stream passing through the control valve.

The first function is called directional control. The second control function — modifying the energy of the fluid stream — can be broken down into two modes of control: flow control and pressure control. This chapter discusses the selection criteria for valves designed to perform each of these control modes.

DIRECTIONAL CONTROL VALVES

Circuit designers usually think of directional control in terms of the type of valve used: 2-way, 3-way, or 4-way — sometimes even one-way (check valve). This hardware orientation toward the directional control function in circuit design can create difficulties to those who are not intimately acquainted with the hardware available.

In a general sense, the directional control function is really a switching function. The pressure connection to the valve is comparable to a "hot" connection in an electrical circuit, and the tank connection is comparable to a ground, Figures 24.2a and b. Thus, each valve cylinder port can be thought of as a pair of contacts such as C_1 and C_2. There is an equivalent to an electrical open circuit when the ports are blocked, since fluid then cannot flow through the valve, but is returned to reservoir. A closed circuit exists when the cylinder ports are connected to the pressure or tank ports. This is accom-

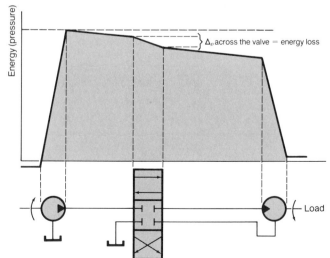

Fig. 24.1. Plot of pressure level at component input and output ports in a typical hydraulic circuit illustrates pressure drop across control valve.

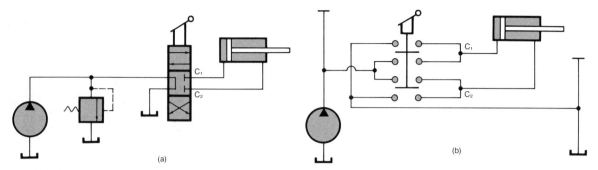

Fig. 24.2. Functions of fluid power directional control valve are analogous to those of electrical switching mechanisms.

plished by shifting the valve.

Each cylinder port can be thought of as a binary device*, that is, it can be in one of two states: open or closed. The fact that shifting the valve changes the state of two or more ports does not alter the legitimacy of the term. Having adopted this point of view, we can now approach the directional control functions of a fluid power circuit as switching functions.

Directional control implies these functions:
a) activating a circuit or a branch of a multibranched system
b) reversing the direction of flow (polarity) within a circuit or a circuit branch (assuming DF — direct flow — hydraulics)‡,
c) diverting return flow from an output device
d) deactivating a circuit or a branch
e) combining flow from two or more branches, and
f) separating flow from one branch to two or more branches.

The method by which a control valve accomplishes or contributes to these functions depends on the design and construction of the valve.

Selection criteria
1. Pressure rating. The maximum design pressure for the system is obtained from the pressure plot in the cycle profile. Component rating must match it.

2. Flow capacity. Maximum flow capacity is also obtained from the cycle profile. It is important to consider the flow plot for the particular branch in which the valve will be used. In sizing a valve, the designer should consider the flow rates in both directions, allowing for area differentials on both sides of the cylinder piston. Most manufacturers currently rate valves in terms of a given flow capacity and a corresponding pressure drop across the valve.

Further consideration of circuit design based on a switching concept can be found in Chapter 22.

---

‡*See "A-F Hydraulics" by Russell W. Henke, Machine Design Magazine, Penton/IPC February 28, 1963.*

3. Flow capacity based on C_v factor. Increasingly, valve manufacturers are turning to C_v factors to rate hydraulic and pneumatic control valves.

Hydraulic valves:
$$C_v = Q/\sqrt{\Delta p/S_G}$$
Note this is a special form of the classical orifice flow vs Δp equation*,
$$Q = C_d A_o \sqrt{2g\Delta p/\gamma}$$
Essentially C_v is a measure of the ability of the valve to conduct fluid and can be used to select or compare similar control valves.

Pneumatic valves:
$$C_v = (Q/22.67)\sqrt{S_G T/(p_1 - p_2)K}$$
where:
S_G — 1 for air
T — absolute temperature (400 + F)
p_1 — absolute inlet pressure (psig + 14.7)
p_2 — absolute outlet pressure (psig + 14.7)
  p_2 must be greater than $0.53\,p_1$
K — a constant
  $K_1 = p_2$, when Δp is no more than $0.1\,p_1$
  $K_2 = p_1$, when $\Delta p \geq 0.25\,p_1$
  $K_3 = (Cp_1 + p_2)/2$,
    when $0.1\,p_1 < \Delta p < 0.25\,p_1$
Q — flow rate in scfm

C_v is a flow coefficient indicating a valve's ability to conduct a compressible fluid (gas); p_2 must be greater than $0.53\,p_1$, to assure subsonic flow through the valve orifice. If Δp across the orifice is greater, flow becomes supersonic and the equation does not work.

4. Operators. Basic types of operators include:
a) manual (lever, cam)
b) electrical (solenoid)
c) fluid pilot (hydraulic or air pilot piston), and
d) mechanical (cam, lever, etc.).

5. Shock pressures. The possibility of pressure transients is an important consideration. Valves must be able to tolerate shock pressures and continue to operate properly.

Introduction to Fluid Mechanics, Russ Henke, Addison-Wesley Publishing Co., 1970. pp. 77, 79-82, 91-98.

6. Single vs multiple valves. Many directional control functions can be performed by a single valve, or by multiple valves in a single body casting, or by stacked valves. If stacked valves are used, additional valve banks can usually be added.

7. Fluid capability. Some valves are limited to applications using mineral oil. Others are compatible with a variety of fluids including synthetic and high water base.

8. Response time. In many applications, the response speed of the directional control valve may affect the performance of the circuit. Response time information can usually be obtained from the manufacturer.

9. Throttling characteristics. In some circuits the directional control valve is used to modulate flow as well as to switch it. Manufacturers can furnish information on flow vs pressure drop as a function of displacement of the valve element.

10. Special options. Different valve manufacturers offer special options with their products, eliminating the need for additional components. For example, sometimes a secondary control function can be obtained as an option in a directional control valve.

11. Available mountings. There are two basic types: foot and manifold. ISO standards manifolds are currently being introduced.

12. Port connections. The available types of piping connections include NPT, SAE Straight thread O-ring, Dri-Seal Thread, etc. For details, see manufacturers' literature and standards. The designer should also be sure to consult appropriate standards.

13. Size and weight. As in the case of pumps and motors, size and weight may be important considerations.

14. Initial cost. The initial cost of the valve should be weighed against other selection criteria.

15. Serviceability. Can the valve be readily serviced, both in the shop and in the field? This may be the deciding factor in the choice between manifold-mounted and foot-mounted valves. It is also an important consideration where special configurations are needed.

16. Availability. Is the valve readily available? This factor may be of particular concern where options or special configurations are required.

17. Compatibility. Relates to customer-acceptance.

Is the valve compatible with the customer's current practice? Is it compatible and/or interchangeable with similar equipment now in use?

18. Product history. What is the history of performance and acceptance of the product?

FLOW CONTROL VALVES

In a general sense, flow control is one of the two basic modes of modulating energy transfer in a system or circuit branch. However, its practical function is as a **speed control** method. Consider, for instance, an output device with a displacement of $V_a \text{in}^3$ and a cycle time of t sec. The average flow rate to the device will be $Q = V_a/t \, \text{in}^3/\text{sec}$. Since V_a is constant, a change in flow rate, Q, will obviously result in a proportionate change in time t. Thus the speed of the output device will change.

There are three types of flow controls:
- *flow rate,* using a flow control valve,
- *flow division,* using a flow-divider device to split a single flow into two streams, and
- *flow integration,* using a flow-integrator device to combine two streams into one.

Load considerations

1. Type of load. If the load the system must move is a resistive one, it is usually best to use a meter-in flow control circuit. A meter-out circuit works best with an overrunning load. If the load is inertial, a flow control valve in meter-out position is probably the better choice. However, in some cases it might be necessary to control both legs of the circuit. For a modulating load (*i.e.,* one subject to minor speed adjustments), a bleed-off control circuit should be used. Note, however, that a bleed-off valve usually does not handle full circuit flow, only part of it.

2. Load cycle. The pressure characteristics of the load cycle determine how various types of valves will perform in a circuit. Consequently, the pressure cycle will affect the designer's choice of valves — for example, whether or not he will use pressure-compensated valves. The time cycle, determined by the requirements of the output device, will tell the designer what the flow rates should be for the various parts of the load cycle. With this information, the designer can establish the flow cycle, which will indicate where flow control valves are needed.

3. Special functions. A flow control valve may be used to maintain steady-state flow during the "feed-in" part of the feed cycle of a machine tool. For this application a pressure-compensated valve would be needed. Deceleration can be accomplished with variable-flow-rate deceleration valves. Larger than normal ambient temperature variations might require the use of a temperature-compensated flow control valve.

4. Compensation requirements. A non-compensated flow control valve operates as a fixed orifice, even though it may be adjusted manually. Both the rate of flow through a non-compensated valve and the pressure drop across it vary with changes in the temperature of the fluid. A pressure-compensated valve adjusts itself for changes in system pressure within the range of the valve, thus maintaining a much more nearly constant flow rate. A temperature-compensated valve adjusts for changes in fluid temperature and corresponding changes in fluid viscosity, thus maintaining closer flow rate control.

Selection criteria

1. System pressure. The valve selected must be able to operate in the range of pressures to be encountered in the system. Consideration must be given to transient pressure conditions in addition to steady state load pressure levels.

2. Maximum flow rate. The maximum flow rate required during the cycle will affect the selection of a valve. The flow control valve selected must be one that can pass maximum flow rate defined in the cycle profile.

3. Flow pattern. Select the type of valve that will provide the type of control required by the flow-rate pattern. See Chapter 10.

4. Flow range. A flow control valve may be required to adjust the maximum and minimum flow rates encountered in the system.

5. Accuracy. Establish the level of accuracy the application requires and specify a flow control valve that can provide this degree of accuracy over the entire control range. Note that accuracies specified as a "% full scale" translate into poorer accuracies at the low end of the flow rate range. See Chapter 10.

6. Repeatability. The valve must be able to deliver as nearly as possible the same flow rate at the same setting from one cycle to the next. Be sure to know the valve's maximum drift from the set point.

7. Modes of operation. Is the valve operated manually, by remote control, or automatically?

8. Pressure compensation. Is pressure compensation available? What are its limits of accuracy? See Chapter 10.

9. Temperature compensation. Is temperature compensation available? What are its limit of accuracy?

Other selection criteria for flow control valves are similar to those for pumps, motors, and directional

control valves (see above and Chapter 23). Note, however, that in the case of serviceability, the designer should consider not only shop and field service, but also recalibration after servicing. Other factors to consider include:

10. Available mountings
11. Porting connections
12. Size and weight
13. Efficiency
14. Serviceability
15. Availability
16. Compatibility
17. Product history

PRESSURE CONTROL VALVES

The second valve control for modulating energy transfer in a fluid power system is pressure control. In Chapter 8, we discussed many of the facets of pressure control. The purpose in controlling fluid pressure is to:
a) limit the system's maximum pressure,
b) modulate the pressure level of the fluid, and
c) use a pressure-level signal to trigger a control function.

When selecting a pressure control valve, the designer must know which of these functions is to be performed, and under what conditions. Once again, the cycle profile provides the answers.

Selection criteria

1. Maximum pressure. The maximum pressure encountered in the system will influence the choice of valve.

2. Controlled pressure. The designer should determine from the cycle profile what the control levels are and how they vary during the work cycle. Check pressure override characteristics.

3. Flow capacity. What will be the rate of flow through the valve while control is being exercised? The pressure drop across the valve is another important consideration. Some pressure control valves require a control by-pass flow in order to function. Refer to Chapter 8.

4. Shock loading. The possibility of pressure transients during the cycle may affect the choice of pressure control valve.

5. Accuracy. What is maximum deviation from set pressure?

6. Repeatability. How well will the valve reproduce control pressure settings from cycle to cycle?

7. Response time. What is the total time the valve will take to begin operating? How long will it take to adjust to a change in conditions? Check on cracking band characteristics for relief valves. Refer to Chapter 8.

8. Available mountings — Refer to NFPA/ANSI standards

9. Porting connections — Refer to NFPA & SAE standards

10. Size and weight

11. Efficiency

12. Initial cost

13. Serviceability (including recalibration after repairs)

14. Availability

15. Compatibility

16. Product history

In addition to the selection criteria listed in this and in the preceding chapter, the designer must be aware of other factors to consider in the selection of all components. Two examples are the ambient environment and compatibility with the fluid. The designer must give due consideration to these factors and call them to the attention of the manufacturer of the fluid power components. These factors do not affect the way a component is supposed to function, but if the components are not properly selected, the potential mismatch may prevent the component from performing its function properly.

The reader is once again reminded that in this book, we are concerned only with open-loop circuits.

Important Terms

Directional control is the process of routing fluid to the appropriate place in the hydraulic circuit at the proper time, as determined by the sequence diagram.

Flow control regulates the quantity of fluid passing per unit time. It is related to speed control of the output device in the circuit.

Flow capacity is a flow rating specified by the manufacturer of a flow control valve, generally associated with a related pressure drop through the control valve.

Pressure control is related to pressure level in the circuit. It is related to force or torque reactions on the output devices.

Pressure rating is the pressure level specified by the manufacturer at which a control component is supposed to function.

Shock pressure (Transient Pressure) is a pressure level of short duration which can be significantly higher than steady state circuit pressure. It is usually associated with "water hammer" effect in a circuit.

Response time is the time interval required for a control valve element to move from an initial specified position to a final specified position in the course of performing a control function.

Throttling characteristic is the flow rate vs pressure differential curve associated with valve elements used to control flow rate. It relates to the accuracy and sensitivity of such control elements.

Accuracy is the ratio of the indicated value to the true value of the variable being controlled.

Uncertainty is the actual deviation in units of the variable being controlled related to accuracy. For example, a 50-gpm flow control with $\pm 2\%$ accuracy would have an uncertainty of ± 1 gpm. At 10 gpm setting, the uncertainty is ± 1 gpm, but the accuracy changes to $\pm 10\%$.

Repeatability expressed as a %, represents the degree of agreement among successive values of the controlled variable at a given setting of the control.

Threshold or resolution of a control is the least change in the variable which can be effected by the control with a specified degree of certainty under specified conditions.

Error is the difference between an indicated controlled variable and the true value of the variable.

Design pressure is the pressure level selected by the circuit designer to correspond to the *maximum* load reaction defined by the Cycle Profile.

System pressure is the actual pressure existing in the circuit as a function of load reaction on the output device at any point in the machine cycle.

24.1. What are the three modes of control in fluid power systems?

24.2. What mode of control relates to routing fluid to the proper place in the circuit at the proper time in the load cycle?

24.3. Discuss the analogy illustrated in Figure 24.2.

24.4. What mode of control relates to speed or velocity of loads? Write the mathematical relationships for system variables involved in load speed control for linear and rotary output devices.

24.5. Given: delivery to a linear actuator is 30 gpm; bore is 5 in; volumetric efficiency is 97%. Calculate load velocity.

24.6. Repeat problem 24.5 using SI metric units.

24.7. Given: delivery to a rotary motor is 25 gpm; motor displacement is 3 in³/rev. Calculate load rotational speed. Calculate equivalent angular velocity.

24.8. Repeat problem 24.7 using SI metric units.

24.9. What mode of control relates to load reaction on the output device? Write mathematical relationships for system variables involved with load reactions for linear and rotary output devices.

24.10. Given: a linear load reaction of 75,000 lbs opposes extension of a linear actuator piston rod; bore is 8 in; rod dia. is 4 in; mechanical efficiency is 85%.

a) Calculate pressure on cap end of cylinder during cylinder extension;

b) Calculate pressure on head end during cylinder retraction;

c) Assuming pressure is limited to that calculated in part a), what would be the maximum retract load reaction?

24.11. Given: a load torque reaction of 1500 lb.-in. opposes rotation of a motor; displacement is 3 in³/rev; mechanical efficiency is 92%. Calculate the pressure differential across the motor required to rotate the load.

24.12. Repeat problem 24.11 using SI metric units.

24.13. Given: a steady state load torque of 1500 lb in; breakaway and inertia torque of 1000 lb-in; mechanical efficiency of 92%; stall torque efficiency of 80%; motor displacement 3 in³/rev.

a) Calculate the pressure differential required to start the load from zero speed and to accelerate it;

b) Assume maximum pressure differential available is that calculated in problem 24.11; calculate motor displacement required to start and accelerate load.

24.14. Repeat problem 24.13 using SI metric units.

24.15. Discuss the difference between load pressure and design pressure. Which is used to establish component pressure ratings?

24.16. Discuss the difference between average piston rod velocity and steady state piston rod velocity. How do they relate to load velocity?

24.17. Do control valves have continuous and intermittent pressure ratings, like pumps and motors?

Discuss.

24.18. What factor(s) are involved in establishing flow rating for directional control valves?

24.19. How many pressure drop characteristics are there for 4-way directional control valves?

24.20. Given: a double acting differential-area-cylinder with a piston area ratio of 3:1; input flow rate of 80 gpm, calculate the back pressure developed from B-T for a type 4 spool during retract stroke.

24.21. In example 24.20, assume the viscosity of the fluid is 350 SUS, instead of 100 SUS. Calculate the Δp, p-A and B-T for the type 4 spool during the retract and extend strokes.

24.22. In the example of 24.20, assume the fluid is phosphate ester with a specific gravity of 1.165 instead of mineral oil with $S_g = .865$. Calculate Δps, p-A and B-T for a type 4 spool in both extend and retract modes.

24.23. Assume the 4 way directional valve of example 24.20 has a pilot pressure back pressure valve with an "R" spring. What is the effect of Δp at normal flow rate? During the retract stroke of the differential cylinder rod, what would back pressure be?

24.24. What is the total back pressure, B-T, under conditions of examples 24.20 through 24.23? How might this back pressure affect cylinder performance?

24.25. Would you expect data provided by some manufacturers to be applicable to all manufacturers of directional control valves? Discuss.

24.26. Referring to examples of 24.20 through 24.23, calculate C_v for the valve for a mineral base fluid. Calculate C_v for the phosphate ester. What is the implication of these two C_v factors?

24.27. Will the back pressures for extend and retract strokes in examples 24.23 and 24.24 be sufficient to supply adequate pilot pressure?

24.28. What choices are offered for this example directional control valve for solenoid operators for the pilot valve? Why the number of options?

24.29. In the example valve, discuss requirements for continuous vs. momentary energizing of solenoid operators.

24.30. Discuss potential for valve spool hangup, if the spool is held shifted for long periods of time. What is the cause of this spool sticking? How can it be prevented?

24.31. Under what conditions might an externally drained pilot valve be required?

24.32. What is the range of spool response times for the example valve?

24.33. What changes in valve seals, are specified to accommodate the change of fluids called for in 24.22?

24.34. Selecting a directional control valve for a

specific application is a simple procedure. ( ) True ( ) False.

24.35. Discuss how potential for shock pressure in a system can be determined, see Chapter 25.

24.36. Discuss the idea of throttling characteristics of control valves, see Chapter 12.

24.37. What are the normal options available for ports in valves?

24.38. In selecting flow control valves, what is one of the principle considerations relative to loads?

24.39. Referring to Chapter 10: Discuss typical flow control valve characteristics as a selection factor.

24.40. What are the implications of load *Cycle Profile* on flow control valve selection?

24.41. Discuss non-compensated, pressure compensated and temperature compensated flow controls from a selection point of view.

24.42. How are flow control valves rated by manufacturers?

24.43. How are valve rating and maximum system flow rate related in the selection process?

24.44. Discuss heat generation in a system related to application of flow control valves. How does adjustment over the flow range of the valve affect heat generation. Why does a flow control valve contribute to heat generation?

24.45. What is typical accuracy, full scale, of a pressure compensated flow control valve? What are the implications of this for settings at the low end of the flow range for the valve?

24.46. Are flow controls or flow dividers accurate enough for precise synchronization of linear and rotary actuators? Discuss.

24.47. Discuss the advantages or disadvantages of manually adjusted vs. remote, electrically controlled flow control valves. If both are used in an open loop, is there any significant difference in performance characteristics?

24.48. Discuss other selection criteria applicable to flow control valves.

24.49. How do the considerations of problems 24.38 through 24.48, relate to flow control using variable displacement motors?

24.51. What are the three basic pressure control functions?

24.52. What type of pressure controls are used to limit maximum system pressure? Referring to

Chapter 8: discuss typical characteristics of these pressure control valves, sketch ANSI symbols. Is there a significant difference between the ANSI and ISO systems for the valve?

24.53. What is the function of a counterbalance valve? How does it differ from a relief valve? Sketch its ANSI and ISO symbols.

24.54. Discuss the selection of an unloading valve vs. a vented relief valve for an application. Refer to Chapter 8. Sketch the ANSI symbol.

24.55. Why use a reducing valve in a hydraulic circuit? What types of reducing valves are available? Sketch ANSI and ISO symbols. Discuss the requirement for a continuous (quiescent) control flow in a reducing valve. What implications does this have for draining the valve? For energy loss in the valve? What happens to valve performance, if we fail to drain it properly?

24.56. What is the function of a sequence valve? Sketch ANSI and ISO symbols. What alternative techniques might be selected? Discuss implications of drain requirements for sequence valves.

24.57. Discuss effect on valve selector of system pressure as defined by the Cycle Profile.

24.58. Discuss flow capacity of a pressure control valve as a selection factor.

24.59. Discuss the difference between rated pressure and controlled pressure, as a selection factor.

24.60. Discuss potential for pressure controls causing shock pressure in a system; or effect of shock pressures on performance.

24.61. Will a relief valve in a system always control shock pressures? Discuss.

24.62. What is meant by pressure override in a pressure control? What is its effect on valve performance?

24.63. Discuss relief valve cracking band characteristic as a selection factor. What are its implications for circuit performance?

24.64. Discuss general selection criteria as they apply to pressure control valve selection.

24.65. Discuss the implication of valve control vs pump control of pressure characteristics of a circuit.

24.66. Selecting a control valve for a circuit application is simply a matter of matching pressure rating to design pressure; and flow capacity to flow requirements defined by the Cycle Profile. ( ) True ( ) False.

CHAPTER 25

SELECTING AUXILIARY COMPONENTS

In Chapter 22, we mentioned the 4th functional section of fluid power systems, *Auxiliaries,* Figure 22.8. We characterized them as passive devices, not directly involved in the control and transmission of energy, but essential to any operative system. These categories of components are classified as auxiliaries:

- electrical controls
- filters and strainers
- fittings
- heat exchangers
- hydraulic fluids
- instrumentation
- manifolds
- lines, and
- reservoirs.

THE CONDUCTING NETWORK

This classification includes all components which interconnect the major components in a system to confine and conduct the fluid, store excess or reserve fluid, provide access to the system for maintenance, repair, servicing, etc. Components under this head include:

- Reservoirs
- Conductors
  - pipe
  - tubing
  - hoses

- Fittings
  - hose
  - reusable
  - quick-acting
  - weld and braze types
  - couplings.

RESERVOIRS

In addition to storing system fluid, a well-designed hydraulic reservoir serves several other purposes; it traps contaminants, separates entrained air from the oil and cools the hydraulic fluid. Generally, reservoirs can be divided into three categories.

Integral. If the reservoir's only function is to store fluid, the integral design is suitable for many applications. "Waste" space within a machine base can be readily converted into a useful reservoir. In some mobile applications, tubular structural members can be made into an efficient hydraulic oil reservoir, without the need for additional structure. However, integral reservoirs also have disadvantages for which appropriate allowances must be made.

Remote. In stationary, industrial applications, where space is not a limiting factor, a remote reservoir is often the best choice.

Rectangular tank with electric motor and hydraulic pump mounted on top, Figure 25.1, provides an efficient, compact arrangement. The top is usually a removable cover, which must be made of material rigid enough to support the electric motor, pump(s), and other components such as valves, and *not* vibrate. A special purpose reservoir may be required to meet application needs a standard reservoir cannot provide.

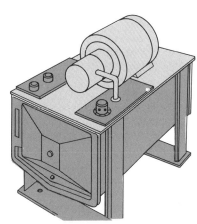

Fig. 25.1. Basic rectangular hydraulic reservoir design. Electric motor and hydraulic pump are mounted on cover.

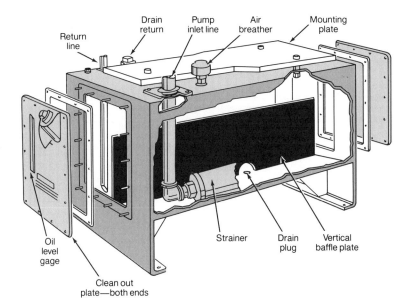

Fig. 25.2. Typical, welded, reservoir for industrial application.

Design criteria

Sound design methods and criteria apply to all reservoirs, Figure 25.2.

Volume. A reservoir should be large enough to hold and cool *all* the fluid a system will need, yet it should not be wastefully large. Minimum required capacity can vary anywhere between 1 and 3 times pump output. The reservoir must be able to hold all of the fluid displaced by *retracted* cylinders when the system is not operating, yet provide space for expansion and foaming.

Lines. The return line to reservoir and inlet-to-the-pump line should both be *submerged*. The pump inlet line should be far enough above the bottom of the reservoir to avoid ingesting contaminants resting on the tank bottom. (See Chapter 20 for additional information on inlet-to-pump filters and strainers).

Return lines should end below fluid level to avoid fluid aeration and should be placed so return flow impinges at a slight angle against a tank wall, to induce oil circulation and cooling.

Another function of a reservoir is to de-aerate the returning fluid by providing enough separation time inside the reservoir before the fluid again flows into the pump inlet line. A 100-mesh screen placed in the reservoir at an angle between 30 and 45 degrees, Figure 25.3, will remove much of the air entrained in the return fluid.

The space above the screen should be isolated from the remaining volume by a full-height baffle (not shown) to prevent foam spill-over. If the reservoir is equipped with a breather, it should *not* be located above that part of the reservoir where de-aeration takes place.

Baffles. The pump inlet line should be separated from the fluid return lines by one or more baffles to prevent continuous recirculation of the same fluid.

The baffles also reduce fluid velocity to help contaminants to settle out and entrapped air to escape.

Some reservoir designers show *one* vertical baffle running the length of the reservoir, Figure 25.2. Many designers prefer two such baffles, Figure 25.4(*a*). This design provides the longer circulating flow path and thus the most time for fluid cooling, de-aeration, and contaminant settling. Note that two baffles provide 1½ times the flow path of a single baffle. The capacity, especially the width of the reservoir, will influence the use of one or two baffles.

Cleaning. Current industry standards include ample provisions for thorough reservoir cleaning, Figure 25.2.

Draining. For periodic cleaning, provide a way to conveniently drain the reservoir, Figure 25.2.

Level indicator. Since fluid level is critical to proper system operation, a liquid level gage should be installed for convenient visual check, Figure 25.2.

Sealing. Cast reservoirs or cast portions of reservoirs should be impregnated and sealed with materials compatible with the fluid used in the system, Figure 25.5.

Filters/breathers. Since the level of the fluid in the reservoir fluctuates during system operation, ambient air must be allowed to move in and out of the space above the fluid. To keep airborne contaminants from entering the reservoir, filters should be added to clean the entering air, Figure 25.2.

Pressurizing. To avoid cavitation, many designers choose to flood the pump inlet to compensate for poor inlet characteristics or to eliminate airborne contaminants. To this end, reservoirs may be sealed and pressurized. The designer must ensure that the reservoir is strong enough to withstand the internal pressure. A relief valve may have to be added to prevent over-pressurization. Several pressurized reservoir designs have been developed to overcome the

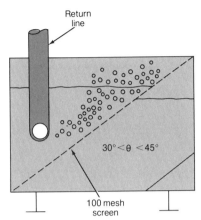

Fig. 25.3. Inside reservoir, 100-mesh screen at 30- to 45-degree angle will remove most entrained air in return fluid.

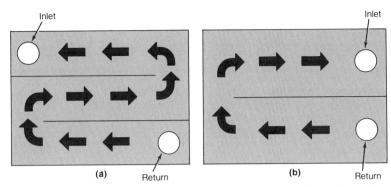

Fig. 25.4. Two baffles in reservoir, (a) provide flow path 1½ times longer than with single baffle (b).

problems inherent to pressurization, Figure 25.6.

Filter access. If the pump inlet filter is submerged in the reservoir, access must be provided for servicing without having to drain the reservoir or "diving" to get to it. An external inlet filter which can be serviced from outside the reservoir can be used to good advantage.

When an overhead reservoir is used, Figure 25.11, a shut-off valve should be installed in the inlet line for convenient servicing. A ball type shut-off valve, for instance, creates minimum restriction or pressure drop when opened.

Plugs, separators. Magnetic plugs and separators help control ferrous contaminants in the fluid. (Also see Chapter 20). These plugs should be placed where return fluid flows past them at *minimum* velocity, Figure 25.7. Magnetic separators are also available as an integral part of filters.

Filler. The filler opening should have a snug fitting cap, be readily accessible, and be fitted with a screeen to keep out foreign matter when fluid is added to the reservoir. The cap should be attached to a small, captive chain.

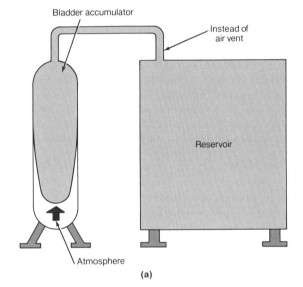

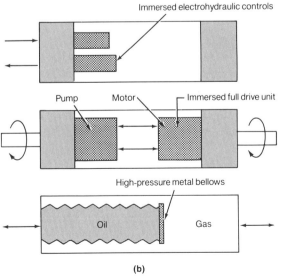

Fig. 25.6. Sealed pressurized reservoirs: (a) oil level fluctuations can be absorbed with accumulator; (b) special designs protect hydraulic system in highly contaminated environments.

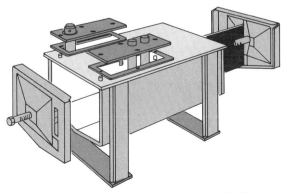

Fig. 25.5. Rectangular reservoir is combination of welded construction with cast iron end covers.

Many designers specify a pre-fill tank, transfer pump, and cleanup filter to ensure that clean fluid is added to the working reservoir, Figure 25.8. Others prefer using a portable filter cart for transferring the oil.

Scavenger systems

If the reservoir is placed at the top of the machine to improve pump inlet conditions or to provide prefill fluid, or if a pressurized reservoir is used, an auxiliary pump system must be provided to return leakage and gravity-drain fluid to reservoir.

This system usually consists of a tank positioned at a low point and a low-pressure pump to transfer the drainage fluid to the main reservoir. A filter should be included to insure system cleanliness. The low-pressure pump should have a float switch so that it operates only when needed. Or, it may be of a type which can run continuously without damage even when there is no fluid to pump back to reservoir.

Two other types of reservoirs are available in addition to the standard ones shown in Figures 25.1 and 25.2: the **overhead** and the **L-shaped.** Both types are taking on new importance because of their use in system operating on high water content fluids. Most manufacturers of components for use with high water content fluids recommend overhead or L-shaped reservoirs to provide a positive head of fluid to the pump inlet port to help avoid cavitation which is apt to be greater with water than petroleum fluids.

Figure 25.9 illustrates a dam design (top) to help trap contaminants in a reservoir and prevent them from being recirculated; a diffuser (bottom) reduces turbulance of return fluid.

The reservoir support structure should include adequate clearance between the bottom of the reservoir and the floor to provide drain space, permit free flow of cooling air, space for cleaning the floor beneath the tank, and room to insert fork-lift tines for lifting.

Removable Tops

The rectangular reservoirs used with L-shaped power units should have a removable top to provide easy access for filter servicing. In addition, various control components often are mounted on the upper vertical surfaces, with the connecting lines inside the reservoir. Here, top access is essential for hook-up and troubleshooting.

The L-shaped power package includes a relatively narrow, tall, rectangular tank with the pump and electric motor mounted beside the tank on a common base, Figure 25.10. The pump inlet line enters the tank through the side. The inlet to the pump must always be *below* oil level. A rectangular tank placed above the pump provides good inlet conditions and easy access to tank for servicing.

The overhead reservoir is functionally similar to the L-shaped design except that the reservoir is mounted above the pump, Figure 25.11.

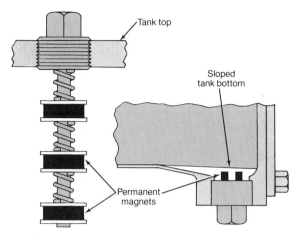

Fig. 25.7. Permanent magnets remove ferrous particles from oil.

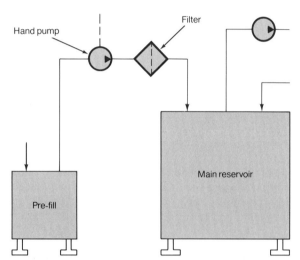

Fig. 25.8. Separate pre-fill tank helps keep contaminants from entering main reservoir.

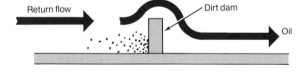

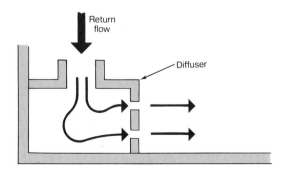

Fig. 25.9. Dams (top) help trap contaminants to keep them from pump inlet. Diffusers (bottom) reduces turbulence of return fluid.

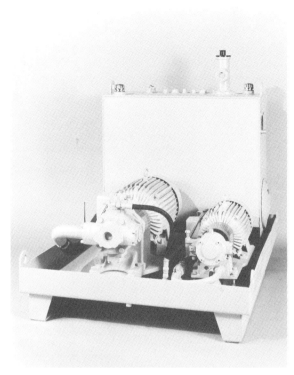

Fig. 25.10. Typical L-shaped hydraulic reservoir with electric motor, pump and various auxiliary components.

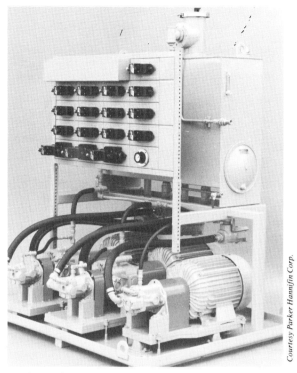

Courtesy Parker Hannifin Corp.

Fig. 25.11. Overhead reservoir provides positive head to pump inlet port.

Special purpose reservoirs

As a practical matter, not every reservoir can be roomy and readily accessible. Mobile vehicles and construction equipment machines often have crowded accommodations, and some are able to carry only a minimum of fluid. If operation is intermittent, this design works well.

Mobile hydraulic systems must be exceptionally well designed to withstand the effects of extreme temperatures, vibration, contaminated environments, and high return-line velocities.

While many reservoirs on mobile equipment are

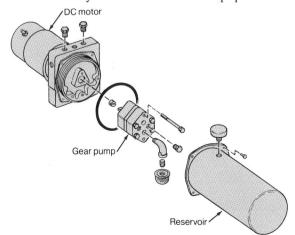

Fig. 25.12. Special design hydraulic power package includes reservoir, DC electric motor, hydraulic gear pump, and other components.

integrated into the machine's structure, a special type is shown in Figure 25.12. In this design, the reservoir is part of a self-contained power unit, commonly used on small mobile machines. For fluid compatibility, see Table 25.5.

Economics.

This factor is important and depends on the number of options and special features the designer incorporates into a basic reservoir. Custom-designed-and-built reservoirs cost more. The "ultimate" reservoir will cost still more. The additional expense must be justified by improved performance and reduced downtime. Machine time availability and productivity are the ultimate design criteria.

CONDUCTORS

Conductors are an integral part of the conducting network.

The almost endless numbers, varieties, and types of pipes, tubing, fittings, hoses, etc., can be overwhelming. However, with appropriate study and care, the system designer can select the proper conductors for the application.

One of the first precepts the designer must remember is that once he has settled on a family of conductors, he must stick with them. For instance, if at all possible, do NOT mix pipe with tubing; metric and CU sizes; ANSI, British, DIN, or other standards. The problems that could arise from their

289

incompatibility could be irresolvable.

Standards as selection criteria

The SAE Handbook lists standards which define primary specifications for various hydraulic conductors. ANSI and NFPA standards generally conform with SAE's, where applicable. However, United States Government standards, such as AN and MS, do not. Pipe and pipe fittings are covered by ANSI standards for American Standard Pipe.

American standard pipe

American standard pipe and pipe fittings are defined by ANSI Standard B36.10, 1970. Note that **nominal** sizes defined in this standard do not factually exist. The outside diameter is held constant for a given nominal size because the threads cut into the OD must always fit those tapped into a mating port or fitting, Figure 25.13. The ID for a given size pipe is a function of the standard OD and wall thickness, which in turn, is a function of "pipe schedule" which refers to wall thicknesses.

There are four schecules: 40, or standard pipe; 80, or extra heavy pipe; 160, and double extra heavy pipe, Figure 25.14.

Designers must select the appropriate schedule to handle the operating pressures anticipated in the system, see Table 25.1. Note that two pressures are given: a working pressure which is the one the designer uses to match system pressures obtained from the cycle profile and a burst pressure which is the pressure at which the pipe will theoretically rupture.

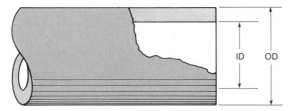

Fig. 25.13. Double extra heavy pipe. Size of pipe is always given by OD.

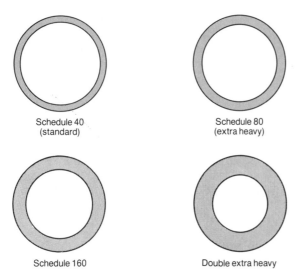

Schedule 40 (standard)
Schedule 80 (extra heavy)
Schedule 160
Double extra heavy

Fig. 25.14. Four standard pipe schedules available for piping hydraulic systems.

Table 25.1—Pressure rating of steel pipe ASTM A53 Grade B or A106 Grade B Seamless

Pipe		Pressure-psi		Water hammer factor
Nom. size inches	Sch. no.	Working	Burst	
1/8	40	3500	20,200	
1/8	80	4800	28,000	
1/4	40	2100	19,500	
1/4	80	4350	26,400	
3/8	40	1700	16,200	
3/8	80	3800	22,500	
1/2	40	2300	15,600	63.4
1/2	80	4100	21,000	
1/2	160	7300	26,700	
1/2	XXS	12,300	42,100	
3/4	40	2000	12,900	36.1
3/4	80	3500	17,600	44.5
3/4	160	8500	25,000	
3/4	XXS	10,000	35,000	
1	40	2100	12,100	22.3
1	80	3500	15,900	26.8
1	160	5700	22,300	36.9
1	XXS	9500	32,700	68.3
1¼	40	1800	10,100	12.9
1¼	80	3000	13,900	15.0
1¼	160	4400	18,100	18.2
1¼	XXS	7900	27,700	30.5
1½	40	1700	9100	9.46
1½	80	2800	12,600	10.9
1½	160	4500	17,700	13.7
1½	XXS	7200	25,300	20.3
2	40	1500	7800	5.74
2	80	2500	11,000	6.52
2	160	4600	17,500	8.60
2	XXS	6300	22,100	10.9
2½	40	1900	8500	4.02
2½	80	2800	11,500	4.54
2½	160	4200	15,700	5.43
2½	XXS	6900	23,000	7.82
3	40	1600	7400	2.60
3	80	2600	10,300	2.92
3	160	4100	15,000	3.56
3	XXS	6100	20,500	4.64
3½	40	1500	6800	1.94
3½	80	2400	9500	2.17
4	40	1400	6300	1.51
4	80	2300	7500	1.67
4	160	4000	14,200	2.08
4	XXS	5300	18,000	2.47

Water hammer effect is used to accommodate shock pressure conditions. Multiply flow rate by water hammer factor: P = Q×WHF. Deduct P from pressure working rating in table to get allowable pressure for design.

290

A method is also given for accommodating anticipated shock pressures.

Dash number system

Because many conducting systems are combinations of pipe, tubing, and hoses, a method was devised to identify all of them by a system of dash numbers.

Nominal pipe thread sizes are identified by dash sizes expressed in 16ths of an inch. A certain pipe thread size is standard for each OD tube dash size, as shown in Table 25.2. These combinations apply to SAE, AN, ANSI and PTT standards. Table 25.2 also shows that pipe thread dash numbers smaller than 1-inch do **not** correspond with the same OD tube dash size. For sizes 1-inch and larger, pipe and tubing dash sizes are the same.

For example, OD **tube** size -4 is equal to **pipe** size -2; and OD **tube** size -16 corresponds to pipe size -16. Also, refer to Table 25.2 for standard pipe and OD tube dash size combinations.

American standard pipe can be connected with American standard fittings which correspond to the pipe sizes listed. When selecting fittings, a designer must make absolutely certain that the fittings will withstand all the pressures (including peak) frequently encountered in hydraulic systems. A common error is to specify a pipe schedule which can sustain the design pressures, then use standard fittings from stock. The pressure mismatch can be disastrous. The pressure rating of pipe fittings MUST match the working pressure of the specified pipe schedule.

THREADED FITTINGS

There are two basic types of threaded joints. One has tapered threads which produce a metal-to-metal seal by wedging surfaces together as the pipe threads are tightened. The other has straight threads and no wedging action, but has a elastomeric element to do the sealing.

Tapered threads have the advantage that an additional fraction of a turn may, in systems operating at moderate pressures, cure a slight leak. Their sealing ability depends on how perfectly the threads are formed. In practice, threads may be machined care-

Table 25.2 — Comparison of dash-numbers for tubing, pipe, and hose

Rigid tube dash size	Pipe thread dash size	Pipe thread size
−4	−2	1/8″
−5	−4	1/4″
−6	−4	1/4″
−8	−6	3/8″
−10	−8	1/2″
−14	−12	3/4″
−16	−16	1″
−20	−20	1 1/4″
−24	−24	1 1/2″
−32	−32	2″
−40	−40	2 1/2″
−48	−48	3″

Aeroquip Corporation

lessly and not seal regardless of how much they are tightened. In such cases, excessive torque often results in cracked component bodies. Because of the frequency of such leaks there is a trend to stop using tapered pipe threads. Some companies limit their use to pressures below 500 psi.

USA Standard-NPT

The USA Standard pipe thread is tapered and shaped to engage mating threads on their **flanks,** Figure 25.15 *(a)*. This design leaves a small spiral groove along the thread tips which must be filled with sealant. The sealing material may also lubricate the threads and prevents galling.

USA Standard Dryseal-NPTF

These are very similar to NPT pipe threads, but are shaped to first make contact at their **roots** and **crests,** Figure 25.15**(b).** When the joint is tightened with a wrench, the thread crests are crushed until the thread flanks make full contact, Figure 25.15**(c).** They do not have the built-in leakage path of NPT threads but can still leak because of machining imperfections. Sealant should be used on these threads for lubricating but it cannot seal a poorly-cut thread.

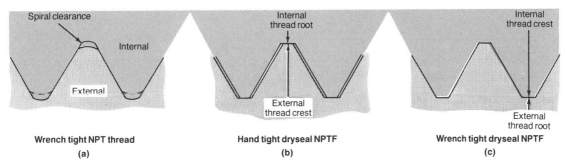

Fig. 25.15. USA standard Dryseal (NPTF) threads seal on their flanks (a), leaving a spiral shaped leakage path; (b) hand-tightened Dryseal and (c) wrench tightened.

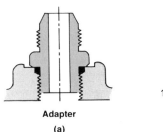
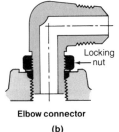

Adapter
(a)

Elbow connector
(b)

Fig. 25.16. SAE straight thread, fittings are sealed with an O-ring. Elbows can be properly oriented before locking nut is tightened.

Straight thread fitting

The SAE straight thread fitting does not depend on thread surfaces for sealing because an O-ring in the fitting becomes compressed and does the sealing. Straight thread fittings may be classified as fixed-hex, as the adapter in Figure 25.16(a), or adjustable as the elbow in Figure 25.16 (b). Used almost universally in mobile machinery, straight thread O-ring fittings are now also becoming more popular in industrial applications.

ISO has adopted straight thread, O-ring fittings as the international standard. However, the ISO thread form and the O-Ring groove are not interchangeable with SAE's.

HYDRAULIC TUBING

Tubing used in hydraulic systems, particularly pressure lines, must conform to standards such as those shown in Table 25.3 or equivalent. Tubing can be seamless carbon steel, aluminum or copper, welded steel; brazed cooper, or plastic. The anticipated operating pressure in a system will control the type of tubing material used.

Seamless steel tubing is normally annealed for convenience in bending and flaring. Tubing referred to as **hydraulic tubing** is most widely used for fluid power applications.

In contrast to American Standard Pipe, tubing is sized by its **outside diameter;** wall thickness varies

Table 25.3 — Relation of dash-numbers to tubing ID and OD and hose ID

Dash size tube & hose in 1/16ths (in.)	Tube O.D.	Tube I.D.	Hose I.D. medium pressure
−4	1/4	.180	.188
−5	5/16	.242	.250
−6	3/8	.305	.313
−8	1/2	.402	.406
−10	5/8	.495	.500
−12	3/4	.620	.625
−16	1	.870	.875
−20	1 1/4	1.120	1.125
−24	1 1/2	1.370	1.375
−32	2	1.810	1.813

all dimensions in inches

The tubing I.D. will depend on the wall thickness, selection of which is determined by the operating pressure. Wall thickness is expressed as a decimal inch or gage number.

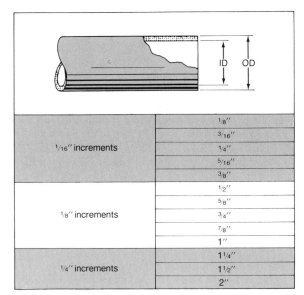

1/16" increments	1/8"
	3/16"
	1/4"
	5/16"
	3/8"
1/8" increments	1/2"
	5/8"
	3/4"
	7/8"
	1"
1/4" increments	1 1/4"
	1 1/2"
	2"

Fig. 25.17. Standard tubing OD sizes are measured in 1/16" increments through 3/8" OD; 1/8" increments from 1/2" to 1" and 1/4" increments above 1".

to match pressure requirements, Figure 25.17.

Tubing is usually measured by its outside diameter and has a thin wall compared to pipe. Two exceptions to this rule are Naval piping, where tubing is based on standard OD, and in refrigeration systems, where tubing is based on standard ID dimensions. Though similar to pipe, tubing is used differently. Since the wall sections of tubing are relatively thin, methods other than threading must be used to connect tubing into systems.

Tubing is flared and attached with swivel nuts, brazed or welded, or connected with flareless fittings.

To use all these connecting methods, the tube must have a standard OD, or it will not fit the various types and combinations of fittings.

Rigid tube dash numbering system

Rigid tubing varies in size from 3/16" to 3" OD. Tubing size is given by dash numbers and is also expressed in 16ths of an inch. For instance a 3/8" size would be 6/16 ths or -6, (dash 6).

Table 23.3 shows the standard rigid tube sizes now used by industry, compared with the ID of medium pressure hoses with identical dash numbers.

Metal tubing is available in steel, aluminum, copper, and stainless steel. While aluminum and copper tubing are generally used only in low-pressure systems, they are ideal for applications where resistance to corrosion is mandatory; stainless steel tubing resists corrosion best. Stainless steel and carbon steel tubing have the mechanical properties required to withstand high-pressure system operations. Plastic tubing most often is used in low-pressure systems where mechanical properties are not stringent.

After the tubing material has been selected, the

292

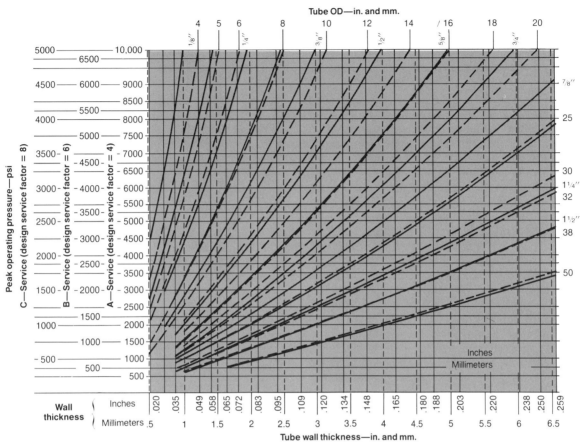

Fig. 25.18. Graph for determining wall thickness of annealed low carbon steel tubing based on relative severity of service, peak operating pressure, and tubing OD. Based on tensile strength of 47,500 psi, per SAE J525. Courtesy Parker Hannifin.

ID and wall thickness must be determined: the calculated ID is based on flow rate, wall thickness, working pressure, and mechanical loads to which the tubing may be subjected. Tubing which meets working pressure and flow requirements can be selected with graphs, such as Figure 25.18. However, in addition to working pressure, wall thickness selection must also consider mechanical stresses and strains and service abuse.

Mechanical stresses and strains are caused by vibration, relative motion of connected parts, and unsupported elements in the line which tend to stretch, bend, shorten, or twist the tubing.

Service abuse can result from:
• careless practices, such as walking on or dropping tools or other heavy and sharp objects on the tubing
• inherent rough wear that can be expected in heavy machinery where production parts, turnings, chips, and other materials may strike or otherwise damage fluid lines, and
• on mobile equipment where rocks and gravel may strike the fluid lines.

Severity of service

Much can be done to minimize these problems

and improve reliability through proper system design. The designer should insure that all components are anchored properly and fluid lines supported and restrained from relative motion.

The severity of service or abuse to which tubing in a system is subjected can be categorized into one of three arbitrary classifications, based on design factors:
• mechanical and hydraulic shocks not excessive. The equipment is stationary and is not subjected to hydraulic shock. Valve shifting and cylinder actuation speeds are relatively slow.
• considerable hydraulic shock and mechanical strain. The equipment may be mobile, with high-velocity fluid flows provided by accumulators or large displacement pumps so valves and cylinders move rapidly, and
• hazardous application with severe service conditions. Lines exposed to potential damage, high shocks, etc.

The graphs in Figure 25.18 help compute wall thickness quickly, based on relative severity of service, working pressure, and tubing OD. When pressures are low and tubing lines small, a design (burst pressure to peak operating pressure) service factor of even 7:1 or 10:1 can be obtained easily, even with

thin-wall tubing. For example, 1/4-in. OD ×
0.035-in. wall thickness low carbon steel tubing
could be rated for 2000 psi at 7:1 design service
factor, or at 1500 psi at 10:1.

Where pressures and severity of service are **not
excessive,** a design service factor of 4:1 is generally
acceptable. **For demanding service,** 6:1 and 8:1 design service factors are recommended. However,
where flow rates and pressures are high, requiring
larger diameter tubing, design service factors dictate
the use of very heavy tubing walls.

For example, the wall thickness for 2-in. OD
tubing for 4000 psi service at 4:1 design service
factor is seen to be beyond the graph, Figure 25.18.
The wall thickness would be calculated at nearly 0.3
inch.

Allowable stress values

Note that this method for determining design service factors is subjective and lends itself to widely
varying interpretations. Thus, as system pressures
have increased, designers have been forced to seek
more practical selection criteria. Many now use a
percentage of tubing material nominal yield strength
as an allowable stress value. Standard practice in
ASME Boiler Codes is to use between 50% and 60%
of nominal yield strength, depending on the type of
material.

Carbon steel tubing that meets SAE specifications J524 and J525 has a minimum ultimate tensile
strength of 45,000 psi and a minimum yield strength
of 25,000 psi. In actual practice these minimums are
exceeded.

The minimum yield strength allowed by SAE
J525 is 56% of the minimum ultimate strength, or
45,000 × 56% = 25,200, or 25,000 psi. Laboratory
test results show that in practice the composite yield
points average 70% (36,100/51,300) of ultimate
strength, ranging between 65 and 82%.

FLEXIBLE CONDUCTORS - HOSE

Piping and tubing are rigid conductors. They are
not suitable for applicatons requiring the two ends of
a conductor to move relative to one another. A typical example would be where machine elements move
during a work cycle.

**Table 25.4—Comparison of working pressures
for four types of wire braid hoses.**

Hose size	Single wire braid	SAE 100R2 Multiple wire braid	SAE 100R10 4 Spiral wire wrap	SAE 100R11 6 Spiral wire wrap
−4	3000	5000	8700	11,250
−6	2250	4000	7500	10,000
−8	2000	3500	6250	7500
−10	1750	2750	—	—
−12	1500	2250	5000	6250
−16	800	1875	4000	5000
−20	600	1625	3000	3500
−24	500	1250	2500	3000
−32	350	1125	2500	3000

In such applications flexible conductors, such as
hoses, are used. There are more hoses to choose from
than pipe or tubing; they come in may types and are
designed for a broad spectrum of uses.

In a hydraulic system, flexible conductors are
called *hose assemblies.* An assembly includes a
length of flexible hose to each end of which an appropriate fitting has been attached.

In addition to the freedom and convenience of
relative motion between components, hoses* provide
other advantages. They help:
- overcome severe vibration
- compensate for manufacturing tolerances in
piping
- provide freedom in routing conductors on a
machine
- absorb hydraulic impulse shocks and smooth fluid flow.

Dash numbering system
for single wire braid hose

Rigid tube dash sizes (tube OD) form the basis for
the dash sizes used to identify single-wire braid
(SAE 100R5) hose and fittings. Sizes for most other
standard hose styles (fabric braid, two-wire braid,
multiple-spiral wire wrap) are also expressed by a

---

*In the United States, hydraulic hose specifications
are set by SAE J517; fittings and couplings by SAE
J514 and SAE J518. See Table 25.4.*

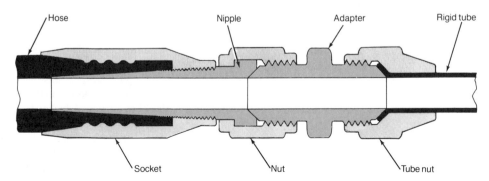

Fig. 25.19. Re-
lationship between
IDs based on the dash
system of elements in
a typical conductor.

Labels: Hose, Nipple, Adapter, Rigid tube, Socket, Nut, Tube nut

dash number but, in these cases, the dash number represents the number of 16ths of an inch of the hose

ID, Table 25.4.

Figure 25.19 shows that the ID of the hose and

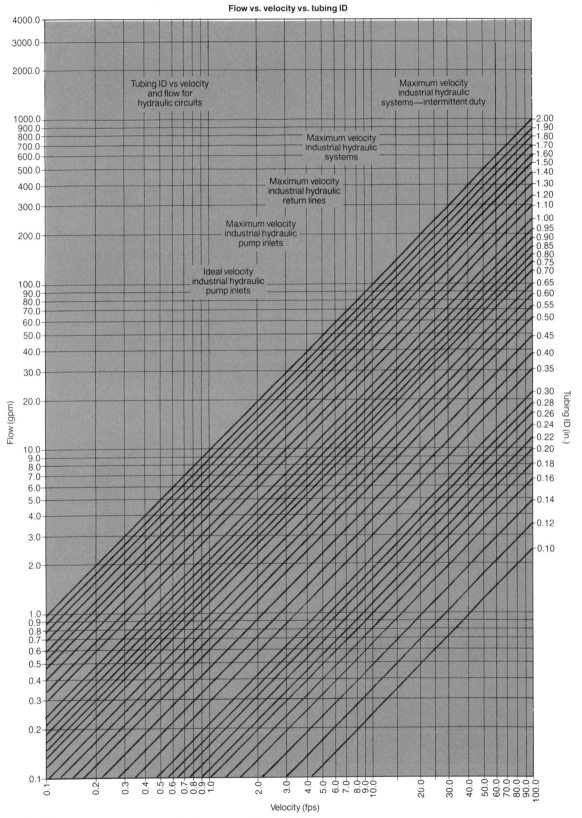

Fig. 25.20. Nomograph relates tube ID to flow rate and flow velocity.

nipple are generally the same as the adapter ID. Note that the IDs of hose and fittings are nearly equal to the ID of the corresponding size rigid tube. Also, the swivel nut on the hose fitting has the same size threads as the adapter and is the same as the flare tube nut that fits the rigid tube. The dash size that indentifies the hose and fittings also applies to the equivalent rigid tube. (A -4 male flare adapter fits a -4 tube nut and a -4 hose fitting which fits a -4 hose.)

The graph in Figure 25.20 shows the relationship between flow, velocity, and tubing ID for hydraulic circuits together with maximum recommended velocity for various systems. Proper use will help select the proper tube ID as a function of flow rate and velocity.

FIVE BASIC TYPES OF INDUSTRIAL HOSE

The five basic types of industrial hose are classified by the amount of fluid pressure they will withstand. The type of reinforcement used is the chief difference between these hose types because high-

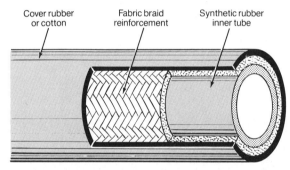

Fig. 25.21. Typical fabric braid reinforced rubber hose.

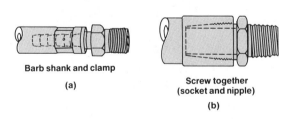

Barb shank and clamp
(a)

Screw together
(socket and nipple)
(b)

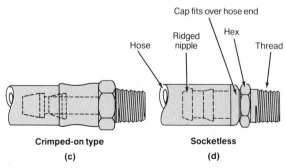

Crimped-on type
(c)

Socketless
(d)

Fig. 25.22. Four methods for connecting fittings to low pressure rubber hose.

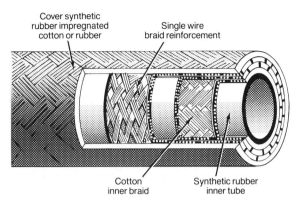

Fig. 25.23. Typical construction of SAE 100R1 single wire/or 2-wire braid (one is fabric) hose.

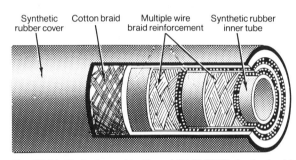

Fig. 25.24. Typical construction of SAE100R2, 2-wire braid high pressure hose.

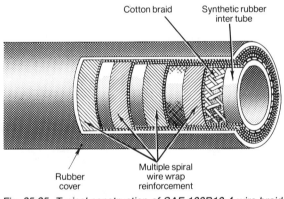

Fig. 25.25. Typical construction of SAE 100R10 4-wire braid very high pressure hose.

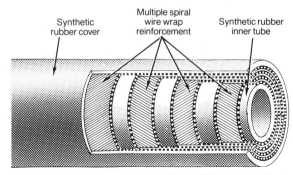

Fig. 25.26. Typical construction of SAE 100R11 4- and 6-wire super high pressure braid hose.

TABLE 25.5—Seal compatibility with common fluids

Fluid name	Military specification	Buna N	Polyurethane	EP	Viton Fluorocarbon
Water Glycol	MIL-H22072	R	U	R	S
		R	U	R	—
		R	U	R	S
		R	U	R	R
		R	U	R	R
Water Oil/Emulsion		R	U	U	R
		R	R	U	R
Water Soluble Oil		R	—	R	—
Water Fresh		R	U	R	R
Water Salt		R	U	R	R
Phosphate Ester	MIL-19547B	U	U	R	R
		U	U	R	R
		U	U	R	R
		U	—	R	U
		U	—	R	U
Diester	MIL-H-7808	S	U	U	R
Silicate Ester	MIL-H-8446B	S	R	U	R
Petroleum Base	MIL-H-5606	R	R	U	R

R = Recommended   S = Satisfactory   M = Marginal   U = Unsatisfactory   — = Insufficient data

pressure hoses require stronger reinforcement to handle the pressurized fluid in a system.

Low pressure hose is generally reinforced with a fabric braid; medium- and high-pressure hoses have single- and multiple-wire braid reinforcement depending on need. Spiral-wire wrap hoses were developed for special, high-impulse pressure applications.

Figure 25.21 illustrates a typical low pressure hose showing a fabric braid reinforcement, a synthetic rubber inner tube, and either a cotton or rubber cover. This hose is used largely in the automotive and trucking industries and is not recommended for hydraulic applications.

Figure 25.22 illustrates four methods of attaching fittings to a low pressure hose:

• a barbed nipple is pushed into the hose and held with a clamp, Figure 25.22(a). This is seen often in industrial applications.
• a screw-together fitting, in which the nipple is screwed into a socket attached to the hose, Figure 25.22(b).
• a crimped-on fitting, which is pressed firmly on the hose by machine, Figure 25.22(c).
• the socketless fitting in which a ridged nipple grips the interior of the hose and holds it fast, Figure 25.22(d). It is engineered to require no exterior clamp as does a barbed nipple. A cap fits over the end of the hose to protect the raw end and give the assembly a finished appearance. The cap determines the position of the hose over the fitting. It can be assembled manually by pushing the fitting into the hose.

Figure 25.23 is a cutaway drawing of a medium pressure hose. SAE specifications 100R1 and 100R5 describe this type hose as having cotton or rubber covers; most manufacturers conform closely to these specifications. The hose is reinforced with a single layer of carbon steel wire-braid, and has a cotton inner braid between the wire and the synthetic rubber inner tube. Available in -4 through -48 sizes, this

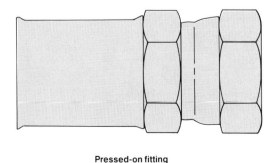

Pressed-on fitting

(a)

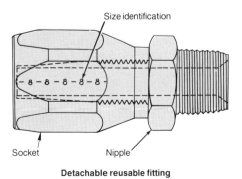

Size identification

Socket   Nipple

Detachable reusable fitting

(b)

Fig. 25.27. Two basic types of hose fittings: (a) crimped, (b) detachable reusable.

297

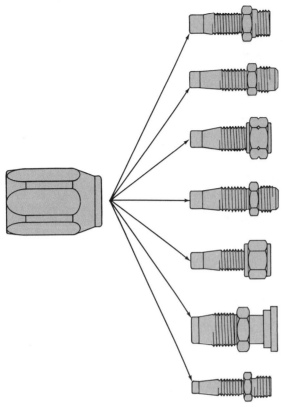

Fig. 25.28. Variety of hose fitting types available with reusable fittings.

TABLE 25.6—Recommended torquing procedure

Nominal tube size	Fitting size	Rotate no. of hex flats
¼	4	2½
5⁄16	5	2½
⅜	6	2
½	8	2
⅝	10	1½-2
¾	12	1
1	16	¾-1
1¼	20	¾-1
1½	24	½-¾

hose is suitable for many industrial applications with hydraulic oil, crude oil, lubricating oil, air, and water. Typical constructions of wire braid hose are illustrated in Figure 25.24: SAE 100R2, high pressure hose; Figure 25.25: SAE 100R10, very high pressure hose; and Figure 25.26: SAE 100R11, super high pressure hose.

Hose fittings

Two types of fittings are manufactured for medium pressure hoses. One is a pressed-on type, Figure 25.27(a), non-reusable, usually swaged-on or crimped-on. These fittings must be installed with a special machine and *discarded* with the hose when the assembly fails.

The second is the detachable, reusable type which has a socket and a threaded nipple, Figure 25.27(b). This type fitting can be reused when hose lines wear out or become damaged. Assembly and disassembly is done with simple hand tools. The socket grips the hose carcass, the nipple is inserted into the hose and

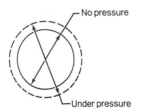

Fig. 25.29. Variations in hose internal geometry caused by system pressure.

No pressure

Under pressure

screwed into the socket. This design provides a firm, strong attachment of hose-to-fitting; the assembly will not leak or wear at connecting points.

One distinct advantage of reusable fittings other than the ability to re-use them with different hose lengths is their versatility. With the reusable fitting, one socket can mate with a variety of nipple assemblies, Figure 25.28. Thus one thread type can be replaced by another simply by changing nipple assemblies in the socket.

Because hoses are flexible, their volumetric expansion must be considered in some applications. Hoses not only bend and flex, they also experience a diametral expansion when pressurized to slightly increase the volume inside the hose, Figure 25.29.

In most systems, this factor can be ignored. However, in some critical applications this volumetric change may have to be taken into account. Hose manufacturers can supply data, generally in terms of a coefficient of cubic expansion, in^3/psi/unit length from which volumetric changes can be calculated.

Another factor which especially concerns wire-braid hoses is the change in hose length with increase in pressure. Because this change cannot be predicted, hoses must be installed "loosely", without rigid longitudinal constraints, Figure 25.29.

Split flange fittings

SAE split flange fittings are available in five basic configurations: straight, 22½, 45, 67½, and 90 degrees, Figure 25.30. Many other shapes are available from most manufacturers. These fittings require two split flanges and an O-ring which provides a positive seal. Split flange fittings were designed for connecting rigid lines 1 inch OD and larger. They are used instead of pipe threads or swivel nuts and can be installed with small tools. Split flange fittings are often installed with adapters; in many cases they are connected to control valves, cylinders and accessories machined to accept flange connections instead of female pipe threads.

The flanged heads are incorporated into fittings attached to tubing pipes or hoses. Because these connect directly to the hydraulic component they eliminate the need for an adapter or connector.

298

Table 25.7 — Typical fluid power fittings

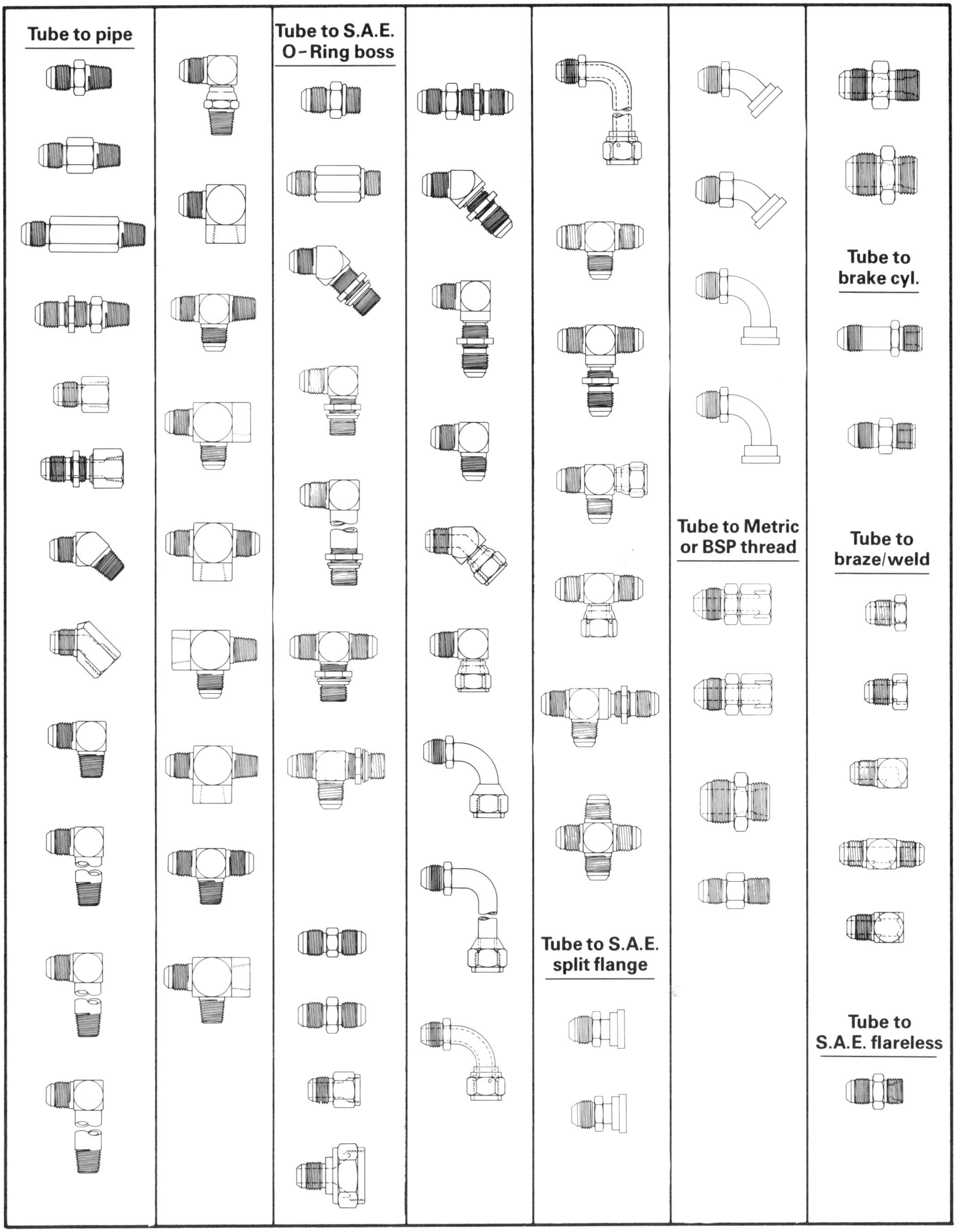

| Tube to pipe | | Tube to S.A.E. O-Ring boss | | | | | Tube to brake cyl. |

Tube to Metric or BSP thread

Tube to S.A.E. split flange

Tube to braze/weld

Tube to S.A.E. flareless

Courtesy Aeroquip Corp.

Elbow fittings and adapters, Figure 25.31, are available in three basic types: 45-, 90-, and 90-degrees with the long tangent. They are often used to prevent abrasion, allow access to hard-to-get-

at connections, permit better flexing, reduce the amount of hose needed in the system, and improve system appearance. They can also help improve flow characteristics.

Hose selection

To choose the right hose for a system, follow this guideline:

1. From the Cycle Profile, determine the *pressures* and *flow rates* to which the hose will be subjected, (refer to Chapters 3, 4, and 5). Be sure to include shock loading.

2. Determine the type of fluid which will fill the system and choose a hose material which will be compatible with it; (refer to section on fluids), Table 25.5.

3. Determine the anticipated operating temperature level for the system; (refer to Chapter 18).

4. Estimate how much flexing the hose will experience during machine operation.

5. Establish the minimum allowable *bend radius* for the hose size as related to the operation of the machine.

6. Examine potentials for abrasion. If the exterior of the hose is likely to get damaged, specify one of several types of protective coverings or sleeves available.

7. Select couplings and adapters for the hose which must mate with other fittings and ports in the system.

8. Select proper dash numbers to match hose and fittings with rigid tubing and fitting sizes.

9. Select the appropriate SAE number for the hose to match system pressure and flow requirements to the capability of the hose.

10. Evaluate the various cost options.

11. Determine how serviceable the hose is. Assess

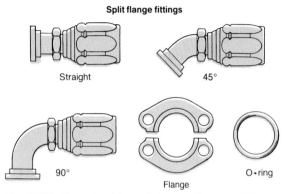

Split flange fittings

Straight   45°

90°   O•ring
Flange

Fig. 25.30. Example of hose fittings available in SAE split flange fittings.

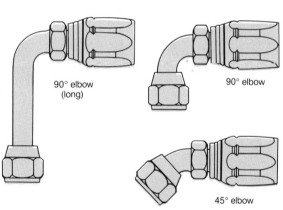

Elbow fittings

90° elbow (long)   90° elbow

45° elbow

Fig. 25.31. Various elbow fittings for hose applications.

Table 25.8 — Relation of tubing sizes, materials and flare types

Material:		Steel, stainless steel, brass aluminum	Steel stainless steel	Steel stainless steel	Brass aluminum
Tube size					
O.D.-in.	Size no.	SAE 37° flare	SAE flareless	Heavy duty	Instrumentation
1/8	2	.010-.035	.010-.035	—	.012-.028
3/16	3	.010-.035	.020-.049	—	.012-.035
1/4	4	.020-.065	.028-.065	.049	.020-.049
5/16	5	.020-.065	.028-.065	—	.020-.065
3/8	6	.020-.065	.035-.095	.065	.028-.065
1/2	8	.028-.083	.049-.120	.083	.035-.083
5/8	10	.035-.095	.058-.120	.095	.035-.083
3/4	12	.035-.109	.065-.120	.109	.035-.095
7/8	14	.035-.109	.072-.120	—	.049-.095
1	16	.035-.120	.083-.148	.134	.049-.120
1-1/4	20	.049-.120	.095-.188	—	—
1-1/2	24	.049-.120	.095-.203	—	—
2	32	.058-.134	.095-.220	—	—

whether it can be repaired in the field and re-used.
12. Establish how readily available the hose is both for initial purchase and replacement. Can the manufacturer and distributor networks meet and supply your requirements. Is the hose available for field service?
13. Establish compatibility with customer requirements. The customer must accept the hose selected. This is often predicated on what the customer already has.
14. Find out whether the product has a good reputation in the field and whether it is generally accepted. Get a history of its performance.

Manifolds

Manifolds have become an effective design tool for minimizing and eliminating leakage. Some manifolds are standard; many are specially made for a given installation. Manifolds may consist of either drilled plates — for smaller applications — or plates in which the conductor pattern has been milled and drilled, after which the plates were brazed together to form the closed system.

More recently, modular manifold systems have been developed. In these, predesigned, modular building blocks can be assembled in many configurations to provide the various types of manifolds needed for different applications. In some instances manifolding is designed into a machine part and cast integrally when the machine is made. In another configuration, a manifold may be a large piece of pipe with multiple connections, sometimes called a header. It is difficult to offer many selection criteria for manifolds, since each is almost a custom design.

Here are a few rules of thumb for using most manifolds:

1. Pressure. The manifold must be able to sustain system design and peak pressures.
2. Pressure drop. Total pressure drop must be acceptable.
3. Access. Pipe or tube fitting taps, valve port patterns, etc., must be compatible with the rest of the system and accessible for servicing.
4. Integrated valves. Cartridge valves, for instance, must have the same pressure rating as other system components.
5. Stacking Systems. Some controls manufacturers have developed modular stacking systems which incorporate the functions of manifolds. These might be considered as an option.
6. Cost. Must be compared to alternative approaches such as subplate mounting, in- line mounting, and tube networks.
7. Acceptability. Will the customer accept a manifold in lieu of a conventional pipe/tube system?

Hydraulic lines, a summary

Lines perform the essential function of closing a circuit. They provide the flow paths for the energy-transmitting fluid from an input device to an output device. They also provide the flow paths for return flow after the energy transfer has been completed at the output component. In some instances, for pilot purposes, lines carry control signals. Primary considerations are:

1. Acceptability. The proposed selection should be acceptable to the customer, the plant engineering department, or other end user.
2. Compatibility with fittings. Many types of fittings are available for both rigid and flexible lines. Be sure they mate.
3. Cost. Economics play a major role in the final selection.
4. Flow rate vs. pressure drop. All lines display a characteristic pressure drop, Δp, usually given in psi per foot, or per hundred feet, at specified flow rates.
5. Fluid compatibility. The material(s) from which the lines are made must not deteriorate or corrode when in contact with the fluid used in the system.
6. Pressure rating. Most lines carry two ratings: operating pressure and burst pressure.
7. Product history. What has been the performance of the proposed selection in similar applications?
8. Rigid vs. flexible. A basic choice must be made between rigid lines, like piping or other metallic tubing, and flexible lines, such as hoses or plastic tubing.
9. Temperature. This is an important consideration, particularly in the case of rubber hoses and plastic tubing, where the basic material may deteriorate at high temperatures.

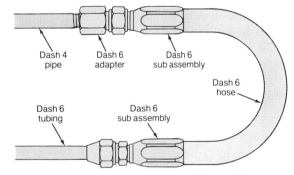

Fig. 25.32. Dash system provides method for matching various conducting elements in hydraulic system.

Low pressure hose ID	Single wire hose ID	Dash No.
1/4″	3/16″	−4
3/8″	5/16″	−6
1/2″	13/32″	−8
5/8″	1/2″	−10
3/4″	5/8″	−12

Fig. 25.33. Comparison of IDs between low pressure and single wire braid hoses referenced to the dash number system.

10. Vibration. Because vibration may cause fatigue failure of a rigid lines, a flexible line may be necessary instead.

USING DASH NUMBERS

Figure 25.32 illustrates the potential problem a designer may encounter when attempting to connect different size conductors. The dash number system provides an orderly basis for connecting components which would otherwise not fit together. Remember, however, that all conductors with the same dash number do not necessarily have the same ID dimension. Figure 25.33 illustrates this by comparing a low pressure hose with a single-wire braid hose. Both carry the same dash number to provide *connecting* consistency.

Low pressure fabric braid hose dash sizes are the actual inside diameter of the hose expressed in 16ths of an inch. Socketless fittings used on a ¼-inch ID low pressure fabric braid hose mate with -4 size adapter flare ends. In keeping with other standards, the ¼-inch ID low pressure how is given the -4 size.

TUBE FITTINGS

Three broad groups

A wide variety of tube fittings is found in hydraulic installations. They fall into three broad groups: flared, flareless, and welded or brazed. None is universal. Each is designed to do a specific job.

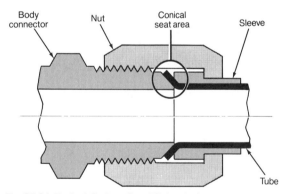

Fig. 25.34. Typical, 3-piece flared fitting design.

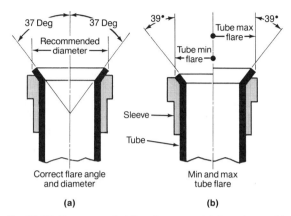

Fig. 25.36. Recommended flare for proper joint made up with 37-degree flare fitting.

Flared fittings are generally less expensive and more readily available in a wider variety of sizes and materials than any other type. Some bite-type flareless models are recommended over flared fittings where vibration fatigue failures may be a problem. However, flareless versions are very sensitive to proper assembly torque. They are prone to leak if over- or under- torqued. In normal service, flared and flareless varieties are equally effective. Welded fittings meet the most severe service requirements of high pressures, temperatures, and severe mechanical loads, and are the most expensive.

Flared fittings

A typical 3-piece flared fitting — body, nut, and sleeve — is shown in Figure 25.34. The metal-to-metal seal is made when the softer tubing is pressed against the hardened, conical seat of the connector body. As the nut is tightened, the sleeve is pushed against the tube. The sleeve absorbs the twisting friction of the nut, transferring only axial forces against the flared tube. This feature eliminates tube twisting found with 2-piece fittings.

Three types of flare fittings are illustrated in Figure 25.35: a 2-piece in Figure 25.35(*a*); a 3-piece in Figure 25.35(*b*); and an inverted flare in Figure 25.35(*c*).

The 37-degree flare

The standard flare angle for hydraulic tubing is

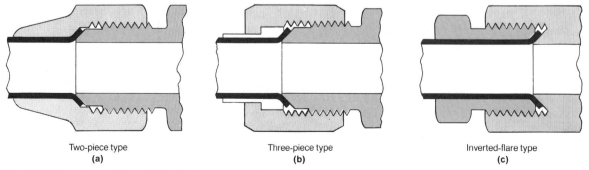

Fig. 25.35. Three types of flared fitting designs.

37-degrees from the centerline, Figure 25.36. Most tube end flares are made by hand or power tools which swage the tube end over a split die. These flares tend to have a ridge of metal extruded from the outer surface at the parting line of the die. This ridge will provide a leak path unless cleaned. A correct flare is shown in Fig. 25.36 (*b*). Common fabrication errors consist of making the flare too broad or too narrow.

The 45-degree flare

Another common flare angle, used mainly in low pressure automotive and refrigeration applications, is 45 degrees from the centerline. Never mix 45- with 37-degree fittings! A simple way to tell a 37- from a 45-degree flare fitting is to use any 90-degree angle such as the edge of a calling card. If placed inside and along one edge of the 37-degree flared tube, the card will bottom out on the outside lip, Figure 25.37(*a*). Inside a 45-degree flare, the card will fit perfectly, Figure 35.37(*b*).

If Joint Leaks

Most leaks in flared tubing fittings are caused by poor tubing flares, irregularities in connector body seat surfaces, or improperly tightened joints. The only cure for poorly flared tubing is to reflare the tubing properly. Several companies make small truncated cones of ductile metal for a quick fix when irregularities in conical seats provide a leak path. Placed between seat and flare, the thin ductile washers tend to fill in non-uniformities in body seat and tubing flare when the joint is tightened.

A method has been devised for gaging tightening of fittings in the field without using a torque wrench. The nut is hand tightened and an index line is marked on adjacent hex flats, Figure 25.38. The nut is then torqued, Figure 25.39. Misalignment of the index lines indicates correct torquing when matched with data shown in Table 25.6.

Never exceed the offsets shown in Table 25.6 or the nut will be overtorqued. It is impossible to stop a leak due to overtorquing by additional torquing of the nut.

Flareless fittings

These were developed because tube flaring becomes more difficult as tube wall thickness increases. A typical bite style flareless tube fitting is shown in Figure 25.40. Other types of flareless fittings appear in Figure 25.41.

The wedging action of the ferrule, when drawn down by the nut, forms a seal between ferrule and connector body. At the same time, the cutting edge of the ferrule bites into the tubing wall forming another positive seal around the circumference of the tube. The keys to reliable operation of the bite style flareless fitting are presetting the ferrule and inspecting for good preset.

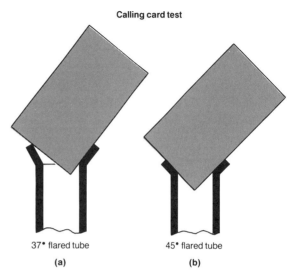
Calling card test

37° flared tube   45° flared tube
(a)   (b)

Fig. 25.37. Simple card test helps field check 37- and 45-degree flared joints.

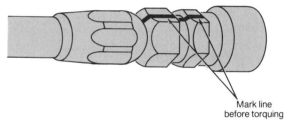
Mark line before torquing

Fig. 25.38. First step in proper torquing of flared fitting is to hand-tighten nut and mark an index line on adjacent hex flats.

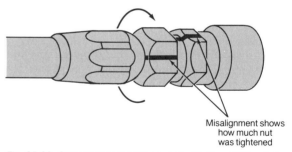
Misalignment shows how much nut was tightened

Fig. 25.39. Second step in properly torquing flared fitting is to rotate nut with wrench until misalignment between two segments of index line corresponds to that recommended in Table 25.6.

Avoid thin-wall tubing

Bite-type fittings are not recommended for thin-wall tubing because the ferrule can collapse the tubing wall before an adequate bite is achieved.

While leakage of the flareless fitting is less prone to poor workmanship than the 37-degree flare, it is more sensitive to torquing or tightening. It will leak if under-tightened or over-tightened. Once over-tightened, this tubing and sleeve must be replaced; the nut and body can be salvaged. As with the flared fitting, follow very closely the manufacturer's recommended assembly procedures for tightening

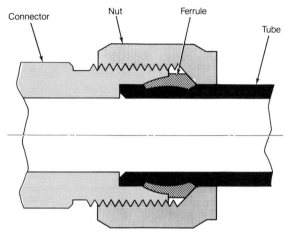

Fig. 25.40. Typical 3-piece bite type flareless fitting.

values. Tightening after preset is usually ½ to ⅓ of a turn from finger tight.

Table 25.7 illustrates the wide variety of tube fittings available to the circuit designer to assemble a fluid conducting system.

Flared or flareless fittings?

Flared fittings are generally used on low- to medium-pressure applications. Tubing-wall thickness becomes the limiting factor, because heavier-wall tubing tends to reduce the sealing surface and shorten thread engagement if assembled on conventional flare fittings.

To use a flared fitting, the tubing must be ductile enough to be flared. For example, in ¾-in OD steel tubing, the wall thicknesses can range from 0.035 to 0.109 in.

Flareless fittings include bite, compression, and collet types. These proprietary designs are suitable for low- to medium-high-pressure applications depending on the fitting used. Tubing wall thickness is not usually a limiting factor. Quality fittings will out-perform the tubing in pressure retention. However, as pressures increase, standard fitting configurations may not be strong enough for the service.

Most flareless fittings exert a uniform stress on the tubing, but the tubing must have an adequate compressive hoop strength to withstand these stresses. Compressive hoop strength relates to the collapse resistance of the tubing when it is subjected to a uniform external pressure at all points on the OD. Hoop strength and durability are also important in flaring.

With a bite-type flareless fitting the tubing must be strong enough to withstand the high compression force exerted by the fitting. In this case the acceptable wall thickness for ¾-in. OD steel tubing is higher: 0.065 in to 0.120 in.

Table 25.8 summarizes data on minimum and maximum tube wall thickness recommended for various fittings and a range of tube sizes.

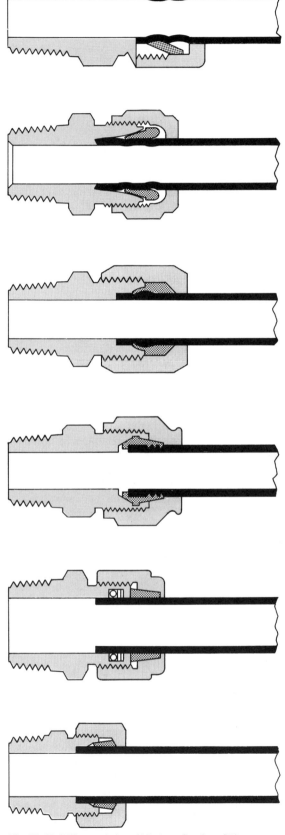

Fig. 25.41. Different styles of bite type flareless fittings.

304

Fitting functions

All tube fittings perform two functions: hold and seal; some do one better than the other. Although all applications require these functions, one is more important or difficult to achieve than the other. There are four possibilities:
- hard to hold, easy to seal
- easy to hold, hard to seal,
- hard to hold and seal
- easy to hold and seal.

Mechanical holding power, defined as the ability to mechanically restrain the tubing against pressure blow-out, is a function of a ratio of system pressure and the pressure area of the tubing plus a safety factor. For example, ¼-in OD tubing presents a pressure area of 0.0491 in² for pressure blowout. This means that when ¼-in OD tubing is exposed to a pressure of 1000 psi, the fitting must grip the tube tightly enough to resist a blowout force of almost 50 lb. (1000 × 0.0491). At 3000 psi, the blowout force is 150 lb; 1-in OD tubing subjected to a pressure of 1000 psi must resist a blowout force of 785 lb.

Sealing power

Sealing capability is a function of the relation of

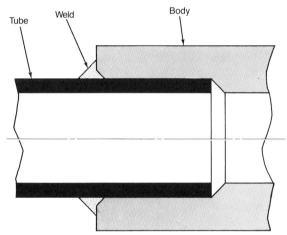

Fig. 25.42. Basic configurations of weld or braze type fitting.

the molecular structure of the contained fluid to the size of any leak path at the fitting seal surfaces.

A hard-to-hold/easy-to-seal application involves containing a large-molecule medium such as hydraulic oil, at high system pressure using fairly large-diameter tubing. One of the best choices is a flared fitting with its very strong holding power. If the tubing wall is too heavy to flare, a well-designed bite-type flareless fitting should work in most cases. On many applications a permanent fitting works best.

An easy-to-hold/hard-to-seal application involves containing a *small* molecule medium such as water-glycol fluids, at low system pressure using fairly small-diameter tubing. Most good bite-type flareless fittings are suitable for these applications.

A hard-to-hold/hard-to-seal applications contains a *small* molecule medium and high system pressure such as nitrogen at 3000 psi and higher in accumulator systems. The permanent weld-type fitting is best for this type application.

Welded fittings

High-pressure and/or high-temperature systems which do NOT require frequent disassembly may use welded or brazed fittings. A typical welded fitting is shown in Figure 25.42. Here, tubing is inserted into a fitting body, positioned, and welded. Chief disadvantages are cost and need for welding.

Low-carbon steel welds are sometimes porous or cracked. In each case, the porous or cracked section must be ground out and the joint rewelded. Then, as with all welded joints, the welded area must be stress-relieved. Heat the weld area with a torch to a dull red, then air cool.

Rigid pipe and tubing require proper alignment before final attachment to avoid inducing high stresses and ultimate line failure. Never attempt to pull a line into place with clamps, bolts, or tube nuts to hold it in position. If a connection is difficult to make, use an appropriate strength flexible hose instead.

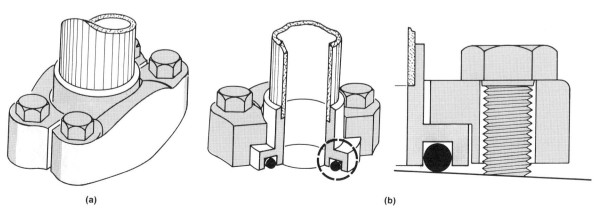

(a)   (b)

Fig. 25.43. Typical SAE, 4-bolt split flange fitting (a) complete assembly, (b) cut-away showing seal.

Fig. 25.44. Low, uneven torquing of split flange bolts can distort flange.

**Table 25.9—Recommended torque values
(use grade 5 bolts)**

Connection size	Torque foot pounds
—8	21
—12	40
—16	40
—20	60
—24	90
—32	90
—40	90
—48	175

Note: Air wrenches tend to cause flange tipping.

Split-flange fittings

SAE split-flange fittings are basically face seals, Figure 25.43. They were developed to overcome two problems. One was to tighten threaded connectors in hard-to-get-at places; the other involved large-diameter hoses and tubing which required high tightening torques.

A flanged member is brazed to a tube end, Figure 25.43. Where a hose coupling is involved, the flanged portion becomes an integral part of the coupling. A groove in the horizontal face of the flange contains the O-ring seal.

When the split-flange halves are positioned over the flange and the retaining bolts torqued, the flange and O-ring are clamped against a mating machined surface and the joint becomes fluid-tight.

This connection can be very sensitive to human error because of uneven bolt torquing. The protruding shoulder and overhanging flange tend to tip the flange when the bolts are tightened unevenly, Figure 25.44. To avoid this problem, tighten the four bolts gradually and torque evenly, Table 25.9.

Quick-acting couplings

When it is necessary to uncouple and recouple a line frequently quick-acting couplings can save much time and money. Quick-acting couplings are used to connect and disconnect quickly and easily one flexible hose to another hose, or to rigid piping *by hand*. Often a valve in one or both halves opens automatically when the parts are joined and closes when separated.

Quick-acting couplings are available in various sizes and designs for use with different materials and at various pressures. For most applications, it is relatively easy to determine which type of coupling to use. However, the designer must take into consideration such factors as pipe and thread sizes, flow characteristics, types of end configurations, sealing materials, finishes, interchangeability, type of fluids, temperatures, etc.

There are three general types of quick-acting couplings:

Single shut-off couplings, Figure 25.45, were used originally to connect portable air tools and equipment to compressed air lines and for that reason, are often called "pneumatic" couplings. However, they are now used on many other applications as well. Single shut-off couplings are usually built to withstand operating pressures to 300 psi.

Where noncompressible fluids such as water or oil are being used, this pressure may sometimes be exceeded safely. Body sizes are compatible with ¼-, ⅜-, and ½-in. pipe and hose.

The coupler body should be installed on the supply end of the line to shut off fluid supply when the coupling is disconnected. The nipple has no valving and when disconnected, exhausts the downstream media. This is no problem with air. Even in a liquid line, this is not mechanically detrimental unless fluid loss interferes with a holding circuit or contaminates the surrounding area.

Double shut-off couplings, Figure 25.46, are used to connect hydraulic lines and those used for a variety of other fluids. These couplings are made to withstand pressures from 800 to 5000 psi depending on size and material. Manufacturers' specifications should always be checked for correct application. They have valves in both halves to prevent loss of fluid when disconnected.

It is recommended that when the coupling is disconnected, an appropriate dust cap be placed over the nipple and a dust plug inside the coupler body. These dust caps not only help prevent contamination, but also increase the life of the coupling by preventing damage during handling and storing.

Double shut-off couplings are available in brass, steel, and 303 stainless steel, in body sizes ranging from ⅛ to 1½ inches. Stainless steel couplers are excellent for use with corrosive fluids, in corrosive atmospheres, or where sanitary requirements dictate

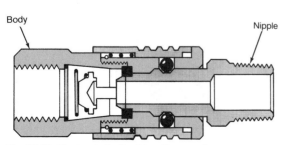

Fig. 25.45. Single, shut off quick acting coupling.

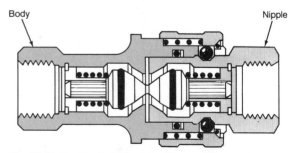

Fig. 25.46. Double shut off quick acting coupling.

306

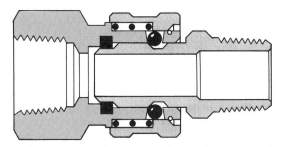

Fig. 25.47. Straight through (no check valve) quick acting coupling.

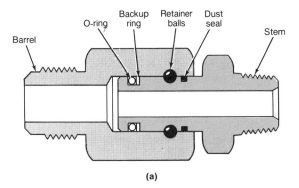

(a)

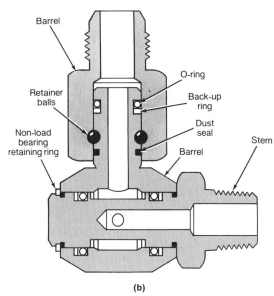

(b)

Fig. 25.48. Rotary couplings, (a) in-line, (b) elbow type.

clean conditions.

Straight-through couplings, Figure 25.47, are designed without valves to provide the least resistance to fluid flow. Therefore, shut-off valves are needed in both lines if fluid loss is to be avoided when the coupling is disconnected.

Coupler bodies of this design are manufactured in brass and 303 stainless steel. Straight-through nipples come in brass, steel, and stainless steel. The wide range of sizes, from ⅛ to 1 inch, makes them suitable for applications ranging from instrumentation to steelmaking.

SIZING QUICK-ACTING COUPLINGS

When sizing quick-acting couplings, consider these factors:
● **valving** — Determine the type of valving you need: remember to consider fluid leakage and safety.
● **pressure** — Calculate system working pressure and establish whether surges or shock conditions are likely.
● **flow** — Determine the volume of fluid to be delivered through the coupling at system working pressure.
● **pressure drop** — Establish pressure drop (Δp) for each coupling size. Remember that pressure drop is cumulative.
● **materials** — Determine what seal materials are compatible with system fluid and temperature. The fluid will also influence the type of metal selected.
● **Ambient conditions** — External conditions such as temperature, corrosive vapors, and other factors should also be considered as they may affect the operation of the coupler.

Swivel joints

These were developed for applications where conductors must rotate with respect to one another, yet where pressure-tight, leak-proof joints must be maintained. Swivel joints are available in in-line, Figure 25.48(*a*), and 90-degree, Figure 25.48(*b*) configurations. The 90-degree swivel joints are most common and are available in single- and double-plane types.

Single plane swivels provide rotation about one axis; **double plane** about two axes at 90 degrees to one another, Figure 25.48(*b*). In addition, various combinations of tube- and pipe-fitting ends are available.

Fitting selection criteria

In summary, the system designer should consider these factors when selecting fittings:
Cycle profile provides pressure and flow-rate information for circuit branches. (Refer to Chapters 3, 4 and 5).
Type of conductor: pipe, tube, or hose, or in what combinations they are to be used.
Type of fitting
● pressure rating must be high enough to contain design pressures.
● pressure drops are introduced by all fittings in the system.
● size of tube fittings is based on tubing OD with which fittings are to be connected. Pipe fittings are sized according to American Standard Pipe sizes and do not correspond, dimensionally, to nominal pipe sizes. Refer to discussion on dash-number system.
● fitting location will determine the type of fitting to be specified.

- fitting material and corrosion resistance must be considered in relation to other selection factors.
- frequency of connect and disconnect is sometimes an important selection consideration.
- vibration, cost, acceptability, and product history.

HYDRAULIC FLUIDS

Hydraulic fluids transfer energy in fluid power systems using liquids.

During the past decade, the fluids technology has become increasingly complex. Here is a summary of the major types of fluids available for hydraulic systems.

1. **Petroleum base fluids** (sometimes called mineral oils)
- straight mineral oils
- mineral oils with complex additive packages to enhance performance
- transmission "Fluid A"
- synthetic oils

2. **Fire-resistant fluids**
- water base
- emulsion
- water-in-oil emulsions nominally 40% water and 60% oil
- oil-in-water emulsions

high water content fluids: 95/5. These fluids contain 90 to 95% water and 5 to 10% miscible oils.
- water glycols 35-60% water in solution with polyglycol fluid
- synthetic fluids
- phosphate esters
- chlorinated compounds
- halogenated compounds
- other synthetics for special applications

3. **Silicones**

4. **Military specification**
   A-MIL-5606
   B-MIL-H-83282

Properties of fluids

Many characteristics affect fluid performance. They must be considered most carefully when selecting a fluid.

1. **Viscosity**[1] is a measure of how the fluid resists flow and is the single most important property of a hydraulic fluid. A hydraulic fluid which is too viscous (thick) usually causes high pressure drops, sluggish operation, results in low mechanical efficiency, and high power consumption. High-pressure, high-precision systems are particularly sensitive to viscosity at low temperatures when fluid is the most viscous (thickest). Such systems are likely to be affected by pump cavitation and sluggish actuator response.

Low-viscosity fluids permit efficient low-drag operation, but tend to increase wear, reduce volumetric efficiency, and increase chances of leakage. In theory, this leakage can be predicted based on fluid viscosity and laminar flow through a known gap. Since the clearance of some pump leakage paths depends on operating pressure and temperature, leakage may deviate considerably from theoretical viscosity-flow curves.

2. **Viscosity index (VI)**[2] is a measure of how viscosity changes with temperature. Ideally, a hydraulic fluid should have the same viscosity regardless of temperature. In reality, this is unattainable. Fluids which approach this goal have high VIs; low VIs, on the other hand, indicate wide flunctuation of viscosity with temperature. Typical VIs for petroleum oils range from 90 to 105; for polyglycols from 160 to 200.

A high VI is most important in applications subject to a wide temperature range, for example, mobile or industrial hydraulic systems which are started and stopped frequently during winter months in an unheated plant. An industrial system in a heated plant should operate satisfactorily on a low VI fluid.

Some fluids, such as paraffinic oils, come with fairly high VIs. The VI of many fluids is commonly raised through use of special additives. Although these additives may be expensive and tend to lose effectiveness under high shear rates and during long service, oils with VI additives can perform well in industrial service.

3. **Pour point** is the lowest temperature at which oil flows when chilled under specified test conditions. Pour point can be important if the system is regularly exposed to low temperatures; it is relatively insignificant if the system is used continuously inside a heated plant. Oil pour point should be about 20 F below the lowest expected temperature.

4. **Compressibility** is a measure of a fluid's elasticity. It is the degree to which a volume of fluid is reduced when under pressure. As a rule of thumb, compressibility is about 0.5% for each 1000 psi of pressure increase, up to 4000 psi. Compressibility is expressed by bulk modulus. Refer to Chapter 27.

Compressibility has its greatest effect on performance in servo applications. It determines system static rigidity and strongly influences system gain, or amplification. Because compressibility increases with pressure and temperature, it is an important factor in high-pressure systems.

Using positive-displacement pumps, the effect of bulk modulus is a loss in volume, which represents a power loss because few actuators recover the compressive energy in the fluid.

5. **Stability** is usually the most important property affecting fluid longevity. Ideally, the properties of hydraulic fluids should not change with use. But stresses from flow and cavitation, thermal degradation, oxidation, and hydrolysis tend to alter fluid properties. Mechanical stress can shear polymer chains, break down viscosity improvers, and reduce viscosity. Chemical changes can form volatile components, insoluble materials, and corrosive products.

6. Lubricity is an important characteristic in hydraulic fluids because the fluid must be able to lubricate properly the moving parts in a system to minimize wear. Most petroleum fluids satisfy the lubrication requirements in hydraulic components. However, because certain types of hydraulic pumps and motors place unusually severe load-carrying requirements on the oil, fluids for these applications should be fortified by *antiwear additives*.

7. Volatility is rarely the cause of pump cavitation because the vapor pressure of most hydraulic fluids is too low to cause boiling at the pump inlet. In most systems, the real cause of cavitation is entrained air.

8. Aeration and foaming resistance is another important indicator of fluid quality. Fluid in a hydraulic system always contains air in the form of entrained bubbles and/or solution. The entrained air increases fluid compressibility, making the system elastic, noisy, and erratic. Compression of this air generates heat and can increase oxidation.

Copper should be avoided in *hydraulic* systems, because it acts as a catalyst to oxidize oils. For this reason, heat exchangers should be of steel, rather than copper or brass.

Pump volumetric efficiency is reduced because air bubbles in the oil in the pump inlet expand as the oil enters the pump. When the bubbles collapse on discharge, they are likely to damage the pump. This is called cavitation erosion. Many high-quality fluids contain *anti-foaming additives* to release air readily.

9. Corrosion prevention capabilities of an oil are important because some moisture is always present in hydraulic systems. Since most hydraulic components have ferrous surfaces, corrosion prevention is essential.

Corrosive agents usually form because of thermal or oxidation decomposition, or hydrolysis. These agents are usually acidic although not all acidic materials are corrosive. In most instances, corrosion simply increases leakage by increasing tolerances of close-fitting parts. Corrosion resistance is normally provided by adding *rust inhibitor* to the oil. The inhibitor plates out on the metal surfaces to form a protective film.

Some antirust additives used in hydraulic systems may attack zinc. Therefore, galvanized and other zinc-coated surfaces should be avoided. Zinc is also objectionable in a hydraulic system because products of oil oxidation can react with it to form metallic soaps.

Other materials susceptible to corrosion are magnesium-based alloys and lead. Magnesium alloys generally corrode heavily in the presence of water. Lead is attacked by products of oxidation.

10. Materials compatibility determines which seals and components can be used with a given fluid. For example, *natural* rubber is not oil-resistant and should not be used in hydraulic systems operating on petroleum oils.

Synthetic rubbers vary widely in their behavior when exposed to different fluids. When in contact with a given fluid, some synthetics are almost unaffected, while others swell, shrink, or otherwise deteriorate.

Most seals used with oil are made from nitrile rubbers. Other suitable materials include neoprene, Thiokol, silicones, fluorocarbon rubbers, and Hypalon. Most tubing and fitting manufacturers offer extensive tables of materials compatibility with their products.

Alternative hydraulic fluids

Petroleum oils are the most common hydraulic fluids used, but they have some limitations. Rising petroleum prices, threats of shortages, high disposal costs, and advances in hydraulic hardware are making non-petroleum hydraulic fluids more attractive. Water base fluids and synthetic fluids offer some alternatives.

All synthetic fluids cost more than oils when used *neat* or undiluted, but water-dilutable synthetics can often be used at water-to-synthetic chemical ratios of 95:5. With these high-water synthetics, in-use costs are reduced considerably while problems of fire hazards, and compatibility are minimized. However, high-water content fluids have a low viscosity which cannot be increased and kept stable.

Multi-purpose fluids serve several functions: they provide:
- antiwear protection for hydraulic systems and other internal parts, and
- the film strength, frictional, and other properties needed for machining operations.

The fluid is used neat in viscosity-dependent hydraulic systems. However, it is diluted with up to 95% water in other systems. It is also diluted with water when used as a coolant. The fluid is compatible with elastomers commonly used in hydraulic systems and is inhibited to protect against metal corrosion in both neat and diluted applications. Used *neat*, the fluid costs more than five times as much as petroleum oil; *diluted* it costs only about one-fourth.

With this fluid, leakage from the hydraulic system to the coolant system introduces no contamination. Also, additive ratios in the coolant are not altered appreciably because the water-diluted coolant is the same as the hydraulic fluid.

Single-purpose fluids. The most commonly used type of synthetic fluid is intended only for hydraulic applications, and is also diluted with 95% water. Since this synthetic is not intended to be a coolant, it does not contain the extreme-pressure additives that give coolants the lubricity required for metal-cutting operations. It costs about one-eighth as much as oil.

The lubricating additives in single-purpose fluids are polar compounds. Like dual-purpose fluids, single-purpose fluids are fully compatible with water-diluted coolants. However, leakage of single-purpose fluid into coolant sumps gradually changes the concentration of extreme-pressure and other coolant additives, so leakage must be minimized.

Water-glycols provide excellent fire resistance because contain 35 to 55% water. However, they are not dilutable and cost about four times as much as oil.

Since water glycols are solutions rather than emulsions, they can be formulated for a range of viscosities similar to those of petroleum oils. Like other synthetics, water glycols include additives which improve viscosity, corrosion resistance, and lubricity. They can be used in existing oil-hydraulic hardware, although some components may be derated when switched from oil to water-glycol service.

Phosphate-esters are fire-resistant, but not to the degree of water glycols or high-water synthetics. Phosphate esters are available in a range of viscosities suitable for single-machine hydraulic systems. Lubricity is equivalent or better than the best petroleum oils. Operating temperatures can range as high as 150 F because of the fluid's inherent oxidation and thermal stabilities.

Phosphate esters are strong solvents for many plastics and elastomers. For this reason, seals in systems using these fluids should be made of butyl rubber, ethylene-propylene rubber, or fluoroelastomer. Phosphate esters cost about eight to ten times as much as petroleum oils.

Oil synthetic blends are a blend of phosphate ester and selected petroleum stocks; they cost about the same as water glycols. Because of the oil content, fire resistance is between that of petroleum oils and phosphate esters.

Emulsions. Water dispersed in continuous oil phase is called an invert emulsion. In an ordinary *oil emulsion*, water is the continuous phase, with oil droplets dispersed throughout (surrounded by) the water. In invert emulsions, the usual concentration of water in oil is 35 to 45%. In ordinary emulsions, the usual concentration of oil in water is 5 to 10%.

The advantage of an invert emulsion is economy — about 1.5 times the cost of petroleum oil — with the high oil content providing good viscosity. However, the high oil content also means that fire resistance is below the level of phosphate esters.

Reprocessed oil

With the advent of the high cost of petroleum base fluids, there has been increased interest in using reprocessed oils as a cost-saving measure. However, there are no standards against which to measure the properties of reprocessed oils.

Reprocessing can range from simple filtering and adjusting of pH to stripping the fluid to its base stock and returning it to its original condition, including additives.

Be careful when considering using reprocessed fluids. Know the reprocessor and what is actually done to the oil. Make certain that the reprocessed oil will perform as well as a new oil.

FILTERS AND STRAINERS

Filters and strainers perform the same function: they remove contaminants from the fluid. They differ only in the size contaminants they can remove. A strainer is a device with a 100-mesh or larger screen which removes particles measuring 144 micrometres and larger. A filter removes smaller particles, though filters differ in the minimum size of particle they will remove.

Filters and strainers can be placed in various parts in a system. Strainers are normally located in the pump-inlet line, filters in the pressure and return lines. The type and construction of a filter or strainer will depend, in part, on where it is placed. (Also refer to Chapter 20).

Other selection factors include:

1. **Pressure.** To what pressures will the filter be subjected? In an inlet line, pressures will be low; in a pressure-line, full system pressure.

2. **Filtration.** Usually expressed in terms of micrometre rating: namely the *smallest* particle which will *not* pass through the filter.

3. **Pressure drop.** This is a function of flow rate and filter micrometre rating size. It is also related to the service of the filter.

4. **Service life.** An index of how long a filter will operate before the element must be cleaned or changed.

5. **Piping.** What types of lines are used on both sides of the filter? What are the port sizes?

6. **Special features.** Some filters are equipped with built-in warning devices which signal when the filter element needs servicing. Some have integral pressure gages, others integral cleaning arrangements.

7. **Fluid compatibility**

8. **Cost**

HEAT EXCHANGERS

Heat exchangers cool the hydraulic fluid. There are two basic types: air-cooled and water-cooled. Because the subject of heat transfer is a specialized one, most circuit designers choose to purchase commercial heat exchangers rather than design and build their own. Refer to Chapter 18. Selection factors include:

1. **Pressure.** Most heat exchangers are installed in the return side of a circuit, where pressure is normally low. However, the system designer should know the maximum pressure level which might be expected to occur in the line.

2. **Capacity.** What is the rated flow capacity of the heat exchanger?

3. **Pressure drop.** What is the pressure drop across the heat exchanger at rated flow?

4. **Heat dissipating capability.** At what rate will the heat exchanger reduce the oil temperature in the system?

5. **Controls.** Sometimes thermostatic controls are used to maintain a constant temperature with varying load conditions.

6. **Piping and connections**
7. **Fluid compatibility**
8. **Cost**

[1]*Introduction to Fluid Mechanics,* Russ Henke, Addison-Wesley Publishing Co. See Appendix C for fluids data.
[2]Ibid, pp 141-142

Important Terms

Auxiliaries. Components belonging to the fourth functional section of fluid power systems. Auxiliary products do not participate in energy transfer or control functions; they may be considered passive components.

Conducting network. All components which interconnect active components, confine and transmit the fluid, and reduce and provide storage for excess or reserve fluid.

Conductor. Interconnecting component such as pipe, tubing or hose.

Compatibility. Characteristic of a component which enables it to perform properly in relation to other components in the system.

Dash number. A system for matching size of components in the conducting network.

Filter. A component designed to remove contaminants from a fluid.

Fitting. A component which interconnects conductors and/or other components in the fluid power system.

Fluid. The component which is the energy transfer medium in a fluid power system. It is a substance which cannot sustain a shear stress under equilibrium conditions.

Heat exchanger. A component designed to transfer heat into or out of the fluid in a fluid power system.

Hose. A flexible conductor capable of sustaining system pressure while bending or flexing.

Instruments. Family of components designed to measure the state of a system variable and provide a proportional output for data gathering or control purposes.

Pipe. A rigid conducting component produced in accordance with ANSI B36.10-1981. Pipe is sized on the basis of a schedule of nominal sizes specified in the standard.

Reservoir. A component which provides the storage capacity for excess or reserve fluid in the fluid power system.

Schedule. The system used to designate wall thicknesses of American standard pipe.

Tubing. A rigid conducting component produced in accordance with SAE J5256b, or equivalent. Tubing is sized on the basis of OD and wall thickness.

Review Exercises

25.1. What is meant by the term auxiliaries?

25.2. What is meant by the term *passive*? Discuss it in relationship to *active*.

25.3. What type of components are considered to be auxiliary components?

25.4. What is the conducting network? Of what components is it made up?

25.5. Discuss the functions of a reservoir.

25.6. What three categories of reservoirs are there? Discuss each.

25.7. Discuss the functional features of the ANSI reservoir illustrated in Fig. 25.2.

25.8. On what factor is the volume of the reservoir based?

25.9. Discuss location of the suction line in a reservoir.

25.10. Why must a return line terminate below fluid level in the reservoir?

25.11. How can a reservoir help de-aerate hydraulic fluid?

25.12. What is a baffle? What is/are its use(s) in a reservoir? Discuss baffling.

25.13. How should suction and return lines be located relative to baffles? Why?

25.14. Why must a reservoir incorporate a fluid level indicator?

25.15. What is the purpose of a breather in a reservoir?

25.16. Why is a reservoir sometimes pressurized? Discuss pressurization.

25.17. Is pressurizing a safety hazard? Discuss.

25.18. What is the function of a magnetic separator?

25.19. Why is it important to provide under clearance for a stationary reservoir?

25.20. Discuss the advantages and disadvantages of overhead reservoirs vs. ANSI reservoir.

25.21. What components make up the classification "conductors"?

25.22. What are the differences between pipe and tubing? How do they affect application in a system?

Is it possible to properly match pipe and tubing in a system? Discuss.

25.23. What is American standard pipe? Do other kinds of pipe exist? Discuss.

25.24. On what basis is American standard pipe dimensioned and how does this affect selection?

25.25. Discuss pipe "schedule" for American standard pipe.

25.26. What is the difference between working pressure and burst pressure?

25.27. Discuss water hammer. Why must it be considered in selecting conductors?

25.28. What is the dash- number system for matching conductors?

25.29. Can pipe fittings be used to connect tubing as well as pipe? Discuss.

25.30. What kinds of threads for fittings are there? Are they interchangeable? Discuss.

25.31. Are American standard threads and metric threads interchangeable? Discuss.

25.32. Is the ISO standard thread O- ring fitting interchangeable with the SAE O- ring standard thread fitting? Discuss.

25.33. What is hydraulic tubing? Are there differing standards for hydraulic tubing? Discuss.

25.34. How is tubing dimensioned? How does this compare to American standard pipe? Are there any matching dimensions between the two?

25.35. Does hydraulic tubing have working and burst pressure ratings?

25.36. What are the standard increments in size for hydraulic tubing?

25.37. Discuss how the dash- numbering system can be used to match tubing with other conductor components in the system.

25.38. Discuss "Severity of Service" considerations for selecting tubing.

25.39. Discuss selection of flow velocity for tubing.

25.40. What is a hose?

25.41. How does hose differ from tubing or pipe?

25.42. Is it feasible to connect hoses with pipe and/or tubing? If so, how? What precautions must be taken?

25.43. What is the primary reason for using hose in place of pipe or tubing? Are there other reasons? Discuss.

25.44. How does heat dissipating ability of hose compared with pipe or tubing? Does this affect design of the conducting system in any way? Discuss.

25.45. What standards primarily govern hose design and construction?

25.46. Does the dash- numbering system apply to hoses? How is it used to match hoses sizes to pipe and tubing?

25.47. Does hose construction affect selection for system application? Discuss.

25.48. What is "minimum bend radius"? How does it affect hose application?

25.49. Are hose fittings different in design or construction from pipe or tube fittings? Discuss.

25.50. Are there any problem areas connected with hose fittings which should be considered in the selection process? Discuss.

25.51. What types of hoses (in terms of rating) are there?

25.52. What is the difference between reusable and permanent hose fittings? Is there any difference in performance capability between the two types?

25.53. What is cubic expansion of a hose? How might it affect performance in a system? Can you do anything about it?

25.54. What effect on hose length might pressure- have? How does this affect application in an actual system?

25.55. What is an SAE split flange fitting? Why and when is it used?

25.56. What is an elbow fitting? When would it be used?

25.57. Discuss the selection factor hose compatibility with fluids and/or ambient environment.

25.58. What is a manifold? How is it used in a fluid power system? How would a manifold be matched to other conducting network components?

25.59. What is a fitting? How are they used in the conducting network?

25.60. Discuss how the dash numbering system applies to fittings.

25.61. What are the three broad groups of tube fittings? Discuss.

25.62. What are the most common causes of leakage in flared fittings?

25.63. Describe the alignment marks method of properly torquing a flared fitting nut.

25.64. What are the types of flareless fittings?

25.65. What is the area of greatest sensitivity during assembly of the flareless fittings? Discuss. Compare to 37 degree flared fitting.

25.66. Why is there such a wide variety of tube fittings available?

25.67. What advantage(s) are claimed for O-ring type tube fittings compared to flared or compression types?

25.68. What is a welded or brazed fitting. When would they be specified?

25.69. What is the significance of minimum/maximum tube wall thickness for various types of fittings and tube materials? How would it be used as a selection factor?

25.70. What is a quick acting fitting? When should it be considered for a system application?

25.71. Describe swivel couplings. When should swivel couplings be used in a system?

25.72. What is the primary function of a hydraulic fluid?

25.73. Why are there so many different kinds of hydraulic fluids?

25.74. Discuss what kinds of fluids are available for use in hydraulic systems.

25.75. What fluid properties are important in selecting a petroleum base fluid for an application?

25.76. Why is oil viscosity important? What effect does it have on a fluid's performance in a system?

25.77. What is viscosity index? Is it the same as viscosity? If not, how does it differ from viscosity? How is it used on a selection criterion?

25.78. Discuss pour point? How does it relate to viscosity? How is it used as a selection criterion?

25.79. What is compressibility of a fluid? Is it the same for hydraulic fluids as for pneumatic fluids? How does it affect fluid performance?

25.80. Why is fluid stability an important consideration?

25.81. What is the greatest single advantage of mineral oils over the other available types of fluids?

25.82. What is aeration? Discuss the effects of air on hydraulic fluids and on system performance.

25.83. Discuss materials compatibility and corrosion prevention as a selection criterion for fluids.

25.84. Why have high water content fluids become important in recent years?

25.85. What are the differences between water-in-oil and oil-in-water emulsion fluids? How do they affect selection?

25.86. What is a water-glycol fluid? How does it compare to the emulsion type water-base fluids? Are they interchangeable?

25.87. Discuss synthetic fluids. What is the principal deterent to wider use of synthetics?

25.88. What is a HWCF? Why is there such great interest in high water content fluids at this time?

25.89. Discuss the implications of mandated use of HWCF on component design and performance.

25.90. What factors must be taken into consideration in applying 95-5 HWCF in a system? Discuss. 25.91. What is reprocessed oil? Discuss the use of it in a hydraulic system.

25.92. discuss general selection criteria for hydraulic filters.

25.93. Discuss general selection criteria for heat exchangers.

25.94. Discuss selection of electrical controls for a fluid power system.

25.95. What is an instrument? Discuss general selection criteria for a fluid power system.

CHAPTER 26

TROUBLESHOOTING
FLUID POWER SYSTEMS

Just as design is the first step in producing a reliable fluid power system, troubleshooting is the last. Chapter 1 characterized design as the synthesis of a hydraulic system by the deductive process. Troubleshooting uses analysis of an existing system to diagnose the causes of system malfunction.

Figure 26.1 illustrates an important concept relating these two processes — they are inversions of one another. In the case of **design,** the designer started with a definition of tasks in the form of *Cycle*

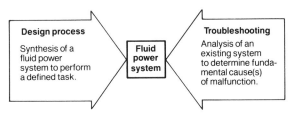

Fig. 26.1. Superior fluid power systems require two parallel processes: design and troubleshooting.

Profile, Chapters 3, 4, and 5. He then synthesized a solution to the problem by starting at the load and working back through the energy output elements, the energy control and input elements, to the machine's energy source. This process yielded a hydraulic system which would perform a defined task.

When **troubleshooting,** the technician starts with an inoperable hydraulic system and attempts to diagnose and locate the cause(s) of malfunction. The mental processes used in design are the same for troubleshooting.

Troubleshooting method

Before discussing a methodical approach to troubleshooting, a distinction must be made between maintenance and troubleshooting.

Maintenance is a mechanical procedure, *i.e.* the repair or replacement of damaged or warn com-

ponents. For instance, maintenance could involve replacing seals, broken hoses, broken shafts, buckled cylinder rods, collapsed or clogged filter elements. While **troubleshooting** often leads to maintenance or changes in maintenance practices, maintenance does not replace troubleshooting.

Having made this important distinction, let us analyze the troubleshooting process.

Step 1. Energy transmission system. This is neither a plumbing nor mass transfer system. Refer to Chapter 1. Figure 26.2 summarizes a fluid power Energy Transmission System, (ETS).

Step 2. Functional sections. Since troubleshooting is an inversion of the design procedure, the system can be divided into its functional sections, Figure 26.3. Each active section has two input and two output variables. In addition to input/output variables, each active section *and* most of the passive section components — *i.e.* auxiliaries — include energy losses which must be accounted for. These are symbolized by q in Figure 26.3. Individual losses have been discussed in various chapters describing the design process.

Step 3. Diagnostic troubleshooting. This process starts at the *output* end of the system because discrepancies in the machine cycle are the first indicators of system malfunction. Also, the interface

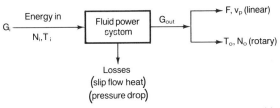

Fig. 26.2. When troubleshooting a hydraulic system, consider the entire circuit.

between hydraulic system output and load may be the only point where physical measurements can be made in the field, Figure 26.4.

Successful diagnosis of machine malfunctions requires that the technician understand and be familiar with the functions and proper operation of the machine. Without this knowledge, successful troubleshooting is virtually impossible.

The *Cycle Profile*, Chapters 3, 4, and 5 provides the best definition of a machine cycle. It is not only a valuable design tool, but one which is essential to intelligent troubleshooting. It is the author's opinion that machine manufacturers should be *required* to include both the *Cycle Profile* and *Sequence Diagram* in the installation, operation, and troubleshooting manuals shipped with all machines. Without this information, the troubleshooter has no starting point.

Step 4. Variable outputs. If the output device is a cylinder, output variables are:
- piston rod velocity, v_p, which is equal to load velocity, and
- load reaction, F_L. Refer to Chapters 4 and 5.

Step 5. How a cylinder overcomes load resistance. Pressure is proportional to load reaction

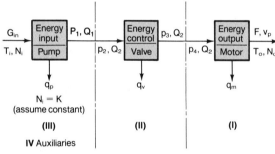

Fig. 26.3. After considering the entire circuit, check major points for performance.

and $F_L = \Delta p \cdot \Delta A_p$ is the form commonly used to express the algebraic relationship. However, in fact, pressure is a function of load reaction.

Some designers refer to the *output force* capability of an actuator. This is an incorrect and misleading term because an actuator has *no* output force. It only has the capability to sustain a load reaction. The magnitude of the load reaction, when distributed over the area of the piston, yields the unit force called *pressure*. Thus,

$$\Delta p = F_L/\Delta A_p.$$

The pressure and area terms are shown as differences (preceded by a Δ) to emphasize two points:
1. There may be backpressure which will add to input pressure, and
2. Unless a double rod end cylinder is used, there is an area differential from one side of the piston to the other which must also be considered, Figure 26.4.

When troubleshooting a hydraulic system, it is important to use pressures at the exact points being investigated. Thus p_4, Figure 26.4, must be measured at the inlet to the cylinder port. Frequently, the only pressure gage on a machine is at the discharge port of the pump, forcing the troubleshooter to use pump discharge pressure to diagnose the performance of an actuator.

That such a procedure can introduce significant errors is implicit in Figure 1.4, which shows the effect of losses throughout a system. In critical situations, where downtime costs are significant, it is economically sound to locate test fittings at the inlet *and* outlet ports of all active components.

In many applications, it may be difficult to measure load reaction F_L. The troubleshooter may have to rely on pressure measurements, the cylinder's actual or estimated mechanical efficiency, and calculated values of F_L to determine the cylinder's output.

Step 6. How a cylinder delivers required load ve-

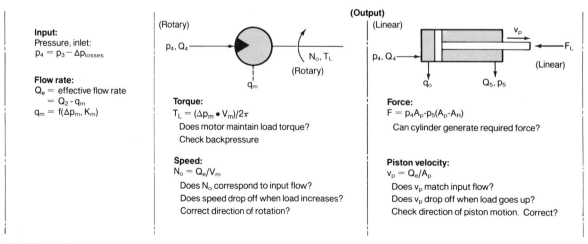

Fig. 26.4. After checking major points, check individual components for performance.

locity. The designer selected parameters to insure that the required load velocities would be attained; the troubleshooter must establish that they are. Load velocity is equal or proportional to cylinder piston rod velocity:

$$v_p = Q_e/A_p,$$

in which Q_e was defined as the effective flow rate, namely $Q_2 - q_p$, which is flow from the motor port of the control valve less cylinder slip.

Internal leakage in a cylinder generally equals the flow bypassing the cylinder's piston seals. When a cylinder is retracting, slip could also include excessive leakage at the piston rod gland seal. Piston rod velocity is one variable which the troubleshooter can check directly. The cylinder stroke can also be measured, while making absolutely certain that safety precautions are followed. The troubleshooter can also time the cylinder stroke,

$$v_p = S/t_s.$$

Working back through the velocity equation, Q_e can be calculated and compared to specified pump outputs. The troubleshooter should observe piston rod velocity as the load increases. Any significant deceleration would indicate that fluid is bypassing somewhere in the system.

To check the cylinder for internal leakage, remove the connection to the return port, block the load to keep the piston rod from moving, and measure any flow from the return port. Any such flow would be due to internal leakage in the cylinder. The procedure can be repeated for various strokes to establish whether slip is position-sensitive.

This discussion emphasizes that load reaction, F_L, is the *independent* variable and pressure the *dependent* variable in the force, area, pressure equation. On the other hand, flow rate Q_4 is the *independent* variable, and piston rod velocity, v_p, is the *dependent* variable in the flow, area, velocity equation.

In Chapter 1, it was stated that flow rate and pressure are essentially independent of one another. The two fundamental equations for hydraulic systems,

$$F = pA_p, \text{ and}$$
$$Q = Av_p$$

demonstrate this fact. The only parameter common to both equations is piston area, which is constant for any given cylinder. The fact that pressure and flow-rate related phenomena can be evaluated independently simplifies the troubleshooter's task.

Step 7. Available outputs. If the output component is a rotary motor, available outputs are, 1) motor shaft speed, N_o = load speed, and 2) load torque reaction, T_L. Refer to Chapters 4 and 5.

Step 8. How a motor overcomes load-torque reac-

tion. This question is similar to that in Step 5. In hydraulic motors, pressure is proportional to torque reaction. The equation

$$T_L = \Delta p \cdot V_m/2\pi$$

expresses algebraically the relationship between motor variables. As in the case of linear actuators, Figure 26.4, pressure is a function of load torque, not vice versa. In hydraulic motors,

$$\Delta p = p_{\text{in}} - p_{\text{out}},$$

and there are no displacement differentials to consider.

Torque measuring instruments are extremely difficult to use in the field. For this reason the troubleshooter may have to rely on *pressure differential*, motor displacement, and mechanical efficiency data to estimate load reaction torque. Another approach, if the application permits, is to apply calibrated test weights to produce a load torque at the motor shaft.

Step 9. How a motor drives a load at required speed. This question is similar to that in Step 6. Load velocity is equal or proportional to motor shaft speed,

$$N_o = Q_e/V_m.$$

Q_e is the effective flow rate, that is

$$Q_e = Q_2 - q_m, \text{ Refer to Figure 16.8.}$$

If the hydraulic motor is drained externally, the troubleshooter could tap into the drain line and actually measure case drain flow, q_m.

On the other hand, the system designer might plan on providing additional flow to offset motor slip with

$$Q_2 = Q_t + q_m.$$

A key point, when troubleshooting a fluid motor, is to watch for a drop in output speed, N_o, as load increases. Such a speed reduction would signal that fluid is bypassing somewhere in the system.

Step 10. Moving the load in the right direction. This becomes a matter of prime importance in troubleshooting, especially where conductors are disconnected and reconnected at directional controls or output devices. Should lines be inadvertently cross-connected, direction of motion of the output devices could be reversed and result in a serious accident.

Step 11. Inputs to actuators. Pressures and flow rates are the hydraulic inputs to energy output components. Input pressure is

$$p_4 = p_3 - \Delta p_{\text{losses}},$$

where p_3 is the fluid pressure at the control valve port, and Δp is the sum of the pressure drops between the control valve and the output component. Refer to Figure 1.4.

From the design and troubleshooting viewpoints, the more important form is

$$p_3 = p_4 + \Delta p_{losses,}$$

because $p_4 \propto$ to the load. Input flow rate $Q_m = Q_2$, where Q_2 is flow from the directional control valve. Remember, however, that it is the effective flow, $Q_e = Q_2 - q_m$, which actually determines load speed. Refer to Figure 16.8.

Step 12. Functional controls. Controls must be defined before pump(s) can be sized and specified, Figure 26.5.

As discussed in Chapter 16, pumps and motors are functional inversions of one another; structurally, they are very similar. Many designers consider pump and motors to be the most vulnerable components in a system. Figure 26.6 shows the analysis of a fixed displacement pump.

Step 13. Pump discharge pressure. Discharge pressure at the pump is the algebraic sum of all the pressure differentials throughout the system, see Figure 1.4:

$$p_1 = p_4 + \Sigma \Delta p_{losses}.$$

The troubleshooter must determine, 1) what p_1 is, and 2) whether p_1 is at design level. Generally, placing a pressure gage at the pump discharge port will provide this information. However, there may possibly be a problem with the pressure gage, especially if it has been in service for a long time.

To maintain a reasonable degree of accuracy, pressure gages must be recalibrated continuously against an established, known standard. The reliable troubleshooter will always make certain that the gages he uses will have been recalibrated recently and are trustworthy before setting out on an assignment.

A key element to consider in checking a pump is whether it can achieve and maintain design system pressure, p_{1max}. *Failure to pass this test may indicate a damaged or worn pump.*

Step 14. Pump delivery. From a design standpoint, pump output should equal:
- the sum of all *simultaneous* branch flows, as determined in Steps 9 and 10. Refer to Figure 3.7.
- all control flows required, and

Next, the controls (II)

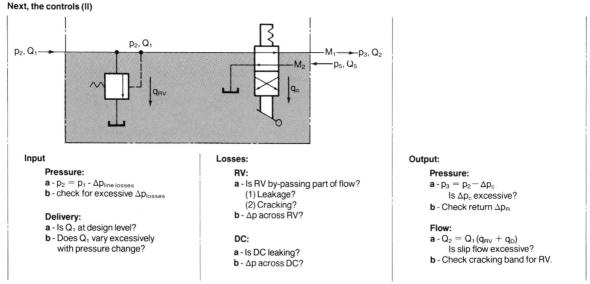

Input

Pressure:
a - $p_2 = p_1 - \Delta p_{line\ losses}$
b - check for excessive Δp_{losses}

Delivery:
a - Is Q_1 at design level?
b - Does Q_1 vary excessively with pressure change?

Losses:

RV:
a - Is RV by-passing part of flow?
  (1) Leakage?
  (2) Cracking?
b - Δp across RV?

DC:
a - Is DC leaking?
b - Δp across DC?

Output:

Pressure:
a - $p_3 = p_2 - \Delta p_c$
  Is Δp_c excessive?
b - Check return Δp_R

Flow:
a - $Q_2 = Q_1 (q_{RV} + q_D)$
  Is slip flow excessive?
b - Check cracking band for RV.

Fig. 26.5. Follow this procedure to check controls.

Next, the pump (III)

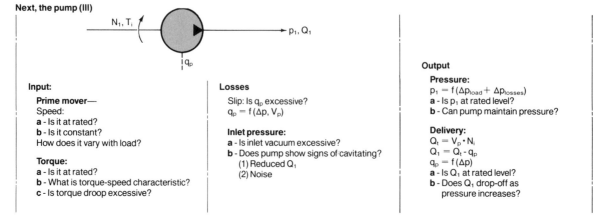

Input:

Prime mover—
Speed:
a - Is it at rated?
b - Is it constant?
How does it vary with load?

Torque:
a - Is it at rated?
b - What is torque-speed characteristic?
c - Is torque droop excessive?

Losses

Slip: Is q_p excessive?
$q_p = f(\Delta p, V_p)$

Inlet pressure:
a - Is inlet vacuum excessive?
b - Does pump show signs of cavitating?
  (1) Reduced Q_1
  (2) Noise

Output

Pressure:
$p_1 = f(\Delta p_{load} + \Delta p_{losses})$
a - Is p_1 at rated level?
b - Can pump maintain pressure?

Delivery:
$Q_t = V_p \cdot N_i$
$Q_1 = Q_t - q_p$
$q_p = f(\Delta p)$
a - Is Q_1 at rated level?
b - Does Q_1 drop-off as pressure increases?

Fig. 26.6. Follow this procedure to check pump.

● unavoidable leakages:

$$Q_1 = \Sigma Q_L + \Sigma Q_c + \Sigma q_i.$$

In the example in Figure 26.6,

$$Q_1 = Q_2 + q_v = (V_p N_i - q_p) + q_v.$$

When troubleshooting the pump, it must be determined whether Q_1 is at design flow rate. A flow meter might measure flow rate directly.

In Step 9, an analog approach was used — that of determining output speed and calculating input flow to the actuator. If a flow meter is available to measure actual pump output, Q_1, it can be compared to Q_2, the calculated input to the actuator as an added diagnostic tool.

Figure 26.6 summarizes the relationship between theoretical flow rate, Q_{t1} and actual delivery Q_1. The difference,

$$q_p = Q_t - Q_1,$$

which equals pump slip, can be measured, as outlined in Step 9, if the pump is drained externally. If slip flow is excessive, it is a sure sign of a worn or damaged pump.

Step 15. Pump inlet conditions. Troubleshooters must be particularly aware of the effects poor inlet conditions can have on pumps.

Figure 26.7 illustrates an equivalent inlet circuit for a pump connected to a reservoir open to atmospheric pressure,[1] (open circuit of Chapter 16). Energy available to introduce fluid into a pump is derived entirely from atmospheric pressure head.

Force to overcome all the inlet pressure drops through piping, fittings, filters and strainers must be supplied by atmospheric pressure head, as must the suction lift Z_o. In addition, the velocity head (kinetic energy of fluid flowing in the inlet system) must also be supplied.

When petroleum base fluid is used in a system, suction lift can be negative, Figure 26.7. When high water content fluids (HWCF) are used, recommended practice calls for a *positive* head at the pump inlet port. Refer to Chapter 25.

Allowable inlet vacuums are much lower than would be available with a hard vacuum because of the changes in saturation of dissolved air in the fluid with reductions in pressure. Excessive inlet vacuums result in air coming out of solution, a phenomenon which contributes to pump cavitation.

Another factor contributing to cavitation is excessive velocities in pump inlet lines. Inlet flow velocity is one of the major limitations on pump speed, N_i. Because of excessive pump speeds, the fluid entering the inlet side of the pump cannot keep up with that

---

1. For a detailed discussion of fluid mechanics involved, see *Introduction to Fluid Mechanics,* Russell W. Henke, P.E., Addison-Wesley Publishing Co., Reading, MA 1970.

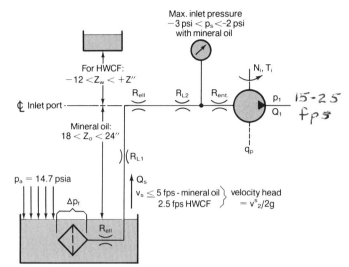

Fig. 26.7. Equivalent inlet circuit for pump connected to reservoir exposed to atmospheric pressure.

exiting on the output side. The result is cavitation. Still another potential contributor to cavitation is associated with changing fluids in an existing system. Assume you want to switch a system designed to operate on petroleum base oil, to run on high water content or synthetic fluid, see Chapter 25.

Other than seal compatibility, the higher density fire-resistant fluids are apt to create pump cavitation which did not occur when the system was operating on lower density petroleum base oils. Some pump manufacturers consider pump cavitation as more damaging to pumps than contamination. *Never starve the pump.*

Step 16. Remember the prime mover. Figure 26.6 summarizes pump input characteristics: speed, N_i and torque, T_i. Remember that these are functions of the prime mover. Refer to Figure 16.4. Unhappily, the hydraulic system is often blamed for (and dismantled) for malfunctions which are ultimately traced to the prime mover. If speed, N_i is below or above rated speed, output flow, Q_1 will not be at rated flow. If

$$T_i < p_1(V_p/2\pi),$$

the pump will be unable to meet system demands. The prime mover's torque-speed curve is the key.

A typical T-N_i curve for an electric motor is shown in Figure 26.8 (a) and for a diesel engine in Figure 26.8(b). Information on prime mover speed characteristics should be included in the machine's installation, operator, and service manuals. The hydraulic system trouble shooter should have access to a copy.

Torque/speed curves show that as the prime mover becomes loaded, it slows down. This characteristic is called *lugging.* Unless something is drastically wrong with the electrical system, electric motors normally experience a relatively small speed droop as load or torque increases.

Internal combustion engines, on the other hand, exhibit more pronounced lugging, particularly diesel engines. When engines become overloaded, the change in their output speeds may be substantial enough to affect pump output. Reduced pump delivery might be a primary indication (short of stalling) that the engine is not functioning properly.

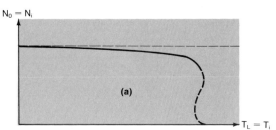

Torque-speed curve for an electric motor prime mover

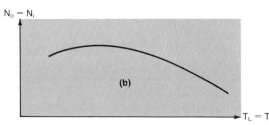

Torque-speed curve for an internal combusion engine prime mover

Fig. 26.8. Torque-speed curves for (a) electric prime mover, (b) internal combustion prime mover.

Step 17. Variable vs fixed displacement pumps. The primary differences, Figure 26.9, relate to variability of pump displacement:

$$0 < Q_1 < Q_{max}, \text{and}$$
$$p_1 = p_4 + \Sigma p_{losses,}$$

as before. Now, however,

$$\Sigma \Delta p_{losses} = f(0 < Q_1 < Q_{max}).$$

Other than accounting for displacement at any operating point, the questions to be answered are the same as when dealing with fixed-displacement pumps.

Step 18. Controls — functional section II. As noted in Step 11, the logical sequence of circuit design would call for controls to be discussed right after output devices. We arbitrarily deferred this discussion to this point.

Figure 26.5 illustrates a simplified control package with one directional and one pressure-control valve. As the functional controls become more complex, the basic technique must be extrapolated to cover additional functions. When multi-branched systems are involved, this technique must first be applied to each branch, then superimposed for the entire system.

Step 19. Directional control valves. To accommodate the 4-way directional control valve shown in Figure 26.5, variables must be specified for both load ports. Output variables at the supply port are:

$$p_3 = p_2 - \Sigma \Delta p_c,$$

or supply pressure, p_2, less the pressure drops through the control valve. See Figure 24.3 for information on Q vs Δp_c; and flow rate

$$Q_2 = Q_1 - (q_{RV} + q_o),$$

or supply flow Q_1 less leakage in the relief valve and leakage in the directional control valve. Refer to Chapter 8 for a discussion of bypass flow in relief valves, particularly as it relates to the cracking band. Also refer to Chapter 24 for information on directional control valve leakage characteristics.

Troubleshooters frequently tend to overlook return port variables. Backpressure at the return port is given by

$$p_5 \propto f(Q_5^2)$$

where, Q_5 is the return flow from the output device. Refer to Figure 24.3. Designers must also remember that Q_5 is not equal to Q_2 when a differential cylinder is used. When a hydraulic *motor* is involved,

$$Q_5 = Q_2 - q_m,$$

When a *cylinder* is involved,

$$Q_5 = Q_2 [A_1/(A_1 - A_r)].$$

What if the pump is variable displacement?

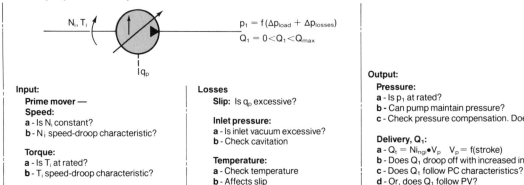

Fig. 26.9. Procedure for checking variable displacement pump.

For high area ratio cylinders, $Q_5 \gg Q_2$ and p_5 can be high, sometimes high enough to cause system malfunction.

For example, in open-center spool-type directional control valves, Bernoulli's jet forces (see Chapter 27) can be so high under conditions of high Q_5 that centering springs cannot shift the spool to neutral. In some closed-center spool valves, the opposite can occur. If the troubleshooter is unaware of these facts, diagnosing such malfunctions is almost impossible.

Crossport leakage in directional control valves is not well understood. All spool-type directional control valves experience some crossport leakage because of the high pressure-differentials from either a supply or load port to a reservoir port, and clearances between the spool and bore. Crossport leakage can be neglected during normal valve operation unless the valve is worn or has been damaged.

However, when a suspended load must be held in place over a long period of time, crossport leakage will result in load drift.

Step 20. Pressure control valves. In Chapter 8, we described how relief valves bypass as they operate in the valve's cracking band. The troubleshooter must understand quiescent control flows in pressure-reducing valves and special characteristics of other types of pressure and flow controls, Chapters 8 and 10. Such controls may also exhibit leakage flows caused by wear or damaged to ports, plugged control orifices, broken springs, etc.

When it comes to troubleshooting control valves, there is no substitute for thorough knowledge and understanding of how they function. When controls are disassembled for inspection and/or repair, it is *imperative* that they be re-assembled properly. While this may seem obvious (as well it should be), it is easy to inadvertently rotate a valve cover, insert a valve spool backwards, omit a seal, etc. and completely alter a valve's characteristics without realizing it.

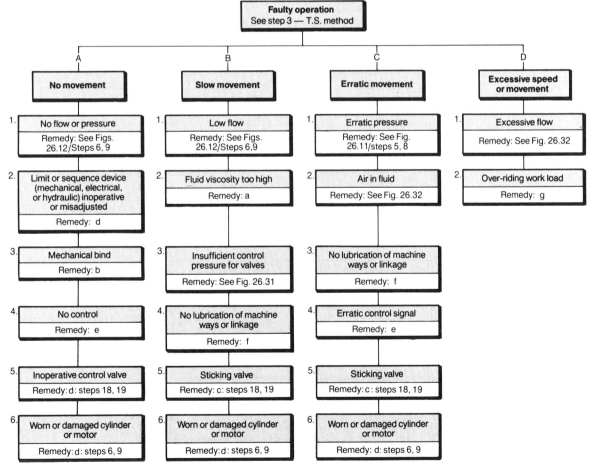

Remedies:
a. Fluid may be too cold or should be changed to clean fluid of correct viscosity, Ref. Chapter 25.
b. Locate bind and repair
c. Clean and adjust or replace — Check condition of system fluid and filters, Ref. chapters 8, 10, 12, 24.

d. Overhaul or replace, Ref. chapter 23
e. Repair control console or interconnecting wires
f. Lubricate
g. Adjust, repair, or replace counterbalance valve. Ref. chapter 8, 24.

Fig. 26.10. Typical malfunctions related to load variables.

Step 21. Inputs to functional section II. Controls include supply pressure

$$p_2 = p_1 - \Delta p_{losses},$$

and supply flow rate, $Q_2 = Q_1$. These variables are essentially the same as delivery characteristics for functional section III energy input. Refer to Figure 1.4.

The preceding steps outline a logical diagnostic procedure for troubleshooting a hydraulic system. The procedure parallels this underlying philosophy:
• the ability to either design or troubleshoot a hydraulic system is predicated on a thorough definition of the load cycle for the machine, and
• any fluid power problem can be handled more readily and efficiently if subdivided into functional sections which can then be considered and analyzed sequentially.

THE TROUBLESHOOTER'S "COOKBOOK"

Maintenance and troubleshooting information is traditionally presented in cause-and-effects tables and/or diagrams. This method is sometimes referred to as a "cookbook" approach. Some of the information is presented here to correlate it with the methodology discussed earlier in this chapter.

Figure 26.10 summarizes some of the primary malfunctions related to load variables and typical causes. References are given to steps in the troubleshooting method and other chapters in this book, detailing specific components or fundamentals relating to the problem area.

Figure 26.11 summarizes typical and malfunctions and causes involving *pressure* variables. Figure 26.12 considers flow variables.

These tables are followed by a series of cause-and-effect troubleshooting charts, typical of those used by the fluid power industry.

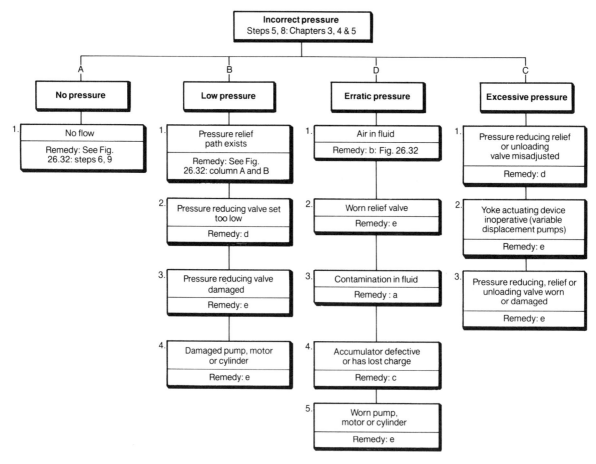

Remedies:
a. Replace dirty filters and system fluid, Ref. Chapters 20 and 25.
b. Tighten leaky connections (fill reservoir to proper level and bleed air from system). Ref. Chapter 25.
c. Check gas valve for leakage — charge to correct pressure — overhaul if defective.

d. Adjust. Ref. Chapters 8 and 24.
e. Overhaul or replace. Ref. Chapters 8 and 24.

Fig. 26.11. Typical malfunctions related to pressure variables.

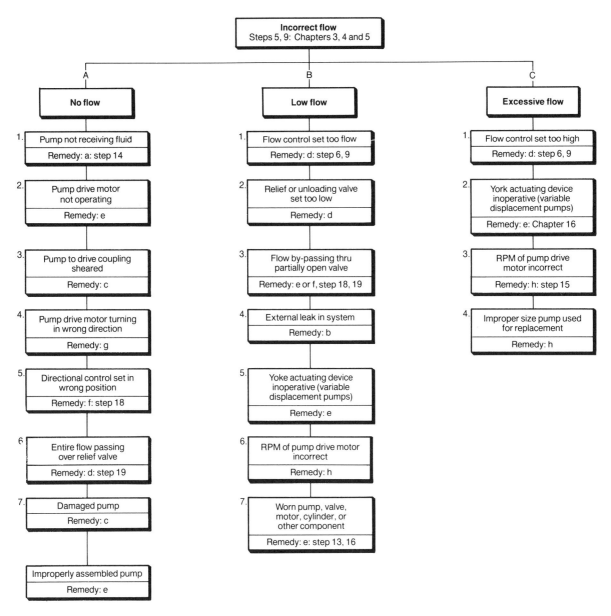

Incorrect flow
Steps 5, 9: Chapters 3, 4 and 5

A

No flow

1. Pump not receiving fluid
   Remedy: a: step 14

2. Pump drive motor
   not operating
   Remedy: e

3. Pump to drive coupling
   sheared
   Remedy: c

4. Pump drive motor turning
   in wrong direction
   Remedy: g

5. Directional control set in
   wrong position
   Remedy: f: step 18

6. Entire flow passing
   over relief valve
   Remedy: d: step 19

7. Damaged pump
   Remedy: c

Improperly assembled pump
Remedy: e

B

Low flow

1. Flow control set too flow
   Remedy: d: step 6, 9

2. Relief or unloading valve
   set too low
   Remedy: d

3. Flow by-passing thru
   partially open valve
   Remedy: e or f, step 18, 19

4. External leak in system
   Remedy: b

5. Yoke actuating device
   inoperative (variable
   displacement pumps)
   Remedy: e

6. RPM of pump drive motor
   incorrect
   Remedy: h

7. Worn pump, valve,
   motor, cylinder, or
   other component
   Remedy: e: step 13, 16

C

Excessive flow

1. Flow control set too high
   Remedy: d: step 6, 9

2. York actuating device
   inoperative (variable
   displacement pumps)
   Remedy: e: Chapter 16

3. RPM of pump drive
   motor incorrect
   Remedy: h: step 15

4. Improper size pump used
   for replacement
   Remedy: h

Remedies:
a. Any or all of the following: replace dirty filters — clean clogged inlet line — clean reservoir breather vent — fill reservoir to proper level — overhaul or replace supercharge pump. Ref. Fig. 26.7, step 14.
b. Tighten leaky connections — bleed air from system. Ref. Chapter 25; Leakage control, Chapter 26.
c. Check for damaged pump or pump drive — replace and align coupling.

d. Adjust. Ref. Chapter 8.
e. Overhaul or replace. Ref. Chapter 23.
f. Check position of manually operated controls — check electrical circuit on solenoid operated controls — repair or replace pilot pressure pump. Chapter 24.
g. Reverse rotation.
h. Replace with correct unit. Ref. Chapter 23.

Fig. 26.12. Typical malfunctions related to flow variables.

Trouble Shooting

Hydraulic System Problems

Trouble	Cause	Remedy	References
No flow or motors fail to turn when operated correctly	1. No oil in system-reservoir	Fill/refill	Steps 6, 9 Chapter 25
	2. Wrong prime mover direction	Correct	
	3. Broken coupling (or insert)	Repair/replace	
	4. Broken coupling key	Replace	Chapters 8, 9
	5. Unloading or relieving valve open	Correct	
	6. Pressure line blockage	Free line	Chapter 25
	7. Pump problem	Check pump	Chapters 16, 23
	8. Actuator malfunction	Check actuator	Chapter 23
	9. Suction line restriction or disconnected	Correct	Step 14, Fig. 26.7
	10. Piping error/s	Check against circuit drawing	Chapter 25
	11. Actuator directional control malfunction	Check directional valve	
Progressively disconnect fittings or test points to verify existence of flow. Rule: Pumps pump flow only, systems and their loads-resistances produce pressure, up to that limit imposed by lowest pressure limiting device exposed to pressure.			Troubleshooting Method, Chapter 26
No pressure or too low a pressure	1. No oil system-reservoir	Fill/refill	Steps 5, 8
	2. Broken or defective pressure gage	Replace	Chapter 25
	3. Unloading valve or relief stuck open	Correct	Chapter 8
	4. Compensator stuck or too low	Check pump	Chapter 16
	5. Excessive leakage	Find source & correct or go through component	
	6. Pressure limiter set too low	Readjust	Chapter 16
Progressively test circuit points to determine pressure existence.			Troubleshooting Method, Chapter 26
Too high flow	1. Pump size incorrect	Correct	Steps 5, 9
	2. Pump speed too fast	Correct	Chapter 25
	3. Improper or lack of flow control	Correct or add	Chapter 25
	4. Incorrect means of finding flow	Check components displacements or instruments	Chapters 10, 11
	5. Too many pumps on line	Check circuit	Steps 5, 9
Too high pressure	1. Pressure limiter set too high	Readjust	Chapters 16, 25
	2. Causing motor (electric) overload	Check requirements	
	3. Prime mover too small	Same	
Once problem area has been defined and pinpointed, go to component section for specific symptom and cure.			Troubleshooting Method, Chapter 26

Hydraulic Motors—Energy Output, Section 1

Motor turning in wrong direction	1. Piping between control valve and motor is incorrect	Check manufacturers literature and circuit to determine correct piping.	Step 19 Troubleshooting Method, Chapter 26
Motor not turning over or not developing proper speed or torque	1. Driven mechanism binding because of misalignment	Remove motor & check torque requirement of driven shaft.	
	2. Free recirculation of oil to reservoir	Check circuit, valving & valve position.	Chapters 8, 9, 10, 11

Hydraulic Motors—Energy Output, Section 1 *(continued)*

Trouble	Cause	Remedy	References
	3. Sticky relief valve (open)	Remove dirt from under pressure adjustment ball or piston.	Chapter 8
	4. Motor yoke not set at proper angle (on adjustable motors)	Set hand wheel to proper pump yoke angle.	Chapter 16
	5. Setting overload relief valve not high enough	Check system pressure & reset relief valve	Chapter 8
	6. Pump not delivering sufficient pressure or volume	Check pump delivery, pressure and motor speed.	Step 12 Troubleshooting Method
	7. Motor mechanism mechanically bound	Remove stoppage or reshim if applicable.	
External oil leakage from motor	1. Gaskets leaking (may be due to reservoir drain not being connected if this is required).	Replace. (If drain line required it must be piped directly to reservoir.)	
Will not hold load	1. No external brake	Hydraulic motors have inherent internal leakage. An external brake should be considered.	Chapter 23
	2. External brake not holding	Check for causes of brake slipping or other malfunction.	

Cylinders—Energy Output, Section 1

Trouble	Cause	Remedy	References
Erratic action	1. Valves sticking or binding	Check for dirt or gummy deposit. Check for contamination of oil. Check for air in system. Check for worn parts. Excessive wear may be due to oil contamination.	Chapter 20
	2. Cylinder sticking or binding	Check for dirt, gummy deposits or air leaks as above. Check for misalignment, worn parts or defective seals.	Chapter 23
	3. Sluggish operation during warm-up period	Viscosity of oil too high or pour point too high at starting temperature. Change to oil with lower viscosity or better viscosity index and lower pour point. An immersion heater placed in the oil may help under severe cold conditions.	Chapter 25
	4. Pilot control pressure too low	Control line may be too small, or metering choke valve not working properly.	Chapter 8
	5. Internal leakage in cylinder	Repair or replace worn parts and loose packing. Check oil to see that viscosity is not too low. Check for excessive contamination or wear.	Step 6
	6. Air in system	Bleed air and check for leaks. Check to see that oil intake is well below surface of oil in reservoir. Check pump packings and line connections on intake side by pouring hydraulic oil over suspected leak. If noise stops, the leak has been located. Tighten joints or change seals or gaskets where necessary.	Chapters 19, 25

Pressure Control Valves — Energy control, Section II

Trouble	Cause	Remedy	References
Reduced pressure too high	1. Incorrect setting 2. Stuck spool 3. Gage broken or inaccurate	Adjust setting at valve Clean valve Replace gage	Chapters 8, 9, 25

Pressure Control Valves—Energy control, Section II *(continued)*

Trouble	Cause	Remedy	References
Reduced pressure	1. Pump pressure too low 2. Main valve setting too low 3. Vent relief setting too low	Check relief or compensator Adjust Adjust vent relief	Chapters 16, 23 Chapters 8, 9 Chapters 8, 9
System excessively hot	1. Excessive slip oil	Check clearances and orifice size of pilot section. Consider control power losses.	Chapter 8

Valves — Directional Control — Energy Control, Section II

Trouble	Cause	Remedy	References
Valve spool fails to move	1. Solenoids inoperative	Check electrical supply for over/under voltage or solenoid burnout.	Chapters 9, 11, 12, 13
	2. No pilot pressure	Check source of pilot pressure.	
	3. Blocked pilot drain	Check plugs, dirt fittings & lines.	
	4. Dirty	Disassemble, clean & flush	Chapter 20
	5. Improper reassembly after overhaul.	Review parts drawing for proper assembly.	
	6. Distortion	Align body & piping to remove strains, check bolt down torque.	
	7. Manufacturing burr	Remove spool, check spool & bore.	Chapter 24
	8. Silted	Remove spool & clean with emery paper. Be sure to clean.	Chapter 20
Valve spool response sluggish	1. Startup oil viscosity too high	Change oil, use tank heater or run pump for oil warmup.	Chapter 25
	2. Restricted drain	Small drain fittings or pipe.	
	3. Distortion valve body	Align body piping to remove strains. Check bolt down torque.	
	4. Malfunctions of solenoids	Check for proper source voltage & frequency. Remove solenoid & check fields, look for double solenoid energization.	
	5. Dirt in system	Drain & flush system. Tear down & clean, if required.	Chapter 20
	6. Pilot pressure low	Check pilot pressure source.	
Valve produces undesired response in work unit	1. Improper installation connections	Check drawings for piping & energization.	Chapter 13
	2. Improper assembly of valves	Compare drawings & parts.	Step 19
	3. Spool end for end	Reverse spool.	Step 19

Check Valves — Energy Control, Section II

Trouble	Cause	Remedy	References
Flow stoppage	1. Valve installed backwards or free flow arrow has incorrect direction	Correct installation	
	2. Parts broken	Disassembly & check	
	3. Pump not pumping	See pump section	
Incorrect pressure drop	1. Valve too small	Change valve	
	2. Incorrect spring (in the case of pilot pressure relief)	Correct	
Fails to hold pressure	1. Seat is damaged (shock)	Change seat or to correct seat type, eliminate cause of damage.	
	2. Seat is "wiredrawn"	Change to larger size.	
	3. Excessive leakage in held component	See component section.	

Relief Valves — Energy Control, Section II

Trouble	Cause	Remedy	References
Lack of pressure	1. Valve stuck open 2. Pump not pumping 3. Incorrect setting or broken spring	Free ball or spool. See pump section. Readjust or replace.	
Pressure not adjustable	1. Spool stuck open 2. Some other relief valve set lower	Free spool. Check other relief valve seeing same pressure.	
Pressure too high	1. Spool stuck closed 2. Incorrect reference pressure 3. Drain line plugged (internal)	Free spool. Check line restrictions. Check valve.	
Valve too slow to open	1. Wrong relief valve type	Change to faster acting type.	
Valve noisy or erratic performance	1. Incorrect design 2. Reseat pressure too low 3. Dirty valve 4. Air in system	Correct type. Change valve type. Clean. Remove cause.	

Pumps — Energy Input, Section III

Trouble	Cause	Remedy	References
Excessive pump noise	1. Pump-motor coupling misalignment	Re-align pump & motor accurately. Align to within .005″ total indicator reading.	Chapter 19
	2. Oil level low	Fill reservoir so that surface of oil well above end of suction line during all of work cycle. About 1½ pipe diameters minimum.	Chapter 25
	3. Pump running too fast	Reduce speed. Speeds above rating are harmful & cause early failure of pumps. Refer to pump rating for maximum speed.	Chapter 19
	4. Wrong type of oil	Use a good, clean hydraulic oil having the viscosity in accordance with manufacturer's recommendations. Anti-foaming additives preferred.	Chapters 19, 25
	5. Air leak in suction line Air leak in case drain line Air leak around shaft packing	Pour hydraulic oil on joints & around shaft while listening for change in sound of operation. Tighten or replace.	Chapter 25
Excessive pump noise	6. Direction of pump rotation not correct.	Arrow on pump case must agree with direction of rotation.	
	7. Reservoirs not vented	Allow reservoir to breathe so oil level may fluctuate as required.	
	8. Air bound pump.	Air is locked in pumping chamber & has no way of escape. Stop pressure line or install special by-pass line back to tank so that air can pass out of the pump. An air bleed valve need is indicated.	
	9. Restricted flow through suction piping.	Check suction piping & fittings to make sure full size is used throughout. Make sure suction line is not plugged with rags or other foreign material.	Chapters 19, 25
	10. Pump case drain does not terminate below oil level.	Extend slip line piping so that it terminates below the oil surface when oil is at its lowest during any part of one machine cycle.	Chapters 20, 25
	11. Pressure ring is worn	Replace. This condition caused by hot, thin dirty oil or no oil at all. An air bound condition will also contribute to the worn pressure ring.	

Pumps—Energy Input, Section III (continued)

Trouble	Cause	Remedy	References
	12. Air bubbles in intake line	Provide reservoir with baffles. All return lines to reservoir must end below oil surface, & on opposite side of the baffle from intake lines. Check for reservoir design violations.	Chapters 20, 25
	13. Restricted filter or strainer	Clean filter or strainer.	Chapters 19, 20
	14. Sticking vane.	Remove cover assembly & check rotor & vane for presence of metal chips or sticky oil. Some pump models have chamfered edges on the vanes. See pump drawings for proper installation.	
	15. Worn or broken parts	Replace	
	16. Reservoir air vent plugged	Air must be allowed to circulate in the reservoir. Clean and/or replace breather.	Chapter 25
System excessively hot	1. Pump operates at higher pressures than required	Reduce pump pressure to minimum required for designed performance.	Chapter 18 Step 12 Chapters 19, 25
	2. Pump discharging through relief valve	Consider removing relief valve. Relief valves are not usually required with pumps having spring or hydraulic pressure compensating governor.	
	3. Pump slip too high	Check fluid viscosity, pump clearances, wear, loose covers	
	4. Cooling inadequate	Install oil cooler and/or increase reservoir capacity.	Chapters 18, 25
	5. High ambient temperature	Relocate power unit or baffle against heat source	Chapter 18
	6. Excessive friction	Internal parts may be too tight.	
	7. Oil in reservoir low	Raise oil level to recommended point.	
	8. Pump drain or return line too close to pump suction.	Separate the drain return & suction lines by a baffle in the reservoir. Place the drain line in a location where it must travel the farthest distance practical before the oil re-enters the pump.	Chapter 25
	9. System leakage excessive	Check progressively through the system for losses.	Steps 6, 9, 13, 18, 19
Leakage at oil seal	1. Seal installed incorrectly	Correct installation.	Chapter 25
	2. Pressure in pump case	Observe case drain line for restriction. Check drain line circuitry for excessive back pressure arrangement.	
	3. Poor coupling alignment	Re-align pump & motor shafts. Align to within .005″ total indicator reading.	Chapter 19
	4. Seals damaged during installation. Damaged or scratched shaft seal	Replace oil seal assembly. Slip packing carefully over keyway avoiding guts.	
	5. Abrasives on pump shaft	Protect shaft from abrasive dust & foreign material.	
Bearing failure	1. Abuse during coupling installation to pump	Most pumps are not designed to handle end thrusts against the drive shaft. Eliminate all end play. Couplings should be a slip fit onto the pump shaft.	Chapter 25
	2. Overhung load	Many pumps are not designed to handle any overhung load or side thrust on the drive shaft. See manufacturers recommendations.	Chapter 25

Trouble	Cause	Remedy	References
	3. Incorrect fluid	See manufacturer's oil recommendations.	Chapter 25
	4. Excessive or shock load	Reduce operation pressure. Observe maximum rating of operating pressure. Make necessary circuit changes.	
	5. Chips or other foreign matter in bearings (contamination)	Make sure clean oil is used. Essential for efficient operation & long life of bearings.	Chapter 20
	6. Coupling misalignment	Re-align pump & motor.	
Pump not delivering oil	1. Wrong direction of pump rotation	Observe arrow on pump case of name-plate. direction of rotation must correspond.	Step 10
	2. Oil level low in reservoir	Maintain oil level in reservoir well above bottom of suction line at all times.	Chapter 25
Pump not delivering oil	3. Air leak in suction line.	Apply good pipe compound nonsoluble in oil, & tighten joints.	Chapters 19, 25
	4. Pump running too slowly	Increase speed. Check manufacturing minimum speed recommendations to be sure of proper priming.	Chapter 25
	5. Suction filter or plugged line	Filters must be cleaned of lint or dirt soon after first start of unit. Periodic checks should be made as a preventive maintenance precaution.	Chapter 20
	6. Bleed-off in other portion of circuit	Check for open center valves or other controls connected to tank.	Step 6, 9, 18, 19
	7. Oil viscosity too high for proper priming	Thinner oil should be used per recommendations for given temperatures & service.	Chapter 25
	8. Pump shaft, mechanism or rotor damaged	Replace broken parts. Study for signs of excessive shock, dirt, foreign material, or other probable causes of failure.	
	9. Sheared key at rotor or coupling	Check and replace.	
	10. Pump cover too loose	Tighten bolts on pump cover.	
Pump not delivering pressure	1. Pump pressure not set high enough	Set adjusting screw to obtain desired minimum operating pressure.	
	2. Oil by-passing to reservoir	Inspect circuit pressure progressively. Watch for open center valves or other valves open to reservoir.	
	3. Pressure being relieved through relief valve	Relief valve is usually not required with pressure-compensated vane pumps. Relief valves may create additional heat and present another pressure to set.	
	4. Vane or vanes stuck in rotor slots	Dismantle pump, inspect for wedged chips or sticky oil.	
	5. Pump running too slowly	Check minimum pump speed recommendations.	
	6. Defective pressure gage or gage line is shut off. Dirt may plug gage orifice.	Install good pressure gage in a line open to pump pressure.	

Accumulators (Gas)—Auxiliaries, Section IV

Slow Reaction	1. Loss of charge or overcharge	Check charge pressure—reset	Chapter 7, 23

Accumulators (Gas)—Auxiliaries, Section IV *(continued)*

Trouble	Cause	Remedy	References
	2. Unloading valve or pump low pressure set too low	Adjust to higher pressure	
	3. Relief valve set too low or stuck open	Reset or clean valve	
	4. Pump not pumping	Check pump	
	5. Unloading pressure switch set too low	Reset pressure switch	
Fails to absorb shock	1. Loss of charge or over-charge	Check & recharge if necessary or reset	

Filters — Auxiliaries, Section IV

Dirty Oil	1. Plugged cartridge	Replace cartridge	Chapters 20, 25
	2. Partial bypass-continuous	Correct filter size and oil viscosity	
	3. Improper micrometre rating	Check particle size and switch to proper size rating	Chapters 20, 25
	4. Improper changes	Correct maintenance procedure or add bypass indicator	

Gages — Auxiliaries, Section IV

Incorrect indication	1. Gage defective	Check zero pressure & remedy or replace broken tube, broken movement, tube spring, broken needle, pegged needle or gage pinion gear.	Chapter 25
	2. Check accuracy	Check gage against calibration standard	Chapter 25
Poor gage life	1. Gage subject to mechanical shock	Isolate shock by switching to glycerin-filled gage	
	2. Bourdon tube fatigue	Use gage isolator to remove continuous pressure on tube.	
	3. Pegged needles	Add pressure flow snubber to restrict needle movement in addition to glycerin (or fluid filled gage).	
Broken housing	1. Too much pressure	Remove downstream restriction or change to corresponding higher pressure or flow rated filter	
	2. Too much mechanical shock	Add shock absorbing material	

TROUBLESHOOTING SYSTEM HEAT

Figure 26.13 summarizes cause-and-effect relationships for excessive heating of hydraulic systems. Refer also to Chapter 18.

High temperatures indicate that the system is producing an unsafe amount of friction and leakage — which generate heat. Many factors can cause oil temperature to rise: sludge, varnish, turbulence, aeration, overly high fluid velocity, cavitation, excessive slip, rubbing and contacting parts, trapped metal particles, etc.

If a system continues to operate with unchecked high oil temperatures, the oil will begin to break down, reducing lubricity and viscosity; transmission of fluidborne noise will increase. Simultaneously, as metal parts expand under higher temperatures, clearances between mating parts increase. Slip flow increases and more contaminants are trapped in the narrow clearances throughout the system. These events further increase friction, wear, particles, clattering and rattling noises, erratic system performance, etc.

An easy and convenient way to check oil temperatures *without* a thermometer is to put the palm of the

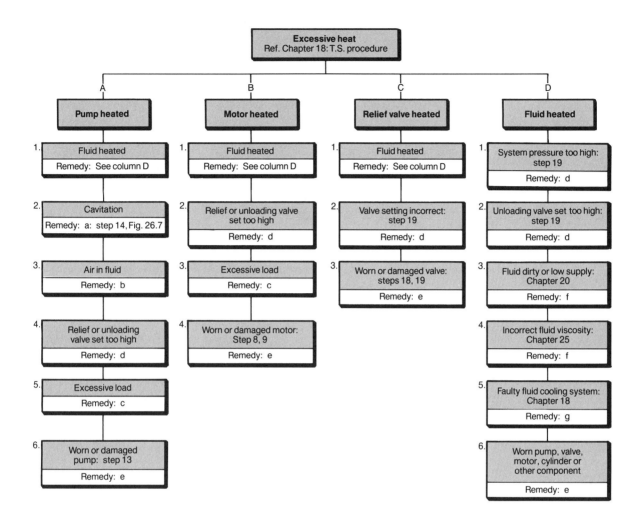

A Pump heated	B Motor heated	C Relief valve heated	D Fluid heated
1. Fluid heated — Remedy: See column D	1. Fluid heated — Remedy: See column D	1. Fluid heated — Remedy: See column D	1. System pressure too high: step 19 — Remedy: d
2. Cavitation — Remedy: a: step 14, Fig. 26.7	2. Relief or unloading valve set too high — Remedy: d	2. Valve setting incorrect: step 19 — Remedy: d	2. Unloading valve set too high: step 19 — Remedy: d
3. Air in fluid — Remedy: b	3. Excessive load — Remedy: c	3. Worn or damaged valve: steps 18, 19 — Remedy: e	3. Fluid dirty or low supply: Chapter 20 — Remedy: f
4. Relief or unloading valve set too high — Remedy: d	4. Worn or damaged motor: Step 8, 9 — Remedy: e		4. Incorrect fluid viscosity: Chapter 25 — Remedy: f
5. Excessive load — Remedy: c			5. Faulty fluid cooling system: Chapter 18 — Remedy: g
6. Worn or damaged pump: step 13 — Remedy: e			6. Worn pump, valve, motor, cylinder or other component — Remedy: e

(At top: Excessive heat — Ref. Chapter 18: T.S. procedure)

Remedies:

a. Any or all of the following: replace dirty filters — clean clogged inlet line — clean reservoir breather vent — change system fluid — change to proper pump drive motor speed — overhaul or replace supercharge pump. Ref. Chapter 19.

b. Any or all of the following: tighten leaky inlet connections — fill reservoir to proper level (with rare exception all return lines should be below fluid level in reservoir) — bleed air from system — replace pump shaft seal (and shaft if worn at seal journal). Ref. Chapters 19, 25.

c. Align unit and check condition of seals and bearings — locate and correct mechanical binding — check for work load in excess of circuit design. Ref. Chapters 3, 4, 5 and 23.

d. Install pressure gauge and adjust to correct pressure (keep at least 125 psi difference between valve settings). Ref. Chapters 3, 4 and 5.

e. Overhaul or replace. Ref. Chapters 8, 16, 23 and 25.

f. Change filters and also system fluid if of improper viscosity — fill reservoir to proper level. Ref. Chapters 20 and 25.

g. Clean cooler and/or cooler strainer — replace cooler control valve — repair or replace cooler. Ref. Chapters 18 and 25.

Fig. 26.13. Typical malfuctions related to elevated temperatures.

hand on the side of an oil reservoir. Most people can withstand temperatures to 120 to 130 degrees, for a few seconds. This is a safe operating temperature. For safety's sake, first test with fingertips, which are tougher than the palm of the hand. Do not perform the finger or palm test on a pump which usually runs hotter than the oil temperature in the reservoir.

TROUBLESHOOTING NOISE

Figure 26.14 summarizes the cause-and-effect relationships of noise generation in a hydraulic system. An increase in noise from a hydraulic circuit im-

plies one and possibly two kinds of trouble. The unquestionable trouble is that some damage is being done inside the system. The potential trouble is that the machinery is generating noise in excess of that permitted. Refer to Chapter 19.

Vibration and contamination—Both vibration and contamination can lead to aeration, cavitation, sticking, and worn parts. It is an unfortunate cycle where one problem leads to another until trouble occurs.

Every pump produces hydraulic and mechanical vibrations at some noise level. Refer to Chapter 19. Vibrations can cause fittings to loosen. If the loose fitting is on the pressure side of the system, it eventually will leak oil. If a substantial amount of oil leaks out, the pump will ingest extra air through the oil in the reservoir. Excessive air causes aeration — the entrainment of tiny air bubbles in the fluid. These bubbles create extra turbulence in the pump and throughout the system. The first noise indication of impending trouble is an increase in overall turbulence noise throughout the system.

Turbulence from aeration generates additional vibration in the pump. It also may cause control valve spools to chatter noisily and work erratically, resulting in spongy or jumpy cylinder operation which further increases vibration. These compounded vibrations enlarge the leakage area allowing more oil to escape. As this cycle repeats the oil can drop to a level which causes cavitation or pump starvation.

Why is cavitation noisy?

The process of cavitation is generally not understood. During cavitation, air bubbles are *imploded*. Under high pressure, the fluid displaces violently the area occupied by the bubbles, causing the air bubbles to dissolve in the fluid.

Noise results when bubbles are touching a metal surface when they implode. The impact is so violent that the fluid actually dents, pits, and erodes the metal surfaces. Additional noise is caused by the expansion and contraction of the housing under this dynamic hammering. Cavitation can increase overall system noise levels by as much as 10 to 15 decibels.

Eroded metal particles from cavitation

These metal particles migrate through the system, lodging in any clearances in which they can enter. If cavitation continues for some time, most working parts in components will wear and add more particulate contamination to the system. Refer to Chapter 20. When caught under rotating or sliding parts like spools and sleeve bearings, these highly-abrasive particles will wear out parts. Even after cavitation has been stopped, the worn, clattering parts can boost system noise four to six decibels.

If cavitation is allowed to continue, bearings will seize or the pump housing will get so work-hardened and brittle that it will crack. Pumping elements can become so battered that they will produce no system pressure. Sometimes the electric drive motor bearings seize before the pump bearings. Remember, noise and leakage are tipoffs to real problems.

If noise continues to increase, first check the oil level and oil leaks; then check the temperature of the oil and its appearance. Also, listen carefully at each component and part, and study any operational irregularities and peculiar noises associated with each. Table 26.1 summarizes troubleshooting by ear.

Oil appearance-Check whether the oil looks milky or frothy. If the machine is not making exces-

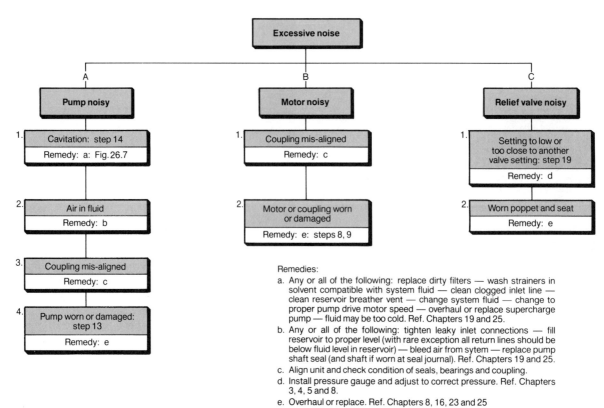

Fig. 26.14. Typical cause-and-effect relationships of noise generation.

sively loud noises and the oil is not clear, it is reasonable to assume that either water or air is getting into the oil, or a small restriction is causing low-grade cavitation. Water can get into the oil through a leak in a water-type heat exchanger, through condensation, or from external sources.

Next, clean the oil filter regardless whether or not it looks dirty, and tighten all connections on the *inlet*

Table 26.1 — Trouble-shooting hydraulic components by ear

Typical noise and source	Probable cause of noise	What to check	How to cure it	Potential reduction (dbA)
Noticeable increase in *overall* noise level at fittings, pipes, valves, and pump or motor (usually accompanied by spongy or jumping operation of hydraulic cylinders in the system.)	High flow turbulence caused by aeration. Air is being leaked into the system.	Look in oil reservoir. See if oil is "milky" or "frothy," but reservoir is *full*.	Find and repair source of air leak. Look especially for leaks in suction side at fittings, oil filter, fill-cap threads, fill-cap O-ring and pump seal. Remove air in system by bleeding at bleed points.	2-4
Same *overall* noise problem as above. (same erratic cylinder operation.)	Turbulence caused by aeration brought on by *oil leaking out* of system while *air is leaking in*.	Check to see if oil in reservoir is frothy but oil level is *down*.	Find and repair source of *oil* leak, refill oil reservoir, bleed lines. Operate the system long enough to see if noise has stopped and operation is smooth. If not, find and repair *air* leak as above and operate again to check results.	2-4
Same *overall* noise as above *continues,* but not quite as loud *after* both remedies have been tried.	Turbulence caused by aeration because oil is *retaining* too high a percentage of air.	Check to see if oil reservoir is full, but *still* frothy.	Change to hydraulic oil with anti-foam additive. (Consult with system manufacturer and oil company to make sure new oil type is compatible with the system.)	1-3
Same *overall* noise as above in system that has *water cooling* unit in it.	Turbulence caused by aeration from air carried in water leaking into oil from cooling coils.	See if oil is cloudy or milky in reservoir. (Boil small quantity of oil — if it clears, cause is water in oil.)	Let system stand overnight. If cloudiness disappears, cause is air leak (find and repair). If cloudiness remains, cause is water homogenized in the oil. Find leak, repair it, drain oil, replace with new oil, bleed lines during check out under no load.	2-4
Pump, motor, or valves make loud rattling or clanking noises under load when first started up . . . but noise disappears shortly.	Cold oil is too viscous — causes cavitation by drawing air from reservoir into the system.	Check oil in reservoir. See if oil is frothy, thick, and much cooler than when running normally.	Warm up the system with a pre-heater or by running it under no load till side of oil reservoir is hot to palm of hand. Bleed lines when system starts to quiet. (Ideal oil temperature is 120° F.)	10-15
Pump, motor, or valves for no apparent reason start making loud rattling or clanking noises. (Accompanied by erratic operation of cylinders.)	Cavitation caused by pronounced restriction in system immediately *ahead* of noisy component, or very low oil level.	Check oil level. If full, then check for foreign object (cleaning rag, bit of Teflon tape, plugged oil filter, crimped suction inlet, etc.)	Fill oil reservoir. Find obstruction and correct it. Clean oil filter. Tighten all connections on suction side. Bleed lines during checkout under no load.	10-15
Single loud "plop" or "clank" repeating at irregular intervals in pump or hydraulic motor.	Single cavitation sound caused by one large air bubble collapsing.	Check oil for froth. Check suction connections for air leak.	Fill reservoir if low. Tighten all connections on suction side. Look for any restricting foreign object. Clean oil filter. Bleed lines on startup.	Peaks of 4-8
Increased noises from pump or hydraulic motor. (Usually accompanied by sluggish performance by cylinders.)	Worn parts in pump or motor caused by abrasive action of wear particles on rotating and working parts.)	Check oil temperature. Probably too high because of friction.	Remove metal particles in suspension; drain entire system, flush piping, clean all components, refill with new oil and bleed lines during checkout under no load. Repeat in 30 days. (If noise level is not reduced, replace worn parts or entire pump.)	4-6
Increased noises from valves, usually chattering sound, sometimes sticking or erratic performance.	Worn spools or orifices caused by wear particles.	Check dimensions and clearances of spool and orifices.	Replace worn parts with new if practical, or replace entire valve unit. Remove metal particles from oil as above.	2-4
Loud slam travels through hydraulic system during erratic performance *after* changing to different type of hydraulic oil in system.	Hydraulic shock waves caused when sticking part suddenly overcomes the constricting force.	Check filter and valve or cylinder parts for sludge, corrosion and varnish.	Clean filter and parts with lacquer thinner. (Have oil analyzed — make changes in contents or switch oil type as recommended.) Flush system thoroughly.	Peaks of 10-20

Courtesy Parker Hannifin Corp.

side, including pump-cover bolts and fittings. Check the fill-cap threads and O-ring seal, Figure 26.15. After tightening all system fittings, operate the system under no-load conditions, bleeding trapped air out of overhead bleed ports. This procedure should quiet the system and improve cylinder response. If

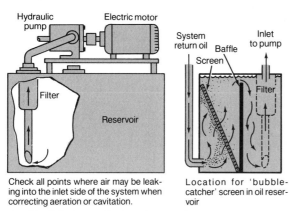

Check all points where air may be leaking into the inlet side of the system when correcting aeration or cavitation.

Location for 'bubble-catcher' screen in oil reservoir.

Fig. 26.15. Points to check and correct for aeration problems.

this does not help, there is likely to be a restriction which would require disassembly and cleaning. Aeration can often be reduced by inserting a bubble-catcher screen in the tank, Figure 26.15. Also see Chapter 25.

Correcting noise caused by high oil temperatures- Because most of these problems are caused by contamination, the best thing is to drain and flush the whole system, being careful to clean out the oil reservoir and filter thoroughly. After adding *new* clean, hydraulic fluid, operate the system under no load, and vent trapped air from all overhead bleed ports. Do not refill with old oil as all contaminants could be put back in the system. Filter new oil as it is charged into the reservoir. Never pour oil directly from the shipping container into a reservoir.

Since the most troublesome noise and operational problems start with contamination, Chapter 20, good maintenance is of utmost importance. There is no substitute for it.

If a system is operated at too high a temperature, some oils will build up varnish. To make sure varnish is removed from a filter, clean the element in lacquer thinner, if a re-usable type is used. Varnish is clear, and almost invisible to the eye, but it can quickly plug small filter holes. It's a good idea to clean filters with lacquer thinner periodically to guard against this problem, Figure 26.16. If a disposable element is used, replace the element.

Lower pressures reduce noise levels - In some applications, it may be possible to reduce noise levels by operating the system at the lowest acceptable pressures. For example, in some systems, relief valves operate frequently because they are used as load controls for cylinders. Relief and other valves — and

even adjustable pumps can often by quieted by lowering the pressure settings to that needed to do the job. This procedure reduces all noise-generating functions.

Reducing mechanical noise in hydraulic system Mechanical noise contributes to overall system noise. Refer to Chapter 19. The types of mechanical couplings used between the prime mover and pump can also contribute to noise.

Noise generated by mechanical interface "slapping" plus lateral vibration in a pump and motor can add one to three decibels to overall noise levels.

Inspect the coupling and check alignment with a gage. Maximum deviation should not exceed 0.003 in. T.I.R. There may be as much as 0.008-in. to 0.010-in. deviation if the machine is making much noise. To rectify this situation, shim the pump and motor feet and correct horizontal alignment. Tighten tie-down bolts. If the old coupling has metal-to-metal interfaces, switch to rubber-faced couplings.

If the pump is mounted on the end of the motor, listen for a popping or crackling that sounds like static. This indicates misalignment. If it is very loud, the basic mount should be reworked or replaced.

Reducing electric motor noise - Most noises originating with the electric motor are caused by the fan and fan cover or shroud. If the motor itself sounds noisy, the bearings could be bad or open gaps in the rotor might be causing windage sounds as they pass the stator bars. The bearings can be oiled and the rotor gaps filled with inert epoxy. However, the latter is a time-consuming job which probably will not reduce overall noise more than one or two decibels.

If the bearings are extremely noisy, they are most likely badly worn because of misalignment or dynamic unbalance. These should be replaced rather than just oiled. If the bearings cannot be replaced,

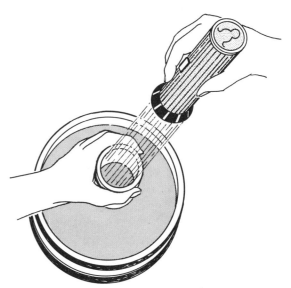

Fig. 26.16. When checking for varnish coating shine flashlight into filter to see how rapidly — or slowly — it fills with oil.

better buy a new motor — one with filled stator gaps and a quieter cooling fan. Due attention should be given the efficiencies of the new motor.

Quieting an existing fan assembly - Because the fan and cover are usually thin and broad, they transmit and amplify all frequencies of structure-borne vibrations and windage noises. However, fan and cover noises can be reduced by five to seven decibels.

The most effective technique is to replace a metal fan with a plastic one. Plastic absorbs rather than transmits vibrations and sounds. Replace a thin sheet metal shroud with one of cast iron. The added mass will help damp out noise-causing vibrations.

Reducing pipe noises - When piping fluid power systems, the basic objectives are to avoid sharp turns, minimize noise transmission, and dampen pump ripple and other vibration.

When metal pipes make 90-degree turns, they become transmitters of pump noise and ripple vibration. Transmission noise can be reduced by inserting sections of flexible hose in the system where bends are most prominent. A flexible hose at the pump discharge port also helps isolate pump ripple and vibration.

Another effective way to dampen transmission and vibration — with pipes or hose — is to anchor the lines at frequent intervals with strong, resilient mounting brackets or with clamps lined with resilient sleeves. These are especially helpful if there is vi-

bration at control or valve panels, Figure 26.17.

Dampening reservoir walls - Reservoir walls cannot be dampened easily. They need to be stiffened or at least divided into smaller resonating panels. The best retrofit procedure is to apply very thick mastic cement on all surfaces to dampen some of the sounds. This will not reduce vibration, but it will dampen the resulting noises — perhaps one or two decibels.

Other low-cost ways to cut system noises - If the system is enclosed in a metal cabinet, as many are, apply mastic cement inside all the walls and doors to dampen sound before it reaches the panels.

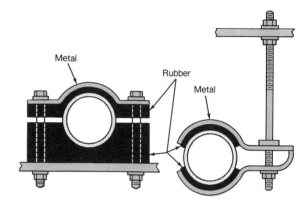

Fig. 26.17. Two examples of typical mounting brackets to dampen conduit vibration.

Table 26.2—How to quiet existing structural noises

Noise area	Probable cause	How to check or cure	Potential reduction (dbA)
Coupling between pump and motor. (High vibration)	Misalignment	Shim where necessary, realign to .003″ T.I.R. or less.	1-2
Coupling (Noise only)	Metal slapping	Change to type with rubber interfacing.	1-2
Electric motor (Vibration)	Dynamic unbalance	Check on balancer.	1-2
Electric motor (Loud windage noises)	Open rotor spaces	Fill with epoxy.	1-2
Electric motor (Clatter)	Dry or worn bearings	Oil or replace.	1-3
Cooling fan (Loud windage)	Thin metal structure	Replace with plastic fan or coat metal fan with plastic.	1-2
Cooling fan (Siren noise)	Too close to motor or cover	Add spacers where needed for more clearance.	1-2
TEFC fan & cover	Loose bolts	Tighten all bolts	1-3
Fan cover (Windage, general noises, high vibration.)	Thin metal structure is amplifying	Replace with cast iron cover or coat with heavy mastic cement inside and out.	1-2
Pipes and fittings (Noise and vibration)	Flow surge and ripple turbulence.	Insert hose in sharp bend areas and at pump.	2-3
Pipes or hoses (Rattling noises)	Hitting floor, panels, etc.	Stabilize with absorbent mounts at frequent intervals.	1-3
Mounting plate of pump/motor (Vibration)	Transmitted vibrations from pump/motor.	Stiffen by welding or bolting angle iron ribs at frequent intervals.	1-3
Oil reservoir (Loud "thrumbing")	Thin walls are amplifying.	Add rubber washers under reservoir and under pump/motor plate; add sound-dampener material to walls.	2-4
Steel enclosure (General noise)	Transmitted vibrations from whole system.	Line interior of walls and doors with sound-dampening or absorbing material.	1-3

Adhesive-backed fiberglass sheet pading material can be also be applied on the inside. Fiberglass is a good absorber of air-borne sound waves, but its mass is so low that it will not stop structure-borne vibration. For best results, it must be applied inside a well-sealed chamber. Table 26.2 summarizes ways of quieting existing structural noise.

LEAKAGE CONTROL

Internal leakage in a hydraulic cylinder (Refer to Step 6, Troubleshooting Methods) may manifest itself in several ways:
- gradual or sudden loss of power or speed
- stalling under light load conditions, or
- failure to shift, even under no load.

These problems occur when too much oil bypasses the cylinder piston during its stroke. Excessive bypass may occur if the piston rings or seals are worn or broken, or if there is heavy the or cylinder bore.

Do not expect zero bypass, cylinders with cast-iron piston rings will normally bypass one to five cubic inches of oil per minute even when they are new.

Excessive bypass

Here are some simple ways to check for excessive oil bypass:

1. Large-volume leakage
- *Retract* cylinder rod until the piston has bottomed against the cap end.
- with the pump running, feel the return line for temperature rise or oil flow.
- if no flow is detected, repeat the test with the cylinder rod fully *extended*.
- if excessive flow is detected, remove the cylinder from the machine, check the piston, rings and seals, and replace worn components.

2. Small volume leakage
- bottom the piston against one end of the cylinder and maintain operating pressure. Make sure cylinder return line is open to reservoir and is not pressurized.
- loosen a fitting in the return line, and check for oil flow. If the line is full of oil, it will drain when the fitting is loosened; or, if the fitting is below reservoir oil level, siphoning may occur. Do not mistake drainage oil for bypass oil.
- after normal drainage flow has stopped, remove the fitting to isolate the line so you can observe or measure bypass oil.
- repeat the test by running the cylinder piston to the opposite end of the cylinder, check again for bypass flow.

The preceding method is highly reliable, because it is performed with the cylinder *isolated* from other components in the circuit.

3. Leakage at various points in the cylinder stroke
Checking for excessive bypass flow at various points in the stroke — in addition to checking at full stroke — will reveal the presence of heavy pitting or scoring in the cylinder bore. You will need a needle valve and a pressure gage to perform this test.
- with the cylinder rod fully retracted and the rod end full of oil, install the metering valve and gage at the head end port
- close the needle valve, and pressurize the cap end port
    a. if the cylinder is in good condition, the gage will show intensified pressure at the head end; however, the piston rod will not move.
    b. if excessive oil is bypassing, the intensified head-end pressure will leak into the cap end, and the piston rod will extend at a rate proportional to leakage.
- if the piston rod is extending because of leakage, slowly open the metering valve until the piston rod stops: it will stop when flow through the valve equals bypass (leakage) flow.
- alternately open or close the metering valve, testing the cylinder through its entire stroke. During this test, mark (on the outside of the cylinder body) the points or areas of leakage.
- remove the cylinder from the machine, disassemble it and check the bore. If it is heavily pitted or scored, replace the cylinder.

Find the leak

The point where a leak is visible is not necessarily where it is taking place. The troubleshooter must know the *exact* location of a leak before he can eliminate it. It is impossible to point to the source of a leak on a machine covered with oil on *all* sides. If such is the case, there might not even be a leak. The real cause might be an over-filled reservoir or a spill.

When locating leakage sources, the first step is to clean the area and watch. Focus on the four general areas where leaks might occur:
- fittings (connectors)
- hoses
- dynamic seals, and
- static seals.

While many leaks occur at fittings, finding the leaking fitting is difficult because the fluid may flow some distance before dripping. Always suspect inaccessible connections, they are often installed carelessly because they are hard to get at. Leaks in high pressure lines sometimes are difficult to pinpoint because the fluid comes out as a mist. Be careful—high pressure leaks can cause personal injury.

Determine cause of leak

Once a leak is located, its cause must be determined before it can be corrected. A scratch in a fitting seat or cut in a seal may be the trouble yet almost invisible to the naked eye. A magnifying glass can help reduce repeat repairs.

If an SAE or ISO straight thread O-ring fitting leaks, either the seal was damaged during assembly or it has lost its flexibility. When it is replaced, make certain the size and material of the new seal are correct.

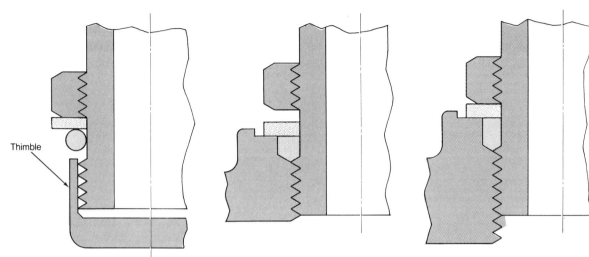

Fig. 26.18. When installing O-ring seal, cover threads with plastic or metal thimble to avoid damage to O-ring.

Fig. 26.19. Tighten by hand until washer squeezes O-ring into O-ring cavity.

Fig. 26.20. Tighten locknut until backup washer contacts spot-face.

Use a set procedure to avoid cutting or trapping the O-ring during assembly of an adjustable straight thread fitting:

1. lubricate the O-ring with the fluid to be sealed or a light grease such as *petrolatum*. Place a plastic or metal thimble over the threads when installing the O-ring to avoid nicks or cuts from the threads. Slide the O-ring over the thimble and onto the undercut section of the fitting and against the backup washer, Figure 26.18.

2. screw the fitting by hand into SAE straight thread boss until backup washer bottoms on spotface with O-ring squeezed into its boss cavity, Figure 26.19. The reason for lubricating the O-ring is to help it slide into the tapered O-ring cavity. Dry O-rings will not slide and will get damaged.

3. next, position the fitting to meet the joining tube by *unscrewing* as far as necessary, but *no more* than one full turn. Tighten locknut with wrench so backup washer contacts boss face: The greater the pressure to be sealed, the greater the nut locking torque, Figure 26.20.

Straight thread leakage troubleshooting hints are summarized in Table 26.3. Table 26.4 analyzes leakage in tapered thread installations.

Seal life — leakage control

Dynamic seals prevent or control leakage between surfaces which move past each other. Since these seals contact moving surfaces, they will eventually wear out or fail. Periodic seal replacement is required. With proper installation and maintenance, however, dynamic seals should last throusands of hours. High pressure, temperature, speed and surface roughness all tend to reduce seal life. Refer to Chapter 25. A typical lip seal is shown in Figure 26.21.

Surface finish

Tests have shown maximum seal life can be expected with a shaft surface finish in the range of 8 to 20 micrometres. If the shaft is too smooth, it will not support the necessary lubricating film of oil; if too rough, it will wear the seal lip prematurely. In either case, early seal failure may occur. Finish marks should be circumferential rather than axial to retain the fluid. A *spiral tool mark* will "pump" oil out or ingest air past a seal, depending on shaft rotation.

Lip seal installation

To operate successfully, lip seals must be installed

Table 26.3—Straight thread leakage analysis

Possible source of trouble	Suggested remedy
1. O-ring cut	Replace O-ring lubricating with petrolatum or fluid to be sealed. Use thimble, Figure 6, to protect ring. Inspect for burr.
2. O-ring pinched on assembly into port	Inspect roughness of port sealing surface. Repair or replace part if finish exceeds 100 micro. Lubricate O-ring before assembly
3. Sealing surfaces of port or fitting are scratched or gouged	Repair if possible, otherwise replace
4. Sealing surfaces of port or fitting are dirty	Clean and lubricate before reassembly of parts
5. Port spotface is too small. Nut or washer hangs up on sport-face shoulder	Enlarge spotface so fitting can seat properly, or replace faulty part
6. O-ring edges nibbled because pressure is lifting fitting	Check pressure relief valve setting. Increase seating torque on fitting

correctly. Follow this procedure:

1. examine the seal to be sure it is the correct part, has not been damaged, nor lost its flexibility.

2. use a press to install the oil seal into the bore. The OD of the press ram or driving tool should not be more than 0.010″ smaller than the bore diameter and should have a flat face to contact the back of the metal case on the seal. If installing the seal in a reverse position, be sure that ram pressure is applied only to the rollover bead around the outer diameter of

Table 26.4—Tapered thread leakage analysis

Possible sources of trouble	Suggested remedy
1. Fitting is under-torqued	Tighten using "General rule of thumb" in text
2. Female part expanded from heat	Retighten while hot
3. Vibration has loosened fitting	Retighten if fitting is not cracked. Use clamps with vibration dampeners for support
4. Hydraulic shock	Retighten fitting if not cracked. Recharge accumulators. Check use of low shock control valves, deceleration and decompression components
5. Female threads in part are oversize	Inspect. Replace if oversize
6. Male threads are undersize on pipe	Inspect. Replace if undersize
7. Straight male thread put into tapered thread port	Inspect. Replace with tapered Dryseal thread fitting
8. Threads galled, dirty or damaged before assembly	Rework, if possible, with sharp taps and dies or replace faulty parts
9. Port cracked from over-torqued pipe	Check for cracks. Replace damage parts

the seal face and not to the inside face or filler ring inside the metal outer case, Figure 26.22.

3. polish the shaft to remove burrs and sharp or rough edges which touch seal lip during assembly. Use a mounting thimble or a sheet of shim stock, Figure 26.23, to protect the seal. The thimble wall should be as thin as possible (0.012 in. max.) to avoid seal lip distortion during assembly. The shaft and oil-seal lip should be lubricated before mounting the seal over the shaft.

4. if a press cannot be used, the seal may be seated with a driving plug or tool, Figure 26.24. This tool is placed into position and tapped with a mallet. When large seals are being seated, in an emergency, a block of wood resting squarely on the seal may be used instead of a driving tool. Never hit the seal directly!

5. check shaft-to-bore misalignment and dynamic runout. *Misalignment* is the distance which the shaft is off center with respect to the bore, Figure 26.25.

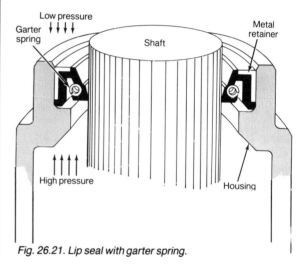

Fig. 26.21. Lip seal with garter spring.

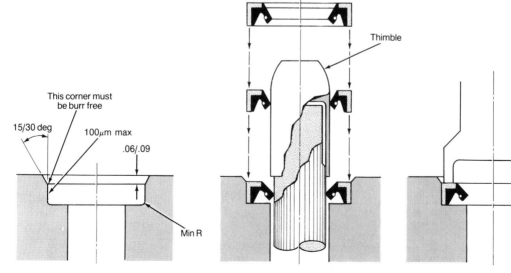

Fig. 26.22. Optimum seal bore dimensions.

Fig. 26.23. Use shim stock or thimble to protect seal.

Fig. 26.24. If press cannot be used, seal may be seated with driving plug or tool.

Runout is the amount by which the shaft does not rotate around its true center, at the sealing surface, Figure 26.26.

The sum of misalignment plus runout is called eccentricity. For a given eccentricity, the probability of shaft-seal leakage increases as shaft speed increases. The recommended maximum eccentricity which should not be exceeded in standard lip seal applications is shown in Figure 26.27.

To reduce misalignment, it is necessary to remove the cause: shaft bearings, housing, or shaft side load.

To reduce runout, replace the shaft.

Table 26.5 offers suggestions for reducing lip seal leakage.

Face seals

The mechanical face seal is most effective in preventing leakage along a rotating shaft which passes in or out of pressurized oil. Two lapped sealing faces are mounted perpendicular to the shaft. The seal seat is attached to and rotates with the shaft, while the spring-loaded seal head is stationary, Figure 26.28. Refer to Chapter 25.

The conventional seal face materials used in hydraulic applications are hard carbon for the *seal head*, and steel or cast iron for the *seal seat*. The two are separated by an oil film. With good matching of sealing forces and seal flatness, oil surface tension can complete the seal and there will be no leakage. Elevated pressures can induce seal wear, but with proper balancing, pressure-induced sealing forces can be kept low.

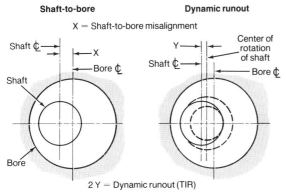

Shaft-to-bore   **Dynamic runout**

X = Shaft-to-bore misalignment

2 Y = Dynamic runout (TIR)

Fig. 26.25. *Misalignment is the distance shaft is off center with respect to bore.*

Fig. 26.26. *Runout is amount by which shaft rotates outside of true center.*

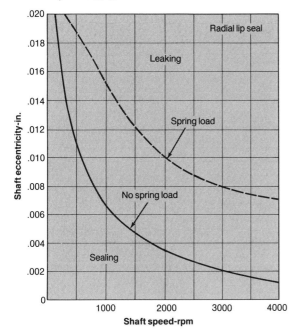

Fig. 26.27. *Sum of misalignment plus runout is called eccentricity. Curves show maximum permissible eccentricity.*

Table 26.5—Lip seal leakage analysis

Possible source of trouble	Suggested remedy
1. Worn shaft	Check shaft sealing surface hardness—Rockwell C 30 minimum necessary. Replace seal. Use wear sleeve on shaft if available. Othewise replace shaft. Lubricate parts.
2. Rough finish on shaft	Finish shaft surface to 8-20 μ in.
3. Damaged shaft	Replace shaft. Protect sealing surfaces during handling and assembly
4. Adhesive or paint on sealing surface	Clean with crocus cloth. Mask shaft during seal assembly into bore or painting of unit.
5. Seal cocked in bore	Use proper driving tool. Install seal at right angle to shaft surface.
6. Seal lip reversed	Check stock seal whether it has double lip before replacement. Some seals have double lips. One lip faces inward to retain fluid, one faces outward to exclude dirt.
7. Seal lip cut or torn	Replace seal. Lubricate seal/shaft. Use thimble to carry lip over keyways, splines and sharp edges. Be sure lip I.D. is not stretched over .035 in.
8. Seal lip worn, glazed or hardened, shaft OK	Check for hot oil, high case pressure, and correct seal size. Is seal lubricant good?
9. Seal spring damaged	Replace seal avoiding excessive spreading of sealing lip and spring. Check for proper storage and handling of seals.
10. Excessive eccentricity or misalignment—seal lip can't follow shaft movement	Align shaft, eliminate shaft side load, or use a better flexible coupling.
11. "Built-in" seal flaw such as contamination, poor rubber bond to metal, or flash on seal lip	Replace seal.

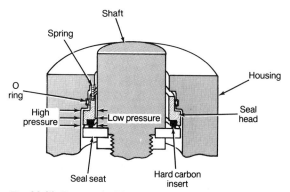

Fig. 26.28. Face seal with stationary head and rotating seat.

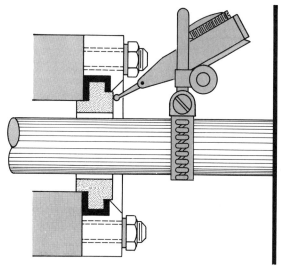

Fig. 26.29. Dial indicator mounted on shaft aligns stationary seal seat to 0.0001" T.I.R.

Only a properly trained technician should attempt to repair the sealing surfaces of face seals. With the new, correct replacement parts, do not touch the sealing surfaces with fingers or an old wiping rag. Make sure the seal seat is perpendicular to the shaft within 0.001 inch T.I.R., Figure 26.29. Lubricate the sealing surfaces well with the fluid to be sealed before installing.

Troubleshooting- Examine the old parts for telltale signs of potential problems. Abrasive wear of the sealing faces means contaminated oil. Burned faces indicate dry running seals. Heavy wear may mean either excessive operating pressure or a hung-up spring. A cracked carbon ring will leak badly. Worn bearings should be replaced if end play exceeds 0.002 in. or radial looseness is greater than 0.004 in. Replace the shaft with a new one if runout exceeds 0.002" T.I.R. Polish the new shaft to remove burrs or scratches that might damage static seals.

Test assembly- To insure against errors, test the mechnical seal assembly with low-pressure filtered air, at 5 to 20 psi *before* installing it on a machine. For example, an externally-drained piston pump housing can be easily pressurized through the drain port

connection.

Molded lip type seals

Lip type seals are molded from rubberized fabric, Nitrile, polyurethane, or PTFE. Two common shapes are U- and V-rings. Table 26.6 summarizes common seal failures and remedies.

Characteristics- Distortion of the seal lips from an interference fit on an assembly creates a counter sealing force adequate for low pressure.

With seal lips facing fluid pressure, any rise in pressure flattens the lips against wall surfaces and raises the sealing force.

Lip-type seals leak less, generate less friction and offer longer life than compressed seals.

The U-ring is an effective seal when used singly. A ring support or pedestal with cross drilled holes assures equal pressure loading on both seal lips.

The V-ring needs a stack of three rings along with male and female adapters to contain low pressure fluid. Five or more rings are needed for high pressure applications.

Molded squeeze packing

Squeeze seals are molded from synthetic rubber, polyurethane or PTFE. Common shapes are the O-, T-, and X-rings.

Characteristics - Distortion of squeeze seals from an assembly interference fit generates an internal sealing force within the seal to contain low pressure fluids.

High pressure puts an additional squeeze on the seal, raising the internal sealing force to counter the pressure force. This action tends to extrude the seal

Table 26.6 — Seal failures

Probable source of failure	Suggested remedy
1. Shaft or rod worn	Replace shaft. For contaminated fluid, change filter. For dirty atmosphere, install protective shield or boot. Check shaft hardness: Rockwell C 30 min.
2. Sealing surfaces are scratched. Seals damaged	Use proper assembly and disassembly tools on overhaul. Replace damaged parts.
3. Dynamic runout of shaft or eccentric motion is excessive	Inspect bearings, replace if too loose. Check side loads on shaft or rod. Seals are not to be used as bearings.
4. Rapid wear out of seal	Seal compressed too much. Loosen if adjustment is available. Otherwise check to be certain of correct seal size.
5. Glazed or hardened seal	Check for high oil temperature. Correct if seal lubrication is inadequate.
6. Seal edges are extruded	Check parts for too much clearance. Replace faulty parts. Use anti-extrusion rings on low pressure side of seal.

340

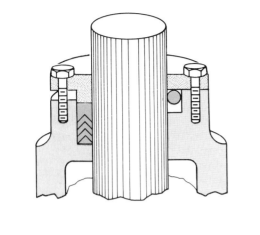

Compression

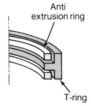

Anti extrusion ring

T-ring

U-ring

X-ring

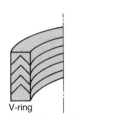

V-ring

O-ring

Fig. 26.30. Several types of seals used to seal piston rod.

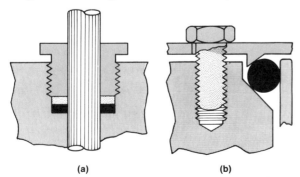

(a)   (b)

Fig. 26.31. Static seals prevent leakage between stationary surfaces. (a) crush washer, (b) jam packing.

through any clearance. Anti-extrusion rings are shown with the T-ring in Figure 26.30.

Squeeze seals generate less friction than either compression or lip-type seals and seal in both directions. When assembled, the O-ring should be squeezed about 10 percent, the T-ring about 5 percent, and the X-ring as little as 1 percent.

STATIC SEALS

Static seals prevent leakage between stationary surfaces. To contain pressure fluid, the seal and its mating parts must be in contact at a pressure higher than the pressure of the fluid being sealed. This pressure may be obtained through the method used to install the parts, as with the crush washer, or jam packing, Figure 26.31.

Pressure-activated seals- In other applications, such as with O-, V-, and X-rings, Figure 26.32, the initial sealing pressure from installation alone is sufficient to contain only *low* pressure oil. High pressure deforms or changes the seal shape and increases the sealing pressure level to complete the seal.

Gaskets- A gasket is an installation-activated seal made of relatively soft material. It must be deformed or compressed to fill surface irregularities and close the fluid leakage path.

O-rings can replace gaskets in many of the new hydraulic designs because of their greater reliability and ease of application. In general, the more compressible (softer) materials are used for low pressure applications. Common materials include cork, paper, plastic, rubber or a combination of these materials.

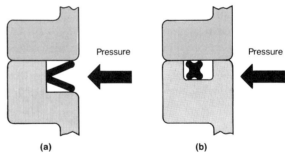

Pressure   Pressure

(a)   (b)

Fig. 26.32. Pressure activated seals: (a) O-ring, (b) X-ring.

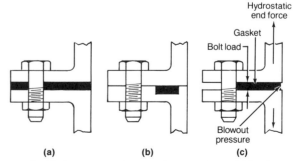

Hydrostatic end force

Gasket

Bolt load

Blowout pressure

(a)   (b)   (c)

Fig. 26.33. Gasket seals for basic flange designs: (a) flat face; (b) grooved face; (c) shows how internal pressures act on gasket joint.

The majority of gasket applications can be represented by two basic flange designs: the flat face, Figure 26.33 (a), and the grooved face, Figure 26.33(b).

For a given gasket cross section, each material requires a minimum clamping load necessary to *close its structure* to fluid leakage and fill surface irregularities to a maximum of 250 micrometres. Higher internal pressures require higher clamping loads. The forces acting on a gasketed joint are shown in Figure 26.33(c).

Most gasket materials relax and creep after being clamped, resulting in a loss in loading, generally within 18 hours. For critical applications, wait a day after initial assembly and retighten to the original loading, preferably at system operating temperature but with no internal pressure.

As pressures rise and operating conditions become more severe, metal or metal-with-soft-core gaskets are necessary. The required clamping force and surface finish to obtain a good seal vary widely, depending on the type of gasket. Follow the manufacturer's recommendations.

O-ring static seals

The O-ring is one of the most commonly used static seals. Recommended surface finish is 32 to 63 micrometres.

With high-pressure applications, the sealing surfaces may either slide or separate. Sliding causes seal wear. The rougher the surface, the greater the rate of seal wear. If sliding cannot be prevented, a surface finish of 16 micrometres may be necessary to obtain satisfactory seal life.

If the sealing surfaces are allowed to separate, the O-ring will extrude into the clearance. Figure 26.34. A sudden pressure drop will trap the extruded edges of the seal. With pressure pulsations, the extruded edges will be nibbled away. Eventually the seal will leak. Table 26.7 summarizes static seal leakage analysis.

Seal extrusion

It has been found that as O-ring hardness or du-

rometer increases, its resistance to extrusion damage also increases. For example, in laboratory tests with 160 F oil, 100,000 pressure pulses at 1500 psi caused significant O-ring extrusion damage when the diametral extrusion gap was greater than:
- 0.004 inches with 70 durometer seals
- 0.008 inches with 80 durometer seals
- 0.014 inches with 90 durometer seals

Caution: Don't jump at the first chance to put in high durometer O-rings. As pressures rise, they do resist extrusion better than softer seals. However, they leak more readily against rougher surfaces. Back-up rings are required where pressures exceed 1500 psi. Remember — if two surfaces slide or separate, seal wear will always be a problem. Try holding the surfaces together. Use a higher class bolt, if necessary, so bolt torque may be increased. Coordinate this action with the parts supplier to avoid product failure, such as stripped bolt threads.

O-rings should always be protected:
- lubricate them with light grease or the fluid to be sealed
- avoid use of sharp tools during parts removal or assembly, and
- use a thin soft metal, paper, or plastic cone or thimble to pass the O-ring over threads.

SAE split flange fitting

The SAE split flange adapter fitting may be joined to either pipe, tube, or hose, Figure 26.35. It makes an excellent, easily removed, high-pressure static seal. Special note is made of this design because of difficulties that may be encountered during assembly of the joint.

The split flange fitting seals on its face. The shoulder which contains the seal must abut squarely against the mating surface and be held there with even tension on all bolts. The shoulder sticks out past the flange halves by 0.010 to 0.030 in. to insure contact with the mating accessory surface before the flange halves do, Figure 26.36.

Surface finish

Before bolting parts together, examine the sealing

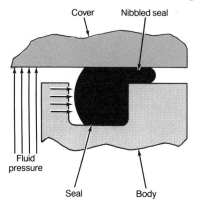

Fig. 26.34. Install seals to avoid extrusion.

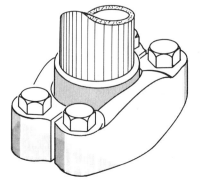

Fig. 26.35. SAE 4-bolt split flange.

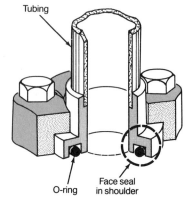

Fig. 26.36. Cutaway view of split flange.

surfaces. The seal will leak if these surfaces are gouged or scratched. The seal will wear if used with rough surface finishes — 32-micrometre finish is recommended but 64 is acceptable. The seal will extrude if the surfaces are not flat — all points over the surface should be within 0.0005 in. of flatness.

The problem

This connection is sensitive to human error. When bolts are tightened on one end, the flanges tend to tip up in a seesaw fashion; the O-ring may be pinched, Figure 26.37. Use a new correct size O-ring to match the flange and of correct material to match the fluid. Apply a light grease to the O-ring before assembly to hold it in place. Be sure all surfaces are clean. Finger tightening with use of feeler gages will help get the flanges and shoulder started squarely.

When the bolts are fully torqued, the flanges often bend down until they bottom on the port face and bolts bend outward, Figure 26.38. Bending of flanges and bolts tends to lift the flange off the shoulder in the center area between the long spacing of the bolts. Much of the high torque on all bolts, which must be Grade 5 or better, is lost in overcoming the bending of the flanges and the bolts.

The solution

As a solution, torque all bolts evenly. Do not tighten one bolt fully before going to the next bolt.

Table 26.8 — Sae 4-bolt flange torque

Nominal tube O.D. inches	Connection size	Torque foot/pounds
½	— 8	21
¾	—12	40
1	—16	40
1¾	—20	60
1½	—24	90
2	—32	90

Table 26.7 — Static seal leakage analysis

Possible source of trouble	Suggested remedy
1. Seal has extruded or been nibbled to death	Replace seal and check the following: a. Sealing surfaces must be flat within .0005 inches, replace part if out of limits. b. Initial bolt torque may have been too low. Check manual for proper torque. c. Pressure pulses may be too high. Check for proper relief valve setting. d. If normal operating presures exceed 1500 psi, back-up rings are required.
2. Seal is badly worn	Replace seal and check the following: a. Sealing surface too rough, polish to 16 μ in. if possible or replace part. b. Undertorqued bolts permit movement. Check manual for correct setting. c. Seal material or durometer may be wrong. Check manual if in doubt.
3. Seal is hard or has taken excessive permanent set	Replace seal and check the following: a. Determine what normal operating temperature is. Check system temperature. b. Check manual to determine that correct seal material is being used.
4. Sealing surfaces are scratched, gouged or have spiral tool marks	Replace faulty parts if marks cannot be polished out.
5. Seal has been pinched or cut on assembly	Use petrolatum to hold seal in place with blind assembly. Use protective shim if seal must pass over sharp threads.
6. Seal leaks for no apparent reason	Check seal size and parts size. Get correct replacement parts.

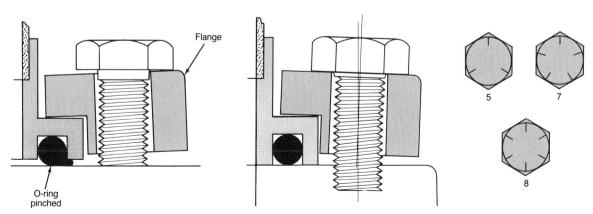

Fig. 26.37. Example of potential problem caused by tipped flange and shoulder.

Fig. 26.38. Bent flanges will cause bent bolts.

Fig. 26.39. Three grades of tightening bolts.

343

Don't use air wrenches because they tend to cause flange tipping. All bolts are not alike. The higher the bolt grade, the stronger the bolt. Always use graded bolts, with head identified as in Figure 26.39, and torque to the values recommended in Table 26.8. Socket-head bolts may be used in place of hex head since they are grade 8 or better.

Important terms

Diagnostics is the art of inferring from symptoms the fundamental cause of a problem.

Maintenance consists of the mechanical procedures applied to correcting the cause(s) of problem(s) determined by troubleshooting.

Prime mover is an energy source for a fluid power system, typically electric motors or internal combustion engines.

Torque-Speed Characteristics: are usually illustrated by the curves defining the relationship between torque delivery capability as a function of speed for a device.

Troubleshooting is the logical procedure for applying diagnostics to determine the cause(s) of a problem(s).

Review Exercises

26.1. Discuss the difference(s) between troubleshooting and design.

26.2. Discuss the implication of Figure 26.1. Why do we say that the thought process is the same for troubleshooting and designing a hydraulic circuit? Relate to Figures 26.2 to 26.8.

26.3. Discuss the difference(s) between troubleshooting and maintenance. Why is the distinction made?

26.4. What are the fundamental equations relating variables in a hydraulic system? Discuss their importance as troubleshooting tools; as design tools.

26.5. What are the implications of Figure 26.2?

26.6. Discuss Figure 26.3: Why is the *Energy Output* shown as Functional Section I? (Refer to Troubleshooting Step 3).

26.7. How does Figure 26.3 apply to troubleshooting? To design procedure?

26.8. Discuss why it is possible to consider flow and pressure related phenomena independently in troubleshooting; in design.

26.9. What is the significance of q_p, q_v and a_m in Figure 26.3?

26.10. What effect would "load malfunction" have on hydraulic system performance? Discuss implications of load malfunction on the Cycle Profile. How would this relate to troubleshooting?

26.11. How would the Sequence Diagram (Refer to Chapters 22 and 26) be helpful in troubleshooting?

26.12. With a linear actuator (cylinder) output what is the first question to be asked in the troubleshooting method? Discuss.

26.13. Why is it said that an actuator has no "output force" capability? Discuss.

26.14. How is pressure defined in Troubleshooting Step 5?

26.15. Referring to Figure 26.4: Why is the $F = pA$ expression written in terms of differential pressures and differential areas? Discuss the implications for both troubleshooting and design.

26.16. What error is frequently made in measuring

pressure in a circuit when trying to diagnose load reaction on an actuator?

26.17. What is the second question to be asked concerning actuator performance in a circuit?

26.18. Discuss effective flow rate, Q_e, and its implication for load velocity.

26.19. Discuss internal leakage in a linear actuator. How can it be measured in an actual circuit?

26.20. When troubleshooting a sustained load, what safety precautions should be taken to protect the service person?

26.21. What is the fundamental purpose for determining piston rod velocity in troubleshooting a circuit?

26.22. What does it mean if piston rod velocity, v_p, drops off as load increases?

26.23. Discuss the statement that load reaction, F_L, is the independent variable and pressure, p_4, is the dependent variable in a linear actuator.

26.24. Discuss the statement that flow rate Q_4 is the independent variable and piston rod velocity v_p, is the dependent variable in a linear actuator.

26.25. Repeat exercise 26.12, for a rotary motor.

26.26. Does the conclusion reached in exercise 26.13 have any bearing on hydraulic motors? Discuss.

26.27. Why is it important to use pressure differential from inlet to output motor ports when calculating torque capability?

26.28. Repeat exercise 26.17 for a motor.

26.29. Does effective flow rate, Q_e, have the same significance for motors as it does for linear actuators? Explain.

26.30. Repeat exercise 26.19 for a motor.

26.31. Repeat exercise 26.21 for a motor.

26.32. Does the conclusion of exercise 26.22 also apply to a motor? Explain.

26.33. Discuss the implication of Troubleshooting Step 10.

26.34. Discuss why we departed from the normal design procedure in Step 11, when we applied the procedure to troubleshooting.

26.35. What factors determine the discharge pressure at the pump?

26.36. A positive displacement pump is (check one) ( ) a pressure generator ( ) a flow generator. Explain your answer.

26.37. What factors determine pump delivery? How are they determined in the troubleshooting process? In the circuit design process?

26.38. Discuss pump inlet conditions as illustrated in Figure 26.7.

26.39. Why must suction lift, Z_s, be less for fire resistant fluids than for mineral oils?

26.40. What recommendations are given for suction head, Z_w, for high water content fluids? Why?

26.41. Discuss cavitation. What effect does it have on pump performance?

26.42. Discuss the implications on hydraulic circuit performance of pump input variables. Where does pump input come from?

26.43. If a pump is "overloaded" by excessive fluid pressure, what are the effects on input variables: torque, T_i and speed, N_i?

26.44. Is it possible to overload a pump with excessive delivery, Q_1?

26.45. What is the principal difference in diagnosing fixed displacement and variable displacement pump performance?

26.47. What effect does pump slip have on circuit performance? How can pump slip be determined?

26.48. What is the effect of discharge pressure, p_i, on pump slip?

26.49. Does pump speed, N_i, have any significant effect on slip? Explain.

26.50. Does pump speed, N_i, have any significant effect on cavitation? Explain.

26.51. Are slip and cavitation related? Explain.

26.52. What functional section is discussed in troubleshooting Step 17? In troubleshooting, Step 17 has been placed after energy output and input. Where would it appear in the design sequence? What figure illustrates it?

26.53. What factors influence pressure, p_3, at the load port of the directional control valve, Figure 26.5?

26.54. What factor influences pressure drop across a directional control valve? Refer also to Chapter 24.

26.55. How many "pressure drops" are there in a 4-way directional control valve? Discuss.

26.56. On what factor(s) does the return port back-pressure, p_5, depend? Is it possible for p_5 to exceed p_3? Explain: Can p_5 affect circuit performance?

26.58. Discuss the effect of area ratio in a differential cylinder on return flow.

26.59. What are some of the causes of bypass flow in a pressure control valve? Does such bypass flow affect circuit performance? Explain. Refer to Chapter 8.

26.60. What is meant by "cracking" pressure and "cracking band" for a relief valve? Refer to Chapter 8. How can this affect circuit performance?

26.61. What factors affect input pressure, p_2, to the controls functional section?

26.62. What determines input flow to the controls functional section? Discuss from a troubleshooting point of view. Discuss from a design point of view. Are the two the same? Discuss.

26.63. Referring to Figure 26.3: Invert the block diagram with the origin (at left) starting with *load* variables as *inputs* and proceeding through functional sections, I, II, and III in that order, to prime mover variables as outputs (at the right). Does this exercise change the way you think about hydraulic circuits at all? Explain.

CHAPTER 27

CONSIDERATIONS
OF CIRCUIT DYNAMICS

We have, so far, considered open loop hydraulic circuit design and performance based on *steady state* conditions. Steady state design and analysis presume no change in the state of a variable with time.

Figure 27.1 shows the velocity profile of Figure 4.1 (*b*) with simple harmonic motion added as Method 4. When we discussed the choice of velocity profile in Chapter 4, Method 1 was presented as a case of steady state velocity, which is true during time interval t_3 -t_1. We accommodated acceleration and deceleration periods, $t_1 - 0$ and t_5 -t_4 by assuming uniform (steady state) acceleration:

$$\overline{a}_a = (v_1 - v_0)/(t_1 - t_0), \text{ and}$$
$$-\overline{a}_a = (v_5 - v_3)/(t_5 - t_4).$$

We thus assumed the slope of the velocity curve in those time intervals to be constant.

For most designs, this approach might be accurate enough, especially since the system designer may be compelled to guess at many machine parameters. Refer to Chapter 22 and Figures 16.8 and 22.2 . However, when variations in a parameter such as velocity must be considered, the more accurate expression for velocity and acceleration would be:

$$v = \dot{x} = dx/dt,$$
and
$$a = \dot{v} = \ddot{x} = d^2x/dt^2 = dv/dt.$$

In the case of Method 4 velocity profile, the variables must be expressed as a function of time since they vary constantly and steady state, as previously discussed, has no meaning.

For simple harmonic motion,

$$S = N \sin \omega t,$$
$$\dot{S} = v = \omega N \cos \omega t,$$
and
$$\ddot{S} = a = \omega^2 N \sin \omega t.$$

This chapter introduces some concepts of circuit dynamics (time variant phenomena) and discusses their effects on open loop hydraulic circuit performance.

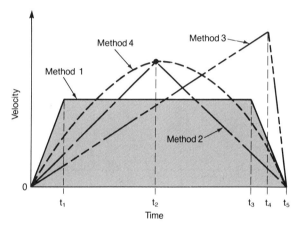

Fig. 27.1. Velocity profile for Figure 4.1(b).

In Figure 16.8, some of these concepts were treated graphically, defining several degrees of refinement in designing a hydraulic circuit.

The first or *approximation level* is as far as many designers go. The *function level* is an attempt to conceptualize the differences between specifying the function and hardware to implement the function. This level shows that *function* actually relates to *performance,* not how hardware achieves the functions.

At the *parametric* level, the designer tries to match specific hardware to load requirements. Figure 16.8 was based on steady-state analysis. Another level is now added: *circuit dynamics*.

The example in Figure 27.2 is based on the overrunning load of Figure 5.2 and the load analysis of Chapter 5.

Figure 27.2 (*a*) shows the *constant flow* version of the circuit (refer to Chapter 6); Figure 27.2 (*b*) the *demand flow* version (refer to Chapter 7); Figure 27.2(*c*) the *circuit variables* for the constant flow case as they vary with time at key points in the system. It is assumed that load- and prime-mover characteristics conform to the cycle plot.

Note that representations of circuit variables in Figure 27.2(*c*) are made in the direction of flow

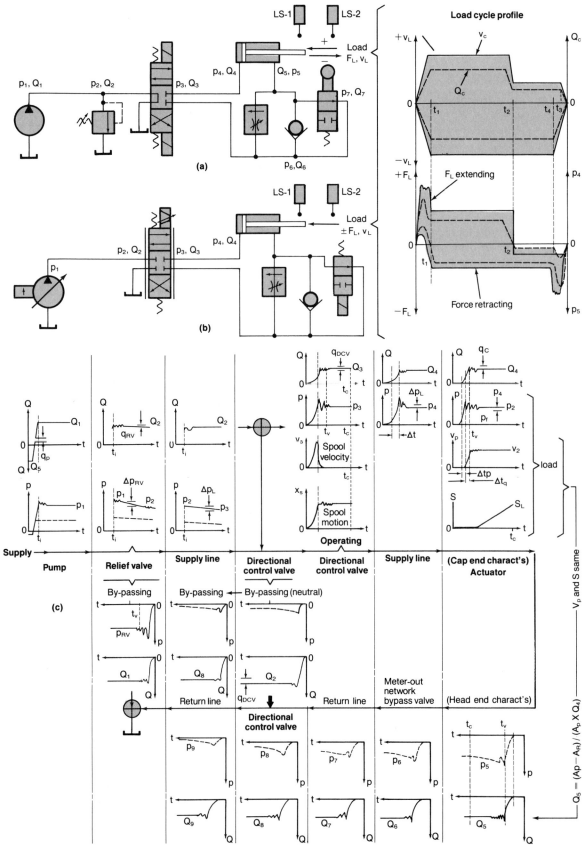

Fig. 27.2. Dynamics of overrunning load of Figure 5.2. Figure 27.2(a) shows a constant flow version; Figure 27.2(b) the demand flow version; and Figure 27.2(c) the circuit variables for the constant flow version as each varies with time.

starting at the source, progressing around the entire circuit and ending at the return to the reservoir. Only the initial segment of the machine cycle is shown (rapid traverse) which occurs during time interval $t_2 - t_0$ in the Cycle Profile, Figures 5.2 and 27.2(*a*)*.

Starting at the energy input (pump) on the supply side, observe the pressure-flow characteristics discussed in Figures 1.4, 1.5 and 16.8. Here, t_1 is the initial time at which pump delivery reaches steady state Q_1. Pump discharge pressure

$$p_1 = p_4 + \Sigma\Delta p_2$$

around the circuit, allowing for the ratio of the cylinder piston differential areas.

Note the wavy line during the initial period as each variable changes, Figure 27.2(*c*). This is a transient period of instability which occurs because of such factors as:

- system compliance,
- fluid compressibility,
- internal leakage caused by pressure variations, and
- energy storage due to elastic deformation of load structure, etc.

These transient periods of instability occur constantly in hydraulic systems. Because they are usually inconsequential as far as system performance is concerned, they are neglected. However, as users come to expect greater precision from a system (Chapters 15 and 16), designers will have to concern themselves with these instability transients. The ultimate design procedure will be to model a circuit mathematically and account for all time variant parameters in the equations. Computers will facilitate this type of analysis.

Relief valves

Relief valve characteristics are represented in Figure 27.2(*c*) for two situations: 1) normal operation with supply flow normally passing through the valve, and 2) relief valve bypassing flow. If there is no leakage, $Q_2 = Q_1$. If there is leakage,

$$q_2 = Q_1 - q_{RV}'.$$

Pressure drop is for a simple orifice, $\Delta p = f(Q^2)$.

Supply line characteristics are simple: assuming no leakage in the line, $Q_2 = Q_3$; pressure drop follows the rule for turbulent flow: $\Delta p = f(Q^2)_1$. If the relief valve is bypassing, as shown in Figure 27.2(*c*), pressure flow characteristics follow those for relief valves, Chapter 8.

Directional control valves

Dynamic interactions are more apparent in directional control valves. Again, two situations are illustrated in Figure 27.2(*c*):

- flow bypassing through a valve with a tandem center in neutral position, and
- valve shifted to direct pressure fluid to the cap end of a cylinder and return fluid to reservoir.

In the bypass mode, flow through the orifice is typical, $\Delta p = f(Q_2^2)$. However, when the solenoid is energized to shift the valve spool, dynamic transient effects become apparent. Response delays — called lags — for the electrical part of the control circuit, Figure 27.2 have not been included.

The analysis starts with spool motor X_s; spool velocity v_s; and related pressure rise and flow rate characteristics. Refer to Figure 27.2(*c*). Note the response lags which build sequentially:

- spool velocity requires a time differential, Δt, to go from 0 to maximum velocity v_{max}
- spool position follows acceleration and steady state velocity until it reaches a limit stop
- pressure builds exponentially as the valve orifice area increases with spool movement, and
- flow rate increases as pressure rises.

During this transient spool shift period, excess flow from the constant flow source bypasses over the relief valve at full pressure setting (refer to Figures 5.7 and 6.3). When steady state conditions are reached, at time t_v, flow rate $Q_3 = Q_2 - q_{\text{dir. valve}}$ is delivered to the supply port at pressure $p_3 = p_4 + \Delta p_{line}$.

Characteristics of the line between the directional control valve load port and the actuator inlet port follow directional control valve outputs. Additional lags could be introduced in long lines due to the compressibility of a larger volume of fluid. As will be discussed later in this chapter, entrained air also contributes to compressibility. Use of hose instead of tubing adds capacitance to the system.

Next, consider cylinder cap-end variables. We have shown characteristics for:

- typical stroke, S
- velocity of loaded piston rod
- load pressure, p_4, and
- input flow rate, Q_4.

These all show the lags characteristic of spring-mass systems and transient instability periods, as previously discussed. These characteristics are linked directly to load variables as defined by the Cycle Profile, Figure 5.2. Additional effects must be considered namely those caused by return flow and pressure variables. As shown in Figure 27.2(*c*), interactions occur across the piston interface. The area ratio across the piston introduces changes in the variables. Return flow rate during the extend stroke is reduced by the area ratio, $(A_p - A_R)A_p$; on the retract stroke, Q_5 is increased by the ratio, $A_p / (A_p - A_R)$.

As discussed in Chapters 24 and 26, amplified return flows result in increased $\Delta p_R = p_7$ across the directional control valve. Large piston area ratios can result in backpressures high enough to cause valves to malfunction and, within limits, could re-

---

**Extrapolation of the diagram to the* feed *and* retract *portions of the cycle is left to the student as is the entire diagram for* demand flow.

duce the load handling capacity of the actuator.

There is an additional impedance in the form of a cam-operated bypass valve in the meter-out flow control network needed for *feed* velocities. This impedance appears as a typical, orifice-type pressure differential, $\Delta p = f(Q^2)$ characteristic. Had the procedure been carried into the feed part of the cycle, a switch would have to be included from the open bypass valve to the pressure compensated flow control (Chapter 10) when the bypass is cammed closed.

Beyond the meter-out network, there is a return line to consider, then the return path characteristics through the directional control valve. Backpressure, p_7, at the return port, is a function of $(Q_7)^2$; Q_7 being equal to Q_5 -$q_{back\ pressure}$. A subtle consideration would involve any cylinder bypass leakage, q_c. Refer to Chapter 26. If there is leakage,

$$Q_e = Q_4 - q_c; \text{ and}$$
$$Q_5 = [(A_p - A_R)\,Q_e/A_p] + q_c.$$

Flow from the directional control valve reservoir port, $Q_8 = Q_7 - q_{DCV}$ and pressure $p_8 = p_7 \Delta p_{DCV}$. As was the case with the supply line, response lags on the return side display the same general characteristics. Pressure, $p_8 = \Delta p_{line}$ between the reservoir port and reservoir. If a return line filter is used in the system, Chapter 20, an additional pressure differential Δp_f must be accounted for.

By definition, this analysis began at the pump and proceeded around the circuit in the direction of flow. This is correct as long as the designer considers the *flow* variables since various leakages are substracted progressively from input flow rate, Q_1:

$$Q_1 = Q_9 + q_{DV_R} + q_{BP} + q_{D_S} + q_{RV} + q_e$$

where Q_9 represents return flow to reservoir.

Conversely, pressure drops around the circuit:

$$P_1 = \Delta p_{RV} + \Delta p_{L_1} + \Delta p_{D_S} + \Delta p_{L_2}$$
$$+ \left\{ F_L + \left[p_5 (A_p - A_p) \right] + F_f \right\} / \Delta P$$
$$+ \Delta p_{BP} + \Delta p_{L_3} + \Delta p_{D_R} + \Delta p_{L_4}$$

Note that the flow and pressure equations are steady state. Should the parameters vary as a function of time, they would have to be stated in differential form, dQ/dt or dp/dt. It follows that the same visualization technique could be applied to a circuit with a continuous rotation motor.

It is not suggested that the concept of Figure 27.2 (c) be used as a design or analytical tool in the same sense as the Cycle Profile. It has fulfilled its mission in illustrating how physical variables in a hydraulic system change as a function of time and in relationship to position in the system. The implications of these interactions are discussed in the balance of this chapter.

CONCEPTS OF BULK MODULUS

The stiffness of a hydraulic system is related to the relative incompressibility of the fluid, called bulk modulus, β.

Bulk modulus units are given in *psi*: the higher the bulk modulus, the stiffer the fluid and, therefore, the hydraulic system.

There are two types of bulk moduli[2]:

1. Secant bulk modulus is the average of the change in pressure, Δp, divided by the total change in volume per unit of initial volume,

$$\beta_s = \Delta p / (\Delta V / V_0)$$

2. Tangent bulk modulus is the inverse of fluid incompressibility at a specific point, or

$$\beta_t = -V_0 (6p/6V).$$

The bulk modulus of a hydraulic fluid *increases slightly* with rising pressure, but *decreases sharply* with rising temperature. Entrained air has a marked adverse effect on bulk modulus: it acts like a soft spring in series with the oil column compliance. Table 27.2 shows the effect of increasing amounts of entrained air on bulk modulus[2].

3. Effective bulk modulus[2], β_e, is to the overall system what *secant* bulk modulus, β_s, is to the hydraulic fluid: it reflects the compliance of all the elements in a system. Components of β_e include:

β_f — bulk modulus of the fluid, gas-free
β_H — bulk modulus of all the hoses in the system
β_t — bulk modulus of the metal tubing, and
β_c — bulk modulus of components structure.

The general expression for the effective bulk modulus, β_e, is:

$$1/\beta_e = 1/\beta_c + 1/\beta_f + 1/\beta_H$$
$$+ (V_g/V_\varrho)(1/\beta g - 1/\beta_l)$$

where:

β_l — bulk modulus of the liquid, gas-free
β_H — bulk modulus of all the hoses in the system
β_c — bulk modulus of the components structure
β_g — bulk modulus of the gas
V_g — volume of entrained gas, and
V_ϱ — volume of liquid, gas-free

The bulk modulus of thick walled cylinders is:

$$1/\beta_{P_c} = 2/E \left\{ \left[(1 + \nu)\,D^2 + (1 + \nu)d^2 \right] \left[2T(D + d) \right] \right\}$$

where:

E — modulus of elasticity, psi
ν — Poisson's ratio of cylinder material
D — OD of cylinder barrel, in
d — ID of cylinder barrel, and
T — wall thickness of cylinder barrel, in.

Table 27.1—Hydraulic Parameters

Hydraulic analogy	Abbreviation	Units	Standard symbol	Typical use	Property
Pressure in a line, cylinder, or accumulator	p	psi		$p_1 - p_2 = QR$	Potential
Flow of fluid through a line or passage	Q	in³/sec (gpm)	Q	$p_1 - p_2 = QR$	Flow
Restriction offered to flow by an orifice	R	psi/in³	R	$p_1 - p_2 = QR$	Resistance
Ability of an orifice to pass flow	g	in³/psi	g	$Q = g(p_1 - p_2)$	Conductance (reciprocal of resistance)
Ability, of a volume of oil, or accumulator, to store pressure	C	in³/psi	c or	$p = \frac{1}{C} \int Q\, dt$ $Q = C\frac{dp}{dt}$	Capacitance

Table 27.2 — Effects of increasing amounts of entrained air in fluid

V_g/V_l	β_e – psi
0.00	2.02×10^5
0.005	1.84×10^4
0.01	9.5×10^3
0.02	5.8×10^3
0.03	3.28×10^3
0.05	1.98×10^3
0.10	10^3

The bulk modulus for thin wall cylinders[2] is:

$$\beta_{ct} = TE/D.$$

Bulk modulus of hydraulic line tubing[2], where D - d = thick wall:

$$\beta_T = E/2(1 + \nu) \approx E/2.5 \text{ for steel tubing.}$$

Bulk modulus of hydraulic line tubing, where $T = d/2$:

$$\beta_t = 3E/2\,(5+3\nu) \approx E/3.83.$$

Bulk modulus of rubber (wire braid) hose[2] is:

$$\beta_H = (V_t \times \Delta p)/V_h;$$
$$V_h = e_c\Delta p V_t)$$

where:

V_t — total volume in hose = $\pi d^2/4L_H$
L_H — length of hose, in.
Δ_p — change in pressure, psi
V_h — change in physical volume of hose, and
e_c — cubic expansion coefficient.

There are two types of bulk moduli of gases[2]:

Isothermal bulk modulus is:

$$\beta_{gI} = V_{go}\Delta_p/\Delta V = p_{go}$$

that is the isothermal bulk modulus of a gas equals the initial pressure of the gas, p_{go}.

Adiabatic bulk modulus is:

$$\beta_{gA} = (C_p/C_V)\,p_{go}$$

where:

C_P — specific heat of gas at constant pressure
C_v — specific heat of gas at constant volume

SPRING RATES AND NATURAL FREQUENCIES

Since the designer is dealing with fluid power *spring-mass* systems, he must concern himself with the spring rates of the system's various elements and their combinations. Bulk modulus is a key factor in determining these spring rates and related natural frequencies.

Natural frequencies in hydraulic systems affect system performance and stability. The designer must be particularly careful to avoid *resonance* between a hydraulic system, its related control system, and the load. Resonant conditions result in oscillations of large magnitude which, at best may cause system malfunction; and at worst may cause it to self-destruct.

The **spring rate** of a column of fluid is:

$$K = A\beta_e/L,$$

where:

A — area of the column of fluid, in^2
L — length of the column, in., and
β_e — effective bulk modulus, psi.

Effective spring rate is:

$$1/K_e = k/K_{load} + \frac{L}{\beta_e \bullet A}$$

Note that K_e will always be less than the spring rate of the softest element in the system, *i.e.*, that having the lowest spring rate.

Application example:

Given a column of fluid 1½ ID, 36 long; bulk modulus $\beta = 2 \times 10^5$ psi. Calculate the spring rate.

$$K = A\beta/L = (1.77 \times 2 \times 10^5)/36$$
$$= 9,833 \text{ lb/in.}$$

Hydraulic natural frequency can be calculated from the general equation:

$$\omega_n = \sqrt{K_e/M_e},$$

where:

ω_n — natural frequency
K_e — effective spring rate
M_e — effective mass $= M_L + M_p + M_f$
M_L — load mass
M_p — piston/rod mass, and
M_f — mass of the fluid.

Example: Calculate the natural frequency of the column of fluid in the previous example:

$$\omega_n = \sqrt{K/M_f} = \sqrt{9833/(5.3 \times 10^{-3})}$$
$$= \sqrt{1.86 \times 10^6}$$
$$= 1.36 \times 10^3 \text{ rad/sec} \equiv 216.5 \text{ Hz}$$

where:

$$M_f = \rho V_f = 8.316 \times 10^{-5} \times 63.72 \text{ in}^3$$
$$= 5.3 \times 10^{-3} \text{ lb. sec}^2/\text{in}$$

Hydraulic natural frequency of an actuator:

$$\omega = \sqrt{[(\beta_e A_p^2)/M_p](1/V_{c_1} + 1/V_{c_2})}$$

where:

V_{c_1} — initial cylinder volume on one side of piston, and
V_{c_2} — initial cylinder volume on other side of piston.

Refer to Figure 27.2(c): the sources of some of the transient periods of instability shown on the curves can be inferred from the discussion of bulk modulus, compliance, spring rates, and natural frequencies.

TRANSMISSION LINE DYNAMICS

Consideration of transmission line dynamics includes concepts of spring rate and natural frequency, discussed above. In addition, the designer must be concerned with transmission line effects on system response. Of special interest are pressure transients or shock or water hammer as these transients are sometimes called.

Celerity

Celerity is the speed at which a pressure wave travels along a fluid transmission line.

$$c = \sqrt{\beta_f/\rho},$$

where:

c — speed of sound in a hydraulic fluid
β_f — fluid bulk modulus, and
ρ — fluid density.

The associated wave length in a tube is:

$$\lambda = c/f = 2\pi c/\omega,$$

where:

λ — wave length
ω — $2\pi f$, and
f — frequency, Hz.

Examples of transmission lines

Several cases must be considered

1. Open end line. Resonance occurs when input impedance is zero as when:

$$L = 0, \lambda/2, \lambda, 3\lambda/2.$$

2. Closed end line. Resonance occurs when

$\omega L/c = \pi/2, 3\pi/2, 5\pi/2 \ldots$
Fundamental frequency is $f_f = c/4L$ Hz.
Pressure ratio $p_{4/p_1} = 1/\cos\omega L/c$,

where:

p_4 is load pressure; p_1 is supply pressure.
$p_4/p_1 = 1$ when $\omega L/c = 0, \lambda, 2\lambda \ldots < \infty$

Given a 7-piston pump rotating at 2400 rpm in a system filled with MIL-H-5606 fluid. A valve is closed at the end of the line. What transmission lengths should be avoided to prevent resonance?

a) Celerity, $c = \sqrt{\beta/\rho}$
$ = 4480$ fps $\times 12 = 53,800$ ips.

b) $\omega = 7 (2400/60) 2\pi = 1759.3$ rad/sec.

c) since resonance occurs at odd multiples of $\pi/2$,

$L_{res} = [(\pi/2) 53,800]/1759.3$

$\phantom{L_{res}} = 48.04$ in. $= 4.01$ ft.

This length, or odd multiples of it, should be avoided to prevent resonance.

3. Line with an end chamber

Refer to Figures 27.2(a) and (b)

a) *Limits*: if the volume of the end chamber $V_c = 0$, the condition is that a *closed* tube. If $V_c = \infty$, the condition is that of an *open* tube. If the cross-sectional area of the cylinder is greater than 10 times its length, the effect of L_f is small; that of R_H is negligible, and the chamber only adds capacitance to the system.

b) *Excluding the above limits*, resonance occurs at $f_{LC} = (n\pi - \phi)(c/2\pi L)$,

c) *Solution* to specific problems involves procedures beyond the scope of this textbook. The reader is referred to Chapter 5, Ref. 2 for a more complete treatment of the problem.

PULSES IN TRANSMISSIONS

Two types of pressure pulses are encountered in hydraulic systems. *Periodic pulses* such as those resulting from pump ripple; and *transient pulses*, as typified by shock or water hammer.

Periodic pulses

Designers may consider three techniques for suppressing pressure ripple: a closed-end side branch, a Quincke tube, or an accumulator.

Case 1: The requisite condition to suppress pressure ripple with a *closed-end side branch* is that its input impedance be zero. Then, all of the ripple will pass into the branch and none into the system. For this to occur, the length of the branch tube must equal one quarter wave length, *i.e.*, $L = \lambda/4$, or an even multiple of it. Such a branch tube will be effective for only one frequency.

Case 2: Quincke tube, Figure 27.3, is constructed so areas

$$A_1 = (A_2 + A_3) = A_4.$$

Then, if the following condition is met,

$$L_3 = L_2 + (2\eta + 1)\lambda/2,$$

excess pressure at the junction of lines 2, 3 and 4 is

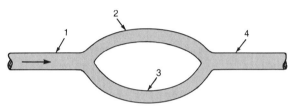

Fig. 27.3. Schematic of Quincke tube

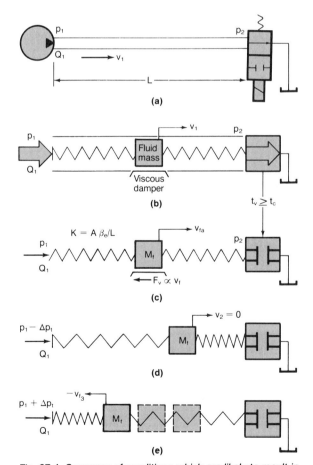

Fig. 27.4. Sequence of conditions which are likely to result in water hammer action. Fig. 27.4(a) circuit schematic; Fig. 27.4(b) equivalent spring-mass system under equilibrium conditions with valve open; Fig. 27.4 (c) instant of valve closure; Fig. 27.4(d) instant when fluid mass comes to rest; Fig. 27.4(e) pressure wave reflected back toward pump.

zero, and a wave traveling from left to right cannot be transmitted into line 4.

Case 3: To be an effective pulse damper, an accumulator must have zero input impedance. This occurs when:

$$\omega\,L/c = \pi/2, 3\pi/2, 5\pi/2\ \text{etc.,}$$
$$\text{or if}\ f_L = c/4L.$$

Transient pulses

One of the most obvious problems encountered in hydraulic systems is that of pressure shock (water hammer) associated with rapid valve closing and opening. Figure 27.4 illustrates the conditions which lead to water hammer.

A simplified hydraulic system is shown in Figure 27.4 (*a*). The mass of fluid in the line is:

$$M_f = \rho_f A_l L.$$

With the valve open (passing) as shown, flow velocity is:

$$v_1 = Q_1/A_l$$

under steady state conditions, Figure 27.4(*b*).

Figure 27.4(*c*) represents the instant of closure when the valve closes *faster* than the critical closing time, t_c. Critical closure time t_c, is the time it takes for the pressure wave to make one round trip from the valve to the source and back at the speed of sound in the fluid. Refer to celerity previously discussed in this chapter.

If the valve closes *within* the time interval, t_c, the pressure wave which produces water hammer will occur, and the pressure rise will be maximum. If valve closure takes longer than time interval, t_c, pressure rise will be less severe. Cause of the pressure wave is represented in the sequence of Figure 27.4 (*b*) through (*e*).

In Figure 27.4(*b*) fluid flow is replaced by a mass equal to m_f, with springs on either side. Since flow is steady state with the valve open, "spring compressions" are in equilibrium.

The viscous effects of fluid flowing through the pipe are represented by a *viscous damper* which is responsible for ultimately damping out the pressure waves caused by rapid valve closure. It is important to recognize that this is a spring-mass system.

It is more difficult to visualize a fluid mass, m_f, moving through the tube and the compliance of the fluid-conductor system being equivalent to springs with a rate K.

Figure 27.4(*c*) shows the valve closed; fluid velocity at the valve face is zero. However velocity is *not* zero throughout the rest of the column of fluid in the tube because of the kinetic energy of the mass, m_f, moving at flow velocity, v_f.

Figure 27.4(*d*) shows what happens as the moving mass of fluid compresses the "spring" against the closed valve and stretches the upstream spring until the mass of fluid comes to a stop against the valve face. At this instant, the kinetic energy of the fluid mass is zero because its velocity is zero.

However, the energy has been stored as potential energy because of the compression of the fluid and stretch of the tube. At this point, there is a force imbalance in the upstream direction — a higher pressure at the valve face than at the inlet to the tube.

A pressure wave will start upstream and move in that direction reversing the process of 27.4 (d) until the conditions shown in Figure 27.4(e) are reached. The pressure wave will oscillate within the tube until damped out by viscous effects as shown by curves in Figure 27.5. The curves are shown for both valve closing and opening conditions. Reduction in amplitude, Figure 27.5, is due to viscous damping which absorbs energy during each cycle.

Here are the equations for estimating system performance:

Valve closing
Fast closure: $t \leq t_c = 2L/c$

$$p_{RMAX} = 0.433\, cv_1 S_G/g.$$

Rule of thumb for typical system
$P_r \approx 50 v_1$ (v_1 is in fps).

Valve Opening
Fast opening: $t \leq t_c = 2L/c$,
$$P_{D\,MAX} = 0.433\, S_G$$
$$[\sqrt{K_f(0.8668 S_G p_1 + K_f)} - K_f],$$
$$K_f = (0.2165\, S_G c^2 v_1^2)/(p_1 g^2).$$

Fast valve closing/and opening produces the highest pressure transients in a hydraulic system. If shock is observed, the most effective way to reduce water hammer is to slow the valve's shifting speed. This can be done most readily in pilot-operated directional control valves with pilot chokes to throttle flow from the pilot valve to the power spool. Another possible solution is to use a throttling spool to eliminate sharp flow cut-off when a spool land passes the end of a flow passage in the valve body.

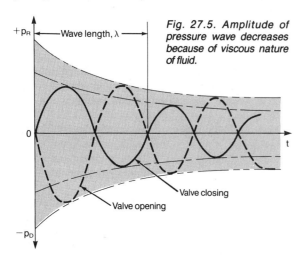

Fig. 27.5. Amplitude of pressure wave decreases because of viscous nature of fluid.

ENERGY OUTPUT DYNAMICS
Dynamics of hydraulic cylinders and motors are considered here qualitatively to provide students with insights into the differences between steady state and dynamic performance.

Linear actuators
An analysis of the dynamics for the cylinder illustrated in Figure 27.2(a) are shown in Figure 27.6.

Figure 27.6(a) represents the steady-state variables which are generally considered during the design stage of a hydraulic system and component selection. Refer to Chapters 3, 4, 5, and 23. Figure 27.6(b) represents force variable components which may be considered for dynamic analysis. The expressions in Figure 27.6(b) are not rigorous mathematical ones. Figure 27.6(c) represents flow-velocity relationships for the linear actuator.

Hydraulic motor
Figure 27.7 represents a continous rotation hydraulic motor resembling that for the cylinder of Figure 27.6.

Figure 27.7(a) shows the steady-state condition of the hydraulic motor. Figure 27.7(b) shows qualitatively the components of resistance torque which the hydraulic motors must overcome to break away, accelerate, and rotate the load, refer to Figure 16.11. Figure 27.7 (c) illustrates flow conditions. To accommodate dynamic changes in all of these variables as well as interactions with other components in a circuit can be a demanding procedure.

ENERGY CONTROLS
Fluid power controls exhibit dynamic characteristics which differ significantly from the steady-state models in general use.

Spool type directional control valves
The most commonly used directional control valves are spool type, Figure 27.8. Also refer to Chapters 12, 13, 14, and 24.

Figure 27.8(a) illustrates the operation of the most common design of spool-type directional control valves. Its switching function is determined by the interactions of spool lands with passages in the valve body. Pressure drop, Δp vs flow (Q^2) characteristics are as discussed on Chapters 7, 12 and 24.

Generally overlooked, however, are two elements: (1) the fact that a typical spring-centered spool valve is a spring mass system and (2) that it is subjected to a number of force-displacement flow rate transients which can affect the response and stability of the valve, Figure 27.8 (b). Spool friction is illustrated in Figure 27.8 (c). Assume the spool is shifted to the right at $v_s = dx/dt$; pilot force is $F_L - F_r \propto dx/dt$; friction force resisting motion is $-F_f$. Flow rate Q $\propto dx/dt$ as well.

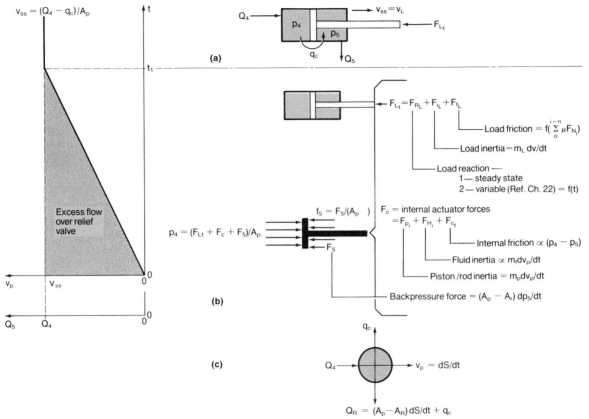

Fig. 27.6. Analysis of parameters of cylinder illustrated in Figure 27.2.

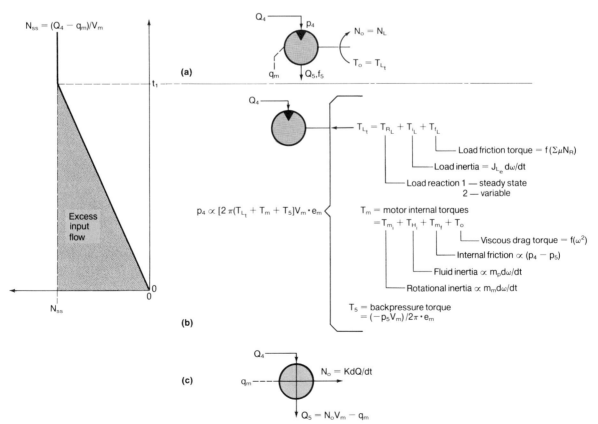

Fig. 27.7. Continuous rotation fluid motor with analysis similar to those of cylinder of Figure 27.6.

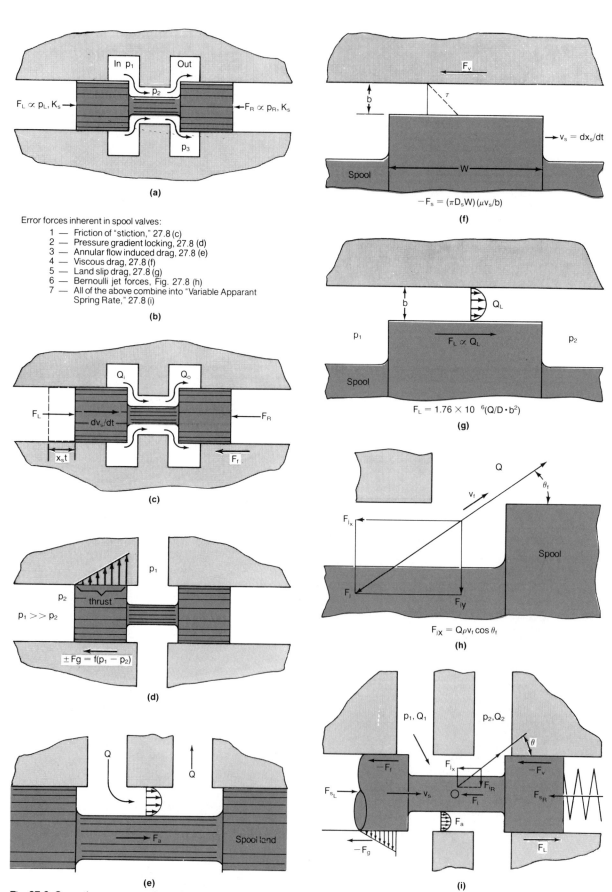

(a)

Error forces inherent in spool valves:
1 — Friction of "stiction," 27.8 (c)
2 — Pressure gradient locking, 27.8 (d)
3 — Annular flow induced drag, 27.8 (e)
4 — Viscous drag, 27.8 (f)
5 — Land slip drag, 27.8 (g)
6 — Bernoulli jet forces, Fig. 27.8 (h)
7 — All of the above combine into "Variable Apparant Spring Rate," 27.8 (i)

(b)

(c)

(d)

(e)

$$-F_s = (\pi D_s W)(\mu v_s/b)$$

(f)

$$F_L = 1.76 \times 10^{-6}(Q/D \cdot b^2)$$

(g)

$$F_{IX} = Q\rho v_f \cos \theta_f$$

(h)

(i)

Fig. 27.8. Operation sequence of spool type directional control valve.

356

Pressure gradient locking is illustrated in Figure 27.8(d). When high-pressure differentials occur across a seal land combined with variations in radial clearances, unbalanced radial pressure distribution results. This can generate a gradient across a land, thrusting the spool against its bore. The metal-to-metal contact under load results in high spool-shift forces, $F_s t = f(p_1 - p_2)$.

Annular flow induced drag, is a force which acts on the spool and is caused by flow through annular flow paths, defined by the spool and its bore, Figure 27.8(e). Viscous drag on the spool results in a force which acts in the direction of flow, Fa.

Viscous drag is a retarding force caused by the viscous shear of the fluid in capillary clearances, b, between spool lands and housing bore, Figure 27.8(f). This force is proportional to spool shift velocity v_s, and fluid viscosity, μ.

Land slip drag is the opposite of viscous drag, Figure 27.8 (g) and is a force which acts on the spool because of cross port leakage through capillary clearance.

Bernoulli jet force is a force which acts on a spool and which is caused by the momentum exchange between the fluid mass flowing through the valve and spool as a result of change in direction of the fluid jet as it progresses through flow passages in the valve, Figure 27.8(h).

The magnitude of the Bernoulli jet force is a function of the exiting angle θ_f of the fluid jet, which in turn is a function of spool position x_s and varies as a function of spool velocity dx/dt. Test have shown that maximum Bernoulli jet forces occur when θ_f equals 69 degrees. The force component of most concern is the axial force, F_{Jx}, because it may be the force which can shift the spool, Chapter 26.

Variable apparent spring rate is the algebraic sum of the spool forces listed in Figure 27.8(b). Figure 27.8(i) shows the various forces acting on a spring centered directional control valve spool. At any point during spool shift, this algebraic sum must be zero, *i.e.*, there must be equlibrium.

The most dominant of the spool error forces discussed are *friction* and the *Bernoulli jet*. Note that an *inertia* force, F_i has been added in Figure 27.8(i) to reflect the mass of the spool during its acceleration and deceleration. When considering spool position, x_s under steady state conditions, the only spring rate considered would be that of the centering spring k_s, which is essentially a linear function of compression of the spring, $F = K_s X_s$. However, when all the dynamic forces summarized in Figure 27.8 are included, a new spring rate, K_e — the variable apparent spring rate — must be used to reflect the changes in spool forces.

The designer can better understand the impact of K_e on the spool valve by applying the concept of the discussions of valves based on steady state criteria, Chapters 7, 12, 15 and 24.

Poppet valves exhibit dynamic characteristics analogous to those of spool valves.

LOAD-ENERGY OUTPUT INTERACTION

In the load analyses in Chapters 3, 4, and 5, and particularly in the Cycle Profile of Figure 5.2, it was assumed that the *load* and *output* device tracked each other perfectly:

- whenever load velocity changed, actuator velocity matched it
- whenever load reaction changed, pressure responded proportionately.

The example of Figure 5.2 in Chapter 5 is used here to illustrate that actual performance is more complicated. Refer also to Figure 27.2(a).

Application example

A 50-lb casting is placed on a machine-tool table which weighs 400 lb; clamps weighing 15 lb hold the casting in place. Horizontal table travel is 18 in. The casting is 9 in. long and is centered on the table. A work cycle consists of 4½ in. of rapid traverse, 9 in. of feed travel, and 4½ in. of travel beyond the work piece. Assume that the coefficient of friction for the machine ways is 0.1. During the milling operation, it takes 5 hp to drive the 6-in. diameter cutter at a speed of 450 rpm.

When we plotted the Cycle Profile (see Figure 5.2 and the accompanying analysis) for the feed and retract cycle, we considered mainly the "steady-state" conditions of the cylinder. We calculated the velocity of the piston rod based on the area of the piston, piston stroke and the time allowed for each part of the cycle. We left the instantaneous, or transient, behavior of the circuit undetermined, hoping that it would fall within the performance capabilities of the components. Figure 27.9 shows what we were doing intuitively when we took this approach.

At time $t = 0$, the piston is fully retracted; stroke, S, piston rod velocity, v, and flow rate into the cylinder, Q are all zero.

At the end of an initial time interval, $t_1 = \Delta t_1$, the piston rod has moved through a stroke increment, $S_1 = \Delta S_1$. The average velocity is:

$$\bar{v} = \Delta S_1 / \Delta t_I$$

and the average flow rate during the time increment is:

$$Q_1 = A_p \bar{v}_1$$

which is illustrated in Figure 27.9(b).

At the end of a second time increment,

$$t_2 = \Delta t_1 + \Delta t_2.$$

The piston rod has moved through a stroke,

$$S_2 = \Delta S_1 + \Delta S_2.$$

The average velocity over the stroke is

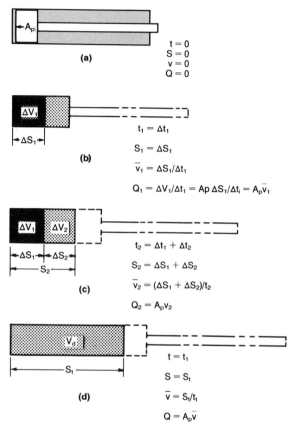

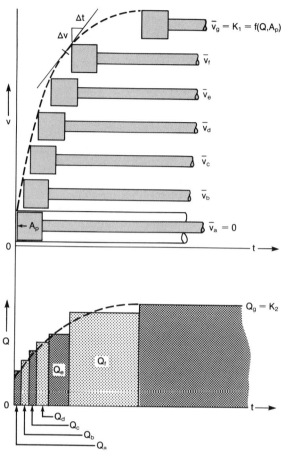

Fig. 27.9. Intuitive calculations for sizing hydraulic cylinder.

Fig. 27.10. Acceleration of cylinder piston from zero to some steady-state velocity and corresponding instantaneous flow rates.

$$\bar{v}_2 = (\Delta S_1 + \Delta S_2)/t_2,$$

and the average flow rate is

$$Q_2 = A_p\bar{v}_2.$$

The time increments Δt_1 and Δt_2 may or may not have been equal; thus the other quantities also may or may not be equal. Refer to Appendix B for a discussion on the difference between average velocity and steady velocity.

The increment-to-increment performance of the cylinder cannot be determined. The total cycle-time increment becomes the total time, t_1, for the full stroke, S_t, of the piston. Piston velocity becomes

$$\bar{v} = S_t/t_t,$$

and flow rate becomes

$$Q = A_p\bar{v}.$$

These relationships are shown in Figure 27.9(d). Refer to Chapter 6, Figure 6.3.

Now consider the application of the cylinder so that output from the system — the stroke of the cylinder — can be modulated on an almost instanteous basis. Now, the use of average values of velocity, flow rate, etc., is no longer feasible. Figure 27.10 illustrates, intuitively, the acceleration of a

piston rod in a cylinder from zero velocity to some steady-state velocity. Refer to Chapter 7, Figure 7.13. The matching flow rates are plotted against time in the lower half of the figure; the upper half shows the plot of piston position versus time.

In Figure 27.10 subscript a indicates that time, velocity, and flow rate are all zero. Subscript b indicates that, after a time differential dt, the piston has just begun to move. The velocity is still very low, as is the flow rate. The subscript g indicates that piston velocity has caught up with the available supply of hydraulic fluid, Q, and that a steady-state or constant-velocity condition prevails.

The curve connecting the various piston positions represents the acceleration curve. The acceleration at any point is the slope of the curve

$$a = \ddot{S} = \dot{v} = dv/dt$$

The flow-rate curve, Figure 27.10 bottom, indicates how flow rate might vary from zero to the constant-velocity condition.

Similar curves might be plotted for changes in state, such as the change which occurs when the casting contacts the milling cutter and switches to *feed*. If we are trying to control the process continuously, we must describe it on an instantaneous, time-related basis. To do this, we use the differential equation. Thus velocity is expressed as

$$v = ds/dt \text{ or } v = S = ds/dt,$$

and acceleration as

$$a = dv/dt = dt^2s/dt^2.$$

These differential equations describe the slopes of the stroke-time and the velocity-time curves at any point. The slope tells how much change in stroke or velocity can be expected in an infinitesimally small period of time, *dt*. A complete set of differential equations describing how a closed-loop system could be expected to act is called a *mathematical model* of the system.

For a simple cylinder, the differential equations are based on an expansion of Newton's Second Law: $F = ma$, where F is the sum of all the forces acting on the piston rod, m is the total mass, and a is the acceleration of the mass. The general form of the equation looks something like this:

$$\begin{aligned} p_s A p - (A_p - A_f) p_b - F_p - F_S - F_t \\ = (W_p + W_l/g)(dv/dt) \end{aligned} \quad (27.1)$$

where:

$p_s A_p$—driving force due to system pressure reacting on piston area
$(A_p - A_r)p_b$—backpressure reacting on rod end of piston
F_p—friction load due to rod seals
F_e—load reaction on rod
$(W_p + W_l)/g$— total mass, and
dv/dt—acceleration.

This equation has a different solution for every point on the acceleration curve of Figure 27.10. The corresponding equation for the flow rate is:

$$dQ = A_p ds/dt. \quad (27.2)$$

These equations would hold true between the positions represented by the subscripts *a* and *g* in Figure 27.10. At *g*, the piston achieves constant velocity as a function of constant flow rate into the cylinder. From this point on, there is a steady-state condition. We can simplify the analysis for purposes of illustration, by combining only load-actuator interaction.

Figure 27.11 is a schematic diagram of the system. Note the refinement in the representation of the load, which is shown as a spring-mass system rather than a simple load reaction. All practical loads have mass and exhibit some elastic characteristics. A precise mathematical analysis of such characteristics, however, is beyond the scope of this discussion. This analysis will include only those mathematical details necessary to illustrate the essential analysis of an open-loop circuit.

The output is the flow of oil from the valve to the cylinder. Total flow can be represented as

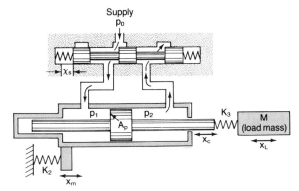

Fig. 27.11. Schematic diagram of load and actuator interactions.

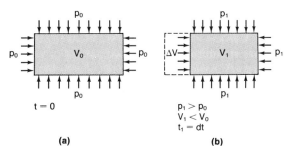

Fig. 27.12. When a fluid undergoes a change in pressure, Δp, it also experiences a corresponding change in volume.

$$Q_4 = d_d + Q_c + Q_\beta \quad (27.3)$$

where:

Q_d—leakage flow past the valve element
Q_c—flow to the cylinder, and
Q_β—compressibility flow.

We see that Q_c is steady-state flow to the actuator, calculated on an average basis; Q_d is leakage flow in the valve—sometimes called the damping flow, for reasons which will be explained later; and Q_β is the apparent loss in volume, as a function of time, because all fluids are compressible. When a hydraulic fluid is pressurizd, its volume is reduced according to the relationship:

$$\begin{aligned} \beta = (p_2 - p_1)/[(V_1 - V_2)/V] \\ = \Delta p/(\Delta v/v). \end{aligned} \quad (27.4)$$

The value obtained for β is called the *bulk modulus* and is the measure of compressibility of a fluid. When a fluid undergoes a change in pressure, Δ_p, it undergoes a corresponding change in volume, (see Figure 27.12). In terms of differential times, this reduction in volume appears to be a flow rate,

$$Q_\beta = \Delta V/dt,$$

which is called the compressibility flow.

In terms of motion of the valve element, the flow can be described as:

$$Q_t = g_f x - b_c p_L \quad (27.5)$$

where:

359

g_f—valve flow gain, [(in.^{3}/sec)/in.]

x—displacement of valve element, in.

b_c—leakage flow gain of element, [(in.^{3}/sec)/psi], and

p_L—load pressure at actuator, psi.

The gain might best be described as the characteristic of the element. Gain is used in writing transfer functions and in determining system response and stability characteristics. Checking Equation (27.5) dimensionally, we get

$$\text{in.}^3/\text{sec} = [(\text{in.}^3/\text{sec})/\text{in}] \times \text{in.}$$
$$- [(\text{in.}^3/\text{sec})/\text{psi}] \times \text{psi})$$

or

total flow = flow through valve ports-leakage flow.

It can be demonstrated that damping flow is:

$$Q_d = C_d L, \qquad (27.6)$$

where C_d is a characteristic coefficient.

Compressibility flow is:

$$Q_\beta = (V_t/4\beta)\,(dp_L/dt), \qquad (27.7)$$

where V_t = total volume.

Actuator flow is

$$Q_c = A_p(dx_c/dt). \qquad (27.8)$$

We can go one step further and include the *compliance* (elastic deformation) of the cylinder, mounting, etc. Then the equation for flow rate to the actuator becomes

$$Q_c = A_p(dx_c/dt) - (dx_m/dt). \qquad (27.9)$$

Figure 27.13 illustrates what is meant by compliance of the cylinder installation. All practical systems exhibit elastic characteristics. Since there is no such thing as a perfectly rigid system, the cylinder could be represented as being supported by a spring (labeled K_2 A, in Figure 27.13). When the load reaction, F_L, is impressed on the piston rod and reacts through the piston, oil, and cylinder barrel to the mounting, the cylinder will move through a distance x_m which is a function of the load and the spring constant, K_s. If this occurs in time dt, the velocity with which the cylinder will recoil is dx_m/dt. The previous equations can now be combined into the following:

$$g_f x - b_c p_L = C_d p_L + [(V_t/4\beta)\,(dp_L/dt)]$$
$$+ A_p(dx_t/dt) - (dx_m/dt). \qquad (27.10)$$

Consider the force equations for the system:

$$\text{piston force} = F_p = A_p p_t,$$
$$\text{compliance force} = K_2 x_m = F_2, \text{and}$$
$$\text{inertial force of mass} = F_M = M(d^2 x_L/dt^2).$$

Note that the load is represented as a spring-mass system in Figure 27.11. The load exhibits much the same characteristics as the cylinder mounting just discussed. That is, it will yield elastically when a force is applied to it. The load structure will have an apparent spring constant, K_3.

When a piston force, F_p, is applied to the load, the force actually transmitted to the load, in an instant of time, is

$$F_3 = K_3(x_t - x_L).$$

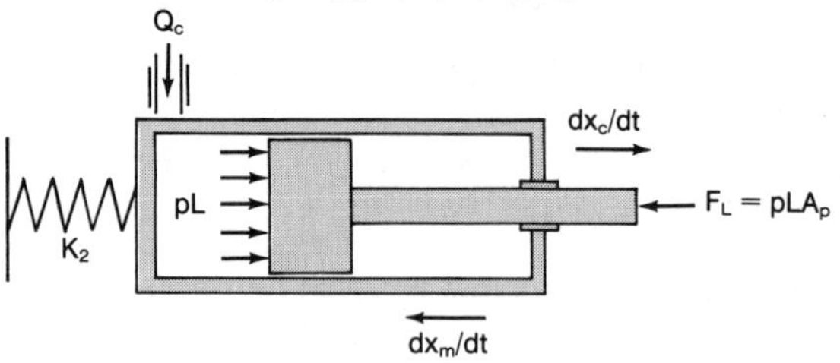

Fig. 27.13. Because perfectly rigid bodies do not exist, a cylinder can be represented as being supported by a spring.

System stability

Because of the compliance of the structural parts of the system and the fact that they exhibit a natural frequency characteristic of any elastic system, it is difficult to maintain system *stability*. Namely the ability of the system to maintain a condition of equilibrium. A stable system will maintain this equilibrium condition, or will quickly return to it if it has been disturbed. An unstable system on the other hand, may make random excursions from the equilibrium point, or, when disturbed, may respond in such a way as to amplify or reinforce the disturbance and oscillate.

It can be demonstrated* that the following natural frequencies exist:

natural frequency of the structure

$$\omega_{N2} = \sqrt{K_2/M}, \qquad (27.11)$$

natural frequency of the load

$$\omega_{N3} = \sqrt{K_3/M}, \qquad (27.12)$$

and hydraulic natural frequency

$$\omega_H = \sqrt{4\beta A^2/V_c M}. \qquad (27.13)$$

Refer to discussion on natural frequencies later in this chapter.

Damping

Damping may be defined as the phenomenon tending to slow the response of a system, with the exception of inertia (mass). Among such phenomena are couloumb friction, viscous drag, leakage flow, etc. Since some of these are extremely difficult to isolate, the damping factor is calculated quantitively as a

---

*For additional information regarding any other points made in this chapter, the student is encouraged to research other texts, such as *Modern Analytical Design of Instrument Servomechanisms*, by Bruce A. Chubb, Addition Wesley Publishing Co.

360

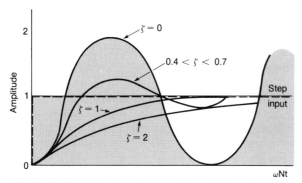

Fig. 27.14. During low damping conditions, a hydraulic system is likely to become unstable.

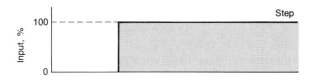

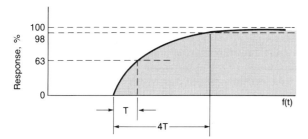

Fig. 27.15. Time constant of a first order system is that needed to reach 63% of the amplitude of a step input.

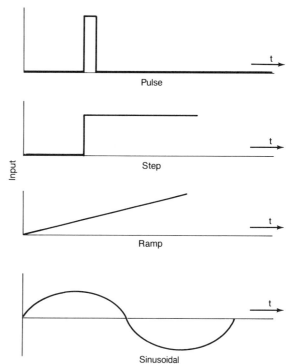

Fig. 27.16. Methods available for analyzing response of a servo system include pulse, step, ramp, and sine wave inputs.

function of some empirically determined system characteristic.

The damping ratio is the ratio of actual-to-critical damping. Critical damping may be defined as the limiting value of damping above which a system will not tend to oscillate. If damping is below the critical value, oscillatory motion will result before a steady-state condition is achieved.

If damping is low enough, the system will be unstable, Figure 27.14. Response and stability characteristics are based on a step input to a system, indicated by the dashed line of Figure 27.14. Since no actual system can respond instantaneously to a step input, it will respond in varying degrees, depending on the damping ration and inertia.

If the damping ratio is zero ($\zeta = 0$), a second-order* system will oscillate continuously at constant amplitude.

---

*The "order" of a system corresponds to the highest derivative in the differential equation describing it. Thus, a differential equation containing an acceleration term, d^2x/dt^2, is a second order differential equation. A first order differential equation contains only velocity dx/dt, and linear f(x) terms.

When $-1 < \zeta < 0$, the system will be unstable and will oscillate with increasing amplitude.

When ζ is positive, the system will be stable.

At $\zeta = 1$, actual damping and critical damping are equal, therefore, the system will not oscillate but will approach the step input line asymptotically.

If $\zeta > 1$, the response time will be slowed by an amount which is a function of the higher damping ratio.

Time constant

Another factor which must be considered is the *time constant*, Figure 27.15. The time constant of a first-order system is the time required for the system to reach 63 percent of the amplitude of a step input. Note from Figure 27.15 that if the "break frequency" is determined from a Bode plot, this amounts to

$$T = \frac{1}{2\pi f_c}$$

System response

Methods available for analyzing the response of a servo system include pulse input, step input, ramp input, and sine-wave input, illustrated graphically in Figure 27.16.

A *pulse* is a short-duration change in the input signal. After the pulse passes, the input signal returns to its original level.

A *step input* changes the level of the input signal and, in that respect, resembles a pulse. However,

361

instead of returning to the original signal level, the step inclrease remains at the changed level.

A *ramp input* changes the input signal level at some predetermined rate — that is, with a constant, known slope.

A *sine-wave input* causes the input signal to vary sinusoidally.

Of these methods, the step and sine input methods are most frequently used in system analysis. We have already considered some of the aspects of system response to step inputs. Figure 27.17 shows similar aspects of response to a sine input.

Figure 27.17(*a*) represents a typical input signal varying sinusoidally. This input signal could be fed into the system from a controller. Figure 27.17(*b*) illustrates the corresponding response, or output, from a typical system. At **low** frequencies the output follows the input very closely. The two curves, Figures 27.17(*a*) and (*b*), peak at the same points, and cross the ordinate at the same points. Also, the amplitude of the output curve is about the same as that of the input curve. When output follows input in this manner, the system is said to be *linear*.

Figure 27.17(*c*) represents the output from a system at **high** frequency. Because of the inertia (mass) and damping characteristics of the system, output *cannot* follow input, as it did at low frequency. Output starts to rise at some point *after* the input signal and reaches a maximum sometime *after* the input signal. Since the input signal starts to decrease before output reaches the same magnitude as the input, output never reaches the same level as the input. The

ratio of output-to-input magnitude is called the *magnitude* (or *amplitude*) *ratio*. This is expressed by the *gain*.

Phase

Referring again to Figure 27.17(*c*), note that the angle (distance along the abscissa) between the input and the output curves is called the *phase angle*. When the output follows input, as it does in this illustration, it is said to *lag*. This type of phase angle is called a *lagging* phase angle. It is also possible to have a *leading* phase angle.

Thus, as frequency is raised higher and higher, lag increases. For every system there is a frequency at which lag reaches 360 deg. When this occurs, the output curve will have shifted until it is back *in phase* with the input signal. If system gain is also unity at that time, the input signal will reinforce the output signal. The system will oscillate and is said to be *unstable*. It is possible to demonstrate these phenomena mathematically and to estimate the values of system parameters at which instability occurs. The student can gain an appreciation for the application of the concepts by referring to Figure 27.2, particularly part (a) and by examining the qualitative parametric representation in light of this discussion.

Hydraulic system parameters

Since we are attempting to bridge the gap between a more elementary steady-state-design-analysis of a hydraulic system and a more rigorous approach encompassing system dynamics it will be useful to consider system parameters mathematically. Table 27.1 summarizes hydraulic (incompressible fluid) parameters.

Resistance

Figure 27.18 shows two fluid resistances in series. The relationship between pressure, flow, and resistance is

$$\Delta p = Q(R_1 + R_2). \qquad (27.14)$$

Hydraulic resistances in parallel are shown in Figure 27.19. The expression relating flow, pressure, and resistance is

$$p_0 = Q(R_1 R_2)/(R_1 + R_2). \qquad (27.15)$$

Figure 27.20 illustrates a condition where a parallel circuit branch is connected between two resistances. The expression for p_1, the pressure in the branch, is

$$p_1 = p_0 R_2/(R_1 + R). \qquad (27.16)$$

Capacitance

The general expression for capacitance is

$$C = \int Q/(dp/dt).$$

For a simple fluid line, Figure 27.21, the capacitance is:

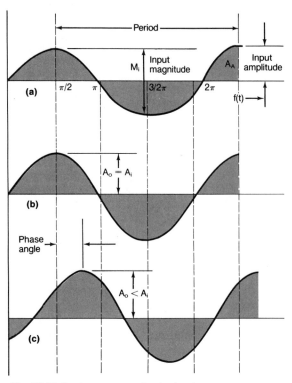

Fig. 27.17. System response to sine input.

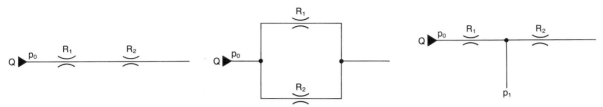

Fig. 27.18. Hydraulic fluid resistances in series.

Fig. 27.19. Hydraulic fluid resistances in parallel.

Fig. 27.20. Parallel circuit branch connected between two resistances.

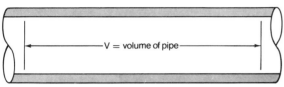

Fig. 27.21. Capacitance for simple fluid line.

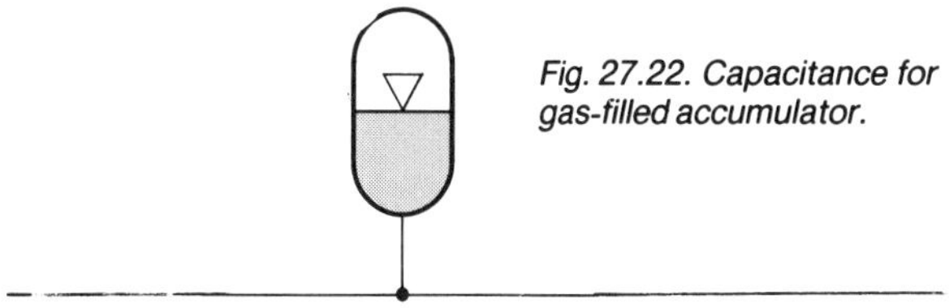

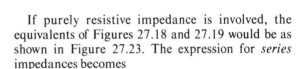

Fig. 27.22. Capacitance for gas-filled accumulator.

$$C = V/\beta$$

where:

V—volume of pipe or tube, and

β—bulk modulus of fluid.

For a gas-filled accumulator, Figure 27.22, capacitance is

$$C_a = (V_0 - V_3)^2/p_0V_0, \qquad (27.17)$$

where:

V_o — accumulator volume,

V_3—stored fluid volume, and

p_o—precharge, pressure.

Inductance

The general expression for fluid inductance is

$$L_f = 1/Q \int p\, dt.$$

For a length of simple tube, such as shown in Figure 27.21, the inductance is:

$$L_f = \rho\, L/A \qquad (27.18)$$

where:

ρ — fluid density,

L — length of tube, and

A — area of tube.

Impedance

It is common practice in electrical technology to denote by *impedance, Z*, the interactive effects of resistance, capacitance, and inductance on flow of current due to a given potential differential. Basically, $E = IZ$, or $I = E/Z$. If impedance is purely *resistive*, this expression reduces to

$$I = E/R \text{ or } E = IR.$$

Similarly, we can write fluid power expressions in terms of potential (pressure), flow, and general impedance, that is,

$$p = QZ.$$

If purely resistive impedance is involved, the equivalents of Figures 27.18 and 27.19 would be as shown in Figure 27.23. The expression for *series* impedances becomes

$$\sqrt{p} = Q(Z_1 + Z_2) \qquad (27.19)$$

and for *parallel* impedances,

$$p = Q Z_1 Z_2/(Z_1 + Z_2). \qquad (27.20)$$

For example if the impedance, due to a conductor is made up of a resistive component and an inductive component, the expression becomes

$$Z = R + L = R + (\rho L/A)$$

Application example

Consider the hydraulic circuit in Figure 27.24(*a*) where a pressure-compensated pump transfers energy to a cylinder through a 3-position, 4-way directional control valve. However, the diagram drawn with ANSI symbols does not begin to tell the story of interaction of pressure and flow phenomena in the circuit.

Figure 27.24(*b*) illustrates the circuit diagram after conversion to an analogous partly-electrical circuit. The components are now represented by equivalent resistance and capacitance. The directional control valve is represented as a resistance, with a leakage path to the tank, which is equivalent to an electrical ground. The cylinder is represented as a capacitance. Note how pump output flow is split into several flow components: flow to the compensator control, leakage flow, and flow to the cylinder.

The following set of equations consitutes a mathematical model, of sorts, of the simple circuit of Figure 27.24.

Step 1. Pump discharge flow, Q_i, is equal to the sum of leakage flow, flow to the cylinder, and flow to the compensator:

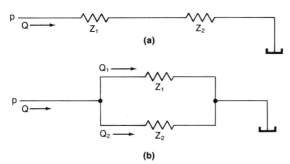

(a)

(b)

Fig. 27.23. Schematic equivalent representation of purely resistive impedances shown in Figures 27.18 and 27.19.

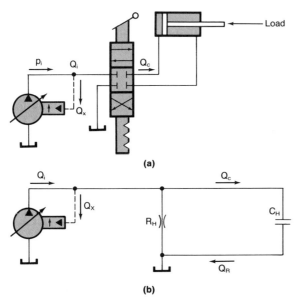

(a)

(b)

Q_i = pump discharge flow Q_R = leakage flow
Q_x = flow to compensator C_H = cylinder capacitance
Q_c = flow to cylinder R_H = valve resistance

Fig. 27.24. Functional circuit diagram does not reveal interaction of pressure and flow phenomena in system.

$$Q_i = Q_R + Q_c + QX.$$

But

$$Q_i = Q_m - D_d X, \qquad (27.22)$$

where:

Q_m — maximum pump discharge flow,
K_d — displacement factor for the compensator control, in^3/in., and
X — compensator displacement, in.;
and, of course,
$Q_m = V_d N$,
where:
V_a — pump displacement, in.^{3}/rev, and
N — rotational speed, rpm.

Thus,

$$Q_i = V_d N - K_d X. \qquad (27.23)$$

Leakage flow, Q_R, is

$$Q_r = g_R p_i, \qquad (27.24)$$

where:
g_R — valve leakage conductance, ^{3}/psi, and
p_i — system pressure, psi.

Flow to cylinder, Q_c, is

$$Q_c = C(dp_i / dt), \qquad (27.25)$$

where C — capacitance.
Flow to the compensator, Q_x, is

$$Q_x = A p_i (dx / dt), \qquad (25.26)$$

where A is the area of compensator piston.
Step 2. By substituting the expressions on the right-hand sides of Equations (27.24), (27.25), and (27.26) into Equation (27.9), we obtain

$$Q_i = g_R p_i + C(dp_i/dt) + A p_i(dx/dt). \qquad (27.27)$$

Substituting for Q_i, the expression on the right-hand side of Equation (27.23) and rearranging terms, we get:

$$dp_i/dt = [V_d N - K_d S - g_R p_i - (dx/dt)] /C. \qquad (27.28)$$

Step 3. Using the formula $F = ma$, we can write,

$$F_v = m(d^2 x /dt^2),$$

where F — viscous (drag) force.
But, since

$$F_v = \Sigma F_x,$$

where F_x — all the various components of force acting on the compensator spool, then,

$$F_v = \Sigma F_x = m(d^2 x /dt^2) + K_v(dx/dt) + K_s(X - X), \qquad (27.29)$$

where:
K_v — viscous drag factor,
K_s — spring constant, lb.in, and
X_0 — initial compensator displacement.
Equation (27.29) can be rewritten as:

$$d^2 x /dt^2 = F_v - K_v(dx/dt) - K_s(X - X_0)/m.$$

But since $F_v = p_i A_p$, where A_p = area of the cylinder piston.
therefore,

$$d^2 x /dt^2 = p_i A_p - K_v(dx/dt) - K_s X + K_s X_0/m. \qquad (27.30)$$

This somewhat oversimplified analysis of the example circuit, very similar to the demand flow case illustrated in Figure 5.2 and Figure 27.2(b), provides insight into the difficulty of going from steady-state to dynamic analysis of hydraulic systems.

Important Terms

Bernoulli jet force. Force acting on a valve spool due to momentum exchange between fluid flowing through a valve and the spool.

Bulk modulus. The characteristic which defines the relative incompressibility (stiffness) of fluid.

Bulk modulus, effective. Bulk modulus of a system which defines the effect of compliance of overall stiffness of the system.

Bulk modulus, secant. The average of the change in pressure divided by the total change in volume per unit of initial volume.

Bulk modulus, tangent. The inverse of fluid compressibility at a specific point.

Celerity. Speed of sound in a hydraulic fluid.

Critical closing time. The smallest time interval for closing a valve in a given hydraulic system which results in pressure shock (water hammer) in the system: $t_c = 2L/c$.

Damping. The sum of those forces and actions which tend to slow down the response of a system to disturbing influences. Damping tends to stabilize a system.

Dynamics. The study of effects of time-variant parameters on system performance.

Natural frequency. Is the number of cycles executed per unit of time by an elastic system undergoing free vibration.

Natural frequency, hydraulic. The natural frequency of a hydraulic system.

Phase. The relationship generally stated in terms of an angle, between input to a system and its output.

Pressure ripple. Cyclic pressure pulses resulting from hydraulic pump ripple characteristics.

Resonance. Conditions which exist when the frequency of an exacting force coincides with the natural frequency of the system.

Response. The manner in which a system output follows its input.

Spring rate. A parameter relating elastic deformation of a system component or member as a function of load applied.

Spring rate, apparent. Spring rate relating dynamic loading to motion of a fluid power device.

Stability. The ability of a system to maintain equilibrium conditions in the face of disturbing actions.

Time constant. Time required (for a first order system) to reach 63% of the amplitude of a step input.

Water hammer. A shock pressure associated with rapid closing of a control valve which shuts off fluid power within the critical closing time for the system.

References

1. Introduction to Fluid Mechanics, Russ Henke, Addison-Wesley Publication Co.
2. Hydraulic System Analysis, George Keller, HYDRAULICS & PNEUMATICS, Cleveland, Ohio.
3. The Control of Fluid Power, D. McCloy and H. R. Martin, John Wiley & Sons, N. Y.
4. Fluid Power Systems, A. B. Goodwin, MacMillan Press, Ltd., London, England.
5. Hydraulic Control Systems - Design and Analysis of Their Dynamics, Dr. Peter Dranfield, Springer-Verlag, LNC15 33, 1981.
6. *Hydraulic & Pneumatic Power& Control,* Louis Dodge, McGraw-Hill, New York, pp. 276-283.
7. Hydraulic Control Systems, Herbert E. Merritt, John Wiley & Sons, New York, N. Y.

Review Exercises

27.1. Discuss what is meant by *steady state* conditions.

27.2. How do *dynamic* conditions vary from steady-state? Discuss.

27.3. What is velocity? Discuss how steady-state velocity, average velocity and instantaneous velocity differ from each other. Ref. Fig. 27.1.

27.4. What are the implications of exercise 27.3 on circuit design and performance?

27.5. What is acceleration? Discuss how steady-state acceleration, average acceleration and instantaneous acceleration differ from each other.

27.6. Why have we characterized the ISO circuit diagram (functional level) in Fig. 16.8 as a "first approximation" in circuit design? Discuss.

27.7. Discuss the differences between *function* and hardware used to implement function.

27.8. Ref. Fig. 27.2(a) and (b) (also Fig. 5.2 in Chapter 5): What type of velocity profile has been selected by the designer? Discuss the implications of this choice and circuit performance.

27.9. In Fig. 27.2, discuss the effect of the velocity profile on the load profile. What is the implication of the point of inflection at time = t_2?

27.10. How is design pressure determined for the application of Fig. 27.2? Discuss.

27.11. What are the major implications of selecting design pressure?

27.12. What effect does selection of p_4 have on Q_4? Discuss.

27.13. Discuss the differences between *design, system* and *rated* pressures.

27.14. Discuss the sequence of 4 steps a circuit designer must make in sizing a hydraulic system, implicit in a Cycle Profile as illustrated in Fig. 27.2.

27.15. Redraw the representations of *circuit variables,* as illustrated in Fig. 27.2(c), for the demand flow case.

27.16. Expand the parametric representations of Fig. 27.2 (c) to include the *feed* portion of the Cycle Profile. What are the difference between this and the Rapid Traverse segment?

27.17. Ref. 27.2(c): Why is there a period of transient instability represented during the initial period as each variable changes? Discuss.

27.18. Discuss the relief valve characteristics represented in Fig. 27.2(c). How do they relate to previous discussions in Chapters 6, 7 and 8?

27.19. Discuss directional control characteristics as represented in Fig, 27.2(c) in light of discussion relating to Fig. 27.8.

27.20. Repeat exercise 27.19 in light of Figs. 27.10 and 27.17.

27.21. How could the relationships illustrated in Fig. 27.11 affect the variables as represented in Fig. 27.2(c)? Discuss.

27.22. Ref. Fig. 27.14: Consider effect on circuit variables as shown in Fig. 27.2(c) for under-damped, critically-damped and over-damped cases. What can be done to the open loop circuits of Figures 27.2(a) and (b) to offset these effects for the three cases of damping? Discuss.

27.23. Discuss piston bypass leakage in Fig. 27.2. How does q_c affect damping?

27.24. Discuss the relationship between delivery flow, Q_1, and the sum of the flows around the circuit(s) of Fig. 27.2.

27.25. Discuss discharge pressure, p_1, and its relationship to the sum of the pressure drop differentials around the circuit.

27.26. (OPTIONAL) Draw a circuit variable representation similar to Fig. 27.2(c) for the rotary drive case shown in Figs. 5.5 and 5.8.

27.27. What is bulk modulus? Why is it important to circuit dynamics?

27.28. Why does entrained air adversely affect bulk modulus? Discuss.

27.29. What is effective bulk modulus? What factors comprise effective bulk modulus?

27.30. Write the mathematical expression for effective bulk modulus.

27.31. Given: a column of fluid 2″ I.D. × 60″long; β_c = 190,000 psi. Calculate the spring rate of the column.

27.32. Reduce the length of the column of examples 27.31 in 10″-in increments and plot a curve of varying spring rate as a function of length.

27.33. In Example 27.31, if load spring rate were 20,000 lb/in, what would the effective spring rate be?

27.34. Recalculate example 27.31 using SI metric units, Ref. Appendix B.

27.35. In example 27.31, calculate the natural frequency for the fluid column if mineral oil is used. Recalculate for phosphate ester.

27.36. Recalculate example 29.35, using SI metric units.

27.37. Recalculate example 27.36 using a 7-piston pump rotating at 2400 rpm on MIL-H-5606 using SI metric units.

27.38. Ref. Fig. 27.4: Discuss the concepts of a fluid spring-mass system and how it relates to the pressure transient known as water-hammer.

27.39. What is meant by critical closure time, t_c? What is the expression for t_c?

27.40. What is meant by *viscous damper* as shown in Fig. 27.4(b)? What is its effect on a hydraulic system?

27.41. Can pressure transients occur on valve opening? Explain.

27.42. What techniques are available to reduce water hammer type pressure transients?

27.43. Discuss the system variables summerized for the actuator case in Fig. 27.6. How does this representation compare with the steady-state analyses of Chapters 3, 4 & 5?

27.44. Repeat example 27.43 for Fig. 27.7.

27.45. Discuss dynamic forces acting on a spool valve, as shown in Fig. 27.8, and how they affect valve performance.

27.46. Which of these forces is the most important?

27.47. How can Bernoulli jet forces affect spool valve performance?

27.48. What is meant by *variable apparent spring rate*? How does it affect valve performance?

27.49. Discuss the implications of Fig. 27.9.

27.50. Discuss Fig. 27.10 and how it compares to Fig. 27.9.

27.51. Ref. Chapter 5, example of Fig. 5.2: Sketch a curve similar to Fig. 27.10 for the transition from rapid traverse to feed in the machine cycle.

27.52. Discuss Newton's Second Law of motion and its implications for hydraulic circuit design and performance. Discuss effects on changing operating conditions for a hydraulic circuit in the field, *i.e.,* increasing or decreasing loads, changing pressure settings, temperature changes, etc.

27.53. Relate the characteristics of a demand-flow circuit to Fig. 27.10.

27.54. Discuss the implications for dynamic performance of the valve-actuator system represented in Fig. 27.11.

27.55. What is the effect of compressibility flow on dymanic performance? Is it significant in open loop circuits? Explain.

27.56. What is meant by *gain* of a hydraulic component? What is its use?

27.57. What is *damping flow*? What is its effect on a hydraulic system?

27.58. What is *compliance* in a hydraulic system? Discuss Fig. 27.13 in terms of compliance.

27.59. Discuss equation 27.10, and its implications for circuit performance.

27.60. What is meant by *system stability*? On what factors does it depend?

27.61. Discuss natural frequencies as expressed in equations 27.11, 27.12, and 27.13.

27.62. Define *damping* in a hydraulic system. Discuss Fig. 27.14.

27.63. What is meant by *damping factor*? How it is determined?

27.64. What is *damping ratio*?

27.65. Define *time constant*. What are its implications for circuit dynamic performance? Sketch a curve showing how time constant is determined.

27.66. What types of *inputs* to hydraulic circuits exist? Sketch them.

27.67. Discuss Fig. 27.17 and its implications for circuit dynamic performance.

27.68. What is meant by *phase angle*? Discuss *lag* and *loads*; and the difference between them.

27.69. What is the effect on phase angle and output magnitude of increasing input signal frequency? Discuss.

27.70. Discuss hydraulic system parameters summarized in Table 27.1.

fluid power graphic symbols

0 Introduction

In fluid power systems, power is transmitted and controlled through a fluid (liquid or gas) under pressure within a circuit.

Graphic symbols are used in diagrams of hydraulic and pneumatic equipment and accessories for fluid power transmission.

1 Scope and field of application

This International Standard establishes principles for the use of symbols and specifies the symbols to be used in diagrams of hydraulic and pneumatic transmission systems and components.

The use of these symbols does not preclude the use of other symbols commonly used for pipework in other technical fields.

2 Reference

ISO 5598, *Fluid power - Vocabulary*[1]
1) In preparation

3 Definitions

For definitions of terms used, see ISO 5598.

4 Identification statement
(Reference to this International Standard)

Use the following statement in test reports, catalogues and sales literature when electing to comply with this International Standard:

"Graphic symbols shown in accordance with ISO 1219, *Fluid power systems and components - Graphic symbols.*"

5 General basic and functional symbols

Symbols for hydraulic and pneumatic equipment and accessories are functional and consist of one or more basic symbols and in general of one or more functional symbols. The symbols are neither to scale nor in general orientated in any particular direction. The relative size of symbols in combination should correspond approximately to those in clauses 11 and 12.

DESCRIPTION		SYMBOL	APPLICATION
5.1	**BASIC SYMBOLS**		
5.1.1	**Line**	2)	
5.1.1.1	— continuous		flow lines *DASHES = PILOT & DRAIN LINES*
5.1.1.2	— long dashes	L > 10E	
5.1.1.3	— short dashes	L < 5E	
5.1.1.4	— double	D < 5E	mechanical connections (shafts, levers, piston-rods)
5.1.1.5	— long chain thin (optional use)		Enclosure for several components assembled in one unit
5.1.2	**Circle, semi-circle**		
5.1.2.1		○	As a rule, energy conversion units (pump, compressor, motor)
5.1.2.2		○	Measuring instruments
5.1.2.3		○	Non-return valve, rotary connection, etc
5.1.2.4		○	Mechanical link, roller, etc
5.1.2.5		D	Semi-rotary actuator

2) L = Length of dash, E = Thickness of line, D = Space between lines

369

DESCRIPTION		SYMBOL	APPLICATION
5.1.3	**Square, rectangle**		As a rule, control valves (valve) except for non-return valves
5.1.4	**Diamond**		Conditioning apparatus (filter, separator, lubricator, heat exchanger)
5.1.5	**Miscellaneous symbols**	3)	
5.1.5.1		$d \approx 5E$	Flow line connection
5.1.5.2			Spring
5.1.5.3			Restriction:
5.1.5.3.1			— affected by viscosity
5.1.5.3.2			— unaffected by viscosity
5.2	**FUNCTIONAL SYMBOLS**		
5.2.1	**Triangle:**		The direction of flow and the nature of the fluid
5.2.1.1	— solid	▼	Hydraulic flow
5.2.1.2	— in outline only	▽	Pneumatic flow or exhaust to atmosphere
5.2.2	**Arrow**		Indication of:
5.2.2.1			— direction
5.2.2.2			— direction of rotation
5.2.2.3			— path and direction of flow through valves.
			For regulating apparatus as in 7.4 both representations, with or without a tail to the end of the arrow, are used without distinction
			As a general rule the line perpendicular to the head of the arrow indicates that when the arrow moves, the interior path always remains connected to the corresponding exterior path
5.2.3	**Sloping arrow**		Indication of the possibility of a regulation or a progressive variability

3) E = Thickness of line

fluid power graphic symbols

	DESCRIPTION	SYMBOL	USE OF THE EQUIPMENT OR EXPLANATION OF THE SYMBOL	
6.1	**PUMPS AND COMPRESSORS**		To convert mechanical energy into hydraulic or pneumatic energy.	
6.1.1 6.1.1.1	**Fixed capacity hydraulic pump:** —with one direction of flow			 OUTLET INLET
6.1.1.2	—with two directions of flow			 BALL CHECK
6.1.2 6.1.2.1	**Variable capacity hydraulic pump:** —with one direction of flow		The symbol is a combination of 6.1.1.1 and 5.2.3 (sloping arrow)	
6.1.2.2	—with two directions of flow		The symbol is a combination of 6.1.1.2 and 5.2.3 (sloping arrow)	
6.1.3	**Fixed capacity compressor (always one direction of flow)**			

	DESCRIPTION	SYMBOL	USE OF THE EQUIPMENT OR EXPLANATION OF THE SYMBOL	
6.2	**MOTORS**		To convert hydraulic or pneumatic energy into rotary mechanical energy	
6.2.1	**Fixed capacity hydraulic motor:**			
6.2.1.1	—with one direction of flow			
6.2.1.2	—with two directions of flow			
6.2.2	**Variable capacity hydraulic motor:**			
6.2.2.1	—with one direction of flow		The symbol is a combination of 6.2.1.1 and 5.2.3 (sloping arrow)	
6.2.2.2	—with two directions of flow		The symbol is a combination of 6.2.1.2 and 5.2.3 (sloping arrow)	
6.2.3	**Fixed capacity pneumatic motor:**			
6.2.3.1	—with one direction of flow			
6.2.3.2	—with two directions of flow			
6.2.4	**Variable capacity pneumatic motor:**			
6.2.4.1	—with one direction of flow		The symbol is a combination of 6.2.3.1 and 5.2.3 (sloping arrow)	
6.2.4.2	—with two directions cf flow		The symbol is a combination of 6.2.3.2 and 5.2.3 (sloping arrow)	
6.2.5	**Oscillating motor:**			
6.2.5.1	—hydraulic			
6.2.5.2	—pneumatic			

	DESCRIPTION	SYMBOL		USE OF THE EQUIPMENT OR EXPLANATION OF THE SYMBOL	
6.3	**PUMP/MOTOR UNITS**			Unit with two functions, either as pump or as rotary motor	
6.3.1	**Fixed capacity pump/motor unit:**				
6.3.1.1	— with reversal of the direction of flow			Functioning as pump or motor according to direction of flow	
6.3.1.2	— with one single direction of flow			Functioning as pump or motor without change of direction of flow	
6.3.1.3	— with two directions of flow			Functioning as pump or motor with either direction of flow	
6.3.2	**Variable capacity pump/motor unit:**				
6.3.2.1	— with reversal of the direction of flow			The symbol is a combination of 6.3.1.1 and 5.2.3 (sloping arrow)	
6.3.2.2	— with one single direction of flow			The symbol is a combination of 6.3.1.2 and 5.2.3 (sloping arrow)	
6.3.2.3	— with two directions of flow			The symbol is a combination of 6.3.1.3 and 5.2.3 (sloping arrow)	
6.4	**VARIABLE SPEED DRIVE UNITS**			Torque converter. Pump and/or motor are of variable capacity. Remote drives, see 12.2	
6.5	**CYLINDERS**			Equipment to convert hydraulic or pneumatic energy into linear energy	
6.5.1	**Single acting cylinder:**	Detailed	Simplified	Cylinder in which the fluid pressure always acts in one and the same direction (on the forward stroke)	
6.5.1.1	— returned by an unspecified force			General symbol when the method of return is not specified	
6.5.1.2	— returned by spring			Combination of the general symbols 6.5.1.1 and 5.1.5.2 (spring)	

	DESCRIPTION	SYMBOL		USE OF THE EQUIPMENT OR EXPLANATION OF THE SYMBOL	
6.5.2	**Double acting cylinder:**			Cylinder in which the fluid pressure operates alternately in both directions (forward and backward strokes)	
6.5.2.1	— with single piston rod				
6.5.2.2	— with double-ended piston rod				
6.5.3	**Differential cylinder**			The action is dependent on the difference between the effective areas on each side of the piston	
6.5.4	**Cylinder with cushion:**				
6.5.4.1	— with single fixed cushion			Cylinder incorporating fixed cushion acting in one direction only	
6.5.4.2	— with double fixed cushion			Cylinder with fixed cushion acting in both directions	
6.5.4.3	— with single adjustable cushion			The symbol is a combination of 6.5.4.1 and 5.2.3 (sloping arrow)	
6.5.4.4	—with double adjustable cushion			The symbol is a combination of 6.5.4.2 and 5.2.3 (sloping arrow)	
6.5.5	**Telescopic cylinder:**				
6.5.5.1	— single acting			The fluid pressure always acts in one and the same direction (on the forward stroke)	
6.5.5.2	— double acting			The fluid pressure operates alternately in both directions (forward and backward strokes)	

	DESCRIPTION	SYMBOL		USE OF THE EQUIPMENT OR EXPLANATION OF THE SYMBOL	
6.6	**PRESSURE INTENSIFIERS:**	Detailed	Simplified	Equipment transforming a pressure x into a higher pressure y	
6.6.1	— for one type of fluid			E.g. a pneumatic pressure x is transformed into a higher pneumatic pressure y	
6.6.2	— for two types of fluid			E.g. a pneumatic pressure x is transformed into a higher hydraulic pressure y	
6.7	**AIR-OIL ACTUATOR**			Equipment transforming a pneumatic pressure into a substantially equal hydraulic pressure or vice versa	
7	**CONTROL VALVES**				
7.1	**METHOD OF REPRE-SENTATION OF VALVES (EXCEPT 7.3 AND 7.6)**			Made up of one or more squares 5.1.3 and arrows In circuit diagrams hydraulic and pneumatic units are normally shown in the unoperated condition	
7.1.1	**One single square**			Indicates unit for controlling flow or pressure, having in operation an infinite number of possible positions between its end positions so as to vary the conditions of flow across one or more of its ports, thus ensuring the chosen pressure and/or flow with regard to the operating conditions of the circuit	
7.1.2	**Two or more squares**			Indicate a directional control valve having as many distinct positions as there are squares. The pipe connections are normally represented as representing the unoperated condition (see 7.1). The operating positions are deduced by imagining the boxes to be displaced so that the pipe connections correspond with the ports of the box in question	

	DESCRIPTION	SYMBOL	USE OF THE EQUIPMENT OR EXPLANATION OF THE SYMBOL	
7.1.3	**Simplified symbol for valves in cases of multiple repetition**	3	The number refers to a note on the diagram in which the symbol for the valve is given in full	
7.2	**DIRECTIONAL CONTROL VALVES**		Units providing for the opening (fully or restricted) or the closing of one or more flow paths (represented by several squares)	
7.2.1	**Flow paths:**		Square containing interior lines	
7.2.1.1	—one flow path			
7.2.1.2	—two closed ports			
7.2.1.3	—two flow paths			
7.2.1.4	—two flow paths and one closed port			
7.2.1.5	—two flow paths with cross connection			
7.2.1.6	—one flow path in a by-pass position, two closed ports			
7.2.2	**Non-throttling directional control valve**		The unit provides distinct circuit conditions each depicted by a square	
7.2.2.1			Basic symbol for 2-position directional control valve	
7.2.2.2			Basic symbol for 3-position directional control valve	
7.2.2.3			A transitory but significant condition between two distinct positions is optionally represented by a square with dashed ends

A basic symbol for a directional control valve with two distinct positions and one transitory intermediate condition | |

	DESCRIPTION	SYMBOL	USE OF THE EQUIPMENT OR EXPLANATION OF THE SYMBOL	
7.2.2.4	**Designation:** The first figure in the designation shows the number of ports (excluding pilot ports) and the second figure the number of distinct positions			
7.2.2.5	**Directional control valve 2/2:**		Directional control valve with 2 ports and 2 distinct positions	
7.2.2.5.1	—with manual control			
7.2.2.5.2	—controlled by pressure operating against a return spring (e.g., on air unloading valve)			
7.2.2.6	**Directional control valve 3/2:**		Directional control valve with 3 ports and 2 distinct positions	
7.2.2.6.1	—controlled by pressure in both directions			
7.2.2.6.2	—controlled by solenoid with return spring		Indicating an intermediate condition (see 7.2.2.3)	
7.2.2.7	**Directional control valve 4/2:**	Detailed	Directional control valve with 4 ports and 2 distinct positions	
7.2.2.7.1	—controlled by pressure in both directions by means of a pilot valve (with a single solenoid and spring return)	 Simplified 		
7.2.2.8	**Directional control valve 5/2:**		Directional control valve with 5 ports and 2 distinct positions	
7.2.2.8.1	—controlled by pressure in both directions			

	DESCRIPTION	SYMBOL	USE OF THE EQUIPMENT OR EXPLANATION OF THE SYMBOL	
7.2.3	**Throttling directional control**		The unit has 2 extreme positions and an infinite number of intermediate conditions with varying degrees of throttling All the symbols have parallel lines along the length of the boxes. For valves with mechanical feedback see 9.3	
7.2.3.1			Showing the extreme positions	
7.2.3.2			Showing the extreme positions and a central (neutral) position	
7.2.3.3	— with 2 ports (one throttling orifice)		For example: Tracer valve plunger operated against a return spring	
7.2.3.4	— with 3 ports (two throttling orifices)		For example: Directional control valve controlled by pressure against a return spring	
7.2.3.5	— with 4 ports (four throttling orifices)		For example: Tracer valve, plunger operated against a return spring	
7.2.4	**Electro-hydraulic servo valve:** **Electro-pneumatic servo valve:**		A unit which accepts an analogue electrical signal and provides a similar analogue fluid power output	Torque motor Spool T B P A T Torque motor armature
7.2.4.1	— single-stage		—with direct operation	
7.2.4.2	— two-stage with mechanical feedback		— with indirect pilot operation	
7.2.4.3	— two-stage with hydraulic feedback		— with indirect pilot operation	

	DESCRIPTION	SYMBOL	USE OF THE EQUIPMENT OR EXPLANATION OF THE SYMBOL	
7.3	NON-RETURN VALVES, SHUTTLE VALVE, RAPID EXHAUST VALVE		Valves which allow free flow in one direction only	
7.3.1	Non-return valve			
7.3.1.1	— free		Opens if the inlet pressure is higher than the outlet pressure	
7.3.1.2	— spring loaded		Opens if the inlet pressure is greater than the outlet pressure plus the spring pressure	
7.3.1.3	—pilot controlled		As 7.3.1.1 but by pilot control it is possible to prevent	
7.3.1.3.1	— a pilot signal closes the valve			
7.3.1.3.2	— a pilot signal opens the valve			
7.3.1.4	— with restriction		Unit allowing free flow in one direction but restricted flow in the other	
7.3.2	Shuttle valve		The inlet port connected to the higher pressure is automatically connected to the outlet port while the other inlet port is closed	
7.3.3	Rapid exhaust valve		When the inlet port is unloaded the outlet port is freely exhausted	
7.4	PRESSURE CONTROL VALVES		Units ensuring the control of pressure. Represented by one single square as in 7.1.1 with one arrow (the tail to the arrow may be placed at the end of the arrow). For interior controlling conditions see 9.2.4.3	
7.4.1	Pressure control valve:		General symbols	
7.4.1.1	— 1 throttling orifice normally closed			

379

	DESCRIPTION	SYMBOL	USE OF THE EQUIPMENT OR EXPLANATION OF THE SYMBOL	
7.4.1.2	— 1 throttling orifice normally open			
7.4.1.3	— 2 throttling orifices, normally closed			
7.4.2	**Pressure relief valve (safety valve):**		Inlet pressure is controlled by opening the exhaust port to the reservoir or to atmosphere against an opposing force (for example a spring)	
7.4.2.1	— with remote pilot control		The pressure at the inlet port is limited as in 7.4.2 or to that corresponding to the setting of a pilot control	
7.4.3	**Proportional pressure relief**		Inlet pressure is limited to a value proportional to the pilot pressure (see 9.2.4.1.3)	
7.4.4.	**Sequence valve**		When the inlet pressure overcomes the opposing force of the spring, the valve opens permitting flow from the outlet port	
7.4.5	**Pressure regulator or reducing valve (reducer of pressure):**		A unit which, with a variable inlet pressure, gives substantially constant output pressure provided that the inlet pressure remains higher than the required outlet pressure	
7.4.5.1	— without relief port			
7.4.5.2	— without relief port with remote control		As in 7.4.5.1 but the outlet pressure is dependent on the control pressure	
7.4.5.3	— with relief port			

fluid power graphic symbols

	DESCRIPTION	SYMBOL		USE OF THE EQUIPMENT OR EXPLANATION OF THE SYMBOL	
7.4.5.4	— with relief port, with remote control			As in 7.4.5.3, but the outlet pressure is dependent on the control pressure	
7.4.6	**Differential pressure regulator**			The outlet pressure is reduced by a fixed amount with respect to the inlet pressure	
7.4.7	**Proportional pressure regulator**			The outlet pressure is reduced by a fixed ratio with respect to the inlet pressure (see 9.2.4.1.3)	
7.5	**FLOW CONTROL VALVES**			Units ensuring control of flow excepting 7.5.3 positions and method of representation as 7.4	
7.5.1	**Throttle valve:**			Simplified symbol (Does not indicate the control method or the state of the valve)	
7.5.1.1	—with manual control			Detailed symbol (indicates the control method of the state of the valve)	
7.5.1.2	— with mechanical control against a return spring (braking valve)				
7.5.2	**Flow control valve:**	Detailed	Simplified	Variations in inlet pressure do not affect the rate of flow	
7.5.2.1	— with fixed output				
7.5.2.2	— with fixed output and relief port to reservoir			As 7.5.2.1 but with relief for excess flow	

	DESCRIPTION	SYMBOL		USE OF THE EQUIPMENT OR EXPLANATION OF THE SYMBOL	
7.5.2.3	— with variable output			As 7.5.2.1 but with arrow 5.2.3 added to the symbol of restriction	Control chamber
7.5.2.4	— with variable output and relief port to reservoir			As 7.5.2.3 but with relief for excess flow	Inlet / Outlet / Tank / Vent connection
7.5.3	Flow dividing valve			The flow is divided into two flows in a fixed ratio substantially independent of pressure variations	
7.6	SHUT-OFF VALVE			Simplified symbol	
8. ENERGY TRANSMISSION AND CONDITIONING					
8.1	SOURCES OF ENERGY				
8.1.1	Pressure source			Simplified general symbol	
8.1.1.1	Hydraulic pressure source			Symbols to be used when the nature of the source should be indicated	
8.1.1.2	Pneumatic pressure source				
8.1.2	Electric motor			Symbol 113 in IEC Publication 117.2	
8.1.3	Heat engine				
8.2	FLOW LINES AND CONNECTIONS				
8.2.1	Flow line:				
8.2.1.1	— working line, return line and feed line				
8.2.1.2	— pilot control line				

fluid power graphic symbols

	DESCRIPTION	SYMBOL	USE OF THE EQUIPMENT OR EXPLANATION OF THE SYMBOL	
8.2.1.3	— drain or bleed line	- - - - - - - - -		
8.2.1.4	— flexible pipe		Flexible hose, usually connecting moving parts	
8.2.1.5	— electric line			
8.2.2	**Pipeline junction**			
8.2.3	**Crossed Pipelines**		not connected	
8.2.4	**Air bleed**			
8.2.5	**Exhaust port:**			
8.2.5.1	— plain with no provision for connection			
8.2.5.2	— threaded for connection			
8.2.6	**Power take-off:**		On equipment or lines, for energy take-off or measurement	
8.2.6.1	— plugged			
8.2.6.2	— with take-off line			
8.2.7	**Quick-acting coupling:**			
8.2.7.1	— connected, without mechanically opened non-return valve			
8.2.7.2	— connected, with mechanically opened non-return valves			
8.2.7.3	— uncoupled, with open end			
8.2.7.4	— uncoupled, closed by free non-return valve (see 7.3.1.1)			

	DESCRIPTION	SYMBOL	USE OF THE EQUIPMENT OR EXPLANATION OF THE SYMBOL	
8.2.8	Rotary connection:		Line junction allowing angular movement in service	
8.2.8.1	— one way			
8.2.8.2	— three way			
8.2.9	Silencer			
8.3	RESERVOIRS			
8.3.1	Reservoir open to atmosphere:			
8.3.1.1	— with inlet pipe above fluid level			
8.3.1.2	— with inlet pipe below fluid level			
8.3.1.3	— with a header line			
8.3.2	Pressurized reservoir			
8.4	ACCUMULATORS		The fluid is maintained under pressure by a spring, weight or compressed gas (air, nitrogen, etc.)	Air or gas
8.5	FILTERS, WATER TRAPS, LUBRICATORS AND MISCELLANEOUS APPARATUS			
8.5.1	Filter or strainer			Bowl — Filter element
8.5.2	Water trap:			

fluid power graphic symbols

	DESCRIPTION	SYMBOL		USE OF THE EQUIPMENT OR EXPLANATION OF THE SYMBOL
8.5.2.1	— with manual control			
8.5.2.2	— automatically drained			
8.5.3	**Filter with water trap:**			
8.5.3.1	— with manual control		Combination of 8.5.1 and 8.5.2.1	Float
8.5.3.2	— automatically drained		Combination of 8.5.1 and 8.5.2.2	
8.5.4	**Air dryer**		A unit drying air (for example, by chemical means)	Desiccant
8.5.5	**Lubricator**		Small quantities of oil are added to the air passing through the unit, in order to lubricate equipment receiving the air	Inlet air — Lubricated air
8.5.6	**Conditioning unit**		Consisting of filter, pressure regulator, pressure gauge and lubricator	
8.5.61	— Detailed symbol			
8.5.6.2	— Simplified symbol			
8.6	**HEAT EXCHANGERS**		Apparatus for heating or cooling the circulating fluid	

	DESCRIPTION	SYMBOL	USE OF THE EQUIPMENT OR EXPLANATION OF THE SYMBOL	
8.6.1	Temperature controller		The fluid temperature is maintained between two predetermined values. The arrows indicate that heat may be either introduced or dissipated	
8.6.2	Cooler		The arrows in the diamond indicate the extraction of heat	
8.6.2.1			— without representation of the flow lines of the coolant	
8.6.2.2			— indicating the flow lines of the coolant	
8.6.3	Heater		The arrows in the diamond indicate the introduction of heat	
9. CONTROL MECHANISMS				
9.1	Mechanical components			
9.1.1	Rotating shaft:		The arrow indicates rotation	
9.1.1.1	— in one direction			
9.1.1.2	— in either direction			
9.1.2	Detent		A device for maintaining a given position	
9.1.3	Locking device	*	* The symbol for unlocking control is inserted in the square	
9.1.4	Over-center device		Prevents the mechanism stopping in a dead center position	
9.1.5	Pivoting devices:			
9.1.5.1	— simple			

fluid power graphic symbols

	DESCRIPTION	SYMBOL	USE OF THE EQUIPMENT OR EXPLANATION OF THE SYMBOL	
9.1.5.2	— with traversing lever			
9.1.5.3	— with fixed fulcrum			
9.2	**CONTROL METHODS**		The symbols representing control methods are incorporated in the symbol of the controlled apparatus, to which they should be adjacent. For apparatus with several squares the actuation of the control makes effective the square adjacent to it.	
9.2.1	**Muscular control:**		General symbol (without indication of control type)	
9.2.1.1	— by pushbutton			
9.2.1.2	— by lever			
9.2.1.3	— by pedal			
9.2.2	**Mechanical control:**			
9.2.2.1	— by plunger or tracer			
9.2.2.2	— by spring			
9.2.2.3	— by roller			
9.2.2.4	— by roller, operating in one direction only			
9.2.3	**Electrical control:**			
9.2.3.1	— by solenoid:			
9.2.3.1.1			— with one winding	
9.2.3.1.2			— with two windings operating in opposite directions	

	DESCRIPTION	SYMBOL	USE OF THE EQUIPMENT OR EXPLANATION OF THE SYMBOL	
9.2.3.1.3			— with two windings operating in a variable way progressively, operating in opposite direction	
9.2.3.2	— by electric motor			
9.2.4	**Control by application or release of pressure**			
9.2.4.1	Direct acting control:			
9.2.4.1.1	— by application of pressure			
9.2.4.1.2	— by release of pressure			
9.2.4.1.3	— by different control areas		In the symbol the larger rectangle represents the larger control area, i.e., the priority phase	
9.2.4.2	Indirect control, pilot actuated:		General symbol for pilot directional control valve	
9.2.4.2.1	— by application of pressure			
9.2.4.2.2	— by release of pressure			
9.2.4.3	Interior control paths		The control paths are inside the unit	
9.2.5	**Combined control:**			
9.2.5.1	— by solenoid and pilot directional valve		The pilot directional valve is actuated by the solenoid	
9.2.5.2	— by solenoid or pilot directional valve		Either may actuate the control independently	

fluid power graphic symbols

	DESCRIPTION	SYMBOL	USE OF THE EQUIPMENT OR EXPLANATION OF THE SYMBOL
9.3	**Mechanical feedback**	1) 2) 1) Controlled apparatus 2) Control apparatus	The mechanical connection of a control apparatus moving part to a controlled apparatus moving part is represented by the symbol 5.1.1.4 which joins the two parts connected. (For examples see 11.1.2 and 12.1.1)

10. SUPPLEMENTARY EQUIPMENT

10.1 MEASURING INSTRUMENTS

10.1.1 10.1.1.1	**Pressure measurement:** — pressure gauge		The point on the circle at which the connection joins the symbol is immaterial
10.1.2 10.1.2.1	**Temperature measurement:** — Thermometer		The point on the circle at which the connection joins the symbol is immaterial
10.1.3 10.1.3.1 10.1.3.2	**Measurement of flow:** — Flow meter — Integrating flow		
10.2 10.2.1	**OTHER APPARATUS** Pressure electric switch		

DESCRIPTION	SYMBOL

11. EXAMPLES OF ASSEMBLIES OF EQUIPMENT

In circuit diagrams, symbols normally represent equipment in the unoperated condition. However, any other condition can be represented, if clearly stated.

11.1 DRIVEN ASSEMBLIES (pumps)

11.1.1	A two-stage pump driven by an electric motor with a pressure relief valve in the second stage and a proprotioning pressure relief valve which maintains the pressure of the first stage at, for example, half the pressure of the second stage.	
11.1.2	A variable displacement pump driven by an electric motor, control being by a servo-motor with differential cylinder and a tracer valve, with two throttling orifices and mechanical feedback	
11.1.3	A single-stage air compressor driven by an electric motor, which is automatically switched on and off as the receiver pressure falls and rises	
11.1.4	A two-stage air compressing assembly driven by an internal combustion engine which idles or takes up the load with the switching over of a 3/2 directional control valve, depending on the receiver pressure	

11.2 DRIVING ASSEMBLIES (motors)

11.2.1	A motor driven in either direction of rotation, with pressure relief valves and flushing valve.	

fluid power graphic symbols

	DESCRIPTION	SYMBOL
11.3	**Control and regulating assemblies**	

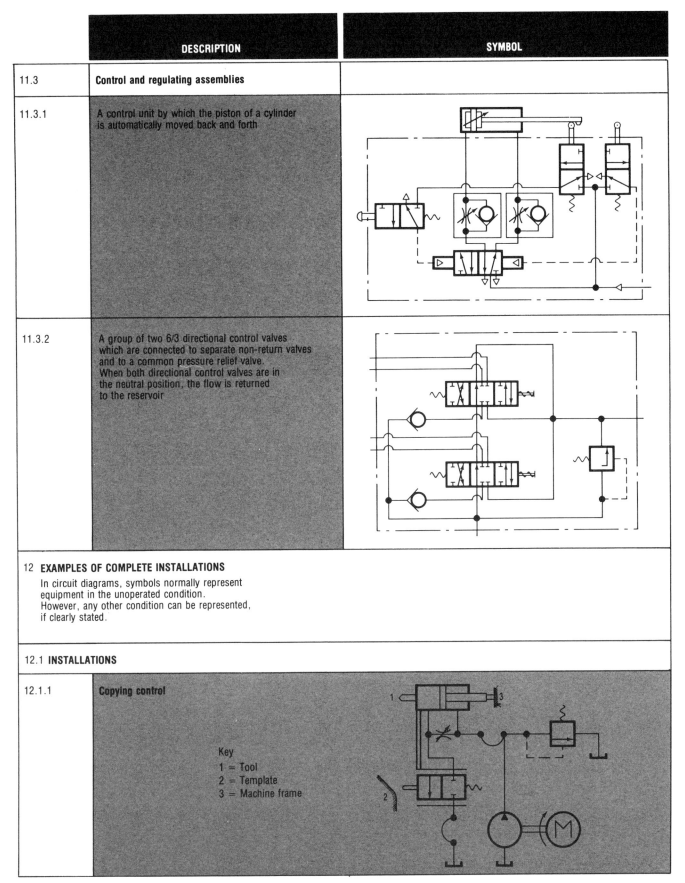

11.3.1	A control unit by which the piston of a cylinder is automatically moved back and forth	
11.3.2	A group of two 6/3 directional control valves which are connected to separate non-return valves and to a common pressure relief valve. When both directional control valves are in the neutral position, the flow is returned to the reservoir	

12 EXAMPLES OF COMPLETE INSTALLATIONS

In circuit diagrams, symbols normally represent
equipment in the unoperated condition.
However, any other condition can be represented,
if clearly stated.

12.1 INSTALLATIONS

12.1.1	**Copying control**

Key
1 = Tool
2 = Template
3 = Machine frame

 fluid power graphic symbols

12.1.2	**Clutch operating control**

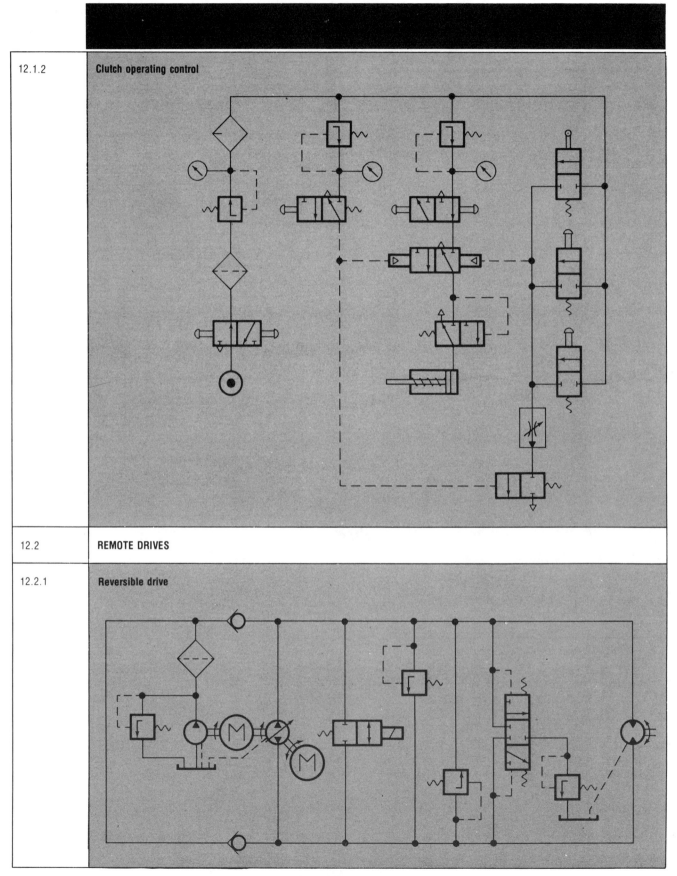

12.2	**REMOTE DRIVES**

12.2.1	**Reversible drive**

INDEX

Normally closed, 238
Normall open, 238
NPT thread port fittings, 338

O

Oil, hydraulic, *See* Hydraulic fluids
Oil, reprocessed, 310
ON-OFF Control, 79-85
Open center circuits
  See Constant flow circuits, 33-38
Open circuit, 30, 33-38
  See also Hydrostatic transmission,
    129, 130, 133, 138
Open loop circuits, 9, 10, 129, 130, 138
Optimum pressure, 47-49, 57
Orifices, 47, 65
Output
  characteristics, 36
  speed control in open center circuit, 35
Overrunning load, 13, 25, 27
  cycle profile, 26

P

Particulate contamination, 196, 197
Phase, 362
Pneumatic power circuits, 103-112
Position control, 235-237
Potential energy, 5
Power plot, 5, 16, 17
Power summing systems, 122, 123
Prefill systems, 74, 75
Pressure,
  control valve selection, 9, 47-62
  drop, 52, 114, 277, 278
  switch, 51, 224, 238
  transducers, 235-238
  troubleshooting, 325, 326
Pressure-compensated pumps, 41, 118, 120-122, 255
Presure drop analysis, 114-115
Pressure-limiting circuits, 2, 54, 55
Pressure-plot, 16, 22, 36, 43
Pressure-transients, shock, 62, 353
Priority valve, 66
Programmable controllers, 229-231, 238
Proportional control, 85-93, 118, 120-123
Pulsating flow effects, 205, 206
Pulsation dampers, 190
Pulse width modulation, 233
Pump, *also see* Energy Input
  charge, 142
  control of flow rate, 41-43, 118, 120-122,
    138, 255
  discharge pressure, 3
  selection criteria, 251-256
Pump-motor interaction, 131-134

Pump performance characteristics, 253-255
  combined, 254
  flow vs pressure, 253
  flow vs speed, 253
  overall efficiency, 254
  power vs speed, 254
  volumetric efficiency, 254
Push-button switch, 224

Q

Quick acting couplings, 306
Quincke tube, 353

R

Radiation heat transfer coefficient G_R, 168, 174
Rate of doing work, 5
Reducing valve, 49, 60
Regenerative circuit, 72, 73
Regulator, 65
Relay, 223-229, 238
Relief valve, 47, 48
  cracking pressure bands, 54
  venting, 52
Reservoirs, 180, 181, 188, 190, 285-289
Resistance, 362
Resistive load, 13, 19-24
Resonant frrequency, 351, 352
Response of a system, 361
Rotory coupling, 307

S

SAE, *see* Society of Automotive Engineers
Seals
  fluid compatibility, 256
  leakage control, 338-344
    face seals, 339, 340
    lip seals, 338, 339
    static seals, 341, 342
Sensors, 235-238
Sequence diagram, 82, 223-229, 238, 241, 242
Sequencing circuits, 50
Shock, suppressing circuit, 62
Society of Automotive Engineers, (SAE), 290
Sound, additive nature of, 185
Sound vs noise, 177
Specific gravity, 174
Specific heat, C_p, 167, 168, 174
Speed regulation, 135
Split flange, SAE fitting
  troubleshooting, 342, 343
Stability, 82, 351, 360
Stephen-Holtzman constant, G, 170
Stiffness of hydrostatic transmissions, 142
Stop tubes, cylinder, 259
Straight thread port, 292
Straight thread, SAE O-ring port, 292, 337
Straight-through coupling, 307
Switches, 224, 238
  steeping, 238